ACCOUNTANT'S HANDBOOK OF FORMULAS AND TABLES

ACCOUNTANTS HANDBOOK OF FORMULAS AND TABLES

Lawrence Lipkin, C.P.A.
Assistant Professor of Accountancy

Irwin K. Feinstein, Ph.D.
Professor Department of Mathematics

Lucile Derrick, Ph.D.
Professor of Economics (Statistics)

All of the University of Illinois, Chicago

PRENTICE-HALL, INC., Englewood Cliffs, N. J.

LIBRARY OF CONGRESS
CATALOG CARD NUMBER: 63-18186

Sixth Printing..... January, 1968

PRINTED IN THE UNITED STATES OF AMERICA

00124-B&P

ACKNOWLEDGMENTS

The authors wish to express their gratitude to the following authors and publishers for granting permission to use the various tables included in this book.

Professor Glover and his publisher, George Wahr Publishing Co., for tables I, II, III, IV, and V which were extracted from that excellent book, TABLES OF APPLIED MATHEMATICS.

Professors Simpson, Pirenian, and Crenshaw, and their publishers, Prentice-Hall, Inc., for tables VI and VII which were taken from their book, MATHEMATICS OF FINANCE, 3rd. Ed.

Professors Croxton and Cowden and their publishers, Prentice-Hall, Inc., for tables VIII, IX, X, XI, and XII taken from their book, APPLIED GENERAL STATISTICS, 2nd Ed.

The Interstate Commerce Commission for table XIII taken from their publication, "105,000 Random Decimal Digits."

PREFACE

This handbook of formulas and tables was compiled primarily for use by accountants. However, it can be a serviceable tool for others working with quantitative data. For any of these users, the book has distinct advantages.

First, the handbook can be a great time saver. It has brought together in one volume materials which ordinarily are widely scattered. Here in one book will be found formulas and tables that would ordinarily require several reference sources covering such topics as: mathematics, finance, accounting theory, cost accounting, statistics, marketing and production.

Second, the handbook is convenient to use. It is compact, fitting readily into a briefcase. The auditor can have access to it on the job as well as in his office. The topical arrangement and the index make for ease and speed in reference. Examples quickly refresh the memory or demonstrate a new technique.

Third, the materials are timely. In addition to the usual formulas pertaining to interest, annuities and statistics, many new methods have been stated in formula form.

L.L.
I.K.F.
L.D.

TABLE OF CONTENTS

ACCOUNTANT'S HANDBOOK OF FORMULAS AND TABLES

1

INTRODUCTION

This handbook of formulas and tables has been compiled for the professional accountant as a reference work. No person is expected to commit to memory all of the many mathematical formulas that he has learned in his professional preparation. However, one is supposed to know where to look for a particular formula should the need arise. The first place to look now will be in this handbook.

Since this handbook is especially intended for the professional accountant, it is assumed that he has a sufficient knowledge of accounting theory, mathematics, and statistics to be able to recognize a problem and know how to use the proper formula in order to solve it. This handbook is not a substitute for a textbook, but is merely a tool to aid one in problem solving. To give one aid in solving problems and recalling theories, every formula is illustrated with a simple problem and its solution. In many cases all one needs to do to solve the problem is merely to substitute the actual data in the formula and perform the indicated operations.

HOW TO USE THIS HANDBOOK

If one is seeking a specific formula, he needs only turn to the index to see if the formula is included in the handbook. When he locates the page on which the formula is presented, a rapid glance over the formula and the illustrative problem will be sufficient to ascertain if the formula is the one he is seeking. The illustrated problem and solution will be of great help in reaching an answer which he seeks when the illustration is considerably like his problem.

The next step is to familiarize himself with the symbols used in the formula for many writers use different symbols to represent the same item. After one is familiar with the symbols, he can then assemble all of the facts for his particular problem. He must be sure that his facts are complete for in many cases, a missing fact makes it impossible to use the given formula.

Now one substitutes his data in the formula and performs the indicated computations, preferably on a calculator. The answer is now obtained. It is wise, however, to validate the answer by checking it through the use of some other technique. This is particularly important if the computations were performed manually.

EXAMPLE

Here is an example of one of the problems which the professional accountant encounters. It serves to illustrate how this handbook can help solve this problem. Suppose that one is examining the books of a client and wishes to verify independently the computation of depreciation by the sum of the years digit method. The facts that have been acertained are: Asset cost $100,000, 20 year estimated life, salvage value $10,000. What should be the correct amount of depreciation for the 14th year?

Referring to the index under the heading Depreciation, we find the formula for "Depreciation by the Sum of the Years Digit Method" located on page 80.

The formula is:

$$D_j = \frac{Y - D}{\Sigma Y} \times (C - S)$$

where

D_j = Depreciation for particular year
Y = Estimated life of asset
D = Number of years of prior depreciation
ΣY = Sum of the years
C = Cost of asset
S = Salvage value of asset

If the above formula is not familiar, it is because to the authors' knowledge this is the first time that it has been thus stated, although the problem is a familiar one.

The facts show the following:

$D_{(14)}$ = Unknown
$Y = 20$
$D = 13$
$\Sigma Y_{(20)} = 210$ (Table VIII, Column 1)
$C = \$100,000$
$S = \$10,000$

$\therefore$ (therefore)

Substituting in formula:

$$D_{(14)} = \frac{20 - 13}{210} \times (\$100{,}000 - \$10{,}000)$$

$$= \frac{7}{210} \times \$90{,}000$$

$$= \$3{,}000$$

Sometimes a problem arises and one does not quite know what to do or how to solve it. If this is the case, it is suggested that you browse through the various formulas and problems under the topic concerned. You may find a problem illustrated that is exactly like the one that you are working on, or a similar problem that will give you further insight into your particular problem. Let us suppose, for example, that you desire to prepare supplemental financial statements that reflect the changing price level. A review of Chapter 13, "Price Level Adjustments," will be very rewarding for it will give you an excellent insight into the problems you will probably encounter. Further, it will suggest the data that will have to be obtained in order to prepare the supplementary financial statements.

USE OF TABLES

It is hardly necessary to explain the use and convenience of the various mathematical tables included in this handbook. An example of the use of the tables was demonstrated in the illustration regarding "Depreciation by the Sum of the Years' Digits." What is the sum of 1 through 20? Merely by referring to the appropriate table one can determine that the sum of 1 through 20 is 210. Most of the tables included in this handbook are most likely quite familiar to you. The convenience of having them in one place and in possession at all times will prove to be very worthwhile.

USE OF FORMULAS

One may ask why bother to express accounting methods in formula form? A mathematician uses a formula because it expresses very simply relationships that would take many pages of complex prose to explain. After spending some time reading the explanation of relationships when language is used, the reader may still not comprehend the explanation due to inept writing. However, formulas with the use of mathematical notations make the expression of complex relationships easy to comprehend. If one understands the formula there is little left to do but substitute the known facts in the formula and perform the indicated operations, mostly simple arithmetic.

USE OF SYMBOLS

Symbols are the mathematicians' shorthand. Everyone knows that (x) represents an unknown quantity. Descartes when designing his mathematical system, decided that the latter part of the alphabet, ... x,y,z, should denote variable quantities, and the beginning part of the alphabet, $a,b,c\cdots$, should denote constant quantitics.[1] However, in working with applied mathematics in many cases the symbols used are the first letter in the word describing the term. Thus, interest is usually expressed by the symbol (i); time by the symbol (t).

In the formulas pertaining to accounting this method of notation has been followed; for instance "inventory" is usually denoted by the symbol (I), "accounts receivable" by the symbol A/R, "accounts payable" by the symbol A/P. Subscripts further identify the term, for instance:

A/R_1 = Accounts Receivable at the beginning of the period
A/R_2 = Accounts Receivable at the end of the period

---

[1]Herbert Western Turnbull, The Great Mathematician, James R. Newman. *The World Book of Mathematics*, Vol. I, Simon and Schuster, New York, 1950, p. 131.

2

SIMPLE INTEREST FORMULAS

SIMPLE INTEREST

Formula:

$$I = P \times R \times T$$

where

I = Interest
P = Principal
R = Rate of Interest
T = Time

Examples:

What is the amount of simple interest on $1,500 for 90 days at 6% interest?

Solution:

$$I = P \times R \times T$$

$$I = 1{,}500 \times .06 \times \frac{90}{360^*}$$

$$I = \$22.50$$

****Note:*** In most business transactions 360 days are used for the number of days in the year. This type of computation is called ordinary simple interest. Exact simple interest is computed by using 365 days in the year.

TIME REQUIRED TO YIELD AN AMOUNT OF INTEREST

Formula:

$$T = \frac{I}{P \times R}$$

where

T = Time
I = Interest
P = Principal
R = Rate of interest

Example:

What is the amount of time required for \$5,000 to yield \$575 at simple interest at 5%?

Solution:

$$T = \frac{I}{P \times R}$$

$$T = \frac{575}{5{,}000 \times .05}$$

$$T = \frac{575}{250}$$

$$T = 2.3 \text{ years}$$

PRINCIPAL OF A LOAN TO OBTAIN SPECIFIC AMOUNT OF CASH

Formula:

$$P = \frac{C}{1 - RT}$$

where

P = Principal of loan
C = Cash required
R = Rate of discount
T = Time

Example:

If \$3,000 net cash is required and the bank will discount a note for 90 days at 6%, what is the principal amount of the note?

Solution:

$$P = \frac{C}{1 - RT}$$

$$P = \frac{3{,}000}{1 - .06 \times \dfrac{90}{360}}$$

$$P = \frac{3{,}000}{1 - .015}$$

$$P = \frac{3{,}000}{.985}$$

$$P = \$3{,}045.69$$

PRESENT VALUE OF AN INTEREST BEARING NOTE (SIMPLE INTEREST)

Formulas:

1. $Mv = P(1 + R_1 T_1)$
2. $Pv = \dfrac{Mv}{1 + R_2 T_2}$

where

Mv = Maturity value
P = Principal of Note
R_1 = Rate of interest on note
T_1 = Time on note
Pv = Present value of note
R_2 = Rate of interest on maturity value (current rate of interest)
T_2 = Time remaining on note at valuation date

Example:

Mr. Jones died on September 14, 1959. In his estate was a note for \$1,500 from Mr. Smith dated August 15, 1959, with interest at 6% for 60 days. What valuation should the executor place on the note, if money cost 7% on September 14, 1959?

Solution:

1. $Mv = P(1 + R_1 T_1)$

$$Mv = 1{,}500\left(1 + .06 \times \frac{60}{360}\right)$$

$$Mv = 1{,}500 + 15$$

$$Mv = \$1{,}515.00$$

$$2.\quad Pv = \frac{Mv}{1 + R_2 T_2}$$

$$Pv = \frac{1{,}515.00}{1 + .07 \times \dfrac{30}{360}}$$

$$Pv = \frac{1{,}515.00}{1.00583}$$

$$Pv = \$1{,}506.22$$

PROCEEDS FROM DISCOUNTING AN INTEREST BEARING NOTE

Formulas:

$$1.\quad Mv = P(1 + R_1 T_1)$$

$$2.\quad C = Mv(1 - R_2 T_2)$$

where

Mv = Maturity value of note
P = Principal of note
R_1 = Rate of interest on note
T_1 = Time on note
C = Cash proceeds
R_2 = Rate of discount by purchaser of note
T_2 = Time remaining on note at discount date

Example:

Able received from Baker a \$1,500, 6%, 60 day note dated August 15, 1959. On September 14, 1959 Able discounted the note at his bank at 7%. How much cash did Able receive from the bank?

Solution:

$$1.\quad Mv = P(1 + R_1 T_1)$$

$$Mv = \$1500\left(1 + .06 \times \frac{60}{360}\right)$$

$$Mv = \$1515.00$$

$$2.\quad C = Mv(1 - R_2 T_2)$$

$$C = 1{,}515.00\left(1 - .07 \times \frac{30}{360}\right)$$

$$C = 1{,}515.00 - 8.84$$

$$C = \$1{,}506.16$$

RATE OF INTEREST CORRESPONDING TO DISCOUNT RATE

Formula:

$$i = \frac{D}{1 - TD}$$

where

i = Interest rate
D = Discount rate
T = Time

Example:

A bank discounts a 90 day note at 6%. What is the actual rate of interest that the borrower must pay?

Solution:

$$i = \frac{D}{1 - TD}$$

$$i = \frac{.06}{1 - \left(\frac{90}{360} \times .06\right)}$$

$$i = \frac{.06}{1 - .015}$$

$$i = \frac{.06}{.985}$$

$$i = .0609 \quad \text{or} \quad 6.09\%$$

EFFECTIVE RATE OF INTEREST ON ACCOUNTS RECEIVABLE FINANCING

Formula:

$$i = \frac{R \times 360}{a}$$

where

i = Effective rate of interest
R = Daily rate of interest charged on the face amount of the invoice financed
a = The percent of the face amount of the invoice.

Example:

The XYZ Commercial Finance Company will loan 75% of the face amount of an invoice which is assigned to it. The charge for the financing is 1/30 th of 1% per day computed on the face amount of the invoice. What is the effective rate of interest?

Solution:

$$i = \frac{R \times 360}{a}$$

$$i = \frac{\frac{.01}{30} \times 360}{.75}$$

$$i = \frac{.12}{.75}$$

$$i = .16 \quad \text{or} \quad 16\%$$

RATE OF INTEREST EQUIVALENT TO CASH DISCOUNT RATE

Formula:

$$i = D \times \frac{360}{N - n}$$

where

i = Effective rate of interest
D = Percent of Cash Discount
N = Number of days credit
n = Number of days in discount period

Example:

If the terms of an invoice are 2/10, N/30, What is the effective rate of interest equivalent to the cash discount?

Solution:

$$i = D \times \frac{360}{N - n}$$

$$i = .02 \times \frac{360}{30 - 10}$$

$$i = .02 \times \frac{360}{20}$$

$$i = .36 \quad \text{or} \quad 36\%$$

3

COMPOUND INTEREST

COMPOUND AMOUNT—USING INTEREST TABLES

Formula:

$$S = P(1 + R)^n$$

where

S = Compound Amount or Future Value
P = Principal
R = Interest Rate per Period
n = Number of Conversion Periods

Example:

How much will \$3,000 accumulate to in 20 years at 6% per year if interest is compounded semi annually?

Solution:

$$\begin{aligned} S &= P(1 + R)^n \\ &= 3{,}000\,(1 + .03)^{40} = 3{,}000\,(1.03)^{40} \\ &= 3{,}000\,(3.262038) \qquad \text{(Table I)} \\ &= \$9{,}786.14 \end{aligned}$$

Example:

What will be the compound amount at the end of 4 years if \$500 is invested at 8% compounded quarterly?

Solution:

$$\begin{aligned} S &= P(1 + R)^n \\ &= 500\,(1 + .02)^{16} = 500\,(1.02)^{16} \qquad \text{(Table I)} \\ &= 500\,(1.372786) = \$686.39 \end{aligned}$$

COMPOUND AMOUNT—USING LOGARITHMS

Formula:

$$S = P(1+R)^n$$

Example:

What will be the compound amount at the end of 4 years if \$500 is invested at 8% compounded quarterly? (This is the same example as in the previous section).

Solution:

$$S = 500(1.02)^{16}$$

Solving for $(1.02)^{16}$ by means of logarithms

$$\log 1.02 = .0086002 \qquad \text{(Table VII)}$$
$$16 \log 1.02 = .1376032$$

Therefore

$$(1.02)^{16} = 1.3728 \qquad \text{(Table VI)}$$
$$S = 500(1.3728) = \$686.40$$

Example:

How much will \$3000 accumulate to in 20 years at 6% interest if interest is compounded semi annually?

Solution:

$$S = P(1+R)^n$$
$$= 3000(1+.03)^{40} = 3000(1.03)^{40}$$

Solving for $(1.03)^{40}$ by means of logarithms

$$\log 1.03 = .0128372$$
$$40 \log 1.03 = .513488 \qquad \text{(Table VII)}$$

Therefore

$$(1.03)^{40} = 3.2621 \qquad \text{(Table VI)}$$
$$S = 3000(3.2621) = \$9{,}786.30$$

PRESENT VALUE—INTEREST BEARING NOTE (FROM TABLES)

Formulas:

1. $S = P(1+R)^n$
2. $P_v = S(1+R)^{-n}$

where

S = Future Value
P = Principal
R = Rate of Interest per Period
P_v = Present Value
n = Number of conversion periods

Example:

The XYZ Company acquired a \$3000 10 year note with interest at 6% compounded semi annually. The company decides to sell the note immediately for a yield of 7%. How much money should the XYZ Company receive for the note?

Solution:

$$S = P(1+R)^n$$
$$= 3000(1+.03)^{20} = 3000(1.03)^{20}$$
$$= 3000(1.806111) \qquad \text{(Table I)}$$
$$= 5418.33$$
$$P_v = S(1+R)^{-n}$$
$$= 5418.33(1+.07)^{-10} = 5418.33(1.07)^{-10}$$
$$= 5418.33(.508349) \qquad \text{(Table II)}$$
$$P_v = 2752.40$$

PRESENT VALUE—NON-INTEREST BEARING NOTE (USING LOGARITHMS)

Formula:

$$P_v = S(1+R)^{-n}$$

(See symbols at top of page)

Example:

A boy is to receive \$1000 10 years from now to help finance his college education. How much should be invested for him if money is worth 4% compounded semi-annually?

Solution:

$$P_v = S(1+R)^{-n}$$
$$= 1000(1+.02)^{-20} = 1000(1.02)^{-20}$$

Using logarithms, we compute $(1.02)^{-20}$.

$$\log 1.02 = .0086002 \qquad \text{(Table VII)}$$
$$-20 \log 1.02 = -.172004 \quad \text{or} \quad 9.827996 - 10$$
$$(1.02)^{-20} = .67297$$

So
$$P_v = 1000(.67297)$$
$$P_v = \$672.97$$

PRESENT VALUE—NON-INTEREST BEARING NOTE (FROM TABLES)

Formula:

$$P_v = S(1+R)^{-n}$$

where

P_v = Present Value
S = Future Value
R = Rate of Interest per Period
n = Number of Conversion Periods

Example:

What is the present value of a \$5000 10 year non-interest bearing note if money is worth 5%?

Solution:

$$P_v = S(1+R)^{-n}$$
$$= 5000(1+.05)^{-10}$$
$$= 5000(1.05)^{-10}$$
$$(1.05)^{-10} = .613913 \qquad \text{(Table II)}$$
$$P_v = 5000(.613913)$$
$$= \$3069.57$$

DETERMINING THE TIME (USING LOGARITHMS) GIVEN S, P, AND R

Formula:

$$n = \frac{\log S - \log P}{\log(1+R)}$$

where

n = Number of Conversion Periods
S = Future Value or Compound Amount
R = Rate of Interest per Period
P = Principal

Example:

How long will it take \$50,000 to amount to \$80,000 if the principal is invested at 4%?

Solution:

$$S = 80{,}000 \qquad P = 50{,}000 \qquad R = 4\%$$

$$\log 80{,}000 = 4.903090 \qquad \log 50{,}000 = 4.698970 \qquad \log 1.04 = .017033$$

$$n = \frac{\log S - \log P}{\log (1 + R)} = \frac{4.903090 - 4.698970}{.017033} = \frac{.204120}{.017033}$$

$$= 11.98 \text{ or } 12 \text{ years approximately}$$

DETERMINING THE TIME (USING TABLES) GIVEN *S*, *P* AND *R*

Formula:

$$(1 + R)^n = \frac{S}{P}$$

Example:

How long will it take \$1000 to amount to \$1373 if the principal is invested at 8% compounded quarterly?

Solution:

$$(1 + .02)^n = \frac{1373}{1000}$$

$$(1.02)^n = 1.373$$

From Table I using tho 2% column, the closest reading is 1.372786 which corresponds to 16 conversion periods. Therefore it will take approximately 4 years.

NOMINAL RATE WHEN PRESENT VALUE AND FUTURE VALUE ARE KNOWN (USING LOGARITHMS) CASE A

Formula (1):

$$R = \left(\frac{S}{P}\right)^{\frac{1}{n}} - 1$$

where

R = Rate of Interest per Period
S = Future Amount
P = Principal
n = Number of Conversion Periods

Example:

If $480 is invested for a period of 4 years after which time $544 is returned, what is the annual rate?

$$R = \left(\frac{S}{P}\right)^{\frac{1}{n}} - 1$$

$$R = \left(\frac{544}{480}\right)^{\frac{1}{4}} - 1 = \left(\frac{17}{15}\right)^{\frac{1}{4}} - 1$$

Let us compute $\left(\frac{17}{15}\right)^{\frac{1}{4}}$ by means of logarithms.

$$\log \left(\frac{17}{15}\right)^{\frac{1}{4}} = \frac{1}{4} (\log 17 - \log 15) = \frac{1}{4} (1.230449 - 1.176091)$$

$$= \frac{1}{4} (.054358) = .0135895$$

Thus $\left(\frac{17}{15}\right)^{\frac{1}{4}} = 1.03179$ (Table VI)

$$R = 1.03179 - 1$$

$$R = .03179 \text{ or } 3.18\%$$

NOMINAL RATE WHEN PRESENT VALUE AND FUTURE AMOUNT ARE KNOWN (USING LOGARITHMS) CASE B

Formula (2):

$$(1 + R)^n = \frac{S}{P}$$

where

R = Rate of Interest per Period (nominal rate)
n = Number of Conversion Periods
S = Future Amount
P = Principal

Example:

What is the required nominal rate of interest compounded annually for $10,000 to double itself in 20 years?

Solution:

$$(1+R)^{20} = \frac{20{,}000}{10{,}000}$$

$$20 \log (1+R) = \log 2$$

$$\log (1+R) = \frac{1}{20} \log 2$$

$$= .05\,(.301030) = .0150515 \qquad \text{(Table VI)}$$

$$1 + R = 1.03528$$

$$R = .03528 \text{ or } 3.53\%$$

RATE OF SIMPLE INTEREST EQUIVALENT TO A COMPOUND INTEREST RATE ON A PER YEAR BASIS: USING INTEREST TABLES

Formula:

$$R_e = (1+R)^m - 1$$

where

R_e = Effective Rate of Interest
R = Nominal Rate of Interest per Period
m = Number of Conversion Periods per Year

Example:

What is the effective rate of interest on a note for 1 year that bears interest at the rate of 7% compounded semi annually?

Solution:

$$R_e = (1+R)^m - 1$$

$$= (1 + .035)^2 - 1 = (1.035)^2 - 1$$

$$(1.035)^2 = 1.071225 \qquad \text{(Table I)}$$

Thus $R_e = 1.071225 - 1 = .071225$ or 7.12%

RATE OF COMPOUND INTEREST ON A PER YEAR BASIS EQUIVALENT TO A SIMPLE INTEREST RATE: USING LOGARITHMS

Formula:

$$R = m[(1+R_e)^{\frac{1}{m}} - 1]$$

where

R = Nominal Rate of Interest

R_e = Effective Rate of Interest

m = Number of Conversion Periods per Year

Example:

What is the nominal rate of interest on a note for 1 year compounded quarterly which will give an effective rate of 3%?

Solution:

$$R = 4[(1 + .03)^{\frac{1}{4}} - 1]$$

$$= 4[(1.03)^{\frac{1}{4}} - 1]$$

Using logarithms, we compute $(1.03)^{\frac{1}{4}}$

$$\log 1.03 = .0128372 \qquad \text{(Table VII)}$$

$$\frac{1}{4}\log 1.03 = .0032093$$

Thus $$(1.03)^{\frac{1}{4}} = 1.00742 \qquad \text{(Table VI)}$$

$$R = 4(1.00742) - 4$$

$$= 4.02968 - 4 = .02968$$

$$R = 2.97\%$$

4

ANNUITIES

AMOUNT OF AN ORDINARY ANNUITY (TABLES)

Formula:

$$S = R \cdot s_{\overline{n}|i} = R \cdot \frac{(1+i)^n - 1}{i}$$

where

S = Amount after a fixed number of years
R = Amount per period
i = Interest rate per period
n = Number of conversion periods
$s_{\overline{n}|i}$ = Amount of Annuity for n interest periods at a rate of i per period

Example:

Find the amount of an annuity in which a payment of $1,000 is made at the end of each year for 10 years, if money is worth 4% compounded annually.

Solution:

$$S = R \cdot s_{\overline{n}|i} = R \cdot \frac{(1+i)^n - 1}{i}$$

$$= \$1000\ s_{\overline{10}|.04} = 1000 \cdot \frac{(1+.04)^{10} - 1}{.04}$$

$$= 1000\ (12.006107) \qquad \text{(Table III)}$$

$$= \$12{,}006.11$$

AMOUNT OF AN ORDINARY ANNUITY (LOGARITHMS)

Formula:

$$S = R \cdot s_{\overline{n}|i} = R \cdot \frac{(1+i)^n - 1}{i}$$

(See above for symbols)

Example:

Mr. Able deposited \$300 in a bank on Jan. 1 and July 1 of each year to provide for his son's education. Interest is 3½% compounded semi-annually. At the end of 10 years what will be the balance in the account?

Solution:

$$S = \$300\ s_{\overline{n}|\,i} = 300 \cdot \frac{(1 + .0175)^{20} - 1}{.0175}$$

We will use logarithms to compute $(1.0175)^{20}$ and then do the rest of the example with ordinary arithmetic.

Let $N = (1.0175)^{20}$

Then $\log N = 20 \log 1.0175$

$= 20\ (.0075344) = 0.150688$ (Table VII)

$N = 1.4148$

$$S = 300 \cdot \frac{1.4148 - 1}{0175} = 300\ \frac{.4148}{.0175}$$

$$S = 300\ (23.701) = \$8{,}110.30$$

PRESENT VALUE OF AN ORDINARY ANNUITY (TABLES)

Formula:

$$A = R \cdot a_{\overline{n}|\,i} = R \cdot \frac{1 - (1 + i)^{-n}}{i}$$

where

A = Present Value
R = Amount per Period
i = Interest Rate per Period
n = Number of Conversion Periods
$a_{\overline{n}|\,i}$ = Present Value of Annuity of \$1 per Period for n periods at a rate of i per period.

Example

Find the present value of an annuity in which a payment of \$2,000 is made at the end of each year for 10 years, if money is worth 4% compounded annually?

Solution:

$$A = \$2{,}000\ a_{\overline{10}|.04} = \$2{,}000\ \frac{1-(1+.04)^{-10}}{.04}$$

$$= \$2{,}000\ (8.110896) \qquad \text{(Table IV)}$$

$$= \$16{,}221.79$$

PRESENT VALUE OF AN ORDINARY ANNUITY (LOGARITHMS)

Formula:

$$A = R \cdot a_{\overline{n}|\,i} = R \cdot \frac{1-(1+i)^{-n}}{i}$$

(See page 20 for symbols)

Example:

Mr. C. C. Smith in his will devised to his grandson \$1,000 per year for 10 years or an equivalent amount in one lump sum payment, payable at the time the will was drawn. If money is worth 5%, how much would the grandson receive if he elected the lump sum settlement?

Solution:

$$A = \$1{,}000 \cdot a_{\overline{10}|.05} = \$1{,}000\ \frac{1-(1+.05)^{-10}}{.05}$$

$$= \$1{,}000\ \frac{1-1.05^{-10}}{.05}$$

We will use logarithms to compute $(1.05)^{-10}$ and then do the rest of the example with ordinary arithmetic.

Let $N = (1.05)^{-10}$

Then $\log N = -10 \log 1.05$

$= -10\ (0.0211893) = -0.211893$ (Table VII)

$= 10.000000 - 0.211893 - 10.000000 = 9.788107 - 10$

$N = 0.61391$

$$A = \$1{,}000\ \frac{1-0.61391}{.05} = \$1{,}000\ \frac{0.38609}{.05}$$

$$= \$1{,}000\ (7.7218) = \$7{,}721.80$$

FINDING THE PERIODIC RENT OF ANNUITY (TABLES)

Formula:

$$R = \frac{1}{a_{\overline{n}|i}} = S \cdot \frac{i}{1 - (1 + i)^{-n}}$$

where

R = Amount per Period
i = Interest Rate per Period
n = Number of Conversion Periods
S = Total Amount

Example:

With money worth 5% compounded annually, what equal payments should be made at the beginning of each year for 20 years to pay off a mortgage on a house amounting to $18,000?

Solution:

$$R = S \cdot \frac{.05}{1 - (1 + .05)^{-20}}$$

$$= \$18{,}000\ (.08024259) \qquad \text{(Table V)}$$

$$= \$1{,}444.37$$

Note: In examples of this kind the first payment is due immediately. The remaining payments can be considered as forming an annuity whose term starts when the first payment is made.

FINDING THE PERIODIC RENT OF ANNUITY (LOGARITHMS)

Formula:

$$R = \frac{1}{a_{\overline{n}|i}} = S \cdot \frac{i}{1 - (1 + i)^{-n}}$$

(See symbols at top of page)

Example:

The XYZ Bank financed a mortgage of $50,000 at $5\frac{1}{2}\%$ compounded quarterly for 20 years payable in equal quarterly installments including interest. How much is the quarterly payment?

Solution:

$$R = \$50{,}000 \frac{0.01375}{1-(1+0.01375)^{-80}}$$

We will use logarithms to compute 1.01375^{-80} and then do the rest by ordinary arithmetic.

Let $N = (1.01375)^{-80}$

Then $\log N = -80 \log 1.01375$

$= -80\ (0.0059308) = -0.474464 = 9.525536 - 10$

$N = 0.33538$ (Tabular value is 0.33537495)

$$R = \$50{,}000 \frac{.01375}{.66462}$$

$= \$50{,}000\ (0.02069)$

$= \$\ 1{,}034.50$

FINDING THE PERIODIC RENT OF ANNUITY WHERE PAYMENT INTERVAL DOES NOT COINCIDE WITH INTEREST PERIOD

Formula:

$$R = \frac{1}{a_{\overline{n}|\,i}} = S \cdot \frac{i}{1-(1+i)^{-n}}$$

(See page 22 for symbols)

Example:

The XYZ Bank financed a mortgage of \$10,000 at 6% interest per annum for 20 years, payable in quarterly installments including interest. How much is the quarterly payment?

Solution:

Since the payment interval does not coincide with the interest period, we need to compute the equivalent rate.

$r = (1+i)^m - 1 = (1+.06)^{\frac{1}{4}} - 1$

Let $N = (1.06)^{\frac{1}{4}}$

Then $\log N = \frac{1}{4} \log 1.06 = \frac{1}{4}(0.025306) = 0.0063265$ (Table VI)

$N = 1.01467$

So $r = 1.467\%$ quarterly

$$R = \$10{,}000 \cdot \frac{0.01467}{1-(1.01467)^{-80}}$$

Let $M = (1.01467)^{-80}$

Then $\log M = -80 \log 1.01467 = -80\ (0.0063265)$ (Table VII)

$$= -0.506120 = 9.493880 - 10$$

$$M = 0.31180$$

$$R = \$10{,}000\,\frac{0.01467}{1 - 0.31180} = \$10{,}000\,\frac{0.01467}{0.68820}$$

$$= \$10{,}000\ (0.02132) = \$213.20$$

Note: Had the interest been 6% compounded quarterly, the problem could have easily been solved by tables. From Table V, we see that the rent would be \$871.85 per year. This compares closely with the results obtained in this example: $4 \times \$213.20 = \$872.20$. Thus the results obtained from quarterly payments with interest computed annually vary only slightly from the results obtained with the interest computed for the period coinciding with the payment period.

FINDING THE TERM OF AN ANNUITY (LOGARITHMS)

Formula:

$$n = \frac{\log\left(1 + \frac{S}{R}\, i\right)}{\log\,(1 + i)}$$

where

n = number of conversion periods
R = Rent
S = Amount of the Annuity
i = Interest Rate per Period

Example:

The controller of the XYZ Co. wishes to set up a fund to accumulate \$75,000.00 for future plant expansion. The controller has budgeted \$2,000.00 per month to be invested for this purpose. The controller has been advised that the funds could be safely invested at a rate of 4% per year. How many months will be required to accumulate the necessary funds?

Solution:

$$n = \frac{\log\left[1 + \frac{75{,}000}{2{,}000} \cdot \frac{1}{300}\right]}{\log\left(1 + \frac{1}{300}\right)}$$

$$= \frac{\log\left[1 + 37.5\ \frac{1}{300}\right]}{\log\left(\frac{301}{300}\right)} = \frac{\log(1 + 0.125)}{\log\left(\frac{301}{300}\right)}$$

$$= \frac{0.051153}{2.478566 - 2.477121} \qquad \text{(Table VI)}$$

$$= \frac{0.051153}{0.001445} = 35.4 \text{ months}$$

Three years should be adequate.

FINDING THE INTEREST RATE OF AN ANNUITY—USING TABLES

Formula:

$$\frac{S}{R} = \frac{(1 + i)^n - 1}{i}$$

where

S = Amount of the Annuity
R = Rent
n = Number of Conversion Periods
i = Interest Rate per Period

Example:

The XYZ Corporation desires to accumulate \$45,000 by the end of 11 years for a proposed expansion program. If the company can set aside \$3,000 at the end of each year, what rate of yearly interest will the fund have to earn?

Solution:

$$\frac{45{,}000}{3{,}000} = \frac{(1 + i)^{11} - 1}{i}$$

or

$$15 = \frac{(1 + i)^{11} - 1}{i}$$

From Table III, we see that $\frac{(1 + .06)^{11} - 1}{.06} = 14.976$.

We conclude that the interest rate per annum must be slightly in excess of 6%.

FINDING THE INTEREST RATE OF AN ANNUITY

Formula:

$$\frac{S}{R} = \frac{(1+i)^n - 1}{i}$$

(See page 25 for symbols)

Example:

The Able Manufacturing Company desires to accumulate \$133,000 by the end of 15 years. The company can set aside \$1,500 quarterly. What yearly rate of interest must the money earn?

Solution:

We first find the quarterly rate.

$$\frac{133{,}000}{1{,}500} = \frac{(1+i)^{60} - 1}{i}$$

$$88.6667 = \frac{(1+i)^{60} - 1}{i}$$

From Table III, we see that $\frac{(1+.0125)^{60} - 1}{.0125} = 88.57$.

The money must earn just in excess of $1\frac{1}{4}\%$ per quarter.
To find the yearly rate, r, we solve

$$\begin{aligned} r &= (1+i)^m - 1 \\ &= (1.0125)^4 - 1 \end{aligned}$$

From Table I, we see that $1.0125^4 = 1.0509$. Thus $r = 5.09\%$. Hence the money must earn about 5.1% per annum.

5

STATISTICS: AVERAGES AND VARIATION FORMULAS

AVERAGE: ARITHMETIC MEAN (UNGROUPED DATA)

Formula:

$$M = \frac{\sum_{1}^{N} fX}{N}$$

where

M – arithmetic mean

$\sum_{1}^{N}$ = add all observations from 1st through last

f = frequency or number of times an observation occurs.

X = magnitude of any one observation

N = total number of observations = $\Sigma\ f$

Example:

What is the average (arithmetic mean) amount outstanding from the following amounts on statements being mailed to customers?

$20.00, $15.20, $43.80, $5.70, $20.00,
$31.20, $43.80, $10.30, $4.20, $43.80.

Solution:

X	f	fX
$20.00	2	$40.00
15.20	1	15.20
43.80	3	131.40
5.70	1	5.70
31.20	1	31.20
10.30	1	10.30
4.20	1	4.20
	10	$238.00

$$\sum_{1}^{N} fX = \$238.00$$

$$N = 10$$

$$M = \frac{\$238.00}{10} = \$23.80$$

AVERAGE: ARITHMETIC MEAN (GROUPED DATA) SHORT-CUT METHOD

Formula:

$$M = M' + \frac{\left(\sum_{1}^{K} f \frac{x'}{i}\right) i}{N}$$

where

M = arithmetic mean

M' = assumed arithmetic mean

K = number of classes

f = frequency or number of observations in a class

x' = deviation = difference between midpoint of a class and assumed mean

i = class range

$\frac{x'}{i}$ = deviation divided by class range

$\sum_{1}^{k}$ = add for all K classes

N = total number of observations = $\sum_{1}^{K} f$

Example and Solution:

What is the average (arithmetic mean) weekly wage when computed from the following frequency distribution:

Wage Class (In Dollars)	*Number of workers* f	$\frac{x'}{i}$	$\frac{fx'}{i}$
60.00–64.99	4	−4	−16
65.00–69.99	8	−3	−24

Wage Class (In Dollars)	*Number of workers* f	$\frac{x'}{i}$	$f\frac{x'}{i}$
70.00–74.99	12	−2	−24
75.00–79.99	15	−1	−15
80.00–84.99	23	0	0
85.00–89.99	18	1	18
90.00–94.99	10	2	20
95.00–99.99	5	3	15
100.00–104.99	3	4	12
105.00–109.99	2	5	10
	100		−4

M' = midpoint of class to left of 0 in x'/i column = \$82.50

$$\sum_1^K f\frac{x'}{i} = -4 \qquad N = 100 \qquad i = \$5.00$$

$$M = \$82.50 + \frac{(-4)\ (\$5.00)}{100} = \$82.50 - \frac{\$20.00}{100} = \$82.30$$

AVERAGE: MEDIAN (UNGROUPED DATA)

Method:

Find value belonging to center position when observations are arranged in order of magnitude.

Example (odd number of observations):

What is the median average amount of assets of the 11 firms having the following assets (expressed in thousands of dollars):

150, 220, 180, 502, 307, 142, 678, 996, 810, 760, 910

Solution:

Arrange observations in order of magnitude and eliminate the 5 lowest. The observation in the 6th position (middle position) is the median.

142, 150, 180, 220, 307, (502), 678, 760, 810, 910, 996

5 lowest observations — Median — 5 highest observations

Median = \$502,000.

Example (even number of observations):

What is the median average amount of assets of the 10 firms having the following assets (expressed in thousands of dollars):

150, 508, 673, 810, 270, 816, 513, 278, 680, 627

Solution:

Arrange observations in order of magnitude and compute the value midway between the 2 center position observations. This value is the median.

150, 270, 278, 508, 513, 627, 673, 680, 810, 816

$\longrightarrow \longleftarrow$

570

Median

Median = $570,000.

AVERAGE: MEDIAN (GROUPED DATA)

Formula:

$$Md. = l_{Md.} + \frac{\left(\frac{N}{2} - \sum_{1}^{Md.\ class} f\right) i}{f_{Md.}}$$

where

$Md.$ = median

$l_{Md.}$ = lower limit of median class

N = total number of observations = Σf

f = frequency = number of observations in a class

$\sum_{1}^{Md.\ class} f$ = add frequencies in classes beginning with smallest class and continuing to median class. (Median class is class containing observation in center position).

i = median class range

$f_{Md.}$ = number of observations in median class

Example:

What is the number of miles traveled daily which has half of the salesmen traveling more and half traveling less? The miles traveled daily were obtained from the expense records and were then classified into the following groups:

Class (*Miles traveled daily*)	*f* (*Number of salesmen's daily reports*)
Under 10	9
10.00 - 13.99	12
14.00 - 17.99	20
18.00 - 21.99	25
22.00 - 25.99	12
26.00 - 29.99	9
30.00 - 33.99	6
34.00 - 37.99	3
38.00 - 41.99	3
42.00 - 45.99	2
46 and over	1
	102

$N = 102$ $\qquad$ $f_{Md.} = 25$

$N/2 = 51$ $\qquad$ Median class = 18.00 – 21.99

$$\sum_{1}^{\text{Md. class}} f = 9 + 12 + 20 = 41 \qquad l_{Md.} = 18.00 \qquad i = 4$$

$$Md. = 18.00 \text{ miles} + \left(\frac{51 - 41}{25}\right) 4 \text{ miles} = 18.00 + 1.6 = 19.6 \text{ miles}$$

AVERAGE: MODE (UNGROUPED DATA)

Method:

Find the observation which occurs most frequently in the set of observations.

Example:

The following errors were reported representing those made in registering sales on the cash registers (expressed in number of cents):

50, 83, 52, 93, 50, 63, 50, 83, 48, 50, 15, 50, 91, 37, 29

50 cents occurs 5 times
83 cents occurs 2 times
52, 93, 63, 48, 15, 91, 37, 29 cents each occurs 1 time

Therefore the mode was 50 cents.

AVERAGE: MODE (GROUPED DATA)

Formula:

$$Mo. = 1_{Mo.} + \left(\frac{\Delta_1}{\Delta_1 + \Delta_2}\right) i$$

where

$Mo.$ = mode

$1_{Mo.}$ = lower limit of modal class

Δ_1 = difference between number of observations falling in modal class and number of observations falling in class *preceding* modal class.

Δ_2 = difference between number of observations falling in modal class and number of observations falling in class *following* modal class

i = range of modal class

Example and Solution:

What is the most frequently occurring amount of a sale when the amounts classified are as follows:

Class (*Amount of sale in dollars*)	*f* (*Number of sales transactions*)
Under 1.00	3
1.00–1.99	4
2.00–2.99	10
3.00–3.99	25
4.00–4.99	15
5.00–5.99	8
6.00–6.99	4
7.00–7.99	4
8.00–8.99	3
9.00–9.99	2
10.00 and over	1
	79

Modal class = class having highest f = \$3.00 – \$3.99

$1_{Mo.} = \$3.00$

$\Delta_1 = 25 - 10 = 15$

$\Delta_2 = 25 - 15 = 10$

$i = \$1.00$

$$Mo. = \$3.00 + \left(\frac{15}{15 + 10}\right) \$1.00 = \$3.00 + \$0.60 = \$3.60$$

VARIATION: QUARTILE DEVIATION (GROUPED DATA)

Formula:

$$Q.\,D. = \frac{Q_3 - Q_1}{2}$$

where

$Q.\,D.$ = quartile deviation

Q_1 = first quartile point. (With respect to magnitude, 25% of observations are below this point and 75% are above it).

Q_3 = third quartile point. (With respect to magnitude, 75% of observations are below this point and 25% are above it).

Example:

What was the range of the middle 50% of the workers' intelligence scores which were grouped into the following classes? (Scores are in whole numbers only).

Class (*Intelligence Score*)	*f* *Number of Workers*
65–69	1
70–74	3
75–79	8
80–84	18
85–89	20
90–94	18
95–99	8
100–104	3
105–109	1
	80

Solution:

Note: Q_1 and Q_3 are positional points comparable to the Median which is Q_2. The computation, therefore is very similar.

$$Q_1 = 80 + \left(\frac{80/4 - 12}{18}\right)4 = 80 + \left(\frac{8}{18}\right)4 = 82 \text{ (rounded to whole number)}$$

$$Q_3 = 90 + \left(\frac{3/4\,(80) - 50}{18}\right)4 = 90 + \left(\frac{10}{18}\right)4 = 92 \text{ (rounded to whole number)}$$

$$Q.\,D. = \frac{92 - 82}{2} = 5 \qquad \text{Median} = 87$$

Middle 50% of workers, according to scores, fell between *Md.* $\pm Q.\ D.$ or 87 ± 5 or between 82 and 92.

Note: This answer was known when Q_1 and Q_3 were computed because this distribution is a symmetrical one. This would not have been true if the distribution had been skewed (not symmetrical). In this latter case the median plus and minus the quartile deviation usually includes more than the middle 50%, the excess over 50% depending upon the amount of the skewness.

VARIATION: STANDARD DEVIATION (VARIATES—UNGROUPED DATA)

Formula:

$$\sigma = \sqrt{\frac{\sum_{1}^{N} f x^2}{N}}$$

where

σ = standard deviation

f = frequency = number of times an observation occurs

x^2 = squared deviation = squared difference between observation and arithmetic mean

$\sum_{1}^{N} fx^2$ = add all products of fx^2 from first through last

N = total number of observations

Example:

What is the standard deviation of the following numbers of days absent during a work year for 20 employees of a unit?

X (*Days absent*)	f (*Number workers*)	x $(X - M)$*	fx *	fx^2
1	1	−9	−9	81
3	1	−7	−7	49
3	1	−7	−7	49
4	1	−6	−6	36
6	1	−4	−4	16
7	1	−3	−3	9
7	1	−3	−3	9

X (*Days absent*)	f (*Number workers*)	x $(X - M)$*	fx *	fx^2
9	1	−1	−1	1
10	1	0	0	0
11	1	1	1	1
11	1	1	1	1
11	1	1	1	1
12	1	2	2	4
14	1	4	4	16
14	1	4	4	16
14	1	4	4	16
15	1	5	5	25
15	1	5	5	25
16	1	6	6	36
17	1	7	7	49
200	20			440

*These two columns have been included for clarity. They can be omitted when computations are made.

Solution:

$$\sum_{1}^{20} fx^2 = 440 \qquad M = 200/20 = 10$$

$$N = 20$$

$$\sigma = \sqrt{\frac{440}{20}} = \sqrt{22} = 4.7$$

VARIATION: STANDARD DEVIATION (VARIATES—GROUPED DATA)

Formula:

$$\sigma = i\sqrt{\frac{\sum_{1}^{k} f\left(\frac{x'}{i}\right)^2}{N} - \left(\frac{\sum_{1}^{k} f\frac{x'}{i}}{N}\right)^2}$$

where

σ = standard deviation

i = class size

f = class frequency (number of observations in a class)

x' = deviation = difference between class midpoint and assumed mean. (Assumed mean is midpoint of class opposite x'/i column value of 0).

k = total number of classes
N = total number of observations
$\sum_{1}^{k}$ = add from first through kth class.

Example:

What is the range of wages paid to approximately the middle 2/3 of the workers having the following wage distribution?

Class (*$ Weekly wage*)	f (*Number workers*)	$\frac{x'}{i}$	$f\frac{x'}{i}$	$f\left(\frac{x'}{i}\right)^2$
60.00–64.99	4	−4	−16	64
65.00–69.99	8	−3	−24	72
70.00–74.99	12	−2	−24	48
75.00–79.99	15	−1	−15	15
80.00–84.99	23	0	0	0
85.00–89.99	18	1	18	18
90.00–94.99	10	2	20	40
95.00–99.99	5	3	15	45
100.00–104.99	3	4	12	48
105.00–109.99	2	5	10	50
	100		− 4	400

Solution:

$$N = 100 \qquad \sum_{1}^{k} f\left(\frac{x'}{i}\right)^2 = 400$$

$$\sum_{1}^{k} f\frac{x'}{i} = -4 \qquad i = 5$$

$$\sigma = 5\sqrt{\frac{400}{100} - \left(\frac{-4}{100}\right)^2} = 5\sqrt{4.00 - .0016} = 5\sqrt{4.00} = 10$$

$\sigma = \$10$ $\qquad$ $M = \$82.30$ (see p. 29 for the computation of mean)

Range of middle 2/3 = \$82.30 ± \$10 = range from \$72.30 to \$92.30.

Note: In a normal distribution:

$M \pm 1\sigma$ includes about the middle 68% of the observations
$M \pm 2\sigma$ includes about the middle 95% of the observations
$M \pm 3\sigma$ includes about the middle 99.7% of the observations.

The above distribution is not normal. For that distribution $M \pm \sigma$ includes the middle 66%.

PROBABLE ERROR

Formula:

$$P.E._s = 0.6745\,S$$

where

$P.E._s$ = probable error based on a statistic (s)

s = standard deviation

Example:

It is known that the arithmetic mean size of sale for all sales is $7.00 and the standard deviation is $2.00. What is the lowest and highest points of sales that have equal probabilities of having sales fall in this range as having sales fall outside this range?

Solution:

$PE_\sigma = 0.6745\ (\$2.00) = \$1.35$

$\$7.00 \pm \$1.35 = \$5.65$ to $8.35. Therefore one might expect (if the sales were normally distributed) to find 50 per cent of the sales falling between $5.65 and $8.35, and the other 50 per cent of the sales less than $5.65 or larger than $8.35.

6

STATISTICS: SAMPLING

STANDARD ERROR OF THE MEAN. Variates. Sample small relative to universe. Standard deviation of universe known.

Formula:

$$\sigma_{\overline{X}} = \frac{\sigma}{\sqrt{n}}$$

where

$\sigma_{\overline{X}}$ = standard error of mean
σ = standard deviation of the universe
n = number of items in sample

Example:

A very large number of samples have been taken where each sample was composed of 9 observations on the number of errors made by a worker during 9 different days. The arithmetic mean of the 9 observations was then found for each of the large number of samples. How variable were these means if it was known that the standard deviation for all errors of all workers like those in the samples taken is equal to 3?

Solution:

$$\sigma_{\overline{X}} = \frac{\sigma}{\sqrt{n}}$$

$$\sigma_{\overline{X}} = \frac{3}{\sqrt{9}} = 1$$

Assuming a normal sampling distribution of means, one would expect the workers with least errors to average about 6 less than the average for the workers with most errors. (If the distribution is normal, six times the standard error of the mean, in this case 1, would include 99.7 per cent of the means).

STANDARD ERROR OF A PROPORTION. Universe large relative to sample.

Formula:

$$\sigma_P = \sqrt{\frac{P(1-P)}{n}}$$

where

σ_P = standard error of a proportion
P = proportion of "successes" in universe (success is a favorable event happening)
$1-P$ = proportion of "failures" in universe (failure is unfavorable event happening)
n = number in the sample

Example:

Can a sample of 100 having a 60 per cent preference of office workers for a 30 minute lunch hour come from a universe of all workers like these where there is actually an even division between preference for a 30 minute and a one-hour lunch period? (Assume that the 1 per cent level of significance is desired).

Solution:

$$\sigma_P = \sqrt{\frac{50\,(1-50)}{100}} = \sqrt{\frac{2500}{100}} = 5$$

$$= 5 \text{ per cent}$$

$$Z = \frac{60\% - 50\%}{5\%} = 2$$

Yes, the sample could come from such a universe of equal division in preferences. Z indicates that the sample proportion (60) differs from the universe proportion (50) by only 2 standard errors. If one is making his decision at the 1 per cent level of significance, this difference would have to be at least as great as 2.33 standard errors. Since this difference is only 2 standard errors, it is therefore not regarded as significant.

STANDARD ERROR OF THE MEAN. Variates. Sample size small relative to size of universe. Standard deviation of universe not known .

Formula:

$$\sigma_{\overline{X}} = \frac{s}{\sqrt{n-1}}$$

where

$\sigma_{\overline{X}}$ = standard error of mean
s = standard deviation for items in sample
n = number of items in sample

Example:

Book inventories have been compared to physical inventories and the size of the discrepancies noted. There are too many figures to use all of them. A random sample of 101 is selected. The standard deviation for these 101 is then computed and found to be $2,000. What is the standard error for a sampling distribution of means for all samples like the one taken? (Thus a measure of the variation among the discrepancies could be obtained).

Solution:

$$\sigma_{\overline{X}} = \frac{s}{\sqrt{n-1}} = \frac{2{,}000}{\sqrt{101-1}} = 200$$

Therefore the standard error of the mean discrepancy is $200.

STANDARD ERROR OF MEAN. Variates. Sample size large relative to size of universe.

Formula:

$$\sigma_{\overline{X}} = \frac{\sigma}{\sqrt{n}}\sqrt{\frac{N-n}{N-1}}$$

where

$\sigma_{\overline{X}}$ = standard error of the mean
σ = standard deviation of the universe
n = number in sample
N = number in universe

Example:

What is the standard error for the sampling distribution of means for samples of petty cash amounts if there are a total of 101 such accounts and a random sample of 36 of the 101 have been studied? It is known that the standard deviation of the 101 accounts is $12.

Solution:

$$\sigma_{\overline{X}} = \frac{\$12}{\sqrt{36}} \sqrt{\frac{101 - 36}{101 - 1}} = \$2.00 \sqrt{\frac{65}{100}} = \$2(.8) = \$1.60$$

Therefore the standard error of the mean is $1.60.

STANDARD ERROR OF PROPORTION. Sample size large relative to size of universe.

Formula:

$$\sigma_P = \sqrt{\frac{P(1-P)}{n}} \sqrt{\frac{N-n}{N-1}}$$

where

σ_P = standard error of a proportion
P = proportion of "successes" in universe. (A success is the occurrence of a favorable event)
$1 - P$ = proportion of "failures" in universe. (A failure is the occurrence of an unfavorable event)
n = number of items in the sample
N = number of items in the universe

Example:

Can a sample of 100 having a 60 per cent preference of office workers for a 30 minute lunch hour come from a universe of 1000 where the workers are evenly divided between preferences for a 30 minute and a 1-hour lunch period, if one is willing to be off in his decision 1 time in 100?

Solution:

$$\sigma_P = \sqrt{\frac{50 \times 50}{100}} \sqrt{\frac{1000 - 100}{1000 - 1}} = (5)\left(\frac{30}{31.6}\right) = 4.74$$

$$= 4.74\%.$$

$$Z = \frac{60\% - 50\%}{4.74\%} = \frac{10}{4.74} = 2.10$$

Yes, the sample could come from the universe where preferences were equally divided. The Z value is 2.10. This value would have to equal or exceed 2.33 in order to make the decision in this case that the 60 is significantly different from the 50.

STANDARD ERROR OF DIFFERENCES BETWEEN ARITHMETIC MEANS

Variates. Assuming independence.

Formula:

$$\sigma_{\overline{X}_1-\overline{X}_2} = \sqrt{\sigma_{\overline{X}_1}^2 + \sigma_{\overline{X}_2}^2}$$

where

$\sigma_{\overline{X}_1-\overline{X}_2}$ = standard error of difference between arithmetic means

$\sigma_{\overline{X}_1}^2$ = standard error squared of mean 1. (See pages 38, 40 for method of computation of this standard error)

$\sigma_{\overline{X}_2}^2$ = standard error squared for mean 2. (See pages 38, 40 for method of computation of this standard error)

Example:

If the average working capital requirement per week this year, based on a sample of 16 representative weeks, was \$200,000, and last year based on the sample of the same number of weeks, it was \$195,000, was this a significant difference this year from last based on the 95 per cent confidence level? The standard deviation for all weeks is known to be \$10,000.

Solution:

$$\sigma_{\overline{X}_1}^2 = \left(\frac{10{,}000}{\sqrt{16}}\right)^2 = \left(\frac{10{,}000}{4}\right)^2 = (2{,}500)^2 = 6{,}250{,}000$$

$$= \$6{,}250{,}000$$

$$\sigma_{\overline{X}_2}^2 = \$6{,}250{,}000 \text{ also}$$

$$\sigma_{\overline{X}_1-\overline{X}_2} = \sqrt{6{,}250{,}000 + 6{,}250{,}000} = \sqrt{12{,}500{,}000} = 3{,}535$$

$$= \$3{,}535$$

$$Z = \frac{\$200{,}000 - \$195{,}000}{\$3{,}535} = \frac{5{,}000}{3{,}535} = 1.41$$

Therefore the difference could be attributed to sampling error and is not significant. Z equals 1.41. It would have to be 1.96 or greater to show significance at the 95% level, where the decision was to be made.

STANDARD ERROR OF DIFFERENCE BETWEEN PROPORTIONS.
Assuming independence.

Formula:

$$\sigma_{P_1-P_2} = \sqrt{\sigma^2_{P_1} + \sigma^2_{P_2}}$$

where

$\sigma_{P_1-P_2}$ = standard error of difference between proportions

$\sigma^2_{P_1}$ = standard error squared of proportion 1. (See pp. 39, 41 for method of computation).

$\sigma^2_{P_2}$ = standard error squared of proportion 2. (See pp. 39, 41 for method of computation).

Example:

The proportion of 100 overdue accounts receivable, which were overdue for as much or more than 3 months, selected at random from this year's list, was 5%. The comparable proportion from last year's list was 3%. Is this a significant increase over last year at the 5% level of significance?

Solution:

$$\sigma^2_{P_1} = \frac{P(1-P)}{n} = \frac{(5)(95)}{100} = 4.75$$

$$= 4.75\%$$

$$\sigma^2_{P_2} = \frac{P(1-P)}{n} = \frac{(3)(97)}{100} = 2.91$$

$$= 2.91\%$$

$$\sigma_{P_1-P_2} = \sqrt{4.75 + 2.91} = \sqrt{7.66} = 2.77$$

$$= 2.77\%$$

$$Z = \frac{5\% - 3\%}{2.77\%} = \frac{2}{2.77} = .72$$

It is therefore not a significant difference at the 5% level of significance. The difference could be attributed to errors of sampling. (The Z value of .72 is less than 1.96 which is necessary at the 95% confidence level.)

STANDARD ERROR OF MEDIAN

Formula:

$$\sigma_{Md.} = 1.25\,\sigma_{\bar{X}}$$

where

$\sigma_{Md.}$ = standard error of median
$\sigma_{\overline{X}}$ = standard error of arithmetic mean

Example:

A random sample of 121 persons having expense accounts was selected. The vouchers belonging to each of these 121 persons were then classified under the appropriate name to whom each belonged. The median amounts of the expenses and the arithmetic mean amounts were then computed for each of the 121 individuals. The standard error of the arithmetic mean amounts was then computed and found to be \$2.20. What was the standard error of the median amounts?

Solution:

$$\begin{aligned}\sigma_{Md.} &= 1.25\,\sigma_{\overline{X}} \\ &= 1.25\,(\$2.20) \\ &= \$2.75\end{aligned}$$

Therefore the standard error of the median amounts in this case is \$2.75.

SAMPLE SIZE. Variables. Sample small in proportion to size of universe. Standard deviation of universe can be determined.

Formula:

$$n = \frac{Z^2 \sigma^2}{E^2}$$

where

n = number of items in sample
Z^2 = square of confidence level in standard error units
σ^2 = square of standard deviation of universe
E^2 = square of maximum difference between true mean and sample mean —the allowance for sampling error.

Example:

A random sample is to be taken from 4000 statements to verify the amounts on the statements. The allowable sampling error is \$5. The sample size is to be large enough that this error is not exceeded more than 1 time in 100. What size should the sample be?

Solution:

$Z^2 = (2.58)^2$

$\sigma^2 = (31.34)^2$

(This was obtained from the knowledge that the total range in the statements was from \$120 to \$276.70 or \$156.70. The standard deviation could be estimated to be 1/5 of \$156.70 or \$31.34)

$E^2 = (\$5)^2$

$$n = \frac{(2.58)^2\,(31.34)^2}{(5)^2} = \frac{6.6564 \times 982.20}{25} = \frac{6538}{25}$$

$$= 262$$

Therefore the required sample size would be 262.

SAMPLE SIZE. Proportions. Sample small in relation to size of universe.

Formula:

$$n = \frac{Z^2 P(1 - P)}{E^2}$$

where

n = number of items in sample

Z^2 = square of confidence level in standard error units

P = proportion of "successes" in universe. (A success is the occurrence of a favorable event)

$1 - P$ = proportion of "failures" in universe. (A failure is the occurrence of an unfavorable event)

E^2 = square of maximum difference between true proportion and sample proportion—the allowance for sampling error.

Example:

From 10,000 items, a random sample is to be taken for verification purposes. It is believed that 90% of the totals on the forms to be studied are correct. The sample size is to be large enough that an observed difference in the sample proportion from the true proportion would not vary more than 3% five times out of 100.

Solution:

$Z^2 = (1.96)^2$

$P = 90$

$1 - P = 10$

$E^2 = (3)^2$

$$n = \frac{(1.96)^2\,(.90)\,(.10)}{(.03)^2} = \frac{(3.84)\,(.09)}{.0009} = \frac{.3456}{.0009}$$

$= 384$, sample size

SAMPLE SIZE. Variables. Finite Universe.

Formula:

$$n = \frac{N}{\dfrac{(N-1)E^2}{Z^2\sigma^2} + 1}$$

where

n = number of items in sample
N = number of items in universe
Z^2 = square of confidence level in standard error units
σ^2 = square of standard deviation of universe
E^2 = square of maximum allowance for sampling error

Example:

A sample is to be taken from a universe of 2,000 items for verification. The universe standard deviation was estimated from a pilot study to be \$50. The error is not to exceed \$10, two times out of 100. How many should be selected for the sample to be verified?

Solution:

$n = ?$

$N = 2{,}000$

$Z^2 = (2.33)^2$

$\sigma^2 = (50)^2$

$E^2 = (10)^2$

$$n = \frac{2{,}000}{\dfrac{(1999)(100)}{(2.33)^2(50)^2} + 1} = \frac{2000}{\dfrac{199900}{13572} + 1} = \frac{2{,}000}{15.7288}$$

$= 127$, sample size

SAMPLE SIZE. Proportions. Finite Universe.

Formula:

$$n = \frac{N}{\dfrac{(N-1)E^2}{Z^2 P(1-P)} + 1}$$

where

n = number in sample
N = number in universe
E^2 = square of maximum allowance for sampling error
Z^2 = square of confidence level in standard error units
P = proportion of successes in universe. (A success is the occurrence of a favorable event)
$1 - P$ = proportion of failures in universe. (A failure is the occurrence of an unfavorable event)

Example:

A sample is to be taken from a total of 2,000 items for verification. It is estimated that the universe proportion of error is 10 per cent. An allowance of .05 is to be made for sampling error. Z is to be 2.33. What size random sample should be selected?

Solution:

$N = 2{,}000$

$E^2 = (.05)^2$

$Z^2 = (2.33)^2$

$P = .90 \qquad 1 - P = .10$

Therefore $$n = \frac{2{,}000}{\dfrac{(2{,}000-1)(.05)^2}{(2.33)^2(.90)(.10)} + 1} = \frac{2{,}000}{\dfrac{4.9975}{.4886} + 1} = \frac{2{,}000}{11.228}$$

$= 178$, sample size

7

STATISTICS: CORRELATION

REGRESSION.

Linear. One independent variable.

Formula:

$$Y' = b_{11} + b_{12}X$$

where

Y' = any value of the dependent variable on the regression line
b_{11} = Y intercept of regression line (value of Y' where $X = O$)
b_{12} = slope of regression line (ratio of the change in Y for a given change in X)
X = any value of the independent variable

Example:

(a) What is the average relationship between total cost and units produced on a given job?

(b) What is the fixed cost, the average variable cost?

Data

Job Lot Number	*Number Units Produced* X	*Total Cost (Dollars)* Y	XY	X^2	Y^2
1	5	9	45	25	81
2	4	8	32	16	64
3	3	6	18	9	36
4	8	12	96	64	144
5	9	14	126	81	196
6	6	12	72	36	144
7	10	14	140	100	196
8	3	8	24	9	64
9	2	7	14	4	49

Data (*continued*)

Job Lot Number	*Number Units Produced* X	*Total Cost (Dollars)* Y	XY	X^2	Y^2
10	2	6	12	4	36
11	3	10	30	9	100
12	6	10	60	36	100
13	9	15	135	81	225
14	7	14	98	49	196
15	5	11	55	25	121
16	7	13	91	49	169
17	6	11	66	36	121
18	6	13	78	36	169
19	7	10	70	49	100
20	5	10	50	25	100
21	5	12	60	25	144
22	6	14	84	36	196
23	4	9	36	16	81
24	8	14	112	64	196
25	9	13	117	81	169
	145	275	1721	965	3197
	ΣX	ΣY	ΣXY	ΣX^2	ΣY^2

Solution (Least Squares Method):

I $\quad \Sigma Y = b_{11} N + b_{12} \Sigma X$ (with summations over all

II $\quad \Sigma XY = b_{11} \Sigma X + b_{12} \Sigma X^2$ values of variables indicated)

$$
\begin{array}{lrl}
\text{I} & 275 = & 25\, b_{11} + 145\, b_{12} \\
\text{II} & 1721 = & 145\, b_{11} + 965\, b_{12} \\
\text{I}(5.8) & 1595 = & 145\, b_{11} + 841\, b_{12} \\
\hline
\text{II-I}(5.8) & 126 = & 124\, b_{12}
\end{array}
$$

$$b_{12} = \frac{126}{124} = 1.02$$

Substituting 1.02 for b_{12} in equation I:

$$b_{11} = \frac{275 - 145\,(1.02)}{25} = 5.11$$

(a) Therefore the average line of relationship is:

$$Y' = 5.11 + 1.02\, X$$

(b) Average fixed cost: \$5.11

Average variable cost: for each additional unit produced, total cost increased \$1.02.

STANDARD ERROR OF ESTIMATE.

Linear Regression. One Independent variable.

Formula:

$$S_{yx} = \sqrt{\frac{\Sigma Y^2 - b_{11}\Sigma Y - b_{12}\Sigma XY}{N - 2}}$$

where

S_{yx} = standard error of estimate

ΣY^2 = sum of all squared values of dependent variable

b_{11} = Y intercept of regression line (Y value where $X = O$)

ΣY = sum of all values of dependent variable

b_{12} = slope of regression line

ΣXY = sum of all individual products formed by multiplying each X value by its corresponding Y value

N = total number of paired observations

Example:

Using the data given on pages 48, 49 and assuming a normal distribution of Y values for each X, what would be the expected total cost of 20 units? What statement could be made concerning the reliability of this result?

Solution:

Expected total cost for 20 units:

$$Y' = \$5.11 + \$1.02(20) = \$5.11 + \$20.40 = \$25.51$$

Statement concerning reliability of the \$25.51:

$$S_{yx} = \sqrt{\frac{3197 - 5.11(275) - 1.02(1721)}{23}} = \sqrt{\frac{36.33}{23}} = \sqrt{1.5796} = 1.26$$

If the statement is made that the cost of producing 20 units will average \$25.51, but that the cost may be anywhere in the range of \$25.51 ± \$1.26 (between \$24.25 and \$26.77), that statement would hold in approximately 2/3 (68%) of the cases like this, but would be expected to be outside this range of \$24.25 to \$26.77 in the other 1/3 of the cases like this.

\$25.51 ±(1.96)(\$1.26) would give a 95% confidence interval, and \$25.51 ± (2.58)(\$1.26) would give a 99% confidence interval, when the above stated assumptions hold.

COEFFICIENT OF DETERMINATION.

Linear regression. One independent variable.

Formula:

$$r^2 = 1 - \frac{S^2_{yx}}{S^2_y}$$

where

r^2 = coefficient of determination
S^2_{yx} = standard error of estimate squared (see page 50)
S^2_y = standard deviation of Y variable squared

Example:

What is the per cent of variation in cost of producing which is associated with the number of pieces produced? (See data on pages 48, 49 and computation of $S_{yx} = 1.26$ on page 50).

Solution:

$$r^2 = 1 - \frac{(1.26)^2}{S^2_y} \quad \text{where} \quad S^2_y = \frac{\Sigma Y^2}{N} - \frac{(\Sigma Y)^2}{N^2} = \frac{3197}{25} - \frac{(275)^2}{(25)^2}$$

$$= 127.88 - 121 = 6.88$$

$$= 1 - \frac{(1.26)^2}{6.88} = 1 - \frac{1.59}{6.88} = 1 - .23 = .77$$

Therefore 77 per cent of the variance in cost of producing is associated with the variation in the number of pieces produced. This leaves 23 per cent of the variation in cost which is *not* related to variation in number of units produced. This 23 per cent might be due to any of several other factors, one of which might be variation in materials quality.

COEFFICIENTOF CORRELATION.

Linear Regression. One independent variable.

A. Where coefficient of determination, r^2, is known:

Formula:

$$r = \pm\sqrt{r^2}$$

where

r = coefficient of correlation
r^2 = coefficient of determination

Example:

What is the coefficient of correlation for the data given on pages 48, 49 where r^2, or coefficient of determination, is .77?

Solution: $$r = \pm\sqrt{.77} = \pm .87$$

Note: The sign given to r depends on the sign of b_{12}, which for this example is plus. (See page 49). Therefore the result would be plus .87.

B. Where coefficient of determination, r^2, is not known:

Formula:

$$r = \frac{N\Sigma XY - (\Sigma X)(\Sigma Y)}{\sqrt{[N\Sigma X^2 - (\Sigma X)^2][N\Sigma Y^2 - (\Sigma Y)^2]}}$$

where

r = coefficient of correlation

$N\Sigma XY$ = Multiply each X by each corresponding Y. Add these products. Then multiply this sum by N, the total number of paired observations.

$(\Sigma X)(\Sigma Y)$ = Add all X values. Add all Y values. Multiply sum of X values by sum of Y values.

$N\Sigma X^2$ = square each X value. Add squared X values. Multiply this sum by N, the total number of paired observations.

$(\Sigma X)^2$ = Add all X values. Square this sum.

$N\Sigma Y^2$ = Square each Y value. Add squares. Multiply sum by N.

$(\Sigma Y)^2$ = Add all Y values. Square sum.

Example:

What is the coefficient of correlation for the data given on page 49 where:

$$N = 25 \qquad \Sigma X = 145$$
$$\Sigma XY = 1721 \qquad \Sigma Y = 275$$
$$\Sigma X^2 = 965 \qquad \Sigma Y^2 = 3197$$

Solution:

$$r = \frac{(25)(1721) - (145)(275)}{\sqrt{[(25)(965) - (145)^2][(25)(3197) - (275)^2]}}$$

$$= \frac{43025 - 39875}{\sqrt{(24125 - 21025)(79925 - 75625)}}$$

$$= \frac{3150}{\sqrt{(3100)(4300)}} = \frac{3150}{3651} = .86$$

Note: the difference in the .86 obtained here and the .87 obtained in A above is due to rounding.

REGRESSION.

Linear relationships. More than one independent variable.

Formula:

$$X_1 = b_{11} + b_{12}X_2 + b_{13}X_3$$

where

X_1 = any value of dependent variable on the net regression line (same as Y' used on page 49).
b_{11} = point of intersection of the regression lines of the planes
b_{12} = rate of change in X_1 as X_2 changes
X_2 = any value of first independent variable
b_{13} = rate of change in X_1 as X_3 changes
X_3 = any value of second independent variable

Example:

(a) What is the average relationship between total cost (X_1), units produced (X_2), and thickness of materials (X_3)?

(b) What total cost would be expected if 10 units were produced and the material thickness were 5 thousands of an inch?

(c) What is the change in cost if pieces produced changed from 10 to 11, while material thickness did not change?

(d) What is the change in cost if materials thickness changed from 4 to 5 thousands of an inch, while pieces produced did not change?

Data

Job Lot Number	*Total Cost ($)* X_1	*Number Units Produced* X_2	*Material Thickness (Thous. inch)* X_3	X_1^2	X_2^2	X_3^2	X_1X_2	X_1X_3	X_2X_3
1	9	5	4	81	25	16	45	36	20
2	8	4	3	64	16	9	32	24	12
3	6	3	2	36	9	4	18	12	6
4	12	8	5	144	64	25	96	60	40
5	12	6	4	144	36	16	72	48	24
6	14	9	6	196	81	36	126	84	54
7	14	10	6	196	100	36	140	84	60

Data (continued)

Job Lot Number	Total Cost ($) X_1	Number Units Produced X_2	Material Thickness (Thous. inch) X_3	X_1^2	X_2^2	X_3^2	X_1X_2	X_1X_3	X_2X_3
8	8	3	4	64	9	16	24	32	12
9	7	2	3	49	4	9	14	21	6
10	6	2	2	36	4	4	12	12	4
11	10	3	6	100	9	36	30	60	18
12	10	6	5	100	36	25	60	50	30
13	15	9	9	225	81	81	135	135	81
14	14	7	7	196	49	49	98	98	49
15	11	5	6	121	25	36	55	66	30
16	13	7	7	169	49	49	91	91	49
17	11	6	5	121	36	25	66	55	30
18	13	6	8	169	36	64	78	104	48
19	10	7	6	100	49	36	70	60	42
20	10	5	5	100	25	25	50	50	25
21	12	5	7	144	25	49	60	84	35
22	14	6	9	196	36	81	84	126	54
23	9	4	4	81	16	16	36	36	16
24	14	8	9	196	64	81	112	126	72
25	13	9	8	169	81	64	117	104	72
	275	145	140	3197	965	888	1721	1658	889
	ΣX_1	ΣX_2	ΣX_3	ΣX_1^2	ΣX_2^2	ΣX_3^2	ΣX_1X_2	ΣX_1X_3	ΣX_2X_3

Solution: (Least Squares method)

I $\quad \Sigma X_1 = b_{11}N + b_{12}\Sigma X_2 + b_{13}\Sigma X_3$

II $\quad \Sigma X_1X_2 = b_{11}\Sigma X_2 + b_{12}\Sigma X_2^2 + b_{13}\Sigma X_2X_3$

III $\quad \Sigma X_1X_3 = b_{11}\Sigma X_3 + b_{12}\Sigma X_2X_3 + b_{13}\Sigma X_3^2$

I $\quad 275 = 25b_{11} + 145b_{12} + 140b_{13}$

II $\quad 1721 = 145b_{11} + 965b_{12} + 889b_{13}$

III $\quad 1658 = 140b_{11} + 889b_{12} + 888b_{13}$

II $\quad 1721 = 145b_{11} + 965b_{12} + 889b_{13}$

I′ = (I)(5.8) $\quad 1595 = 145b_{11} + 841b_{12} + 812b_{13}$

IV = II − I′ $\quad 126 = 124b_{12} + 77b_{13}$

III	$1658 = 140b_{11} + 889b_{12} + 888b_{13}$
$I'' = I(5.6)$	$1540 = 140b_{11} + 812b_{12} + 784b_{13}$
$V = III - I(5.6)$	$118 = 77b_{12} + 104b_{13}$
IV	$126 = 124b_{12} + 77b_{13}$
$V' = V(1.61)$	$190 = 124b_{12} + 167b_{13}$
$V' - IV$	$64 = 90b_{13}$ $\qquad b_{13} = .71$

Substituting in V: $b_{12} = \dfrac{118 - 104b_{13}}{77} = \dfrac{118 - (104)(.71)}{77}$ $\qquad b_{12} = .57$

Substituting in I: $b_{11} = \dfrac{275 - 145b_{12} - 140b_{13}}{25}$

$$= \frac{275 - 145(.57) - 140(.71)}{25} = \frac{93}{25} \qquad b_{11} = 3.72$$

(a) Therefore the average relationship is: $X_1 = 3.72 + .57X_2 + .71X_3$

(b) If 10 units were produced and material thickness were 5 thousands of an inch, a total cost of $12.97 would be expected:

$$X_1 = 3.72 + .57(10) + .71(5) = 12.97$$

(c) If pieces produced is increased one piece, say from 10 to 11, while materials thickness does not change, the expected change in total cost would be $0.57.

(d) If materials thickness changed one thousands of an inch, say from 4 to 5 thousands of an inch, while number of pieces produced remained constant, the total cost would be expected to change $0.71 (the value of b_{13}).

MULTIPLE COEFFICIENT OF DETERMINATION.

Linear regression. More than one independent variable.

Formula:

$$R^2_{1.23} = 1 - \frac{S^2_{1.23}}{S_1^2}$$

where

$R^2_{1.23}$ = the coefficient of determination for variable 1 (the dependent variable) with variables 2 and 3 (the two independent variables)

$S^2_{1.23}$ = standard error of estimate squared for variable 1 as the dependent and variables 2 and 3 as independent

S^2_1 = standard deviation squared for variable 1 (dependent variable)

Example:

What is the per cent of variation in cost of producing dependent upon the number of pieces produced and the thickness of the materials used? (See data on page 54. See $S^2_1 = 6.88$ computed on page 51 and there indicated as S_y^2). (See page 54 for values of data needed for $S^2_{1.23}$).

Solution:

$$R^2_{1.23} = 1 - \frac{S^2_{1.23}}{S^2_1} = 1 - \frac{S^2_{1.23}}{6.88}$$

where

$$S^2_{1.23} = \frac{\Sigma X_1^2 - b_{11}\Sigma X_1 - b_{12}\Sigma X_1 X_2 - b_{13}\Sigma X_1 X_3}{n-3}$$

$$= \frac{3197 - (3.72)(275) - (.57)(1721) - (.71)(1658)}{22} = .72$$

$$R^2_{1.23} = 1 - \frac{.72}{6.88} = 1 - .11 = .89$$

Therefore 89 per cent of the variation in cost of producing is dependent upon number of pieces produced and thickness of material. By referring to page 51, it can be noted that the coefficient of determination is increased from 77 per cent to 89 per cent by adding a second independent variable.

PARTIAL CORRELATION.

Linear relationship. Two independent variables.

Formula:

$$r_{12.3} = \frac{r_{12} - (r_{13})(r_{23})}{\sqrt{(1 - r^2_{13})(1 - r^2_{23})}}$$

where

$r_{12.3}$ = the partial correlation coefficient, i.e. the relationship between variables 1 and 2 with the effects of variable 3 taken out.

r_{12} = zero order correlation coefficient for variables 1 and 2

r_{13} = zero order correlation coefficient for variables 1 and 3

r_{23} = zero order correlation coefficient for variables 2 and 3

r^2_{13} = the zero order correlation coefficient squared for variables 1 and 3

r^2_{23} = the zero order correlation coefficient squared for variables 2 and 3

Example:

It can be seen by reference to page 52 that the correlation between total cost of producing and number of pieces produced is .86. This is a gross relationship. How much would this relationship be reduced if the effect on either one or both of the given variables of the thickness of material used were to be taken out?

Solution:

$r_{12} = .86$ (see page 52 for computations).

$$r_{13} = \frac{(25)(1658) - (275)(140)}{\sqrt{[(25)(3197) - (275)^2][(25)(888) - (140)^2]}}$$

$$= \frac{41450 - 38500}{\sqrt{(79925 - 75625)(22200 - 19600)}} = \frac{2950}{\sqrt{11{,}180{,}000}} = .88$$

$$r_{23} = \frac{25(889) - (145)(140)}{\sqrt{[25(965) - (145)^2][25(888) - (140)^2]}}$$

$$= \frac{22225 - 20300}{\sqrt{(24125 - 21025)(22200 - 19600)}} = \frac{1925}{\sqrt{8{,}060{,}000}} = .68$$

Therefore:

$$r_{12.3} = \frac{.86 - (.88)(.68)}{\sqrt{[1 - (.88)^2][1 - (.68)^2]}} = \frac{.86 - .60}{\sqrt{(1 - .77)(1 - .46)}}$$

$$= \frac{.26}{\sqrt{(.23)(.54)}} = \frac{.26}{\sqrt{.1242}} = \frac{.26}{.35} = .74$$

Partialling out the effects of material thickness reduced the gross relationship between total cost and number of units produced from .86 to .74.

RANK ORDER COEFFICIENT OF CORRELATION

Formula:

$$\rho = 1 - \frac{6\Sigma d^2}{N(N^2 - 1)}$$

where

ρ = rank order correlation coefficient

Σd^2 = sum of squared differences between each pair of corresponding ranks

N = total number of pairs of ranks

Example:

For 20 jobs, it was possible to know their relative positions with respect to time spent and cost, but not possible to measure either variable precisely enough to have confidence in its exact size. The time spent and costs were therefore ranked as to their relative position among the 20 jobs as follows:

Job number	*Rank in amount of time spent on job*	*Rank in cost of job*	*Difference in ranks*	*Difference squared*
1	3	1	2	4
2	7	9	2	4
3	13	15	2	4
4	17	16	1	1
5	20	18	2	4
6	1	2	1	1
7	8	8	0	0
8	2	4	2	4
9	14	12	2	4
10	10	7	3	9
11	16	19	3	9
12	4	5	1	1
13	19	20	1	1
14	11	10	1	1
15	5	6	1	1
16	18	14	4	16
17	15	13	2	4
18	12	17	5	25
19	6	3	3	9
20	9	11	2	4
				$106 = \Sigma d^2$

$$\rho = 1 - \frac{6\,(106)}{20\,(20^2 - 1)} = 1 - \frac{636}{7980} = 1 - .08 = .92$$

The rank order correlation coefficient is .92.

RELIABILITY OF CORRELATION COEFFICIENTS.

Linear Relationships

Formula:

$$\sigma_r = \frac{1 - r^2}{\sqrt{N - 2}}$$

where

σ_r = standard error of the correlation coefficient, r.
r^2 = coefficient of correlation, squared
N = number of pairs of observations used to compute r

Example:

A correlation coefficient of .40 was found from a sample of 51 clerical workers when the total number of minutes late reporting for work each morning for a month was matched against the total job production for that month for each of the 51. How reliable was this .40? Could the .40 have arisen due to sampling error while in reality there was no real basis for believing that there was a relationship between "reporting on time for work in the morning" and "production."

Solution:

The hypothesis to be tested is that there is no correlation in this type of universe.

Therefore:
$$\sigma_r = \frac{1 - 0}{\sqrt{51 - 2}} = \frac{1}{7} = .14$$

If one wishes to maintain his confidence at the 95 per cent level, he will have to reject the above hypothesis and say there does seem to exist a relationship between the two variables since .40 is outside the limits of $0 \pm 1.96\,\sigma_r$, outside the range of $\pm .2744$.

RELIABILITY OF CORRELATION COEFFICIENTS

Formula:

$$Z = \frac{1}{2}\log_e \frac{1 + r}{1 - r} = 1.15129 \log_{10} \frac{1 + r}{1 - r}$$

where

Z = a transformation of r and a statistic whose sampling distribution is approximately normal
r = zero order coefficient of correlation between two variables

Formula:

$$\sigma_z = \frac{1}{\sqrt{N - m - 1}}$$

where

σ_z = standard error of Z
N = number of pairs of observations used to compute r
m = number of variables used to compute r

Example:

A correlation coefficient of .40 was found from a sample of 52 clerical workers when the total number of minutes late reporting for work each morning for a month was matched against the total job production for that month for each of the 52. What is the probable range within which the true value of the universe relationship probably falls if one accepts a 95 per cent confidence interval?

Solution:

$$Z = 1.15129 \log_{10} \frac{1 + .40}{1 - .40} = 1.15129 \log_{10} \frac{1.40}{.60} = (1.15129)(0.367915)$$

$$= .42$$

$$\sigma_z = \frac{1}{\sqrt{52 - 2 - 1}} = \frac{1}{7} = .14$$

Therefore, a 95 per cent confidence interval = (1.96)(.14) = .27 on each side of the mean.

$$Z \pm 1.96\,\sigma_Z = .42 \pm .27 = .15 \text{ to } .69$$

The true correlation would therefore have a Z value range of .15 to .69.

8

STATISTICS: INDEX NUMBER FORMULAS

INDEX NUMBERS. Aggregative of Prices Weighted with Fixed Weights.

Formula:

$$I = \frac{\Sigma p_n q_o}{\Sigma p_o q_o}$$

where

p_n = price of item in period for which index is being computed
p_o = price of item in base year
q_o = fixed weight
$\Sigma p_n q_o$ = sum of products formed by multiplying each present period price by its corresponding fixed weight
$\Sigma p_o q_o$ = sum of products formed by multiplying each base year price by its corresponding fixed weight

Example:

If data are as given below, what are the aggregative price indexes for 1949 and 1950, using 1948 weights and 1948 as base?

	Prices (p)			*Quantities (q)*		
Item	*1948*	*1949*	*1950*	*1948*	*1949*	*1950*
1	20	22	30	103	106	99
2	18	15	18	43	46	45
3	15	15	19	71	70	80

Solution:

$$I_{1949} = \frac{(22)(103) + (15)(43) + (15)(71)}{(20)(103) + (18)(43) + (15)(71)} = \frac{3976}{3899} = 102, \text{ price index for 1949}$$

$$I_{1950} = \frac{(30)(103) + (18)(43) + (19)(71)}{(20)(103) + (18)(43) + (15)(71)} = \frac{5213}{3899} = 134, \text{ price index for 1950}$$

INDEX NUMBERS. Aggregative Price Index Weighted with Variable Weights.

Formula:

$$I = \frac{\Sigma p_n q_n}{\Sigma p_o q_n}$$

where

p_n = price of item in period for which I is being constructed.
p_o = price of item in base period
q_n = variable weight
$\Sigma p_n q_n$ = sum of products formed by multiplying the price of each item in the present period by its corresponding weight for the same period
$\Sigma p_o q_n$ = sum of products formed by multiplying the price of each item in the base period by its corresponding weight in the present period

Example:

If data are as given below, what are the aggregative price indexes for 1949 and 1950 using variable weights and 1948 as base?

	Prices (p)			*Quantities (q)*		
Item	*1948*	*1949*	*1950*	*1948*	*1949*	*1950*
1	20	22	30	103	106	99
2	18	15	18	43	46	45
3	15	15	19	71	70	80

Solution:

$$I_{1949} = \frac{(22)(106) + (15)(46) + (15)(70)}{(20)(106) + (18)(46) + (15)(70)} = \frac{4072}{3998} = 102, \text{ price index for 1949}$$

$$I_{1950} = \frac{(30)(99) + (18)(45) + (19)(80)}{(20)(99) + (18)(45) + (15)(80)} = \frac{5300}{3990} = 133, \text{ price index for 1950}$$

INDEX NUMBERS. Arithmetic mean of Price Relatives with Fixed Weights.

Formula:

$$I = \frac{\sum\left(\frac{p_n}{p_o} \times p_o q_o\right)}{\Sigma p_o q_o}$$

where

p_n = price of an item in present period

p_o = price of an item in base period

$p_o q_o$ = fixed weight (product of base period price and fixed quantity).

$\frac{p_n}{p_o}$ = price of an item in the present period relative to price of the same item in base period.

$\sum\left(\frac{p_n}{p_o} \times p_o q_o\right)$ = sum of weighted price relatives

$\Sigma p_o q_o$ = sum of fixed weights

Example:

What is the arithmetic mean of the price relatives for 1949 if 1948 is the base year and fixed weights (from 1948) are used for the following data?

	Prices (p)		*Quantities (q)*	
Item	*1948*	*1949*	*1948*	*1949*
1	20	22	103	105
2	18	19	98	100
3	15	14	70	60

Solution:

$$I_{1949} = \frac{\left[\frac{22}{20} \times (20)(103)\right] + \left[\frac{19}{18} \times (18)(98)\right] + \left[\frac{14}{15} \times (15)(70)\right]}{(20)(103) + (18)(98) + (15)(70)}$$

$= \frac{5107}{4874} = 105$, arithmetic mean of price relatives weighted by fixed weights.

INDEX NUMBERS. Arithmetic mean of Price Relatives with Variable Weights.

Formula:

$$I = \frac{\sum\left(\frac{p_n}{p_o} \times p_n q_n\right)}{\Sigma p_n q_n}$$

where

p_n = price of an item in present period

p_o = price of an item in base period

q_n = variable quantity

$p_n q_n$ = variable weight

$\sum\left(\frac{p_n}{p_o} \times p_n q_n\right)$ = sum of price relatives weighted by variable weights

$\Sigma p_n q_n$ = sum of variable weights

Example:

What is the arithmetic mean of the price relatives for 1949 if 1948 is the base year and variable weights are employed for the following data?

	Prices (p)		*Quantities (q)*	
Item	*1948*	*1949*	*1948*	*1949*
1	20	22	103	105
2	18	19	98	100
3	15	14	70	60

Solution:

$$I_{1949} = \frac{\left[\frac{22}{20} \times (22)(105)\right] + \left[\frac{19}{18} \times (19)(100)\right] + \left[\frac{14}{15} \times (14)(60)\right]}{(22)(105) + (19)(100) + (14)(60)}$$

$= \frac{5330}{5050} =$ 106, the arithmetic mean of price relatives weighted by variable weights.

9

STATISTICS: TIME SERIES FORMULAS

SECULAR TREND—LINEAR. Least Squares Method. Odd number of time periods.

Formula:

$$Y' = a + bX \qquad a = \frac{\Sigma Y}{N} \qquad b = \frac{\Sigma XY}{\Sigma X^2}$$

where

Y' = trend value
a = average (arithmetic mean) trend value
b = rate of change in trend
X = any time value
ΣY = sum of values of variable
N = Number of time periods for which there are observations.
ΣXY = Sum of products formed by multiplying the value of each Y by each corresponding X
ΣX^2 = Sum of all X's after they have been squared

Example:

(a) What is the secular trend in sales for the following data?

(b) With this formula, what level of secular trend in sales might be estimated for 1970?

Time Period		*Sales (thous. $)*		
X	X	Y	XY	X^2
1910	−5	6	−30	25
1915	−4	9	−36	16
1920	−3	15	−45	9
1925	−2	20	−40	4
1930	−1	21	−21	1

Time Period X	X	*Sales (thous \$)* Y	XY	X^2
1935	0	22	0	0
1940	1	25	25	1
1945	2	36	72	4
1950	3	45	135	9
1955	4	48	192	16
1960	5	50	250	25
	0	297	502	110
	ΣX	ΣY	ΣXY	ΣX^2

Solution:

$$a = \frac{\Sigma Y}{N} = \frac{297}{11} = 27 \qquad b = \frac{\Sigma XY}{\Sigma X^2} = \frac{502}{110} = 4.56$$

(a) $Y' = 27 + 4.56X$ (with origin at 1935)

(b) 1970 is time period number 7. Therefore $Y' = 27 + 4.56(7) = 58.92$, or approximately \$59,000 in 1970 if the straight line trend continues.

SECULAR TREND—LINEAR. Least Squares Method. Even number of time periods.

Formula:

$$Y' = a + bX \qquad a = \frac{\Sigma Y}{N} = \qquad b = \frac{\Sigma XY}{\Sigma X^2}$$

where

Y' = trend value
a = average (arithmetic mean) trend value
b = rate of change in trend
X = any time value
ΣY = sum of values of variable
N = number of time periods for which there are observations
ΣXY = sum of products formed by multiplying the value of each Y by its corresponding X
ΣX^2 = sum of all X's after they have been squared

Example:

(a) What is the secular trend for the following sales data?

(b) With this formula, what would the estimate of secular trend in sales be for 1975?

Time Period		*Sales (Thous. $)*		
X	X	Y	XY	X^2
1915	−9	9	−81	81
1920	−7	15	−105	49
1925	−5	20	−100	25
1930	−3	21	−63	9
1935	−1	22	−22	1
	0			
1940	1	25	25	1
1945	3	36	108	9
1950	5	45	225	25
1955	7	48	336	49
1960	9	59	531	81
	0	300	854	330
	ΣX	ΣY	ΣXY	ΣX^2

Solution:

$$a = \frac{\Sigma Y}{N} = \frac{300}{10} = 30 \qquad b = \frac{\Sigma XY}{\Sigma X^2} = \frac{854}{330} = 2.59$$

(a) $Y' = 30 + 2.59\ X$ (with origin at June 30, 1935).

(b) 1975 is time period number 15 in this problem. Therefore $Y' = 30 + 2.59\ (15) = 30 + 38.85 = 68.85$, or approximately $68,850 if the straight line secular trend continues.

SECULAR TREND. Moving Average Method. Odd number of periods averaged.

Formula:

$$A = \frac{V_1 + V_2 + \ldots + V_n}{n}$$

where

A = moving average
V_1 = value belonging to first time period in average
V_n = value belonging to nth or last time period in average
n = number of time periods in average

Example:

What is the secular trend for the following production values which show a three-year cyclical fluctuation on the average?

Year	*Production (in thousands of tons)*	*3-year Moving Average*
1920	30	
1921	35	31
1922	28	30
1923	27	29
1924	32	29
1925	28	29
1926	27	30
1927	35	
...	...	
...	...	
...	...	

Solution:

For the 31, the first moving average shown above:

$$V_1 = 30 \qquad V_2 = 35 \qquad V_3 = 28$$

$$A = \frac{V_1 + V_2 + V_3}{3} = \frac{30 + 35 + 28}{3} = 31$$

The same method would be followed to obtain the moving averages for all the data. The data would then be plotted. Then points would be placed on the graph showing the location of the moving averages. These points would form the guide points for drawing in the secular trend line. The trend line would not necessarily pass through all of these points. For the data given above, it appears that although the level of production fluctuates from year to year, it does so because of cycle. The secular trend appears so far to be moving almost horizontally.

SECULAR TREND. Moving Average Method. Even number of periods averaged and centered.

Formula:

$$A = \frac{V_1 + 2V_2 + 2V_3 + \ldots + V_n}{2n}$$

where

A = moving average
V_1 = value belonging to first time period in average
$2V_2$ = 2 times value belonging to second time period in average
V_n = value belonging to nth or last time period in average
n = number of time periods in average

Example:

Year	Production (in thousands of tons)	4-Year Moving (Centered) Sum	4-Year Moving (Centered) Average
1920	15		
1921	20		
1922	22	144	18
1923	14	152	19
1924	17	164	20.5
1925	26	...	...
1926	28	...	...
1927	15	...	...
...	...	...	...
...	...		
...	...		

Solution:

An even number moving average centered is equivalent to an odd number moving average weighted, where the end values are weighted by 1 and each of the non-end values weighted by 2. Hence for the 4-year centered moving average above with the first result of 18:

$$A = \frac{V_1 + 2V_2 + 2V_3 + 2V_4 + V_5}{2n} = \frac{15 + 2(20) + 2(22) + 2(14) + 17}{8} = 18$$

Computations can be speeded if the method indicated above is followed where the moving centered sums are obtained first, then multiplication of each of these sums by the reciprocal of "2n" (in this case 8) to obtain the averages. After the averages are obtained, they would be plotted on the graph showing the original time series data. These averages would then form the guides for drawing in the secular trend line. All the averages will not necessarily fall on the smooth secular trend line.

SEASONAL. Ratio to Moving Average Method. Data assumed to contain seasonal, cycle, and secular trend, related to each other as multiplied factors.

Formula:

$$S = \frac{T \times C \times S}{T \times C}$$

where

S = seasonal value
T = secular trend value
C = cycle value
$T \times C \times S$ = original data
$T \times C$ = measurement of trend and cycle

Example:

(a) What is the seasonal index for sales of the second quarter?
(b) What is the seasonal pattern for sales for each of the four quarters?
(c) What would be the estimated sales level for the fourth quarter, 1958, if the seasonal effects were eliminated?

Year	*Quarter*	*Sales (In thousands of $, $T \times C \times S$*	*4-quarter moving centered sum*	*4-quarter moving centered average $T \times C$*	*Seasonal $T \times C \times S \div T \times C$ (in per cent) (in per cent)*
1954	1	2			
	2	5			
	3	6	36	4.500	133
	4	5	37	4.625	108
1955	1	2	40	5.000	40
	2	6	44	5.500	109
	3	8	47	5.875	136
	4	7	48	6.000	117
1956	1	3	49	6.125	49
	2	6	51	6.375	94
	3	9	52	6.500	138
	4	8	54	6.750	118
1957	1	3	57	7.125	42
	2	8	59	7.375	108
	3	10	61	7.625	131
	4	9	62	7.750	116
1958	1	4	63	7.875	51
	2	8	65	8.125	98
	3	11			
	4	10			

Solution:

Quarterly Averages, in per cents: (Seasonal)

	Quarter 1	*Quarter 2*	*Quarter 3*	*Quarter 4*
	40	109	133	108
	49	94	136	117
	42	108	138	118
	51	98	131	116
Total	182	409	538	459
Average (Seasonal Index)	46	102	135	115

(a) Seasonal index for the second quarter, from above, is 102. This indicates that seasonal effects tended to push sales up about 2 per cent on the average in the second quarter.

(b) Seasonal Pattern:

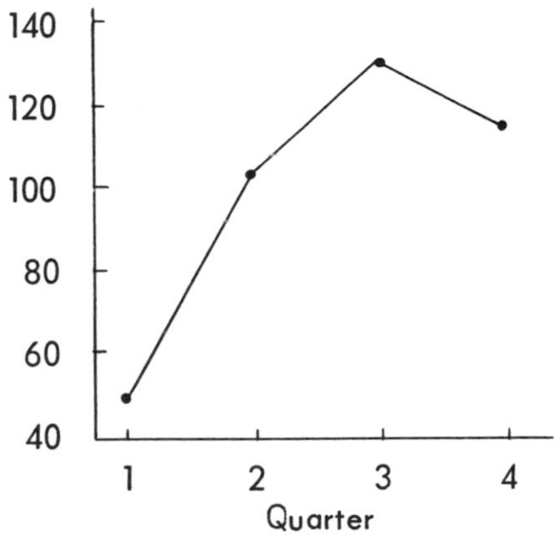

(c) Sales for fourth quarter = \$10,000 (1958)

Seasonal index for fourth quarter = 115%

Sales adjusted for seasonal effect: $\frac{\$10,000}{1.15} = \$8,696$

CYCLE.

Assuming data contain secular trend, cycle, seasonal and random elements, related to each other as multiplied factors.

Formula:

$$C \times R = \frac{T \times C \times S \times R}{T \times S}$$

where

T = Secular trend value
C = Cycle value
S = Seasonal index
R = Value of random element

Example:

What is the cyclical pattern for the following sales data:

Year	Quarter	Sales $T \times C \times S \times R$	Secular Trend[a] T	Seasonal Index[b] S (in %)	$S \times T$	Cycle X Random $\frac{T \times C \times S \times R}{S \times T} = C \times R$
1954	1	8	15.00	70	10.500	76
	2	21	16.25	110	17.875	117
	3	31	17.50	120	21.000	148
	4	34	18.75	100	18.750	181
1955	1	27	20.00	70	14.000	192
	2	47	21.25	110	23.375	201
	3	55	22.50	120	27.000	204
	4	47	23.75	100	23.750	197
1956	1	32	25.00	70	17.500	183
	2	44	26.25	110	28.875	152
	3	40	27.50	120	33.000	121
	4	24	28.75	100	28.750	83
1957	1	15	30.00	70	21.000	71
	2	22	31.25	110	34.375	64
	3	23	32.50	120	39.000	59
	4	25	33.75	100	33.750	74
1958	1	16	35.00	70	24.500	65
	2	27	36.25	110	39.875	68
	3	36	37.50	120	45.000	80
	4	36	38.75	100	38.750	93
1959	1	30	40.00	70	28.000	107
	2	58	41.25	110	45.375	128
	3	80	42.50	120	51.000	157
	4	77	43.75	100	43.750	176

[a] See pp. 65–69 for a method of obtaining secular trend values.
[b] See pp. 70–71 for a method of obtaining seasonal indexes.

10

INVENTORY FORMULAS

ESTIMATING INVENTORY—GROSS PROFIT METHOD

Formula:

$$I_2 = I_1 + P - [S(1 - R)]$$

where

I_2 = Ending Inventory
I_1 = Beginning Inventory
P = Purchases
S = Sales
R = Estimated Gross Profit Percentage on Sales

Example:

It is desired to prepare interim financial statements for the quarter ended March 31, 19__. However, it is not considered practicable to take a physical inventory and the company does not maintain a perpetual inventory. The following data are obtained from the firm's books and other records, sales for the period \$100,000, purchases for the period \$60,000. Inventory: Jan. 1, 19__ \$20,000. For the prior year the profit and loss statement showed a gross profit ratio of 38%. However, management has indicated that the costs have risen, but the selling price has remained more or less constant and they believe that a 35% gross profit ratio is probably being maintained. Compute the ending inventory.

Solution:

$$I_2 = I_1 + P - [S(1 - R)]$$
$$I_2 = 20{,}000 + 60{,}000 - [100{,}000(1 - .35)]$$
$$I_2 = 20{,}000 + 60{,}000 - [100{,}000(.65)]$$
$$I_2 = 20{,}000 + 60{,}000 - 65{,}000$$
$$I_2 = 80{,}000 - 65{,}000$$
$$I_2 = \$15{,}000$$

ESTIMATING INVENTORY—RETAIL INVENTORY METHOD

Formula:

$$I_{r2} = (I_{r1} + P_r + M_u) - (S + M_j + E + W_r)$$

$$I_{c2} = I_{r2} \times \frac{I_{c1} + P_c + T}{I_{r1} + P_r + M_u}$$

where

I_{c2} = Ending Inventory at Cost (Approximate Lower of Cost or Market)
I_{r2} = Ending Inventory at Retail
I_{r1} = Beginning Inventory at Retail
P_r = Purchases at Retail
M_u = Net Additional Markups (Additional Markup Minus Markup Cancellation)
S = Sales
M_j = Net Markdowns (Markdown Minus Markdown Cancellation)
E = Employee Discounts (If not recorded on Books)
W_r = Worthless Inventory at Retail—Due to Breakage, spoilage etc. or possibly known theft
I_{c1} = Beginning Inventory at Cost
P_c = Purchases at Cost
T = Transportation—In

Example:

The Downtown Department Store uses the retail inventory method of accounting. At the end of the first quarter of operations it is necessary to evaluate the inventories of the various departments in order to prepare financial statements. An actual physical inventory is taken only at the end of the fiscal year. From the data obtained from the books and other records estimate the inventory for the Junior Miss Department at the end of the first quarter.

Information obtained from the General Ledger:

	Retail	*Dr.*	*Cr.*
Sales			\$36,625
Purchases	\$80,000	\$52,000	
Transportation In		3,666	
Inventory	30,000	20,000	

The Buyer's records on markups and markdowns is summarized as follows:

Additional Markups	$4000	
Markup Cancellations	500	$3500
Markdowns	$3500	
Markdown Cancellations	2000	$1500

10 suits damaged—shop worn and completely unsaleable or returnable to manufacturer price at retail $20 each or $200.

Employee Discounts totaled $175.

Solution:

$$I_{r2} = (I_{r1} + P_r + M_u) - (S + M_j + E + W_r)$$

$$I_{c2} = I_{r2} \times \frac{I_{c1} + P_c + T}{I_{r1} + P_r + M_u}$$

$$I_{r2} = (30{,}000 + 80{,}000 + 3{,}500) - (36{,}625 + 1{,}500 + 175 + 200)$$

$$I_{r2} = \$113{,}500 - 38{,}500$$

$$I_{r2} = \$75{,}000$$

$$I_{c2} = 75{,}000 \times \frac{20{,}000 + 52{,}000 + 3{,}666}{30{,}000 + 80{,}000 + 3{,}500}$$

$$I_{c2} = 75{,}000 \times \frac{75{,}666}{113{,}500}$$

$$I_{c2} = 75{,}000 \times .66\ 2/3$$

$$I_{c2} = \$50{,}000$$

MAXIMUM INVENTORY LIMIT

Formula:

$$I_2 = O + P$$

where

I_2 = Maximum Inventory
O = Standard Order
P = Order Point

Example:

From the following information determine what the maximum amount of inventory of part X532 could be. When the inventory reaches 4050 units an order is automatically placed for 5000 units.

Solution:

$$I_2 = O + P$$

$$I_2 = 5{,}000 + 4{,}050$$

$$I_2 = 9{,}050$$

MINIMUM INVENTORY LIMIT

Formula:

$$I_1 = D \times U$$

where

I_1 = Minimum Inventory
D = Number of Days Inventory Desired on Hand
U = Maximum Daily Inventory Usage

Example:

Determine the minimum inventory from the following information. The inventory control manager has ascertained that the stock for item X532 should never fall below an 8 day supply. The company uses this part in several products and for the past 2 years the number of parts placed into production for the various products averaged 150 units per day. However, it is possible if all product lines are producing at capacity that 225 units per day would be required. What should be established as the minimum inventory?

Solution:

$$I_1 = D \times U$$
$$I_1 = 8 \times 225$$
$$I_1 = 1800$$

DETERMINING THE ORDER POINT

Formula:

$$P. = (T \times U) + I_1$$

where

$P.$ = Order Point
T = Number of Days Required to Fill Order
U = Maximum Usage
I_1 = Minimum Inventory

Example:

From the following information determine the order point for item X532. The purchasing agent has informed you that on the average it takes 10 working days from the time the order is initiated from inventory control until it is received and placed in stock by the company. The maximum possible usage 225 units per day, and the minimum inventory is 1800 units.

Solution:

$$P. = (T \times U) + I_1$$
$$P. = (10 \times 225) + I_1$$
$$P. = 2250 + 1800$$
$$P. = 4050$$

OPTIMUM ORDER SIZE

Formula:

$$Q = \sqrt{\frac{2(CN)}{UI + A}}$$

where

Q = Optimum Order Size
C = Cost of Placing an Order
N = Number of Units Consumed in One Year
U = Unit Price of Material
I = Assumed Rate of Interest
A = Annual Carrying Cost Per Unit

Example:

A purchasing agent desires to know the optimum order size for material #X53. A study of the inventory records for the past several years indicated the average annual consumption per year is 2,500 units. Cost studies showed that the average cost to prepare a purchase order and handle the invoices and other paper work amounted to $20 per order. The standard price of the material obtained from the cost accounting department is $10 per unit. A review of the financial pages of a leading business paper revealed that the current market for a relatively "risk free" investment is yielding 4%. Statistical studies prepared for the warehouse operations revealed that, on the average, annual carrying costs amounted to 5% of the inventory cost. Determine the optimum order size.

Solution:

$$Q = \sqrt{\frac{2(CN)}{UI + A}}$$

$$Q = \sqrt{\frac{2(20 \times 2{,}500)}{10 \times .04 + .50}}$$

$$Q = \sqrt{\frac{100{,}000}{.90}} = \sqrt{90{,}000}$$

$$Q = 300 \text{ units}$$

Note: A equals \$10 times 5% or .50.

11

DEPRECIATION FORMULAS

DEPRECIATION—STRAIGHT LINE

Formula:

$$D_j = \frac{C - S}{L}$$

where

D_j = Depreciation for particular year
C = Cost
S = Salvage Value
L = Estimated Life of asset

Example:

An asset cost $70,000 and has an estimated salvage value of $10,000. It is estimated that the life of the asset will be 15 years. What is the annual charge for depreciation?

Solution:

$$D_j = \frac{C - S}{L}$$

$$D_j = \frac{70,000 - 10,000}{15}$$

$$D_j = \frac{60,000}{15}$$

$$D_j = \$4,000$$

DEPRECIATION—UNITS OF PRODUCTION

Formula:

$$D_j = (C - S)\,\frac{U_x}{U_n}$$

where

D_j = Depreciation for Particular Year
C = Cost
S = Salvage Value
U_x = Units Produced in Particular Year
U_n = Estimated Number of Units That Asset Will Produce During its Life.

Example:

The XYZ Company purchased a machine that cost $100,000. From past experience and future projections it is estimated that the asset will have a salvage value of $20,000 at the end of its useful life. Engineering estimates indicate that with adequate maintenance the machine will probably produce 500,000 units during its efficient life. During the 8th year of its life the machine produced 30,000 units. What is the annual charge for depreciation by the units of production method of depreciation?

Solution:

$$D_j = (C - S)\,\frac{U_x}{U_n}$$

$$D_8 = (\$100{,}000 - 20{,}000)\,\frac{30{,}000}{500{,}000}$$

$$D_8 = 80{,}000 \times .06$$

$$D_8 = \$4{,}800$$

Note: Units may be interpreted to be units, labor hours, machine hours, etc.

DEPRECIATION—SUM OF THE YEARS' DIGITS METHOD

Formula:

$$D_j = \frac{Y - D}{\Sigma Y} \times (C - S)$$

where

D_j = Depreciation for particular year
Y = Estimated life of asset
D = Number of years of prior depreciation ($D = 1 - j$)
ΣY = Sum of the years
C = Cost of the asset
S = Estimated salvage value

Example:

An asset cost \$100,000 and has an estimated life of 20 years. The expected salvage value is \$10,000. What is the amount of depreciation for the 14th year?

Solution:

$$D_j = \frac{Y - D}{\Sigma Y} \times (C - S)$$

$$D_{14} = \frac{20 - 13}{210} \times (100{,}000 - 10{,}000)$$

$$D_{14} = \frac{7}{210} \times 90{,}000$$

$$D_{14} = \$3{,}000$$

Note: If the ΣY is not included in the tables, it may be calculated by the following formula:

$$\Sigma Y = \frac{Y + 1}{2} \times Y$$

$$\Sigma Y = \frac{20 + 1}{2} \times 20$$

$$\Sigma Y = 210$$

DEPRECIATION—DECLINING BALANCE (REAL)

Formulas:

1. $R = 1 - \sqrt[L]{\frac{S}{C}}$

2. $D_j = R(C - A)$

where

R = Constant Rate
L = Estimated Life of Asset
D_j = Depreciation for Particular Year
C = Cost of Asset
S = Salvage Value
A = Accumulated Depreciation balance at beginning of year

Example:

What is the amount of depreciation for the third year, if an asset cost \$20,000, has a salvage value of \$5,000 and an estimated life of 10 years?

The accumulated depreciation per books on the first day of the fiscal year is \$4,884.60

Solution:

1. $R = 1 - \sqrt[L]{\frac{S}{C}}$

   $R = 1 - \sqrt[10]{\frac{5,000}{20,000}}$

   $R = 1 - \sqrt[10]{.25}$ (See Note for Solving.)

   $R = 1 - .8705$

   $R = .1295$ or 12.95%

2. $D_j = R\,(C - A)$

   $D_3 = .1295\ (20,000.00 - 4,844.60)$

   $D_3 = .1295\ (15,155.40)$

   $D_3 = 1,962.62$

Note: Solution for $\sqrt[10]{.25}$.

Log .25 = 9.397940 − 10
Divide by 10 = .939794 − 1
Antilog Closest = 8,705
Place decimal point .8705

$$\therefore \sqrt[10]{.25} = .8705$$

DEPRECIATION—200% DECLINING BALANCE

Formula:

$$D_j = 2\left[\frac{(C - S) - A}{L}\right]$$

where

D_j = Depreciation for Particular year
C = Cost of Asset
S = Salvage Value of Asset
A = Balance in Reserve at beginning of year
L = Estimated Life of Asset

Example:

What is the amount of depreciation in year 2 of an asset that cost \$11,000, has a 10 year life and an estimated salvage value of \$1,000, and the balance in the reserve account at the beginning of the fiscal year is $2,000?

Solution:

$$D_j \text{ or } D_2 = 2\left[\frac{(C-S)-A}{L}\right]$$

$$D_2 = 2\left[\frac{(\$11{,}000 - \$1{,}000) - \$2{,}000}{10}\right]$$

$$D_2 = 2\left[\frac{8{,}000}{10}\right]$$

$$D_2 = 2\ (800)$$

$$D_2 = \$1{,}600$$

DEPRECIATION—COMPOSITE RATE

Formulas:

1. $$R = \frac{\dfrac{(C-S)_1}{L_1} + \dfrac{(C-S)_2}{L_2} + \dfrac{(C-S)_3}{L_3} + \cdots + \dfrac{(C-S)_n}{L_n}}{\Sigma C}$$

2. $D_j = \Sigma C_x \times R$

where

R = Composite Rate of Depreciation
C = Cost
S = Salvage Value
ΣC = Sum of the Cost
ΣC_x = Sum of the Asset Costs at end of Particular accounting period
D_j = Depreciation for a particular year
$L_1 - L_2 - L_3$ = Estimated Life of Assets

Example:

At the end of the year 19A a composite rate of depreciation was computed for office equipment from the following facts:

Item	*Cost*	*Salvage*	*Estimated Life*
Typewriters	300	50	5 years
Calculator	600	100	10 years
Adding Machine	400	40	9 years
Desks & Chairs	1,500	0	15 years
Total	2,800		

What is the composite rate of Depreciation?

If at the end of the fiscal year 19C the total assets in the group amounted to \$3,500, what amount should be charged to depreciation expense for that year?

Solution:

$$1.\ R = \frac{\frac{(C-S)_1}{L_1} + \frac{(C-S)_2}{L_2} + \frac{(C-S)_3}{L_3} + \frac{(C-S)_4}{L_4}}{\Sigma C}$$

$$R = \frac{\frac{300-50}{5} + \frac{600-100}{10} + \frac{400-40}{9} + \frac{1{,}500-0}{15}}{2{,}800}$$

$$R = \frac{50+50+40+100}{2{,}800}$$

$$R = \frac{240}{2{,}800}$$

$$R = .0857 \text{ or } 8.57\%$$

$$2.\ D_j = \Sigma C_x \times R$$

$$D_j = 3{,}500 \times .0857$$

$$D_j = \$299.95$$

DETERMINING ACCUMULATED DEPRECIATION BALANCE DECLINING BALANCE METHOD OF DEPRECIATION (REAL)

Formula:

$$A_n = C\,[1-(1-R)^n]$$

where

A_n = Accumulated Depreciation at the end of a series of accounting periods

C = Cost of Asset

R = Constant rate of depreciation

n = The number of years

Example:

What should be the balance in the reserve account at the end of year two, if an asset cost \$20,000 and has a scrap value of \$5,000, and the constant rate is 12.95%.

Solution:

$$A_n = C\,[1 - (1 - R)^n]$$
$$A_2 = 20{,}000\,[1 - (1 - .1295)^2]$$
$$A_2 = 20{,}000\,[1 - (.8705)^2]$$
$$A_2 = 20{,}000\,[1 - .75{,}777{,}025]$$
$$A_2 = 20{,}000 \times .24{,}222{,}975$$
$$A_2 = 4844.60$$

DETERMINING ACCUMULATED DEPRECIATION BALANCE DECLINING BALANCE METHOD OF DEPRECIATION (200% METHOD)

Formula:

$$A_n = C - S\left[1 - \left(1 - \frac{2}{L}\right)^n\right]$$

where

A_n = Accumulated depreciation at the end of a series of accounting periods
C = Cost of Asset
S = Salvage value (if used)
L = Estimated life of the asset
n = Number of years of life expired

Example:

An asset cost $11,000, has a salvage value of $1,000, and an estimated life of 10 years. If 200% declining balance method is used, what is the balance in the accumulated depreciation account at the end of the 2nd year?

Solution:

$$A_n = C - S\left[1 - \left(1 - \frac{2}{L}\right)^n\right]$$
$$A_2 = 11{,}000 - 1{,}000\left[1 - \left(1 - \frac{2}{10}\right)^2\right]$$
$$A_2 = 10{,}000\,[1 - (1 - .20)^2]$$
$$A_2 = 10{,}000\,[1 - .80^2]$$
$$A_2 = 10{,}000\,[1 - .64]$$
$$A_2 = 10{,}000 \times .36$$
$$A_2 = \$3{,}600$$

DETERMINING ACCUMULATED DEPRECIATION BALANCE SUM OF THE YEARS' DIGIT METHOD OF DEPRECIATION

Formula:

$$A_n = C - S \times \left[1 - \frac{R\,(R+1)}{2\,\Sigma Y}\right]$$

where

A_n = Accumulated depreciation at the end of a series of accounting periods

C = Cost of the asset

S = Salvage value of the asset

Y = Estimated life of the asset

ΣY = Sum of the years

R = Remaining life of the asset ($R = Y - n$)

Example:

An asset cost $7,000 and has an estimated useful life of 8 years; the salvage value is estimated to be $2,000. What should be the balance in the accumulated depreciation account at the end of the 5th year?

Solution:

$$A_n = C - S \times \left[1 - \frac{R\,(R+1)}{2\,\Sigma Y}\right]$$

$$A_5 = 7{,}000 - 2{,}000 \times \left[1 - \frac{3\,(3+1)}{2 \times 36}\right]$$

$$A_5 = 5{,}000 \times \left[1 - \frac{12}{72}\right]$$

$$A_5 = 5{,}000 \times .8333$$

$$A_5 = \$4{,}166.50$$

12

FINANCE

VALUE OF A BOND (Approximate Yield to Maturity)

Note: Bonds are generally valued on a yield basis.

Formulas:

Discount / *Premium*

1. $\bar{I} = I + \frac{d}{n}$ or $\bar{I} = I - \frac{p}{n}$

2. $\bar{C} = \frac{C + M}{2}$

3. $Y = \frac{\bar{I}}{\bar{C}}$

where

$\bar{I}$ = Average Income
$\bar{C}$ = Average Cost
Y = Yield (approximate)
I = Coupon Interest
M = Maturity Value
d = Discount
p = Premium
n = Number of years to maturity
C = Cost of Bond

Example:

A 20 year, 5% bond is purchased at 102. What is the approximate yield to maturity?

Solution:

1. $\bar{I} = I - \frac{p}{n} = 50 - \frac{20}{20} = \$49$

2. $\overline{C} = \dfrac{C + M}{2} = \dfrac{1{,}020 + 1{,}000}{2} = \$1{,}010$

3. $Y = \dfrac{\overline{I}}{C} = \dfrac{49}{1{,}010}$

$Y = 4.85\%$

VALUE OF A BOND (Known Yield)

Formulas:

1. $A = S(1 + r_e)^{-n}$

2. $A_{\overline{n}|r} = RS \dfrac{1 - (1 + r_e)^{-n}}{r_e}$

3. $V = A + A_{\overline{n}|r}$

where

A = Present value of the face value of the bond
S = Sum, face value, or maturity value
r_e = Effective rate of interest
R = Nominal rate of interest
$A_{\overline{n}|r}$ = Present value of the series of interest payments
V = Value of the bond

Example:

On January 1, 19A the XYZ Co. issued \$100,000, 6%, 20 year bonds, interest payable semi-annually. The bonds were issued to yield 4%. How much did the XYZ company receive for each \$1,000 bond?

Solution:

1. $A = S(1 + r_e)^{-n}$

$A = 1000\,(1 + .02)^{-40}$

$A = 1000\,(.45289)$ (Table II)

$A = \$452.89$

2. $A_{\overline{n}|r} = RS \dfrac{1 - (1 + r_e)^{-n}}{r_e}$

$A_{\overline{n}|r} = .03 \times 1000 \dfrac{(1 - (1 + .02)^{-40}}{.02}$

$A_{\overline{n}|r} = 30\ (27.3555)$ (Table IV)

$A_{\overline{n}|r} = \$820.66$

3. $V = A + A_{\overline{n}|r}$

$V = 452.89 + 820.66$

$V = \$1{,}273.55$

THEORETICAL VALUE OF A STOCKRIGHT

Formula:

$$V = \frac{M - S}{n + 1}$$

where

V = Theoretical Value of a Stockright
M = Market value of the Stock
S = Subscription price of the stock
n = Number of rights required to subscribe to one share of stock.

Example:

Mr. Smith owns 10 shares of A T & P Co. $100 par value common stock. He received 40 rights in the mail along with a notice stating that he could purchase one share of additional stock of the A T & P Co. for $170 plus 4 rights. The market value of the stock on the date the rights were received was $200. What is the theoretical value of the rights?

Solution:

$$V = \frac{M - S}{n + 1}$$

$$V = \frac{200 - 170}{4 + 1} = \frac{30}{5}$$

$$V = \$6$$

ALLOCATION OF COST TO RIGHTS

Formula:

$$V.R. = \frac{M.V.R.}{M.V.S. + M.V.R.} \times C$$

where

$V.R.$ = Value allocated to rights
$M.V.R.$ = Market value of rights on date of issuance
$M.V.S.$ = Market value of the stock ex rights
C = Cost

Example:

Mr. Smith owns 10 shares of A T & P Co. $100 par value common stock which cost him $120 per share or $1,200. He received 40 rights. On the date the rights were issued the stock was quoted ex rights at $195 per share and the rights were quoted separately at $5 per right. What cost shouldbe assigned to each right?

Solution:

$$V.R. = \frac{M.V.R.}{M.V.S. + M.V.R.} \times C$$

$$V.R. = \frac{5}{195 + 5} \times 120 = \frac{1}{40} \times 120$$

$$V.R. = \$3$$

COMPUTING GOODWILL

Formula:

$$G = \frac{E_f - (A \times r)}{R}$$

where

G = Goodwill

E_f = Estimated annual future earnings

A = Fair market value or appraised value of the net assets exclusive of goodwill.

r = Normal industry rate of return.

R = Capitalization rate of excess earnings.

Example:

The President of the XYZ Co. requests that you advise him as the possible value of the goodwill, if any, of the A.B.C. Co. which the President is investigating as a possible new subsidiary company.

After analyzing the income statements for the past 5 years and eliminating unusual and nonrecurring items you have determined that the average normal operating income is $622,000 per year. You have concluded from various studies that it would be reasonable to expect that if your firm "took over," the annual future earnings for the next 5 years would be in the vicinity of $600,000 per year.

The A.B.C company's tangible assets have been appraised by a reputable firm of appraisers at approximately $10,000,000. The most recent balance sheet of the A.B.C. Co. reveals that approximately $2,000,000 of liabilities would be involved in the purchase.

From statistics obtained from the industry trade association it appears that the average industry rate of return on net assets for the past five years is 7%. You have also learned from sources active in the industry that goodwill is generally valued at 5 years annual earnings in excess of normal.

Solution:

$$G = \frac{E_f - (A \times r)}{R}$$

$$G = \frac{600{,}000 - (8{,}000{,}000 \times .07)}{.20}$$

$$G = \frac{40{,}000}{.20}$$

$$G = \$200{,}000$$

AMORTIZATION OF BOND DISCOUNT OR PREMIUM BY BONDS OUTSTANDING METHOD

Formula:

$$A_j = \frac{B/O_n}{\Sigma B/O} \times D \text{ or } P$$

where

A_j = Amortization for a particular year

B/O_n = Face value of the bonds outstanding at the end of a particular year

$\Sigma B/O$ = Sum of the bonds outstanding at the end of each year ($\Sigma B/O = B/O_1 + B/O_2 + B/O_3 + B/O_n$)

D = Discount

P = Premium

Example:

On January 1, 19X1 the ABC Co. issued $500,000, 6% serial bonds, interest payable annually. The bonds sold for $490,000. The bonds are to be retired in the amount of $100,000 at the end of each year. What amount of discount should be amortized for the year 19X3 using the bonds outstanding method?

Solution:

$$A_j = \frac{B/O_n}{\Sigma B/O} \times D$$

$$A_3 = \frac{300{,}000}{1{,}500{,}000} \times 10{,}000$$

$$A_3 = \frac{1}{5} \times 10{,}000$$

$$A_3 = 2{,}000$$

13

PRICE LEVEL ADJUSTMENTS

CONVERTING DEPRECIATION EXPENSE TO COMMON DOLLARS

Formula:

$$D_2 = D_1 \times \frac{P_2}{P_1}$$

where

D_2 = Adjusted Depreciation Expense

D_1 = Depreciation Expense based on historical cost.

P_1 = Index of general price level (or special index) on date asset was acquired.

P_2 = Index of general price level (or special index) at the end of the current year.

Example:

A building was purchased on January 1, 1944 at a cost of $150,000. The estimated economic life of the building is 50 years. The index of the general price level on the date of acquisition was 60 and the index of the general price level at the end of the current year, December 31, 1959 was 240. Determine the economic depreciation for the current year.

Solution:

Historical depreciation based on cost and straight line method

$$\$150,000 \div 50 = \$3,000$$

$$D_2 = D_1 \times \frac{P_2}{P_1}$$

$$D_2 = 3,000 \times \frac{240}{60}$$

$$D_2 = \$12,000$$

Note: For simplicity purposes salvage value is ignored.

CONVERTING ASSET VALUES TO COMMON DOLLARS

Formula:

$$C_2 = C_1 \times \frac{P_2}{P_1}$$

where

C_2 = Adjusted cost
C_1 = Original historical cost
P_2 = Index of general price level (or special index) at the end of the current year.
P_1 = Index of general price level (or special index) on date asset was acquired.

Example:

See example for converting depreciation expense to common dollars, page 93.

Solution:

$$C_2 = C_1 \times \frac{P_2}{P_1}$$

$$C_2 = 150{,}000 \times \frac{240}{60}$$

$$C_2 = \$600{,}000$$

CONVERTING THE ALLOWANCE FOR DEPRECIATION TO COMMON DOLLARS

Formula:

$$A_2 = A_1 \times \frac{P_2}{P_1}$$

where

A_2 = Adjusted allowance.
A_1 = Allowance based on historical cost.
P_1 = Index of general price level (or special index) on date asset was acquired.
P_2 = Index of general price level (or special index) at the end of the current year.

Example:

See example for converting depreciation expense to common dollars, page 93.

Solution:

Allowance per books:

$3,000 annual depreciation on cost times years elapsed (15) equals $45,000

$$A_2 = A_1 \times \frac{P_2}{P_1}$$

$$A_2 = 45,000 \times \frac{240}{60}$$

$$A_2 = \$180,000$$

CONVERTING LONG TERM DEBT TO COMMON DOLLARS

Formula:

$$L_2 = L_1 \times \frac{P_2}{P_1}$$

where

L_2 = Adjusted liability.
L_1 = Liability based on historical cost.
P_2 = Index of general price level (or special index) at the end of the current year.
P_1 = Index of general price level (or special index) on the date liability was acquired.

Example:

On January 1, 19A the XYZ Co. issued $600,000, 6%, 30 year bonds which was sold at par. The index of the general price level on the date the bonds were sold was 150. Ten years later the index of the general price level was 100. What amount should be shown as the liability for Bonds Payable at the later date?

Solution:

$$L_2 = L_1 \times \frac{P_2}{P_1}$$

$$L_2 = 600,000 \times \frac{100}{150}$$

$$L_2 = \$400,000$$

14

MARKETING FORMULAS

CALCULATING THE SELLING PRICE
(Markup Based on Cost)

Formula:

$$S = C(1 + R)$$

where

S = Selling Price
C = Cost
R = Markup % based on Cost

Example:

The buyer of the mens' shoe department is charged with the responsibility of setting the selling price for the merchandise that he purchases for his department. It has been his policy to markup new merchandise at 66 2/3% of cost. Determine the selling price of a pair of shoes that cost $12.

Solution:

$$S = C(1 + R)$$
$$S = 12(1 + .66\ 2/3)$$
$$S = 12 + 8$$
$$S = \$20$$

CALCULATING THE SELLING PRICE
(Markup Based on Selling Price)

Formula:

$$S = \frac{C}{1 - R}$$

where

S = Selling Price
C = Cost
R = Markup % based on Selling Price

Example:

The cost accounting department has estimated that the standard manufacturing cost of a proposed new product will be $240. Determine the selling price of the product, if the gross profit margin is 40% based on selling price.

Solution:

$$S = \frac{C}{1 - R}$$

$$S = \frac{240}{1 - .40}$$

$$S = \frac{240}{.60}$$

$$S = \$400$$

LOADING THE SELLING PRICE
(Markup Based on Selling Price)

Formula:

$$S = \frac{C}{1 - (R + r)}$$

where

S = Selling Price
C = Cost
R = Markup % based on Selling Price
r = Load Factor % based on Selling Price (For instance, sales commissions)

Example:

The General Manufacturing Company desires to establish the selling price of its product, so as to yield a 40% gross profit rate, computed after paying a 10% sales commission to its sales agents. The standard manufacturing cost of the product is $240. Determine the selling price.

Solution:

$$S = \frac{C}{1 - (R + r)}$$

$$S = \frac{240}{1 - (.40 + .10)}$$

$$S = \frac{240}{1 - .50}$$

$$S = \frac{240}{.50}$$

$$S = \$480$$

LOADING THE SELLING PRICE
(Markup Based on Cost)

Formula:

$$S = \frac{C(1 + R)}{1 - r}$$

where

S = Selling Price
C = Cost
R = Markup % Based on Cost
r = Load Factor % based on Selling Price (For instance, sales commissions)

Example:

The buyer of the mens' shoe department desires to allow a 10% sales commission to his sales people and still maintain the same profit on his sales. If a pair of shoes cost $12 and the usual markup based on cost is 66 2/3%, determine the selling price of the pair of shoes.

Solution:

$$S = \frac{C(1 + R)}{1 - r}$$

$$S = \frac{12(1 + .66\ 2/3)}{1 - .10}$$

$$S = \frac{12 + 8}{.90}$$

$$S = \frac{20}{.90}$$

$$S = \$22.22$$

15

COST AND PRODUCTION FORMULAS

EQUIVALENT UNITS OF PRODUCTION

Formula:

$$E.U. = T - \%_1 (W/P_1) + \%_2 (W/P_2)$$

where

$E.U.$ = Equivalent units of production
T = Number of units transferred to next department
$\%_1$ = Percentage of completion of beginning work in process
$\%_2$ = Percentage of completion of ending work in process
W/P_1 = Number of units in beginning work in process
W/P_2 = Number of units in ending work in process

Example:

From the following information compute the equivalent number of units for department No. 10 of the General Manufacturing Company. The production records of the department showed that 200,000 units were actually transferred to Dept. No. 11. The physical inventory at the end of the year revealed that there were 15,000 units of production still in process. The department foreman estimated that these units were on the average 80% completed. Reference to prior records revealed that at the beginning of the accounting period there were 45,000 units in process which were estimated to be on the average 20% completed.

Solution:

$$E.U. = T - \%_1 (W/P_1) + \%_2 (W/P_2)$$
$$E.U. = 200{,}000 - .20\,(45{,}000) + .80\,(15{,}000)$$
$$E.U. = 200{,}000 - 9{,}000 + 12{,}000$$
$$E.U. = 203{,}000$$

BREAKEVEN POINT

Formula:

$$B/E = \frac{F/E}{1 - \frac{V}{S}}$$

where

B/E = Breakeven point
F/E = Total fixed expenses
V = Total variable expenses
S = Normal, budget, or capacity sales volume

Example:

The following data were assembled from the company's flexible budget.

Budget sales volume $1,800,000

Item	*Amount*	*Fixed*	*Variable*
Materials	$ 400,000		$ 400,000
Labor	175,000		175,000
Manufacturing Expenses	600,000	$100,000	500,000
Selling Expenses	100,000	30,000	70,000
General Expenses	300,000	245,000	55,000
Totals	$1,575,000	$375,000	$1,200,000

Determine the estimated breakeven point.

Solution:

$$B/E = \frac{F/E}{1 - \frac{V}{S}}$$

$$B/E = \frac{375{,}000}{1 - \frac{1{,}200{,}000}{1{,}800{,}000}}$$

$$B/E = \frac{375{,}000}{1 - .6667} = \frac{375{,}000}{.3333}$$

$$B/E = \$1{,}125{,}000$$

NORMAL BURDEN RATE
(Job Order Cost)

Formula:

$$N.B.R. = \frac{M/E}{B}$$

where

$N.B.R.$ = Normal burden rate
M/E = Estimated manufacturing expenses at normal capacity
B = Base at normal capacity (direct labor cost, direct labor hours, machine hours, etc.)

Example:

Determine the normal burden rate from the following data gathered from the books and records of the General Manufacturing Company for department number 3.

Estimates of the departmental capacity:

Engineering Estimate	100,000 units	Theoretical
Foreman's Estimate	80,000 units	Practical
Controller's Estimate	60,000 units	Normal

The controller's staff made the following estimate of manufacturing expenses based on normal capacity:

Fixed Expenses	\$ 80,000
Variable Expenses	40,000
Total	\$120,000

Solution:

$$N.B.R. = \frac{M/E}{B}$$

$$N.B.R. = \frac{120,000}{60,000}$$

$$N.B.R. = \$2.00$$

VOLUME VARIATION
(Job Order Cost)

Formula:

$$V_v = A\left(\frac{V/E}{B}\right) + F/E - A(N.B.R.)$$

where

V_v = Volume variance
A = Attained capacity
V/E = Variable expenses at normal capacity
B = Base at normal capacity
F/E = Fixed expenses at normal capacity
$N.B.R.$ = Normal burden rate

Example:

From the following data determine the volume variation for dept No. 3 of the General Manufacturing Co..

Manufacturing expense per general ledger: $115,000
Normal burden rate: $2.00 per direct labor hour.
Normal capacity: 60,000 direct labor hours
Attained capacity per production records: 50,000 hours
Budgeted expenses at normal capacity:

Fixed expenses	$80,000
Variable expenses	40,000

Solution:

$$V_v = A\left(\frac{V/E}{B}\right) + F/E - A(N.B.R.)$$

$$V_v = 50{,}000\left(\frac{40{,}000}{60{,}000}\right) + 80{,}000 - 50{,}000(2.00)$$

$$V_v = 33{,}333.33 + 80{,}000 - 100{,}000$$

$$V_v = \$13{,}333.33$$

BUDGET VARIATION
(Job Order Cost)

Formula:

$$V_b = M/E - A\left(\frac{V/E}{B}\right) - F/E$$

where

V_b = Budget variation
M/E = Actual manufacturing expenses for the period
A = Attained capacity
V/E = Variable expenses at normal capacity
B = Base at normal capacity
F/E = Fixed expenses at normal capacity

Example:

See example for volume variation, page 102.

Solution:

$$V_b = M/E - A\left(\frac{V/E}{B}\right) - \mathrm{F/E}$$

$$V_b = 115{,}000 - 50{,}000\left(\frac{40{,}000}{60{,}000}\right) - 80{,}000$$

$$V_b = 115{,}000 - 33{,}333.33 - 80{,}000$$

$$V_b = \$1{,}666.67$$

Proof of Variations:

Actual Manufacturing Expenses	$115,000.00
Less: Applied Manufacturing	
Expenses (2.00 × 50,000)	100,000.00
Total Variation	15,000.00
Represented By:	
Volume Variation	13,333.33
Budget Variation	1,666.67
Total Variation	$ 15,000.00

QUANTITY VARIATION
(Standard Cost)

Formula:

$$V_q = P_s (Q_a - Q_s)$$

where

V_q = Quantity Variation
P_s = Standard Price
Q_a = Actual Quantity
Q_s = Standard Quantity

Example:

The bill of materials for assembly No. 56 shows that 2 units of part No. 137 are required for each assembly. The standard price for part No. 137 is 30¢ each. The production records indicate that 3,000 assemblies were produced during the period. The material requisition register shows that 6,100 units of part No. 137 were consumed.

Determine the quantity variation.

Solution:

$$V_q = P_s (Q_a - Q_s)$$
$$V_q = .30 \, (6{,}100 - 6{,}000)$$
$$V_q = .30 \times 100$$
$$V_q = \$30$$

PRICE VARIATION
(Standard Cost)

Formula:

$$V_p = Q_a (P_a - P_s)$$

where

V_p = Price Variation
Q_a = Actual Quantity
P_a = Actual Price
P_s = Standard Price

Example:

The General Manufacturing Company has established that the standard price for part No. 137 should be 30¢ per unit. The accounting department received an invoice for 5,000 units at 33¢ per unit.

Determine the price variation.

Solution:

$$V_p = Q_a (P_a - P_s)$$
$$V_p = 5{,}000 \, (.33 - .30)$$
$$V_p = 5{,}000 \times .03$$
$$V_p = \$150$$

LABOR WAGE RATE VARIATION
(Standard Cost)

Formula:

$$V_w = T_a (w_a - w_s)$$

where

V_w = Wage Rate Variation
T_a = Actual Time
W_a = Actual Wage Rate
W_s = Standard Wage Rate

Example:

From the following data taken from the records of Dept. No. 15 of the General Manufacturing Company determine the labor wage rate variation.

Data

Standard	*Actual*
Wage Rate \$2.00 per hour	\$2.10 per hour
Direct Labor hours 250	260

Solution:

$$V_w = T_a (W_a - W_s)$$
$$V_w = 260\ (2.10 - 2.00)$$
$$V_w = 260 \times .10$$
$$V_w = \$26.00$$

LABOR EFFICIENCY VARIATION
(Standard Cost)

Formula:

$$V_E = W_s (T_a - T_s)$$

where

V_E = Labor Efficiency Variation
W_s = Standard Wage Rate
T_a = Actual Time
T_s = Standard Time

Example:

See example for labor wage rate variation, page 104.

Solution:

$$V_E = W_s (T_a - T_s)$$
$$V_E = 2.00\ (260 - 250)$$
$$V_E = 2.00 \times 10$$
$$V_E = \$20.00$$

VOLUME VARIATION
(Standard Cost—3 Factor Analysis)

Formula:

$$V_v = F/E + A\left(\frac{V/E}{B} - S.B.R.\right)$$

where

V_v = Volume variation
F/E = Fixed expenses at normal capacity
A = Attained capacity
V/E = Variable expenses at normal capacity
B = Base at normal capacity
$S.B.R.$ = Standard burden rate

Example:

See example for budget variation below.

Solution:

$$V_v = F/E + A\left(\frac{V/E}{B} - S.B.R.\right)$$

$$V_v = 30{,}000 + 170{,}000\left(\frac{70{,}000}{200{,}000} - .50\right)$$

$$V_v = 30{,}000 + 59{,}500 - 85{,}000$$

$$V_v = 89{,}500 - 85{,}000$$

$$V_v = \$4{,}500$$

BUDGET VARIATION
(Standard Cost—3 Factor Analysis)

Formula:

$$V_b = M/E_a - A\left(\frac{V/E}{B}\right) - F/E$$

where

V_b = Budget variation
M/E_a = Actual manufacturing expenses
A = Attained capacity
V/E = Variable expenses at normal capacity
F/E = Fixed expenses at normal capacity
B = Base at normal capacity
C = Percentage of normal capacity attained

Example:

From the following data pertaining to manufacturing expenses under a standard cost system, analyze the variation by the following factors: budget, volume, efficiency.

Data

	Standard	*Actual*
Capacity	Normal 100%	80%
Fixed Expenses	\$ 30,000	\$ 32,000
Variable Expenses	70,000	56,000
Total	\$100,000	\$ 88,000
Direct Labor Hours (base)	200,000	170,000
Standard Overhead Rate	\$.50	...

Solution:

$$V_b = M/E_a - A\left(\frac{V/E}{B}\right) - F/E$$

$$V_b = 88{,}000 - 170{,}000\left(\frac{70{,}000}{200{,}000}\right) - 30{,}000$$

$$V_b = 88{,}000 - 59{,}500 - 30{,}000$$

$$V_b = -\$1{,}500$$

EFFICIENCY VARIATION
(Standard Cost—3 Factor Analysis)

Formula:

$$V_e = S.B.R.\ [A - C(B)]$$

where

V_e = Efficiency variation
$S.B.R.$ = Standard Burden Rate
A = Attained capacity
C = Percentage of normal capacity attained
B = Base at normal capacity

Example:

See example for budget variation, page 106.

Solution:

$$V_e = S.B.R.\ [A - C(B)]$$

$$V_e = .50\ [170{,}000 - .80\ (200{,}000)]$$

$$V_e = .50\ (170{,}000 - 160{,}000)$$

$$V_e = .50\ (10{,}000)$$

$$V_e = \$5{,}000$$

CONTROLLABLE VARIATION
(Standard Cost—2 Factor Analysis)

Formula:

$$V_c = M/E_a - F/E - C(V/E)$$

where

V_c = Controllable variation
M/E_a = Actual manufacturing expenses
F/E = Fixed expenses at normal capacity
C = Percentage of normal capacity attained
V/E = Variable expenses at normal capacity

Example:

See example for budget variation, page 106.

Solution:

$$V_c = M/E_a - F/E - C(V/E)$$
$$V_c = 88{,}000 - 30{,}000 - .80\,(70{,}000)$$
$$V_c = 88{,}000 - 30{,}000 - 56{,}000$$
$$V_c = \$2{,}000$$

VOLUME VARIATION
(Standard Cost—2 Factor Analysis)

Formula:

$$V_v = F/E + C[V/E - S.B.R.\,(B)]$$

where

V_v = Volume variation
F/E = Fixed expenses at normal capacity
C = Percentage of normal capacity attained
V/E = Variable expenses at normal capacity
$S.B.R.$ = Standard Burden Rate
B = Base at normal capacity

Example:

See example for budget variation, page 106.

Solution:

$$V_v = F/E + C[V/E - S.B.R.(B)]$$
$$V_v = 30{,}000 + .80[70{,}000 - .50(200{,}000)]$$
$$V_v = 30{,}000 + .80(70{,}000 - 100{,}000)$$
$$V_v = 30{,}000 + .80(-30{,}000)$$
$$V_v = 30{,}000 - 24{,}000$$
$$V_v = \$6{,}000$$

16

RATIO ANALYSIS FORMULAS

CURRENT RATIO

Formula:

$$C.R. = \frac{C/A}{C/L}$$

where

$C.R.$ = Current Ratio
C/A = Current Assets
C/L = Current Liabilities

Example:

From the following data extracted from the balance sheet compute the current ratio.

Current Assets		*Current Liabilities*	
Cash	\$ 2,000	Accounts Payable	\$15,000
Accounts Receivable	18,000	Notes Payable	5,000
Inventories	25,000	Withholding Taxes	2,000
Prepaid Expenses	5,000	Accrued Expenses	3,000
Total	\$50,000		\$25,000

Solution:

$$C.R. = \frac{C/A}{C/L}$$

$$C.R. = \frac{50,000}{25,000}$$

$$C.R. = \frac{2}{1}$$

$$C.R. = 2:1$$

ACID TEST RATIO

Formula:

$$A.T.R. = \frac{C/A - I}{C/L}$$

where

$A.T.R.$ = Acid Test Ratio
C/A = Current Assets
I = Inventories
C/L = Current Liabilities

Example:

See data given for example for current ratio, page 110.

Solution:

$$A.T.R. = \frac{C/A - I}{C/L}$$

$$A.T.R. = \frac{50{,}000 - 25{,}000}{25{,}000}$$

$$A.T.R. = \frac{1}{1}$$

$$A.T.R. = 1:1$$

Note: Since the purpose of the acid test ratio is to determine the degree of absolute liquidity, prepaid expenses (P/P) should be excluded from current assets if material in amount. Therefore, the correct formula should be:

$$A.T.R. = \frac{C/A - I - P/P}{C/L}$$

INVENTORY TURNOVER

Formula:

$$T_i = \frac{C}{\frac{I_1 + I_2}{2}}$$

where

T_i = Inventory Turnover
C = Cost of Goods Sold
I_1 = Beginning Inventory
I_2 = Ending Inventory

Example:

From the following cost of goods sold section of a statement of income, compute the inventory turnover.

Cost of Goods Sold:

Beginning Inventory	$17,000	
Purchases	56,000	
Total Goods Available For Sale	73,000	
Less: Ending Inventory	13,000	
Cost of Goods Sold		$60,000

Solution:

$$T_i = \frac{C}{\frac{I_1 + I_2}{2}}$$

$$T_i = \frac{60{,}000}{\frac{17{,}000 + 13{,}000}{2}} = \frac{60{,}000}{\frac{30{,}000}{2}}$$

$$T_i = \frac{60{,}000}{15{,}000}$$

$$T_i = 4$$

Note: For a manufacturing firm the inventory turnover refers to the finished goods inventory only, and is computed by the same formula.

RAW MATERIAL INVENTORY TURNOVER

Formula:

$$T_{r/m} = \frac{C}{\frac{I_{r_1} + I_{r_2}}{2}}$$

where

$T_{r/m}$ = Raw Material Inventory Turnover
C = Raw Material Consumed
I_{r_1} = Beginning Inventory of Raw Materials
I_{r_2} = Ending Inventory of Raw Materials

Example:

From the following data abstracted from a manufacturing statement, compute the raw material inventory turnover.

Materials Consumed:

Beginning Inventory	\$15,000	
Purchases	78,000	
Total Available	93,000	
Less: Ending Inventory	9,000	
Materials Consumed		\$84,000

Solution:

$$T_{r/m} = \frac{C}{\frac{I_{r_1} + I_{r_2}}{2}}$$

$$T_{r/m} = \frac{84{,}000}{\frac{15{,}000 + 9{,}000}{2}}$$

$$T_{r/m} = \frac{84{,}000}{\frac{24{,}000}{2}}$$

$$T_{r/m} = \frac{84{,}000}{12{,}000}$$

$$T_{r/m} = 7$$

ACCOUNTS RECEIVABLE TURNOVER

Formula:

$$T_{a/r} = \frac{S}{\frac{A/R_1 + A/R_2}{2}}$$

where

$T_{a/r}$ = Accounts Receivable Turnover
S = Sales on Account
A/R_1 = Accounts Receivable at Beginning of Period
A/R_2 = Accounts Receivable at End of Period

Example:

From the following data abstracted from a firm's financial statements, compute the accounts receivable turnover for the current year.

	Current Year	*Prior Year*
Cash	\$20,000	\$10,000
Accounts Receivable	50,000	30,000
Inventory	45,000	35,000
Sales on Account	400,000	300,000
Usual terms of sale	2/10, *n*/30	2/10, *n*/30

Solution:

$$T_{a/r} = \frac{S}{\frac{A/R_1 + A/R_2}{2}}$$

$$T_{a/r} = \frac{400{,}000}{\frac{30{,}000 + 50{,}000}{2}}$$

$$T_{a/r} = \frac{400{,}000}{\frac{80{,}000}{2}}$$

$$T_{a/r} = \frac{400{,}000}{40{,}000}$$

$$T_{a/r} = 10$$

COLLECTION PERIOD FOR ACCOUNTS RECEIVABLE

Formula:

$$C.P. = \frac{360}{T_{a/r}}$$

where

$C.P.$ = Collection Period
$T_{a/r}$ = Accounts Receivable Turnover
360 = Number of Days in Year

Example:

See example for accounts receivable turnover, page 113.

Solution:

$$C.P. = \frac{360}{T_{a/r}}$$

$$C.P. = \frac{360}{10}$$

$$C.P. = 36 \text{ days}$$

ACCOUNTS PAYABLE TURNOVER

Formula:

$$T_{a/p} = \frac{P}{\dfrac{A/P_1 + A/P_2}{2}}$$

where

$T_{a/p}$ = Accounts Payable Turnover
A/P_1 = Accounts Payable at Beginning of Period
A/P_2 = Accounts Payable at End of Period
P = Purchases on Account

Example:

From the following data extracted from a firm's financial statements, compute the accounts payable turnover for the current year.

	Current Year	*Prior Year*
Accounts Payable	\$ 10,000	\$ 5,000
Purchases on Account	300,000	250,000
Terms of Purchase	mostly 2/10, *n*/30	

Solution:

$$T_{a/p} = \frac{P}{\dfrac{A/P_1 + A/P_2}{2}}$$

$$T_{a/p} = \frac{300{,}000}{\dfrac{5{,}000 + 10{,}000}{2}}$$

$$T_{a/p} = \frac{300{,}000}{\dfrac{15{,}000}{2}} = \frac{300{,}000}{7{,}500}$$

$$T_{a/p} = 40$$

PAYMENT PERIOD FOR ACCOUNTS PAYABLE

Formula:

$$P.P. = \frac{360}{T_{a/p}}$$

where

$P.P.$ = Payment Period
$T_{a/p}$ = Accounts Payable Turnover
360 = Number of Days in Year

Example:

See example for accounts payable turnover, page 115.

Solution:

$$P.P. = \frac{360}{T_{a/p}}$$

$$P.P. = \frac{360}{40}$$

$$P.P. = 9 \text{ days}$$

RETURN ON INVESTMENT—NETWORTH

Formula:

$$R.I._{n/w} = \frac{N/I}{\frac{N/W_1 + N/W_2}{2}}$$

where

$R.I._{n/w}$ = Return on Investment Based on Networth
N/I = Net Income for the period
N/W_1 = Networth at beginning of period
N/W_2 = Networth at end of period

Example:

From the data tabulated below compute the return on investment as measured by the networth or total capital per books.

	Current Year	*Prior Year*
Assets	$300,000	$200,000
Liabilities	120,000	60,000
Networth	$180,000	$140,000
Sales	$400,000	$350,000
Expenses	360,000	330,000
Net Income	$ 40,000	$ 20,000

Solution:

$$R.I._{n/w} = \frac{N/I}{\dfrac{N/W_1 + N/W_2}{2}}$$

$$R.I._{n/w} = \frac{40{,}000}{\dfrac{140{,}000 + 180{,}000}{2}} = \frac{40{,}000}{\dfrac{320{,}000}{2}}$$

$$R.I._{n/w} = \frac{40{,}000}{160{,}000}$$

$$R.I._{n/w} = .25 \text{ or } 25\%$$

RETURN ON INVESTMENT—TOTAL ASSETS

Formula:

$$R.I._a = \frac{N/I}{\dfrac{A_1 + A_2}{2}}$$

where

$R.I._a$ = Return on Investment Based on Total Assets
N/I = Net Income
A_1 = Total Assets at Beginning of Period
A_2 = Total Assets at End of Period

Example:

See example for return on investment—networth, page 116.

Solution:

$$R.I._a = \frac{N/I}{\dfrac{A_1 + A_2}{2}}$$

$$R.I._a = \frac{40{,}000}{\dfrac{200{,}000 + 300{,}000}{2}}$$

$$R.I._a = \frac{40{,}000}{\dfrac{500{,}000}{2}} = \frac{40{,}000}{250{,}000}$$

$$R.I._a = .16 \text{ or } 16\%$$

TIMES BOND INTEREST EARNED

Formula:

$$x_{i/e} = \frac{N/I + i}{i}$$

where

$x_{i/e}$ = Times Bond Interest Earned
N/I = Net Income
i = Bond Interest Expense

Example:

From the following condensed statement of income, compute the number of times the bond interest was earned.

Condensed Statement of Income

Sales	$1,400,000
Operating Expenses	860,000
Net Income Before Bond Interest and Federal Income Taxes	540,000
Bond Interest	60,000
Net Income Before Federal Income Taxes	480,000
Federal Income Taxes	240,000
Net Income	$ 240,000

Solution:

$$x_{i/e} = \frac{N/I + i}{i}$$

$$x_{i/e} = \frac{240{,}000 + 60{,}000}{60{,}000}$$

$$x_{i/e} = \frac{300{,}000}{60{,}000}$$

$$x_{i/e} = 5$$

BOOK VALUE PER SHARE OF COMMON STOCK

Formula:

$$B.V._{c/s} = \frac{T/C - P/C}{n}$$

where

$B.V._{c/s}$ = Book value per share of common stock
T/C = Total capital
P/C = Capital assigned to preferred shares
n = number of shares of common stock outstanding

Example:

The stockholders' equity section of the General Manufacturing Company is presented below. From this and the other additional data given, determine the book value per share of common stock.

Stockholders' Equity

Preferred Stock, 5%, Cumulative, $50 par	
Authorized 10,000 shares	
Issued 7,000 shares	$ 350,000
Common Stock, $100 par	
Authorized 3,000 shares	
Issued 2,500 shares	250,000
Capital in Excess of Par	75,000
Retained Income	525,000
Total Stockholders' Equity	$1,200,000

The preferred stock dividend is 2 years in arrears, including the current year.

Solution:

$$B.V._{c/s} = \frac{T/C - P/C}{n}$$

$$B.V._{c/s} = \frac{1{,}200{,}000 - 385{,}000}{2{,}500}$$

$$B.V._{c/s} = \frac{815{,}000}{2{,}500}$$

$$B.V._{c/s} = \$326.00$$

Note: A suitable general formula for P/C is difficult to formulate because of the various rights and privileges of individual preferred stock issues.

P/C is this example is computed as follows:

Par Value of Preferred Stock Outstanding	$350,000

Dividend Arrearage 2($350,000 × .05)	35,000
Capital Assigned to Preferred Stock	$385,000

EARNINGS PER SHARE OF COMMON STOCK

Formula:

$$E.P.S. = \frac{N/I - P/D}{n}$$

where

$E.P.S.$ = Earnings per share of common stock
N/I = Net Income
P/D = Preferred Dividends due
n = Number of common shares outstanding

Example:

From the following data abstracted from a firm's financial statements, determine the earnings per share of common stock.

Net Income		$125,600
Preferred Stock, 8%, $100 par		
Authorized	1,000 shares	
Issued	700 shares	$ 70,000
Common Stock, $10 par		
Authorized	50,000 shares	
Issued	30,000 shares	$300,000

Solution:

$$E.P.S. = \frac{N/I - P/D}{n}$$

$$E.P.S. = \frac{125{,}600 - 5{,}600}{30{,}000}$$

$$E.P.S. = \frac{120{,}000}{30{,}000}$$

$$E.P.S. = \$4.00$$

TIMES PREFERRED DIVIDENDS EARNED

Formula:

$$x_{D/e} = \frac{N/I}{P/D}$$

where

$x_{D/e}$ = Times preferred dividends earned
N/I = Net Income
P/D = Preferred dividend requirement

Example:

See example for earnings per share of common stock page 120.

Solution:

$$x_{D/e} = \frac{N/I}{P/D}$$

$$x_{D/e} = \frac{125{,}600}{5{,}600}$$

$$x_{D/e} = 22.4 \text{ times}$$

17

SINGLE ENTRY FORMULAS

DETERMINING SALES

Formula:

$$S = C + A/R_2 - A/R_1$$

where

S = Net Sales
C = Cash Collected
A/R_1 = Accounts Receivable at beginning of year
A/R_2 = Accounts Receivable at end of year

Example:

You are required to determine the net sales of the XYZ company from an incomplete set of records. An examination of the bank statement reveals that $50,000 was collected from customers. A schedule of accounts receivable at the beginning of the year totaled $32,000, and a similar schedule at the end of the year totaled $24,000.

Solution:

$$S = C + A/R_2 - A/R_1$$
$$S = 50{,}000 + 24{,}000 - 32{,}000$$
$$S = \$42{,}000$$

***Note*:** In the absence of adequate accounting records the determination of sales discounts and gross sales is generally not practicable.

DETERMINING PURCHASES

Formula:

$$P = D + A/P_2 - A/P_1$$

where

P = Purchases (net)
D = Payments made to suppliers
A/P_1 = Accounts payable at beginning of year
A/P_2 = Accounts payable at end of year

Example:

From the following incomplete data determine the net purchases of the XYZ company. An analysis of the check stubs for the year revealed that $63,000 was paid to suppliers of merchandise. Unpaid invoices for merchandise at the end of the year were determined to be $12,000. Analysis of payments made during the year indicated that $27,000 were invoices applicable to the prior year.

Solution:

$$P = D + A/P_2 - A/P_1$$
$$P = 63{,}000 + 12{,}000 - 27{,}000$$
$$P = \$48{,}000$$

Note: In the absence of adequate records the determination of purchase discounts and gross purchases is generally not practicable.

DETERMINING AN EXPENSE
(Simple Case)

Formula:

$$E = E_d + E_{a2} - E_{a1}$$

where

E = Expense
E_d = Expense paid in cash during year
E_{a1} = Accrual at beginning of year
E_{a2} = Accrual at end of year

Example:

During the course of your review of incomplete records you have determined the following facts. Wages paid during the year as determined from examination of payroll records amounted to $15,000. Your computations of accrued wages at the beginning and end of the year are $400 and $700 respectively. What should be the proper expense for wages shown on the income statement?

Solution:

$$E = E_d + E_{a2} - E_{a1}$$
$$E = 15{,}000 + 700 - 400$$
$$E = \$15{,}300$$

DETERMINING AN EXPENSE
(Complex Case)

Formula:

$$E = E_d + (E_{a2} - E_{a1}) + (P/P_1 - P/P_2)$$

where

E = Expense
E_d = Expense paid in cash during year
E_{a1} = Accrual at beginning of year
E_{a2} = Accrual at end of year
P/P_1 = Prepaid expense at beginning of year
P/P_2 = Prepaid expense at end of year

Example:

The following facts were determined during your review of advertising accounts. Examination of cancelled checks revealed that $1500 was paid for advertising of which $200 represents payment for an advertisement that will be run in the next year. An inventory of advertising suppliers, circulars etc., at the end of the year aggregated $400. From the balance sheet at the end of the prior year it was learned that $150 of supplies were on hand and that there were $63 accrued advertising expense. Unpaid bills at the end of the year for advertising amounted to $150.

Solution:

$$E = E_d + (E_{a2} - E_{a1}) + (P/P_1 - P/P_2)$$
$$E = \$1{,}500 + (150 - 63) + (150 - 600)$$
$$E = \$1{,}500 + 87 - 450$$
$$E = \$1{,}137$$

DETERMINING EXPENSE (Prepaid Expenses)

Formula:

$$E = E_d + P/P_1 - P/P_2$$

where

E = Expense for year
P/P_1 = Prepaid amount at beginning of period
P/P_2 = Prepaid amount at end of period
E_d = Expenses actually paid during the period

Example:

Examination of insurance transactions revealed the following facts. \$600 was paid out during the year. Prepaid insurance at the beginning of the year amounted to \$175 and analysis of the insurance policies revealed that \$215 was unexpired as of the end of the current year. What is the amount of insurance expense for the year?

Solution:

$$E = E_d + P/P_1 - P/P_2$$
$$E = \$600 + \$175 - \$215$$
$$E = \$560$$

DETERMINING INVENTORY

See Gross Profit Method in Chapter 10.

18

MISCELLANEOUS FORMULAS

BONUS AFTER FEDERAL INCOME TAXES
(Single Tax Rate)

Formulas:

1). $B = r(N/P_1 - B - T)$
2). $T = R(N/P_1 - B)$

where

B = Bonus
T = Federal Income Taxes
r = Rate of Bonus
N/P_1 = Net Profit before Bonus and Taxes
R = Rate of Tax

Example:

The General Manufacturing Company has an agreement with its President whereby he is to receive a bonus of 15% of the net profits calculated after deducting the bonus and the Federal Income Taxes. The net profit before bonus and taxes amounted to $50,000. The Federal Income Tax rate is 30%. What is the amount of the bonus?

Solution:

1). $B = r(N/P_1 - B - T)$
2). $T = R(N/P_1 - B)$

$$B = .15\ (50{,}000 - B - T)$$
$$T = .30\ (50{,}000 - B)$$

Substituting T in formula (1) and solving for B:

$$B = .15\ [50{,}000 - B - .30\ (50{,}000 - B)]$$
$$B = .15\ [50{,}000 - B - 15{,}000 + .30B]$$
$$B = .15\ (35{,}000 - .70B)$$
$$B = 5250 - .105B$$
$$B + .105B = 5250$$
$$1.105B = 5250$$
$$B = \$4{,}751.13$$

BONUS AFTER FEDERAL INCOME TAXES
(Multiple Tax Rates)

Formulas:

$$1). \quad B = r(N/P_1 - B - T)$$
$$2). \quad T = R_{1+2}(N/P_1 - B) - R_2(A)$$

where

B = Bonus
T = Amount of Federal Income Tax
r = Rate of Bonus
R_{1+2} = Combined Normal and Sur Tax Rate
N/P_1 = Net Profit Before Bonus and Federal Income Taxes
R_1 = Normal Tax Rate
R_2 = Sur Tax Rate
A = Amount of Profit exempt from Sur Tax.

Example:

The General Manufacturing Company has an agreement with its President whereby he is to receive a bonus of 10% of the net profits calculated after deducting the Bonus and Federal Income taxes. The net profit before bonus and taxes amounted to \$100,000. The Federal Income Tax rates are 30% normal tax and 22% sur tax on net income in excess of \$25,000. What is the amount of the bonus?

Solution:

$$1). \quad B = r(N/P_1 - B - T)$$
$$2). \quad T = R_{1+2}(N/P_1 - B) - R_2(A)$$
$$B = .10\ (100{,}000 - B - T)$$
$$T = .52\ (100{,}000 - B) - .22\ (25{,}000)$$
$$T = .52\ (100{,}000 - B) - 5{,}500$$

Substituting T in formula (1) and solving for B

$$B = .10\ [100{,}000 - B - .52\ (100{,}000 - B) + 5{,}500]$$
$$B = .10\ (100{,}000 - B - 52{,}000 + .52B + 5{,}500)$$
$$B = .10\ (53{,}500 - .48B)$$
$$B = 5{,}350 - .048B$$
$$B + .048B = 5{,}350$$
$$1.048B = 5{,}350$$
$$B = \$5{,}104.96$$

DETERMINING NET SALES WHEN SALES TAX COLLECTIONS ARE NOT RECORDED

Formula:

$$S = \frac{T}{1 + R}$$

where

S = Net Sales
T = Total Receipts (sales plus tax)
R = Rate of Sales Tax

Example:

The cash receipts of the XYZ Retail Store amounted to $20,600 for the month of October, 19A. There is a 3% sales tax in effect. The sales tax is added to the sale and rung up on the cash register as one amount. What amount should be shown as Sales for the month of October, 19A?

Solution:

$$S = \frac{T}{1 + R}$$

$$S = \frac{20{,}600}{1 + .03}$$

$$S = \frac{20{,}600}{1.03}$$

$$S = \$20{,}000$$

DETERMINING GROSS AMOUNT WHEN PARTIAL DISCOUNTS ARE ALLOWED

Formula:

$$G = \frac{A}{1 - R}$$

where

G = Gross Amount
A = Amount of Partial Payment
R = Rate of Discount

Example:

On February 1, 19A Jones Manufacturing Company purchased materials from the Able Supply Co. The amount of the invoice was $1,000, the terms stated were 2/10, *n*/30. On February 8, 19A the bookkeeper of the Jones Manufacturing Company was instructed to send a check in the amount of $400 to the Able Supply Co. to apply on account. Assuming that partial discounts will be allowed what is the amount that should be debited to accounts payable?

Solution:

$$G = \frac{A}{1 - R}$$

$$G = \frac{400}{1 - .02}$$

$$G = \frac{400}{.98}$$

$$G = \$408.16$$

DETERMINING GROSS WAGES WHEN NET WAGES IS GIVEN

Formula:

$$G = N + R_w [G - D(A)] + R_f(G)$$

where

G = Gross Wages
N = Net Wages
R_w = Rate of Withholding by Percentage Method
A = Amount of Exemption per Dependent
D = Number of Dependents Claimed
R_f = F.I.C.A. Tax Rate Imposed on Employee

Example:

Smith an employee agrees to work for Jones & Co. Smith wants $75 per week take home pay regardless of deductions required by law for withholding and F.I.C.A. taxes. Smith claimed 3 dependents on his W-4 form. The current rate of F.I.C.A. tax is 3% on employer and 3% on employee. The current withholding regulations allow a $13.00 exemption for each dependent on a weekly wage basis and an 18% tax rate for computing the amount to be withheld by the percentage method. What is the gross amount of wages that should be recorded in the payroll records for Smith?

Solution:

$$G = N + R_w[G - D(A)] + R_f(G)$$
$$G = 75 + .18[G - 3(13)] + .03(G)$$
$$G = 75 + .18(G - 39) + .03G$$
$$G = 75 + .18G - 7.02 + .03G$$
$$G = 67.98 + .21G$$
$$G - .21G = 67.98$$
$$.79G = 67.98$$
$$G = \$86.05$$

DETERMINING CONSOLIDATED RETAINED INCOME

Formula:

$$R_c = R_{p\,2} + \%_s(R_{s\,2} - R_{s\,1})$$

where

R_c = Consolidated Retained Income
$R_{p\,2}$ = Parent Company's Retained Income at Balance Sheet Data
$R_{s\,1}$ = Retained Income of Subsidiary Company on date control was obtained
$R_{s\,2}$ = Retained Income of Subsidiary Company at balance sheet date
$\%_s$ = Percentage of Subsidiary Company's Outstanding Stock owned by the Parent Company

Example:

P Company purchased 800 shares of S Company on January 1, 19A for $250,000. The retained income on S Company's books on the date of purchase was $150,000. On December 31, 19C the following information is obtained from the trial balances and books of Company P and Company S:

	Company P	*Company S*
Retained Income	$500,000	$290,000
Common Stock Co. P. $100 par value authorized & issued 1,000 shares	100,000	
Common Stock Co. S $10 par value authorized & issued 1,000 shares		10,000

Determine the consolidated retained income that will appear on the consolidated balance sheet at December 31, 19C.

Solution:

$$R_c = R_{p2} + \%_s (R_{s2} - R_{s1})$$
$$R_c = 500{,}000 + .80(290{,}000 - 150{,}000)$$
$$R_c = 500{,}000 + .80(140{,}000)$$
$$R_c = 500{,}000 + 112{,}000$$
$$R_c = \$612{,}000$$

DETERMINING THE MINORITY INTEREST

Formula:

$$M = \%_m (C_s + R_{s2})$$

where

M = Minority Interest

$\%_m$ = Percentage of subsidiary common stock outstanding owned by minority shareholders

C_s = Value assigned to subsidiary outstanding common stock

R_{s2} = Retained Income of Subsidiary Company on Balance Sheet Date

Example:

See example for consolidated retained income on page 130.

Solution:

$$M = \%_m (C_s + R_{s2})$$
$$M = .20(100{,}000 + 290{,}000)$$
$$M = .20(390{,}000)$$
$$M = \$78{,}000$$

DETERMINING CONSOLIDATED RETAINED INCOME
(Mutual Stock Holdings)

Formulas:

1. $\theta_p = R_{p2} + \%_s (\theta_s - R_{s1})$
2. $\theta_s = R_{s2} + \%_p (\theta_p - R_{p1})$
3. $R_c = \theta_p (1 - \%_p)$

where

R_c = Consolidated Retained Income

θ_p = True Retained Income of the Parent Company

θ_s = True Retained Income of the Subsidiary Company

R_{p2} = Retained Income on the Books of the Parent Company at the Consolidated Balance Sheet Date

R_{s2} = Retained Income on the Books of the Subsidiary Company at the Consolidated Balance Sheet Date

R_{p1} = Retained Income on the Books of the Parent Company on the date the Subsidiary Company acquired its Interest in the Parent Company

R_{s1} = Retained Income on the Books of the Subsidiary Company on the Date the Parent Company Achieved Control of the Subsidiary Company.

$\%_s$ = Percentage of the Outstanding Common Stock of the Subsidiary Company owned by the Parent Company.

$\%_p$ = Percentage of the Outstanding Common Stock of the Parent Company owned by the Subsidiary Company.

Example:

On January 2, 19A Company P purchased 800 of the 1,000 outstanding share of Company S at a cost of $150,000. On the date of this acquisition the capital stock account of Company S was $100,000 and the retained income account was $25,000. On the same date Company S acquired 200 shares of the 2,000 outstanding shares of Company P at a cost of $30,000. On the date of this purchase the capital stock account of Company P was $200,000 and the retained Income account was $70,000.

The condensed balance sheets of companies P & S as of December 31, 19C are presented below:

	Co. P	*Co. S*
Assets		
All other assets	$269,600	$160,000
Investment in Co S (cost)	150,000	
Investment in Co P (cost)		30,000
Total Assets	$419,600	$190,000
Equities		
Liabilities	$ 50,000	$ 40,000
Capital Stock, $100 par	200,000	100,000
Retained Income	169,600	50,000
Total Equities	$419,600	$190,000

From the foregoing data determine the consolidated retained income that will appear on the consolidated balance sheet as of December 31, 19C.

Solution:

$$1.\ \theta_p = R_{p2} + \%_s\,(\theta_s - R_{s1})$$
$$2.\ \theta_s = R_{s2} + \%_p\,(\theta_p - R_{p1})$$
$$3.\ R_c = \theta_p\,(1 - \%_p)$$
$$\theta_p = 169{,}600 + .80\,(\theta_s - 25{,}000)$$
$$\theta_s = 50{,}000 + .10\,(\theta_p - 70{,}000)$$

Substitute equation (2) in equation (1) and solve for θ_p

$$\theta_p = 169{,}600 + .80\,[50{,}000 + .10\,(\theta_p - 70{,}000) - 25{,}000]$$
$$\theta_p = 169{,}600 + .80\,(50{,}000 + .10\,\theta_p - 7{,}000 - 25{,}000)$$
$$\theta_p = 169{,}600 + 40{,}000 + .08\,\theta_p - 5{,}600 - 20{,}000$$
$$\theta_p = 184{,}000 + .08\,\theta_p$$
$$\theta_p - .08\,\theta_p = 184{,}000$$
$$.92\,\theta_p = 184{,}000$$
$$\theta_p = \$200{,}000$$

$$R_c = 200{,}000\,(1 - .10)$$
$$R_c = 200{,}000\,(.90)$$
$$R_c = \$180{,}000$$

CO-INSURANCE

Formula:

$$R = \frac{C}{\%\,(F.V.)} \times L$$

where

R = Recovery from insurance company
$\%$ = Co-insurance requirement
$F.V.$ = Fair value or sound value of property at date of disaster
L = Loss due to peril insured against
C = The coverage or face value of the policy

Example:

The XYZ Company had a fire insurance policy on its building for a face value of $100,000. The policy contained an 80% co-insurance requirement. On February 17, 19__ a fire occurred which caused damage in the amount of $60,000. Several days later insurance appraisers estimated the fair value of the building before the fire to be $150,000. What amount is recoverable from the insurance company?

Solution:

$$R = \frac{C}{\%(F.V.)} \times L$$

$$R = \frac{100,000}{.80\,(150,000)} \times 60,000$$

$$R = \frac{100,000}{120,000} \times 60,000$$

$$R = 50,000$$

***Note* (1)**: Insurer will never pay more than the face value of the policy.

***Note* (2)**: Fair value for insurance purposes is sometimes called sound value. Sound value is the replacement cost minus accrued depreciation. For instance, if in the above example the replacement cost is $300,000 for the building new and it would have a 50 year life and the old building is 25 years old, the sound value would be (300,000 – 150,000) = $150,000.

APPENDIX

I. FUNDAMENTALS OF ALGEBRA

The Language of Algebra

An *algebraic expression* is composed of symbols (numbers, letters, etc.) which are combined by one or more of the operations of algebra (addition, subtraction, multiplication, division, roots, etc.).

Illustrations:

$$xy^2,\ \frac{3}{x^3} - y^2 + 6,\ 4\sqrt{x} + \frac{a^3}{3},\ (a^2 - 3nx^3)^4$$

A *term* is composed of a single symbol, or of symbols, combined by any of the operations of algebra except addition or subtraction.

Illustrations:

$$\frac{5}{4},\quad 3x^2y^3,\quad \sqrt{x-3},\quad \frac{\sqrt{5}}{a^2b^2}\quad \text{are all terms}$$

$$\sqrt{x} - \sqrt{3}\quad \text{two terms}$$

When a term is composed of the product of two or more symbols, any one of these is a *factor,* or divisor, of the term. Likewise, the product of two or more of these factors is also a factor of the term. For example, in the term $6xy^2$, 6, x and y^2 are factors or divisors of the term. Any of the symbols $2, 3, x, y$, or the product of two or more of these would be a factor or divisor of $6xy^2$.

Any factor of a term is the *coefficient* of the remaining factor, or of the product of the remaining factors of the term. For example, in the term $2xy$, 2 is the coefficient of xy, x is the coefficient of $2y$, and y is the coefficient of $2x$. Most frequently, we are interested in the numerical coefficient; that is, the factor which is an explicit number, and sometimes refer to it as the *coefficient of the term.*

Some Basic Assumptions

Expressions are often referred to by more specific names describing the number of terms in the particular expression. Thus an expression of one term is called a *monomial*; an expression of two terms, a *binomial*;

an expression of three terms, a *trinomial*; etc. An expression of two or more terms is often referred to by the name *multinomial*.

Illustrations:

$3x, \quad \sqrt{7}\,x^3, \quad 5y^2z^3$	monomials
$4x+6, \quad 3z^2-5y^3, \quad 2y^3+2y^2$	binomials
$3x^2-7x+4, \quad \sqrt{2}\,y^3-5y+2$	trinomials

If an algebraic expression can be written so that a particular symbol has only integral (whole number) exponents wherever it appears in the expression, and does not appear under a radical sign, the expression is called *rational* with respect to that symbol; otherwise, *irrational*.

Illustrations:

$\sqrt{x^2+4}$	irrational with respect to x
$\sqrt[3]{s^2+2ts}$	irrational with respect to s and t
$\sqrt{2}\,x^2-\sqrt[3]{3}\,x$	rational with respect to x
$\sqrt{s}\,y^2-2y^3+6$	rational with respect to y but irrational with respect to s

A *polynomial* in a particular symbol (or symbols) is an algebraic expression each of whose terms is the product of an explicit number and the symbol (or symbols) with nonnegative integral exponents.

Illustrations:

$3x^3-6x^2+7x-3$	polynomial in x
$\frac{1}{3}y^3-\frac{3}{7}y+\sqrt{2}$	polynomial in y
$\frac{1}{4}x-\sqrt{3}\,y+xy$	polynomial in x and y

In a polynomial the degree of a term in a certain letter is the exponent of that letter. The degree of a term in certain letters is the sum of the exponents of those letters. For example, the term $8x^3y^2$ is of third degree in x, second degree in y, and fifth degree in x and y. The degree of a polynomial in a certain letter or letters is the degree of the term having the highest degree in that letter or letters.

Illustrations:

$5x^3-6x+5$	a polynomial of degree three in x
$s^3-s^2t^2+t^2$	a polynomial of third degree in s, second degree in t, and fourth degree in s and t

Symbols of Grouping

Parentheses ( ), brackets [ ], braces { }, and the vinculum ——— are the four commonly used symbols for grouping terms. These symbols may be thought of as the punctuation marks which, along with the order of operations, comprise the grammatical structure of the language of algebra.

There are three important principles of grouping.

1. We may remove parentheses (or insert terms within parentheses) or any other symbols of grouping preceded by a plus sign by simply rewriting the enclosed terms (or the terms to be enclosed) each with its original sign. What this amounts to is multiplying each term within the parentheses by $+1$.

Illustration: Remove the symbols of grouping

$$(r + s) + (3x - y)$$

Solution:

$$(r + s) + (3x - y) = r + s + 3x - y$$

Illustration: Enclose the terms $4s - 3t$ within parentheses preceded by a plus sign

Solution:

$$4s - 3t = +(4s - 3t) = (4s - 3t)$$

If no sign precedes the parentheses the sign is taken as positive.

2. We may remove parentheses (or insert terms within parentheses) or any other symbols of grouping preceded by a minus sign by rewriting the enclosed terms (or the terms to be enclosed) each with its own sign changed. What this amounts to is multiplying each term within the parentheses by -1.

Illustration: Remove the symbols of grouping and simplify

$$-(3 + 4a - 5b) - (-2 - a + 3b)$$

Solution:

$$\begin{aligned} -(3 + 4a - 5b) - (-2 - a + 3b) &= -3 - 4a + 5b + 2 + a - 3b \\ &= -1 - 3a + 2b \end{aligned}$$

Illustration: Enclose the terms $3z - 4w^2 + x^3$ within parentheses preceded by a minus sign

Solution:

$$3z - 4w^2 + x^3 = -(-3z + 4w^2 - x^3)$$

3. We may remove parentheses or any other symbols of grouping preceded by a multiplier or factor, by multiplying every term within the parentheses by the multiplier or factor.

Illustration: Remove the symbols of grouping

$$-5\,(3c - 2de + 5f^3)$$

Solution:

$$-5(3c - 2de + 5f^3) = -15c + 10de - 25f^3$$

Illustration: Remove the symbols of grouping and simplify

$$3x - \{-4 - [8x^2 + x(5 - x)] + 6\}$$

Solution:

$$3x - \{-4 - [8x^2 + x(5 - x)] + 6\} =$$
$$3x - \{-4 - [8x^2 + 5x - x^2] + 6\} =$$
$$3x - \{-4 - 8x^2 - 5x + x^2 + 6\} =$$
$$3x + 4 + 8x^2 + 5x - x^2 - 6 = 7x^2 + 8x - 2$$

Order of Operations

An apparently clear expression such as $150 - 10 \div 2$ could be interpreted in two distinct ways:

$$150 - 10 \div 2 = 140 \div 2 = 70$$
$$150 - 10 \div 2 = 150 - 5 = 145$$

To avoid any possible duplication of meaning of algebraic expressions mathematicians have agreed that powers and roots shall take priority over multiplications and divisions (which are to be performed left to right), which in turn shall take priority over additions and subtractions (except where some symbols of grouping indicate otherwise).

Illustrations:

$$8 - 4 \div 2 = 8 - 2 = 6$$
$$(8 - 4) \div 2 = 4 \div 2 = 2$$
$$4 \cdot 3 - 1 = 12 - 1 = 11$$
$$4(3 - 1) = 4 \cdot 2 = 8$$
$$\sqrt{5^2 + 12^2} = \sqrt{25 + 144} = \sqrt{169} = 13$$

Addition of Polynomials

Like terms or similar terms are terms whose literal factors are identical.

Illustrations:

$$6y^2z, \quad -y^2z, \frac{9}{2}y^2z, \quad \sqrt[3]{3}\,y^2z \qquad \text{are similar terms}$$

The sum of two similar terms is a similar term whose coefficient is the sum of the coefficients of the terms added.

Illustrations:

$$3y^2z^3 + 7y^2z^3 = (3 + 7)y^2z^3 = 10y^2z^3$$
$$-4aBC^2d + 4aBC^2d - 11aBC^2d = (-4 + 4 - 11)aBC^2d = -11aBC^2d$$

The sum of two polynomials is found by adding the terms of one polynomial to the terms of the other.

Illustration: Add $7x - 11y + 13$ and $7x - 13y - 14$

Solution:

$$(7x - 11y + 13) + (7x - 13y - 14) =$$
$$7x - 11y + 13 + 7x - 13y - 14 = 14x - 24y - 1$$

We may sometimes prefer to write one polynomial under the other, with similar terms in the same column.

Illustration: Add $7x - 11y + 13$ and $7x - 13y - 14$

Solution:

$$\begin{array}{r} 7x - 11y + 13 \\ 7x - 13y - 14 \\ \hline 14x - 24y - 1 \end{array}$$

Illustration: Add $5z^3 - 7z + 3$ and $-z^3 + 2z^2 - 7$

Solution:

$$\begin{array}{r} 5z^3 + 0z^2 - 7z + 3 \\ -z^3 + 2z^2 + 0z - 7 \\ \hline 4z^3 + 2z^2 - 7z - 4 \end{array}$$

Subtraction of Polynomials

The difference of two similar terms is a similar term whose coefficient is the difference of the coefficients of the terms subtracted.

Illustration: Subtract $6x^2y^3$ from $13x^2y^3$

Solution: $13x^2y^3 - 6x^2y^3 = (13 - 6)x^2y^3 = 7x^2y^3$

Illustration: Subtract $4a^2 - 3ab + 3b^2$ from $2a^2 - 5b^2 + 2ba$

Solution: $(2a^2 + 2ab - 5b^2) - (4a^2 - 3ab + 3b^2) =$

$$2a^2 + 2ab - 5b^2 - 4a^2 + 3ab - 3b^2 = -2a^2 + 5ab - 8b^2$$

We may prefer to write the subtrahend under the minuend, with like terms in the same column, and then subtract.

Illustration: Subtract $4a^2 - 3ab + 3b^2$ from $2a^2 - 5b^2 + 2ba$

$$\begin{array}{rl} 2a^2 + 2ab - 5b^2 & \text{minuend} \\ 4a^2 - 3ab + 3b^2 & \text{subtrahend} \\ \hline -2a^2 - 5ab - 2b^2 & \text{difference} \end{array}$$

Multiplication of Polynomials

The product of two monomials can be found by utilizing the commutative and associative properties of real numbers.

Illustrations:

$$-3x^2 \cdot 4y^3 = -3 \cdot 4 \cdot x^2 \cdot y^3 = -12x^2y^3$$

$$-8x^2yz^3 \cdot 2x^3yz = -8 \cdot 2 \cdot x^2 \cdot x^3 \cdot y \cdot y \cdot z^3 \cdot z = -16x^5y^2z^4$$

To multiply a polynomial by a monomial, we merely apply the distributive law.

Illustration:

$$-2xy(x^2y - xy^2 + y^3) = -2x^3y^2 + 2x^2y^3 - 2xy^4$$

$$xyz(xy - yz + xz) = x^2y^2z - xy^2z^2 + x^2yz^2$$

To multiply two polynomials, we multiply each term in one polynomial by each term in the other. This can be justified by applying the distributive law as follows:

$$\begin{aligned}(ax + by)(cx - dy) &= ax(cx - dy) + by(cx - dy)\\ &= ax \cdot cx - ax \cdot dy + by \cdot cx - by \cdot dy\\ &= acx^2 - adxy + bcxy - bdy^2\end{aligned}$$

Illustration: Multiply $2x^2 - x + 7$ by $3x - 2$

Solution:

$$\begin{array}{rrrr} & 2x^2 & -\ x & +\ 7 \\ & & 3x & -\ 2 \\ \hline & -\ 4x^2 & +\ 2x & -\ 14 \\ 6x^3 & -\ 3x^2 & +\ 21x & \\ \hline 6x^3 & -\ 7x^2 & +\ 23x & -\ 14 \end{array}$$

Division of Polynomials

When we divide a polynomial by a monomial, we divide each term of the polynomial by the monomial.

Illustration: Divide $14x^4y - 21x^2y^3 + 7xy^4$ by $-7xy$

Solution 1:

$$\frac{14x^4y - 21x^2y^3 + 7xy^4}{-7xy} = \frac{14x^4y}{-7xy} + \frac{-21x^2y^3}{-7xy} + \frac{7xy^4}{-7xy}$$

$$= -2x^3 + 3xy^2 - y^3$$

Solution 2:

$$\begin{array}{rrrr} & -2x^3 & +\ 3xy^2 & -\ y^3 \\ \hline -7xy\ / & 14x^4y & -\ 21x^2y^3 & +\ 7xy^4 \\ & \underline{14x^4y} & & \\ & & -\ 21x^2y^3 & \\ & & \underline{-21x^2y^3} & \\ & & & +\ 7xy^4 \\ & & & \underline{+\ 7xy^4} \end{array}$$

The division of a polynomial by a polynomial is illustrated by the following:

Illustration: Divide $x^4 - y^4$ by $x - y$

Solution:

$$
\begin{array}{r|l}
 & x^3 + x^2y + xy^2 + y^3 \\
\hline
x - y & x^4 \qquad\qquad\qquad\qquad - y^4 \\
 & \underline{x^4 - x^3y} \\
 & \quad + x^3y \\
 & \quad \underline{+ x^3y - x^2y^2} \\
 & \qquad\quad + x^2y^2 \\
 & \qquad\quad \underline{+ x^2y^2 - xy^3} \\
 & \qquad\qquad\quad + xy^3 - y^4 \\
 & \qquad\qquad\quad \underline{+ xy^3 - y^4}
\end{array}
$$

Factoring

Certain types of products of two polynomials occur so frequently that it is expedient to utilize special techniques which will facilitate and shorten the work of multiplication and assist in the work of factoring.

The type products are

1. $a(x + y) = ax + ay$
2. $(x + y)(x - y) = x^2 - y^2$
3. $(x + y)^2 = x^2 + 2xy + y^2; \quad (x - y)^2 = x^2 - 2xy + y^2$
4. $(x + a)(x + b) = x^2 + (a + b)x + ab$
5. $(ax + b)(cx + d) = acx^2 + (bc + ad)x + bd$
6. $(x + y - z)^2 = x^2 + y^2 + z^2 + 2xy - 2xz - 2yz$
7. $(x + y)^3 = x^3 + 3x^2y + 3xy^2 + y^3$
8. $(x - y)^3 = x^3 - 3x^2y + 3xy^2 - y^3$

Illustrations:

$$4s^3t - 6s^2t^2 + 12st^3 = 2st(2s^2 - 3st + 6t^2)$$

$$3x(z - 8) - 4w(z - 8) = (z - 8)(3x - 4w)$$

$$\begin{aligned} x^2 - (3y + 2z)^2 &= [x - (3y + 2z)][x + (3y + 2z)] \\ &= (x - 3y - 2z)(x + 3y + 2z) \end{aligned}$$

$$-4xz^2 + 8xzw - 4xw^2 = -4x(z^2 - 2zw + w^2) = -4x(z - w)^2$$

$$\begin{aligned} (a - c)^2 - (a - c) - 20 &= [(a - c) - 5][(a - c) + 4] \\ &= (a - c - 5)(a - c + 4) \end{aligned}$$

$$10s^2 - 7st - 12t^2 = (5s + 4t)(2s - 3t)$$

$$27x^3 - 8y^3 = (3x - 2y)(9x^2 + 6xy + 4y^2)$$

$$1 + 64a^6 = (1 + 4a^2)(1 - 4a^2 + 16a^4)$$

$$\begin{aligned} a^2 - b^2 - a + b &= (a - b)(a + b) - 1(a - b) \\ &= (a - b)[(a + b) - 1] = (a - b)(a + b - 1) \end{aligned}$$

$$\begin{aligned} x^4 + 64 &= x^4 + 16x^2 + 64 - 16x^2 \\ &= (x^2 + 8)^2 - (4x)^2 \\ &= [(x^2 + 8) - 4x][(x^2 + 8) + 4x] \\ &= (x^2 - 4x + 8)(x^2 + 4x + 8) \end{aligned}$$

Multiplication and Division of Fractions

The product of two fractions is a fraction whose numerator is the product of the two numerators and whose denominator is the product of the two denominators.

$$\frac{a}{b} \cdot \frac{c}{d} = \frac{ac}{bd} \qquad b, d \neq 0$$

Illustration:

$$\begin{aligned} \frac{2x + 2y}{x + y} \cdot \frac{x^2 - y^2}{x^2 + 2xy + y^2} &= \frac{2(x + y)}{x + y} \cdot \frac{(x - y)(x + y)}{(x + y)(x + y)} \\ &= \frac{2(x - y)}{x + y} \end{aligned}$$

The quotient of a fraction $\frac{a}{b}$ divided by a fraction $\frac{c}{d}$, that is, $\frac{a}{b} \div \frac{c}{d}$, is the product of $\frac{a}{b}$ and the reciprocal of $\frac{c}{d}$. In symbols

$$\frac{a}{b} \div \frac{c}{d} = \frac{a}{b} \cdot \frac{d}{c} \qquad b, d \neq 0$$

Illustration:

$$\begin{aligned} \frac{x^2 - x - 30}{x - 4} \div \frac{x - 6}{x^2 - 5x + 4} &= \frac{(x - 6)(x + 5)}{x - 4} \div \frac{x - 6}{(x - 4)(x - 1)} \\ &= \frac{(x - 6)(x + 5)(x - 4)(x - 1)}{(x - 4)(x - 6)} \\ &= (x + 5)(x - 1) \end{aligned}$$

Oftentimes exercises involve combinations of multiplication and division. However, no new difficulties are introduced.

Illustration:

$$\frac{3x^2+x-10}{x^2-16}\cdot\frac{x^2-3x-4}{3x-5}\div\frac{x^2-1}{x+4}$$
$$=\frac{(3x-5)(x+2)}{(x+4)(x-4)}\cdot\frac{(x-4)(x+1)}{3x-5}\cdot\frac{x+4}{(x-1)(x+1)}$$
$$=\frac{x+2}{x-1}$$

Addition and Subtraction of Fractions

The algebraic sum of two or more fractions having the same denominators is a fraction having the same denominator, whose numerator is the algebraic sum of the numerators of the fractions being added.

$$\frac{a}{d}+\frac{b}{d}+\frac{c}{d}=\frac{a+b+c}{d} \qquad d\neq 0$$

Illustration:

$$\frac{7}{3ax^2}-\frac{2y}{3ax^2}+\frac{6x}{3ax^2}=\frac{7-2y+6x}{3ax^2}$$

To add two or more fractions not having the same denominator we transform each fraction into an equivalent fraction whose denominator is the L.C.D. of the given fractions. Then we add as in the case of fractions whose denominators are alike.

Illustration:

$$\frac{3x-1}{x+1}-\frac{3x+1}{x-1}+\frac{8}{x^2-1}=\frac{(3x-1)(x-1)-(3x+1)(x+1)+8}{(x+1)(x-1)}$$
$$=\frac{3x^2-4x+1-3x^2-4x-1+8}{(x+1)(x-1)}$$
$$=\frac{-8x+8}{(x+1)(x-1)}$$
$$=\frac{-8(x-1)}{(x+1)(x-1)}=\frac{-8}{(x+1)}$$

Illustration:

$$m+\frac{1}{2m-1}=\frac{m(2m-1)}{2m-1}+\frac{1}{2m-1}$$
$$=\frac{2m^2-m+1}{2m-1}$$

Complex Fractions

If the numerator or denominator (or both) of a fraction is also a fraction, we call the entire fraction a *complex* fraction. There are several suitable techniques for simplifying such a fraction. We illustrate two of them.

Illustration:

$$\frac{s + \dfrac{t^2}{s+2t}}{s - \dfrac{3t^2}{s-2t}} = \frac{\dfrac{s(s+2t)}{s+2t} + \dfrac{t^2}{s+2t}}{\dfrac{s(s-2t)}{s-2t} - \dfrac{3t^2}{s-2t}} = \frac{\dfrac{s^2+2st+t^2}{s+2t}}{\dfrac{s^2-2st-3t^2}{s-2t}}$$

$$= \frac{(s+t)(s+t)}{(s+2t)} \cdot \frac{(s-2t)}{(s-3t)(s+t)}$$

$$= \frac{(s+t)(s-2t)}{(s+2t)(s-3t)}$$

Illustration:

$$\frac{m+n-\dfrac{n^2}{m+n}}{m-n-\dfrac{n^2}{m+n}} = \frac{m+n-\dfrac{n^2}{m+n}}{m-n-\dfrac{n^2}{m+n}} \cdot \frac{m+n}{m+n} = \frac{m^2+2mn+n^2-n^2}{m^2-n^2-n^2}$$

$$= \frac{m^2+2mn}{m^2-2n^2}$$

Laws of Exponents

The symbol $a \cdot a \cdot a \cdots a$ to x factors a) means a taken x times as a factor in a product, and is denoted by a^x. a^x is referred to as a power; x is called the exponent; and a is called the base. We define

$$a^1 = a$$
$$a^n a^1 = a^{n+1}$$

Exponents obey five basic laws. We state them without proof.[1]

In the following laws x and y are positive integers, and a and b are any positive numbers.

I. $\quad a^x \cdot a^y = a^{x+y}$

II. $\quad (a^x)^y = a^{xy}$

IIIa. $\quad \dfrac{a^x}{a^y} = a^{x-y}, \quad x > y$

---

[1]For a detailed proof of the laws see: Feinstein, I. K. and Murphy, K. H., *College Algebra*, Ames, Iowa: Littlefield, Adams & Co., 1959.

IIIb. $\dfrac{a^x}{a^y} = \dfrac{1}{a^{y-x}}, \quad x < y$

IV. $(ab)^x = a^x b^x$

V. $\left(\dfrac{a}{b}\right)^x = \dfrac{a^x}{b^x}$

Illustrations:

$s^4 \cdot s^5 = s^{4+5} = s^9$	Law I
$\dfrac{t^{12}}{t^3} = t^{12-3} = t^9$	IIIa
$(r^2)^3 = r^6$	II
$\dfrac{y^7}{y^4} = y^{7-4} = y^3$	IIIa
$\dfrac{w^4}{w^8} = \dfrac{1}{w^{8-4}} = \dfrac{1}{w^4}$	IIIb
$(-2z)^3 = (-2)^3 z^3 = -8z^3$	IV
$\left(\dfrac{3x}{2y}\right)^2 = \dfrac{(3x)^2}{(2y)^2} = \dfrac{3^2x^2}{2^2y^2} = \dfrac{9x^2}{4y^2}$	V
$\left(\dfrac{c^3}{d^2}\right)^m = \dfrac{(c^3)^m}{(d^2)^m} = \dfrac{c^{3m}}{d^{2m}}$	II and IV
$\left(\dfrac{ab^2}{2m^3n}\right)^3 = \dfrac{a^3b^6}{8m^9n^3}$	II, IV and V

Zero, Negative and Fractional Exponents

It is desirable to use zero as an exponent of a power and to so define the power as to be consistent with the laws of exponents. It is easy to show that to do this we must define

$$a^0 = 1, \quad a \neq 0$$

Illustrations:

$$(3x^2)^0 = 1; \quad (2x^3 - 3x^2 + 7)^0 = 1; \quad (1 + .03)^0 = 1$$

What meaning can we give to a negative exponent that would be consistent with the properties or laws of exponents previously stated?

We must define

$$a^{-y} = \frac{1}{a^y} \qquad a \neq 0,\ y > 0$$

Illustrations:

$$y^{-4} = \frac{1}{y^4} \qquad -3^{-2} = -\frac{1}{3^2} = -\frac{1}{9} \qquad \frac{3a}{b^{-2}} = 3ab^2$$

If p and q are integers and if $\frac{p}{q}$ is expressed with a positive denominator, we define

$$a^{\frac{p}{q}} = \sqrt[q]{a^p}$$

Illustrations:

$$(8)^{\frac{2}{3}} = \sqrt[3]{8^2} = (\sqrt[3]{8})^2 = 4$$

$$(25)^{-\frac{3}{2}} = (5^2)^{-\frac{3}{2}} = 5^{-3} = \frac{1}{5^3} = \frac{1}{125}$$

$$\left(\frac{a^{-5}b^3}{a^2b^{-3}}\right)^2 = \frac{a^{-10}b^6}{a^4b^{-6}} = \frac{b^{6-(-6)}}{a^{4-(-10)}} = \frac{b^{12}}{a^{14}}$$

$$a^{-1} + b^{-1} = \frac{1}{a} + \frac{1}{b} = \frac{b}{ab} + \frac{a}{ab} = \frac{b+a}{ab}$$

$$\frac{9 - a^{-4}}{3a^{-1} + a^{-3}} = \frac{(3 - a^{-2})(3 + a^{-2})}{a^{-1}(3 + a^{-2})} = \frac{3 - a^{-2}}{a^{-1}} \cdot \frac{a^2}{a^2}$$

$$= \frac{3a^2 - 1}{a}$$

Radicals

An indicated root of some number or expression, such as $\sqrt[n]{a}$, is called a *radical*; n is the index or order of the radical; the symbol $\sqrt{\ }$ is the radical sign; the number or expression, a, of which the root is taken is called the radicand. In $k\sqrt[n]{a}$, k is the coefficient of the radical.

A number x is an nth root of a if the nth power of x equals a. In symbols

$$x \text{ is an } n\text{th root of } a, \text{ if } x^n = a$$

There are n distinct nth roots of a real number a. Some of these may be complex numbers. Mathematicians have agreed that the symbol $\sqrt[n]{a}$ will stand for the principal nth root of a, unless otherwise specified. The principal nth root of a real number a is the positive real nth root if a is positive; and is the negative real nth root if a is negative and n is odd.

Illustration:

In $x^4 = 16$, the solutions, x, are the fourth roots of 16; $x = 2$ is the principal fourth root; $\sqrt[4]{16} = 2$.

In $x^3 = -27$, the solutions, x, are the cube roots of -27; $x = -3$ is the principal cube root; $\sqrt[3]{-27} = -3$.

The laws of exponents, together with the relation between a power with a rational exponent and a root, enable us to formulate several useful properties for operations on radicals. (In the following laws consider n, p, q and r positive integers and assume $a,b > 0$.)

Law I $\quad \sqrt[q]{a^p} = (\sqrt[q]{a})^p$

Law II $\quad \sqrt[q]{a} \cdot \sqrt[q]{b} = \sqrt[q]{ab}$

Law III $\quad \dfrac{\sqrt[q]{a}}{\sqrt[q]{b}} = \sqrt[q]{\dfrac{a}{b}}$

Law IV $\quad \sqrt[qr]{a^{pr}} = \sqrt[q]{a^p}$

Law V $\quad k\sqrt[n]{a} = \sqrt[n]{k^n a}$

Illustrations:

$$\sqrt[3]{3^3} = 3; \ \sqrt{4^2} = 4$$

$$\sqrt[3]{27} \cdot \sqrt[3]{8} = \sqrt[3]{27 \cdot 8} = \sqrt[3]{216} = 6$$

$$\sqrt[3]{-64s^6t^{-3}} = \sqrt[3]{-64} \cdot \sqrt[3]{s^6t^{-3}} = -4s^2t^{-1}$$

$$\frac{\sqrt[3]{8t^6}}{\sqrt[3]{27s^3}} = \sqrt[3]{\frac{8t^6}{27s^3}} = \frac{2t^2}{3s}$$

$$\sqrt[6]{16x^4} = \sqrt[6]{2^4 \cdot x^4} = \sqrt[3]{2^2 \cdot x^2} = \sqrt[3]{4x^2}$$

$$\sqrt[8]{64z^6} = \sqrt[8]{2^6z^6} = \sqrt[4]{2^3z^3} = \sqrt[4]{8z^3}$$

$$2\sqrt[3]{3} = \sqrt[3]{2^3 \cdot 3} = \sqrt[3]{24}$$

$$\sqrt[3]{\frac{128z}{9x^2y}} = \sqrt[3]{\frac{128z}{9x^2y} \cdot \frac{3xy^2}{3xy^2}}$$

$$= \sqrt[3]{\frac{64 \cdot 2 \cdot 3xy^2z}{27x^3y^3}} = \frac{4}{3xy}\sqrt[3]{6xy^2z}$$

II. LOGARITHMS

Definition. If

$$b^x = N \quad \text{then} \quad x = \log_b N$$

where

b = base (positive number different from 1)

x = logarithm of N, base b
N = number (positive)

The *logarithm* of a positive number N to a positive number b ($b \neq 1$) is that exponent x which must be applied to b so that $b^x = N$. This definition implies that the following two forms are equivalent:

$$b^x = N \quad \text{and} \quad x = \log_b N$$

Illustrations:

Base	*Number*	*Logarithm*	*Exponential Form*	*Logarithmic Form*
3	81	4	$3^4 = 81$	$\log_3 81 = 4$
$\frac{1}{4}$	64	-3	$\left(\frac{1}{4}\right)^{-3} = 64$	$\log_{\frac{1}{4}} 64 = -3$
3	1	0	$3^0 = 1$	$\log_3 1 = 0$
2	2	1	$2^1 = 2$	$\log_2 2 = 1$

Remember:

$$\text{If } b^x = N \quad \text{then} \quad x = \log_b N \qquad (b > 0, \neq 1)$$

Some Properties of Logarithms

Property 1: The logarithm of a *product* is equal to the sum of the logarithms of its factors. In symbols

$$\log_b MN = \log_b M + \log_b N$$

Property 2: The logarithm of a *quotient* equals the logarithm of the numerator minus the logarithm of the denominator. In symbols

$$\log_b \frac{M}{N} = \log_b M - \log_b N$$

Property 3: The logarithm of the kth *power of a number* equals k times the logarithm of the number. In symbols

$$\log_b M^k = k \log_b M$$

Illustration 1:

$$\log_b 81 = \log_b 3^4 = 4 \log_b 3$$

Illustration 2:

$$\log_5 125 = \log_5 5^3 = 3 \log_5 5 = 3$$

Illustration 3:

$$\begin{aligned} \log_{10} 16 + \log_{10} 5 &= \log_{10} (16 \cdot 5) = \log_{10} (10 \cdot 8) \\ &= \log_{10} 10 + \log_{10} 8 \\ &= 1 + \log_{10} 8 \end{aligned}$$

Illustration 4:

$$\log_{10} 14 - \log_{10} 7 = \log_{10} \frac{14}{7} = \log_{10} 2$$

Illustration 5: Show that

$$\log_{10} \frac{24}{7} - \log_{10} \frac{18}{21} = 2 \log_{10} 3$$

Solution:

$$\log_{10} \frac{24}{7} - \log_{10} \frac{8}{21} = \log_{10} \left(\frac{24}{7} \cdot \frac{21}{8}\right) = \log_{10} 9$$

$$= \log_{10} 3^2 = 2 \log_{10} 3$$

Common Logarithms: Common logarithms use the base 10 and are the most convenient for computation in our decimal numeration system. Let us

$\log 10{,}000 = 4$	$10^4 = 10{,}000$
$\log 1{,}000 = 3$	$10^3 = 1{,}000$
$\log 100 = 2$	$10^2 = 100$
$\log 10 = 1$	$10^1 = 10$
$\log 1 = 0$	$10^0 = 1$
$\log 0.1 = -1$	$10^{-1} = 0.1$
$\log 0.01 = -2$	$10^{-2} = 0.01$
$\log 0.001 = -3$	$10^{-3} = 0.001$
$\log 0.0001 = -4$	$10^{-4} = 0.0001$

We see that numbers which are integral powers of 10 will have integral logarithms; all other numbers will not. We assert that the larger of two positive numbers will have the larger logarithm, and conversely. We expect the log 368 to be between 2 and 3 since it must be greater than log 100 = 2 and less than log 1000 = 3. It would be composed of the integer 2 and some decimal fraction. The log 0.04 would be between −2 and −1 since it would be greater than log 0.01 = −2 and less than log 0.10 = −1. We may think of it as being composed of the integer −2 and a positive decimal fraction. The integer or the whole number part of the logarithm of a number is called the *characteristic*; the decimal fraction part is called the *mantissa*.

The logarithms of all numbers with the same digit sequence have the same mantissa. In actual computation the mantissa of the log of a number will be found in a table prepared for that purpose. The mantissas will usually be irrational and will be approximated to five places, six places, etc., according to the particular table used. The technique of using the table will be explained presently.

The characteristic of the log of any positive number depends on the position of the decimal point and is independent of the digit sequence of of the number. The log of a number is found by determining the characteristic by inspection and calculating the mantissa from a table.

The simplest way to find the characteristic of the logarithm of a number is to observe the number of places the decimal point in the number would have to be moved—and whether to the right or left—to give a number between 1 and 10. If the decimal point must be moved to the right, the characteristic is negative; to the left, positive.

Illustrations: Find the characteristic of the log 148.49; of log 0.000053; of log 0.00852; of log 88.295; of log 1.8632.

Solutions: The characteristic of

log 148.49 = 2 because the decimal point would have to be moved 2 places to the left to get a number between 1 and 10.

log 0.000053 = −5 because the decimal point would have to be moved 5 places to the right to get a number between 1 and 10.

log 0.00852 = −3 because the decimal point would have to be moved 3 places to the right to get a number between 1 and 10.

log 88.295 = 1 because the decimal point would have to be moved 1 place to the left to get a number between 1 and 10.

log 1.8632 = 0 because the number already is between 1 and 10.

Suppose the characteristic of log 33.254 is 1 and the mantissa is .520536. Then log 33.254 = 1.520536. Suppose the log of .33254 is required to be found. The characteristic is −1; the mantissa again will be .520536. Then log .33254 = −1 + .520536. The characteristic here is negative yet the mantissa is positive. It would be incorrect to write log 0.33254 = −1.520536 since this is not equivalent to −1 + .520536. We may write log 0.33254 = $\bar{1}.530536$, the bar above the characteristic indicating that it is negative. However, it is more useful to subtract the characteristic from a suitable multiple of 10, append the mantissa to this and write minus that multiple of 10 following the mantissa. Then log 0.33254 = 9.520536 − 10.

Illustrations:

$$\log 0.003951 = 7.596707 - 10; \quad \log 0.000009342 = 4.970440 - 10$$

Tables of Logarithms

The logarithms of numbers between 1 and 10 are found in tables. We shall use in this treatment 6-place mantissas (Table VI) which will enable us to obtain directly mantissas correct to six significant figures for any four digit numbers. By the process of interpolation these tables will yield mantissas for five digit numbers as well. Table VII will yield directly mantissas correct to seven significant figures for any five digit number between 1 and 1.1, and by interpolation for any six digit number between 1 and 1.1.

Illustration 1: Find the mantissa of the logarithm of 33.267.

Solution: The mantissas of 33260 and 33270 can be found directly trom Table VI. Since 33267 lies $\frac{7}{10}$ of the way from 33260 to 33270 we calculate a mantissa which is $\frac{7}{10}$ of the way from the mantissa of 33260 to the mantissa of 33270. We have structured the problem below.

$$\begin{array}{ccc} & \textit{Number} & & \textit{Mantissa} & \\ 10\left\{\begin{array}{l} \quad 33270 \\ 7\left\{\begin{array}{l} 33267 \\ 33260 \end{array}\right. \end{array}\right. & & \left.\begin{array}{r} 522053 \\ \left.\begin{array}{r} N \\ 521922 \end{array}\right\} d \end{array}\right\} 131 \end{array}$$

Then

$$\frac{d}{131} = \frac{7}{10} \quad \text{or} \quad d = 91.7$$

This correction 92 when added to 521922 produces 522014. The logarithm of 33.267 = 1.522014.

Illustration 2: Find the mantissa for the logarithm of .103556.

Solution: Since this number lies between 1 and 1.1, Table VII may be used. Since 103556 lies $\frac{6}{10}$ of the way between 103550 and 103560 we calculate a mantissa which is $\frac{6}{10}$ of the way from the mantissa of 103550 to the mantissa of 103560. We have structured the problem below.

$$\begin{array}{ccc} & \textit{Number} & & \textit{Mantissa} & \\ 10\left\{\begin{array}{l} \quad 103560 \\ 6\left\{\begin{array}{l} 103556 \\ 103550 \end{array}\right. \end{array}\right. & & \left.\begin{array}{r} 0151920 \\ \left.\begin{array}{r} N \\ 0151501 \end{array}\right\} d \end{array}\right\} 419 \end{array}$$

Then

$$\frac{d}{419} = \frac{6}{10} \quad \text{or} \quad d = 251.4$$

This correction 251 when added to 0151501 produces 0151752. The logarithm of .103556 = 9.0151752 − 10.

Illustration 3: Find N if $\log N = 7.966339 - 10$.

Solution: The mantissa of the number N we are seeking is $\frac{10}{47}$ of the way from the mantissa of 92540 to the mantissa of 92550. We therefore calculate N to be $\frac{10}{47}$ of the way from 92540 to 92550. Thus the first four digits of N will be 9254. The fifth digit will then be found by solving the proportion $\frac{x}{10} = \frac{10}{47}$. We have structured the problem below.

$$\begin{array}{ll} \textit{Number} & \textit{Mantissa} \\ 10\left\{\begin{array}{l} \quad 92550 \\ x\left\{\begin{array}{l} N \\ 92540 \end{array}\right. \end{array}\right. & \left.\begin{array}{l} 966376 \\ \left.\begin{array}{l} 966339 \\ 966329 \end{array}\right\} 10 \end{array}\right\} 47 \end{array}$$

Then

$$\frac{x}{10} = \frac{10}{47} \quad \text{or} \quad x = 2.1$$

The digit sequence of N is consequently 92542. The characteristic $7 - 10$ indicates that the decimal point in N will have to be moved 3 places to the right to yield a number between 1 and 10. Therefore if log $N = 7.966339 - 10$, then $N = 0.0092542$.

Logarithmic Computation

Logarithms serve as an excellent means of (or aid to) computation. They are especially adaptable to problems where multiplication, division, powers and roots are the sole or principal operations involved.

Illustration 1: By means of logarithms, find x if

$$x = 1{,}000\,(1.045)^{20}$$

Solution:

$$\begin{aligned} \log x &= \log\,[1{,}000\,(1.045)^{20}] = \log 1{,}000 + 20 \log 1.045 \\ &= 3 + 20 \log 1.045 \end{aligned}$$

We are now ready to structure the problem.

$$\begin{aligned} \log 1.045 &= 0.019116 \qquad \text{(Table VI)} \\ 20 \log 1.045 &= 0.382320 \\ \log x &= 3 + 0.382320 = 3.382320 \\ x &= 2{,}411.70 \end{aligned}$$

As a check on our work, from Table I we find that

$$(1.045)^{20} = 2.41171 \quad \text{so} \quad 1{,}000\,(2.41171) = 2{,}411.71$$

Illustration 2: By means of logarithms, find x if

$$x = (1.035)^{-12}$$

Solution:

$$\log x = -12 \log 1.035 \qquad \text{(Table VI)}$$
$$\log 1.035 = 0.014940$$
$$-12 \log 1.035 = -.179280$$
$$\log x = -.179280 = 10.000000 - 10 - .179280$$
$$= 9.820720 - 10$$
$$x = 0.66179$$

As a check on our work, from Table II, we find that

$$(1.035)^{-12} = 0.661783$$

Illustration 3: Evaluate r given

$$(1 - r)^{20} = \frac{185}{1775}$$

Solution:

$$\log (1 - r)^{20} = \log 185 - \log 1775$$
$$20 \log (1 - r) = \log 185 - \log 1775$$
$$\log (1 - r) = \frac{1}{20} (\log 185 - \log 1775)$$
$$= \frac{1}{20} (2.267172 - 3.249198)$$
$$= \frac{1}{20} (19.017974 - 20)$$
$$= 0.9508987 - 1$$
$$= 9.950899 - 10 \qquad \text{(Table VI)}$$
$$1 - r = 0.8931$$
$$r = 0.1069 \text{ or } 10.7\%$$

Illustration 4: Evaluate

$$\sqrt[10]{\frac{4,797}{23,546}}$$

Solution:

$$\text{Let } N = \sqrt[10]{\frac{4,797}{23,546}}$$

$$\log N = \log \left(\frac{4{,}797}{23{,}546}\right)^{\frac{1}{10}}$$

$$= \frac{1}{10}\,[\log 4{,}797 - \log 23{,}546]$$

$$= \frac{1}{10}\,[3.680970 - 4.371917] \qquad \text{(Table VI)}$$

$$= \frac{1}{10}\,[33.680970 - 4.371917 - 30]$$

$$= \frac{1}{10}\,[29.309053 - 30]$$

$$= \frac{1}{10}\,[99.309053 - 100]$$

$$= 9.930905 - 10$$

$$N = 0.85291$$

Illustration 5: Evaluate x given $x = \dfrac{1500 \times (1.06)^{25}}{29}$

Solution: The chief difficulty here is to evaluate $(1.06)^{25}$ assuming that tables are not available. Once this has been done then the rest of the example can be performed by ordinary arithmetic.

$$\text{Let } N = (1.06)^{25}$$

Then $\log N = 25 \log 1.06$

$$= 25 \times (.0253059) = 0.6326475 \qquad \text{(Table VII)}$$

$$N = 4.2919 \qquad \text{(Tabular value is 4.29187072)}$$

$$x = \frac{1500 \times 4.2919}{29} = \frac{6437.85}{29}$$

$$= 221.994$$

TABLES

TABLE I.—Amount of 1 at Compound Interest

$$s = (1 + i)^n$$

n	$\frac{1}{4}\%$	$\frac{7}{24}\%$	$\frac{1}{3}\%$	$\frac{5}{12}\%$	n
1	1.0025 0000	1.0029 1667	1.0033 3333	1.0041 6667	1
2	1.0050 0625	1.0058 4184	1.0066 7778	1.0083 5069	2
3	1.0075 1877	1.0087 7555	1.0100 3337	1.0125 5216	3
4	1.0100 3756	1.0117 1781	1.0134 0015	1.0167 7112	4
5	1.0125 6266	1.0146 6865	1.0167 7815	1.0210 0767	5
6	1.0150 9406	1.0176 2810	1.0201 6741	1.0252 6187	6
7	1.0176 3180	1.0205 9618	1.0235 6797	1.0295 3379	7
8	1.0201 7588	1.0235 7292	1.0269 7986	1.0338 2352	8
9	1.0227 2632	1.0265 5834	1.0304 0313	1.0381 3111	9
10	1.0252 8313	1.0295 5247	1.0338 3780	1.0424 5666	10
11	1.0278 4634	1.0325 5533	1.0372 8393	1.0468 0023	11
12	1.0304 1596	1.0355 6695	1.0407 4154	1.0511 6190	12
13	1.0329 9200	1.0385 8736	1.0442 1068	1.0555 4174	13
14	1.0355 7448	1.0416 1657	1.0476 9138	1.0599 3983	14
15	1.0381 6341	1.0446 5462	1.0511 8369	1.0643 5625	15
16	1.0407 5882	1.0477 0153	1.0546 8763	1.0687 9106	16
17	1.0433 6072	1.0507 5732	1.0582 0326	1.0732 4436	17
18	1.0459 6912	1.0538 2203	1.0617 3060	1.0777 1621	18
19	1.0485 8404	1.0568 9568	1.0652 6971	1.0822 0670	19
20	1.0512 0550	1.0599 7829	1.0688 2060	1.0867 1589	20
21	1.0538 3352	1.0630 6990	1.0723 8334	1.0912 4387	21
22	1.0564 6810	1.0661 7052	1.0759 5795	1.0957 9072	22
23	1.0591 0927	1.0692 8018	1.0795 4448	1.1003 5652	23
24	1 0617 5704	1.0723 9891	1.0831 4296	1.1049 4134	24
25	1.0644 1144	1.0755 2674	1.0867 5344	1.1095 4526	25
26	1.0670 7247	1.0786 6370	1.0903 7595	1.1141 6836	26
27	1.0697 4015	1.0818 0980	1.0940 1053	1.1188 1073	27
28	1.0724 1450	1.0849 6508	1.0976 5724	1.1234 7244	28
29	1.0750 9553	1.0881 2956	1.1013 1609	1.1281 5358	29
30	1.0777 8327	1.0913 0327	1.1049 8715	1.1328 5422	30
31	1.0804 7773	1.0944 8624	1.1086 7044	1.1375 7444	31
32	1,0831 7892	1.0976 7849	1.1123 6601	1.1423 1434	32
33	1.0858 8687	1.1008 8005	1.1160 7389	1.1470 7398	33
34	1.0886 0159	1.1040 9095	1.1197 9414	1.1518 5346	34
35	1.0913 2309	1.1073 1122	1.1235 2679	1.1566 5284	35
36	1.0940 5140	1.1105 4088	1.1272 7187	1.1614 7223	36
37	1.0967 8653	1.1137 7995	1.1310 2945	1.1663 1170	37
38	1.0995 2850	1.1170 2848	1.1347 9955	1.1711 7133	38
39	1.1022 7732	1.1202 8648	1.1385 8221	1.1760 5121	39
40	1.1050 3301	1.1235 5398	1.1423 7748	1.1809 5142	40
41	1.1077 9559	1.1268 3101	1.1461 8541	1.1858 7206	41
42	1.1105 6508	1.1301 1760	1.1500 0603	1.1908 1319	42
43	1.1133 4149	1.1334 1378	1.1538 3938	1.1957 7491	43
44	1.1161 2485	1.1367 1957	1.1576 8551	1.2007 5731	44
45	1.1189 1516	1.1400 3500	1.1615 4446	1.2057 6046	45
46	1.1217 1245	1.1433 6010	1.1654 1628	1.2107 8446	46
47	1.1245 1673	1.1466 9490	1.1693 0100	1.2158 2940	47
48	1.1273 2802	1.1500 3943	1.1731 9867	1.2208 9536	48
49	1.1301 4634	1.1533 9371	1.1771 0933	1.2259 8242	49
50	1.1329 7171	1.1567 5778	1.1810 3303	1.2310 9068	50

TABLE I.—Amount of 1 at Compound Interest

$$s = (1 + i)^n$$

n	$\frac{1}{4}\%$	$\frac{7}{24}\%$	$\frac{1}{3}\%$	$\frac{5}{12}\%$	n
51	1.1358 0414	1.1601 3165	1.1849 6981	1.2362 2002	51
52	1.1386 4365	1.1635 1537	1.1889 1971	1.2413 7114	52
53	1.1414 9026	1.1669 0896	1.1928 8277	1.2465 4352	53
54	1.1443 4398	1.1703 1244	1.1968 5905	1.2517 3745	54
55	1.1472 0484	1.1737 2585	1.2008 4858	1.2569 5302	55
56	1.1500 7285	1.1771 4922	1.2048 5141	1.2621 9033	56
57	1.1529 4804	1.1805 8257	1.2088 6758	1.2674 4946	57
58	1.1558 3041	1.1840 2594	1.2128 9714	1.2727 3050	58
59	1.1587 1998	1.1874 7935	1.2169 4013	1.2780 3354	59
60	1.1616 1678	1.1909 4283	1.2209 9659	1.2833 5868	60
61	1.1645 2082	1.1944 1641	1.2250 6658	1.2887 0601	61
62	1.1674 3213	1.1979 0013	1.2291 5014	1.2940 7561	62
63	1.1703 5071	1.2013 9400	1.2332 4730	1.2994 6760	63
64	1.1732 7658	1.2048 9807	1.2373 5813	1.3048 8204	64
65	1.1762 0977	1.2084 1235	1.2414 8266	1.3103 1905	65
66	1.1791 5030	1.2119 3689	1.2456 2093	1.3157 7872	66
67	1.1820 9817	1.2154 7171	1.2497 7300	1.3212 6113	67
68	1.1850 5342	1.2190 1683	1.2539 3891	1.3267 6638	68
69	1.1880 1605	1.2225 7230	1.2581 1871	1.3322 9458	69
70	1.1909 8609	1.2261 3813	1.2623 1244	1.3378 4580	70
71	1.1939 6356	1.2297 1437	1.2665 2015	1.3434 2016	71
72	1.1969 4847	1.2333 0104	1.2707 4188	1.3490 1774	72
73	1.1999 4084	1.2368 9816	1.2749 7769	1.3546 3865	73
74	1.2029 4069	1.2405 0578	1.2792 2761	1.3602 8298	74
75	1.2059 4804	1.2441 2393	1.2834 9170	1.3659 5082	75
76	1.2089 6291	1.2477 5262	1.2877 7001	1.3716 4229	76
77	1.2119 8532	1.2513 9190	1.2920 6258	1.3773 5746	77
78	1.2150 1528	1.2550 4179	1.2963 6945	1.3830 9645	78
79	1.2180 5282	1.2587 0233	1.3006 9068	1.3888 5935	79
80	1.2210 9795	1.2623 7355	1.3050 2632	1.3946 4627	80
81	1.2241 5070	1.2660 5547	1.3093 7641	1.4004 5729	81
82	1.2272 1108	1.2697 4813	1.3137 4099	1.4062 9253	82
83	1.2302 7910	1.2734 5156	1.3181 2013	1.4121 5209	83
84	1.2333 5480	1.2771 6580	1.3225 1386	1.4180 3605	84
85	1.2364 3819	1.2808 9086	1.3269 2224	1.4239 4454	85
86	1.2395 2928	1.2846 2680	1.3313 4532	1.4298 7764	86
87	1.2426 2811	1.2883 7362	1.3357 8314	1.4358 3546	87
88	1.2457 3468	1.2921 3138	1.3402 3575	1.4418 1811	88
89	1.2488 4901	1.2959 0010	1.3447 0320	1.4478 2568	89
90	1.2519 7114	1.2996 7980	1.3491 8554	1.4538 5829	90
91	1.2551 0106	1.3034 7054	1.3536 8203	1.4599 1603	91
92	1.2582 3882	1.3072 7233	1.3581 9510	1.4659 9902	92
93	1.2613 8441	1.3110 8520	1.3627 2242	1.4721 0735	93
94	1.2645 3787	1.3149 0920	1.3672 6483	1.4782 4113	94
95	1.2676 9922	1.3187 4435	1.3718 2238	1.4844 0047	95
96	1.2708 6847	1.3225 9069	1.3763 9512	1.4905 8547	96
97	1.2740 4564	1.3264 4825	1.3809 8310	1.4967 9624	97
98	1.2772 3075	1.3303 1706	1.3855 8638	1.5030 3289	98
99	1.2804 2383	1.3341 9715	1.3902 0500	1.5092 9553	99
100	1.2836 2489	1.3380 8856	1.3948 3902	1.5155 8426	100

TABLE I.—Amount of 1 at Compound Interest

$$s = (1 + i)^n$$

n	¼%	7/24%	⅓%	5/12%	n
101	1.2868 3395	1.3419 9131	1.3994 8848	1.5218 9919	101
102	1.2900 5104	1.3459 0546	1.4041 5344	1.5282 4044	102
103	1.2932 7616	1.3498 3101	1.4088 3395	1.5346 0811	103
104	1.2965 0935	1.3537 6802	1.4135 3007	1.5410 0231	104
105	1.2997 5063	1.3577 1651	1.4182 4183	1.5474 2315	105
106	1.3030 0000	1.3616 7652	1.4229 6931	1.5538 7075	106
107	1.3062 5750	1.3656 4807	1.4277 1254	1.5603 4521	107
108	1.3095 2315	1.3696 3121	1.4324 7158	1.5668 4665	108
109	1.3127 9696	1.3736 2597	1.4372 4649	1.5733 7518	109
110	1.3160 7895	1.3776 3238	1.4420 3731	1.5799 3091	110
111	1.3193 6915	1.3816 5047	1.4468 4410	1.5865 1395	111
112	1.3226 6757	1.3856 8029	1.4516 6691	1.5931 2443	112
113	1.3259 7424	1.3897 2186	1.4565 0580	1.5997 6245	113
114	1.3292 8917	1.3937 7521	1.4613 6082	1.6064 2812	114
115	1.3326 1240	1.3978 4039	1.4662 3202	1.6131 2157	115
116	1.3359 4393	1.4019 1742	1.4711 1946	1.6198 4291	116
117	1.3392 8379	1.4060 0635	1.4760 2320	1.6265 9226	117
118	1.3426 3200	1.4101 0720	1.4809 4327	1.6333 6973	118
119	1.3459 8858	1.4142 2001	1.4858 7979	1.6401 7543	119
120	1.3493 5355	1.4183 4482	1.4908 3268	1.6470 0950	120
121	1,3527 2693	1.4224 8166	1.4958 0212	1.6538 7204	121
122	1.3561 0875	1.4266 3057	1.5007 8813	1.6607 6317	122
123	1.3594 9902	1.4307 9157	1.5057 9076	1.6676 8302	123
124	1.3628 9777	1.4349 6471	1.5108 1006	1.6746 3170	124
125	1.3663 0501	1.4391 5003	1.5158 4609	1.6816 0933	125
126	1.3697 2077	1.4433 4755	1.5208 9892	1.6886 1603	126
127	1.3731 4508	1.4475 5731	1.5259 6858	1.6956 5193	127
128	1.3765 7794	1.4517 7935	1.5310 5514	1.7027 1715	128
129	1.3800 1938	1.4560 1371	1.5361 5866	1.7098 1181	129
130	1.3834 6943	1.4602 6042	1.5412 7919	1.7169 3602	130
131	1.3869 2811	1.4645 1951	1.5464 1678	1.7240 8992	131
132	1.3903 9543	1.4687 9103	1.5515 7151	1.7312 7363	132
133	1.3938 7142	1.4730 7500	1.5567 4341	1.7384 8727	133
134	1.3973 5609	1.4773 7147	1.5619 3256	1.7457 3097	134
135	1.4008 4948	1.4816 8047	1.5671 3900	1.7530 0485	135
136	1.4043 5161	1.4860 0204	1.5723 6279	1.7603 0903	136
137	1.4078 6249	1.4903 3621	1.5776 0400	1.7676 4365	137
138	1.4113 8214	1.4946 8302	1.5828 6268	1.7750 0884	138
139	1.4149 1060	1.4990 4252	1.5881 3889	1.7824 0471	139
140	1.4184 4787	1.5034 1472	1.5934 3269	1.7898 3139	140
141	1.4219 9399	1.5077 9968	1.5987 4413	1.7972 8902	141
142	1.4255 4898	1.5121 9743	1.6040 7328	1.8047 7773	142
143	1.4291 1285	1.5166 0801	1.6094 2019	1.8122 9763	143
144	1.4326 8563	1.5210 3145	1.6147 8492	1.8198 4887	144
145	1.4362 6735	1.5254 6779	1.6201 6754	1.8274 3158	145
146	1.4398 5802	1.5299 1707	1.6255 6810	1.8350 4588	146
147	1.4434 5766	1.5343 7933	1.6309 8666	1.8426 9190	147
148	1.4470 6631	1.5388 5460	1.6364 2328	1.8503 6978	148
149	1.4506 8397	1.5433 4293	1.6418 7802	1.8580 7966	149
150	1.4543 1068	1.5478 4434	1.6473 5095	1.8658 2166	150

TABLE I.—Amount of 1 at Compound Interest

$$s = (1 + i)^n$$

n	$\frac{1}{4}\%$	$\frac{7}{24}\%$	$\frac{1}{3}\%$	$\frac{5}{12}\%$	n
151	1.4579 4646	1.5523 5889	1.6528 4212	1.8735 9591	151
152	1.4615 9132	1.5568 8660	1.6583 5160	1.8814 0256	152
153	1.4652 4530	1.5614 2752	1.6638 7943	1.8892 4174	153
154	1.4689 0842	1.5659 8169	1.6694 2570	1.8971 1358	154
155	1.4725 8069	1.5705 4913	1.6749 9045	1.9050 1822	155
156	1.4762 6214	1.5751 2990	1.6805 7375	1.9129 5580	156
157	1.4799 5279	1.5797 2403	1.6861 7566	1.9209 2645	157
158	1.4836 5268	1.5843 3156	1.6917 9625	1.9289 3031	158
159	1.4873 6181	1.5889 5253	1.6974 3557	1.9369 6752	159
160	1.4910 8021	1.5935 8697	1.7030 9369	1.9450 3821	160
161	1.4948 0791	1.5982 3493	1.7087 7067	1.9531 4254	161
162	1.4985 4493	1.6028 9645	1.7144 6657	1.9612 8063	162
163	1.5022 9129	1.6075 7157	1.7201 8146	1.9694 5264	163
164	1.5060 4702	1.6122 6032	1.7259 1540	1.9776 5869	164
165	1.5098 1214	1.6169 6274	1.7316 6845	1.9858 9893	165
166	1.5135 8667	1.6216 7888	1.7374 4068	1.9941 7351	166
167	1.5173 7064	1.6264 0878	1.7432 3215	2.0024 8257	167
168	1.5211 6406	1.6311 5247	1.7490 4292	2.0108 2625	168
169	1.5249 6697	1.6359 1000	1.7548 7306	2.0192 0469	169
170	1.5287 7939	1.6406 8140	1.7607 2264	2.0276 1804	170
171	1.5326 0134	1.6454 6672	1.7665 9172	2.0360 6645	171
172	1.5364 3284	1.6502 6600	1.7724 8035	2.0445 5006	172
173	1.5402 7393	1.6550 7928	1.7783 8862	2.0530 6902	173
174	1.5441 2461	1.6599 0659	1.7843 1658	2.0616 2347	174
175	1.5479 8492	1.6647 4799	1.7902 6431	2.0702 1357	175
176	1.5518 5488	1.6696 0350	1.7962 3185	2.0788 3946	176
177	1.5557 3452	1.6744 7318	1.8022 1929	2.0875 0129	177
178	1.5596 2386	1.6793 5706	1.8082 2669	2.0961 9921	178
179	1.5635 2292	1.6842 5518	1.8142 5411	2.1049 3338	179
180	1.5674 3172	1.6891 6760	1.8203 0163	2.1137 0393	180
181	1.5713 5030	1.6940 9433	1.8263 6930	2.1225 1103	181
182	1.5752 7868	1.6990 3544	1.8324 5720	2.1313 5483	182
183	1.5792 1688	1.7039 9096	1.8385 6539	2.1402 3547	183
184	1.5831 6492	1.7089 6094	1.8446 9394	2.1491 5312	184
185	1.5871 2283	1.7139 4541	1.8508 4292	2.1581 0793	185
186	1.5910 9064	1.7189 4441	1.8570 1240	2.1671 0004	186
187	1.5950 6836	1.7239 5800	1.8632 0244	2.1761 2963	187
188	1.5990 5604	1.7289 8621	1.8694 1311	2.1851 9683	188
189	1.6030 5368	1.7340 2909	1.8756 4449	2.1943 0182	189
190	1.6070 6131	1.7390 8667	1.8818 9664	2.2034 4474	190
191	1.6110 7896	1.7441 5901	1.8881 6963	2.2126 2576	191
192	1.6151 0666	1.7492 4614	1.8944 6352	2.2218 4504	192
193	1.6191 4443	1.7543 4811	1.9007 7840	2.2311 0272	193
194	1.6231 9229	1.7594 6496	1.9071 1433	2.2403 9899	194
195	1.6272 5027	1.7645 9673	1.9134 7138	2.2497 3398	195
196	1.6313 1839	1.7697 4347	1.9198 4962	2.2591 0787	196
197	1.6353 9669	1.7749 0522	1.9262 4912	2.2685 2082	197
198	1.6394 8518	1.7800 8203	1.9326 6995	2.2779 7299	198
199	1.6435 8390	1.7852 7393	1.9391 1218	2.2874 6455	199
200	1.6476 9285	1.7904 8098	1.9455 7589	2.2969 9565	200

TABLE I.—Amount of 1 at Compound Interest

$$s = (1 + i)^n$$

n	½%	$\frac{7}{12}$%	⅝%	⅔%	n
1	1.0050 0000	1.0058 3333	1.0062 5000	1.0066 6667	1
2	1.0100 2500	1.0117 0069	1.0125 3906	1.0133 7778	2
3	1.0150 7513	1.0176 0228	1.0188 6743	1.0201 3363	3
4	1.0201 5050	1.0235 3830	1.0252 3535	1.0269 3452	4
5	1.0252 5125	1.0295 0894	1.0316 4307	1.0337 8075	5
6	1.0303 7751	1.0355 1440	1.0380 9084	1.0406 7262	6
7	1.0355 2940	1.0415 5490	1.0445 7891	1.0476 1044	7
8	1.0407 0704	1.0476 3064	1.0511 0753	1.0545 9451	8
9	1.0459 1058	1.0537 4182	1.0576 7695	1.0616 2514	9
10	1.0511 4013	1.0598 8865	1.0642 8743	1.0687 0264	10
11	1.0563 9583	1.0660 7133	1.0709 3923	1.0758 2732	11
12	1.0616 7781	1.0722 9008	1.0776 3260	1.0829 9951	12
13	1.0669 8620	1.0785 4511	1.0843 6780	1.0902 1950	13
14	1.0723 2113	1.0848 3662	1.0911 4510	1.0974 8763	14
15	1.0776 8274	1.0911 6483	1.0979 6476	1.1048 0422	15
16	1.0830 7115	1.0975 2996	1.1048 2704	1.1121 6958	16
17	1.0884 8651	1.1039 3222	1.1117 3221	1.1195 8404	17
18	1.0939 2894	1.1103 7182	1.1186 8053	1.1270 4794	18
19	1.0993 9858	1.1168 4899	1.1256 7229	1.1345 6159	19
20	1.1048 9558	1.1233 6395	1.1327 0774	1.1421 2533	20
21	1.1104 2006	1.1299 1690	1.1397 8716	1.1497 3950	21
22	1.1159 7216	1.1365 0808	1.1469 1083	1.1574 0443	22
23	1.1215 5202	1.1431 3771	1.1540 7902	1.1651 2046	23
24	1.1271 5978	1.1498 0602	1.1612 9202	1.1728 8793	24
25	1.1327 9558	1.1565 1322	1.1685 5009	1.1807 0718	25
26	1.1384 5955	1.1632 5955	1.1758 5353	1.1885 7857	26
27	1.1441 5185	1.1700 4523	1.1832 0262	1.1965 0242	27
28	1.1498 7261	1.1768 7049	1.1905 9763	1.2044 7911	28
29	1.1556 2197	1.1837 3557	1.1980 3887	1.2125 0897	29
30	1.1614 0008	1.1906 4069	1.2055 2661	1.2205 9236	30
31	1.1672 0708	1.1975 8610	1.2130 6115	1.2287 2964	31
32	1.1730 4312	1.2045 7202	1.2206 4278	1.2369 2117	32
33	1.1789 0833	1.2115 9869	1.2282 7180	1.2451 6731	33
34	1.1848 0288	1.2186 6634	1.2359 4850	1.2534 6843	34
35	1.1907 2689	1.2257 7523	1.2436 7318	1.2618 2489	35
36	1.1966 8052	1.2329 2559	1.2514 4614	1.2702 3705	36
37	1.2026 6393	1.2401 1765	1.2592 6767	1.2787 0530	37
38	1.2086 7725	1.2473 5167	1.2671 3810	1.2872 3000	38
39	1.2147 2063	1.2546 2789	1.2750 5771	1.2958 1153	39
40	1.2207 9424	1.2619 4655	1.2830 2682	1.3044 5028	40
41	1.2268 9821	1.2693 0791	1.2910 4574	1.3131 4661	41
42	1.2330 3270	1.2767 1220	1.2991 1477	1.3219 0092	42
43	1.2391 9786	1.2841 5969	1.3072 3424	1.3307 1360	43
44	1.2453 9385	1.2916 5062	1.3154 0446	1.3395 8502	44
45	1.2516 2082	1.2991 8525	1.3236 2573	1.3485 1559	45
46	1.2578 7892	1.3067 6383	1.3318 9839	1.3575 0569	46
47	1.2641 6832	1.3143 8662	1.3402 2276	1.3665 5573	47
48	1.2704 8916	1.3220 5388	1.3485 9915	1.3756 6610	48
49	1.2768 4161	1.3297 6586	1.3570 2790	1.3848 3721	49
50	1.2832 2581	1.3375 2283	1.3655 0932	1.3940 6946	50

TABLE I. —Amount of 1 at Compound Interest

$$s = (1 + i)^n$$

n	½%	7/12%	⅝%	⅔%	n
51	1.2896 4194	1.3453 2504	1.3740 4375	1.4033 6325	51
52	1.2960 9015	1.3531 7277	1.3826 3153	1.4127 1901	52
53	1.3025 7060	1.3610 6628	1.3912 7207	1.4221 3713	53
54	1.3090 8346	1.3690 0583	1.3999 6843	1.4316 1805	54
55	1.3156 2887	1.3769 9170	1.4087 1823	1.4411 6217	55
56	1.3222 0702	1.3850 2415	1.4175 2272	1.4507 6992	56
57	1.3288 1805	1.3931 0346	1.4263 8224	1.4604 4172	57
58	1.3354 6214	1.4012 2990	1.4352 9713	1.4701 7799	58
59	1.3421 3946	1.4094 0374	1.4442 6773	1.4799 7918	59
60	1.3488 5015	1.4176 2526	1.4532 9441	1.4898 4571	60
61	1.3555 9440	1.4258 9474	1.4623 7750	1.4997 7801	61
62	1.3623 7238	1.4342 1246	1.4715 1736	1.5097 7653	62
63	1.3691 8424	1.4425 7870	1.4807 1434	1.5198 4171	63
64	1.3760 3016	1.4509 9374	1.4899 6881	1.5299 7399	64
65	1.3829 1031	1.4594 5787	1.4992 8111	1.5401 7381	65
66	1.3898 2486	1.4679 7138	1.5086 5162	1.5504 4164	66
67	1.3967 7399	1.4765 3454	1.5180 8069	1.5607 7792	67
68	1.4037 5785	1.4851 4766	1.5275 6869	1.5711 8310	68
69	1.4107 7664	1.4938 1102	1.5371 1600	1.5816 5766	69
70	1.4178 3053	1.5025 2492	1.5467 2297	1.5922 0204	70
71	1.4249 1968	1.5112 8965	1.5563 8999	1.6028 1672	71
72	1.4320 4428	1.5201 0550	1.5661 1743	1.6135 0217	72
73	1.4392 0450	1.5289 7279	1.5759 0566	1.6242 5885	73
74	1.4464 0052	1.5378 9179	1.5857 5507	1.6350 8724	74
75	1.4536 3252	1.5468 6283	1.5956 6604	1.6459 0782	75
76	1.4609 0069	1.5558 8620	1.6056 3896	1.6569 6107	76
77	1.4682 0519	1.5649 6220	1.6156 7420	1.6680 0748	77
78	1.4755 4622	1.5740 9115	1.6257 7216	1.6791 2753	78
79	1.4829 2395	1.5832 7334	1.6359 3324	1.6903 2172	79
80	1.4903 3857	1.5925 0910	1.6461 5782	1.7015 9053	80
81	1.4977 9026	1.6017 9874	1.6564 4631	1.7129 3446	81
82	1.5052 7921	1.6111 4257	1.6667 9910	1.7243 5403	82
83	1.5128 0561	1.6205 4090	1.6772 1659	1.7358 4972	83
84	1.5203 6964	1.6299 9405	1.6876 9920	1.7474 2205	84
85	1.5279 7148	1.6395 0235	1.6982 4732	1.7590 7153	85
86	1.5356 1134	1.6490 6612	1.7088 6136	1.7707 9868	86
87	1.5432 8940	1.6586 8567	1.7195 4175	1.7826 0400	87
88	1.5510 0585	1.6683 6134	1.7302 8888	1.7944 8803	88
89	1.5587 6087	1.6780 9344	1.7411 0319	1.8064 5128	89
90	1.5665 5468	1.6878 8232	1.7519 8508	1.8184 9429	90
91	1.5743 8745	1.6977 2830	1.7629 3499	1.8306 1758	91
92	1.5822 5939	1.7076 3172	1.7739 5333	1.8428 2170	92
93	1.5901 7069	1.7175 9290	1.7850 4054	1.8551 0718	93
94	1.5981 2154	1.7276 1219	1.7961 9704	1.8674 7456	94
95	1.6061 1215	1.7376 8993	1.8074 2328	1.8799 2439	95
96	1.6141 4271	1.7478 2646	1.8187 1967	1.8924 5722	96
97	1.6222 1342	1.7580 2211	1.8300 8667	1.9050 7360	97
98	1.6303 2449	1.7682 7724	1.8415 2471	1.9177 7409	98
99	1.6384 7611	1.7785 9219	1.8530 3424	1.9305 5925	99
100	1.6466 6849	1.7889 6731	1.8646 1570	1.9434 2965	100

TABLE I. —Amount of 1 at Compound Interest

$$s = (1 + i)^n$$

n	½%	7/12%	⅝%	⅔%	n
101	1.6549 0183	1.7994 0295	1.8762 6955	1.9563 8585	101
102	1.6631 7634	1.8098 9947	1.8879 9624	1.9694 2842	102
103	1.6714 9223	1.8204 5722	1.8997 9621	1.9825 5794	103
104	1.6798 4969	1.8310 7655	1.9116 6994	1.9957 7499	104
105	1.6882 4894	1.8417 5783	1.9236 1788	2.0090 8016	105
106	1.6966 9018	1.8525 0142	1.9356 4049	2.0224 7403	106
107	1.7051 7363	1.8633 0768	1.9477 3824	2.0359 5719	107
108	1.7136 9950	1.8741 7697	1.9599 1161	2.0495 3024	108
109	1.7222 6800	1.8851 0967	1.9721 6105	2.0631 9377	109
110	1.7308 7934	1.8961 0614	1.9844 8706	2.0769 4840	110
111	1.7395 3373	1.9071 6676	1.9968 9010	2.0907 9472	111
112	1.7482 3140	1.9182 9190	2.0093 7067	2.1047 3335	112
113	1.7569 7256	1.9294 8194	2.0219 2923	2.1187 6491	113
114	1.7657 5742	1.9407 3725	2.0345 6629	2.1328 9000	114
115	1.7745 8621	1.9520 5822	2.0472 8233	2.1471 0927	115
116	1.7834 5914	1.9634 4522	2.0600 7785	2.1614 2333	116
117	1.7923 7644	1.9748 9865	2.0729 5333	2.1758 3282	117
118	1.8013 3832	1.9864 1890	2.0859 0929	2.1903 3837	118
119	1.8103 4501	1.9980 0634	2.0989 4622	2.2049 4063	119
120	1.8193 9673	2.0096 6138	2.1120 6464	2.2196 4023	120
121	1.8284 9372	2.0213 8440	2.1252 6504	2.2344 3784	121
122	1.8376 3619	2.0331 7581	2.1385 4795	2.2493 3409	122
123	1.8468 2437	2.0450 3600	2.1519 1387	2.2643 2965	123
124	1.8560 5849	2.0569 6538	2.1653 6333	2.2794 2518	124
125	1.8653 3878	2.0689 6434	2.1788 9685	2.2946 2135	125
126	1.8746 6548	2.0810 3330	2.1925 1496	2.3099 1882	126
127	1.8840 3880	2.0931 7266	2.2062 1818	2.3253 1828	127
128	1.8934 5900	2.1053 8284	2.2200 0704	2.3408 2040	128
129	1.9029 2629	2.1176 6424	2.2338 8209	2.3564 2587	129
130	1.9124 4092	2.1300 1728	2.2478 4385	2.3721 3538	130
131	1.9220 0313	2.1424 4238	2.2618 9287	2.3879 4962	131
132	1.9316 1314	2.1549 3996	2.2760 2970	2.4038 6928	132
133	1.9412 7121	2.1675 1044	2.2902 5489	2.4198 9507	133
134	1.9509 7757	2.1801 5425	2.3045 6898	2.4360 2771	134
135	1.9607 3245	2.1928 7182	2.3189 7254	2.4522 6789	135
136	1.9705 3612	2.2056 6357	2.3334 6612	2.4686 1635	136
137	1.9803 8880	2.2185 2994	2.3480 5028	2.4850 7379	137
138	1.9902 9074	2.2314 7137	2.3627 2559	2.5016 4095	138
139	2.0002 4219	2.2444 8828	2.3774 9263	2.5183 1855	139
140	2.0102 4340	2.2575 8113	2.3923 5196	2.5351 0734	140
141	2.0202 9462	2.2707 5036	2.4073 0416	2.5520 0806	141
142	2.0303 9609	2.2839 9640	2.4223 4981	2.5690 2145	142
143	2.0405 4808	2.2973 1971	2.4374 8950	2.5861 4826	143
144	2.0507 5082	2.3107 2074	2.4527 2380	2.6033 8924	144
145	2.0610 0457	2.3241 9995	2.4680 5333	2.6207 4517	145
146	2.0713 0959	2.3377 5778	2.4834 7866	2.6382 1681	146
147	2.0816 6614	2.3513 9470	2.4990 0040	2.6558 0492	147
148	2.0920 7447	2.3651 1117	2.5146 1916	2.6735 1028	148
149	2.1025 3484	2.3789 0765	2.5303 3553	2.6913 3369	149
150	2.1130 4752	2.3927 8461	2.5461 5012	2.7092 7591	150

TABLE I. —Amount of 1 at Compound Interest

$$s = (1 + i)^n$$

n	$\frac{1}{2}\%$	$\frac{7}{12}\%$	$\frac{5}{8}\%$	$\frac{2}{3}\%$	n
151	2.1236 1276	2.4067 4252	2.5620 6356	2.7273 3775	151
152	2.1342 3082	2.4207 8186	2.5780 7646	2.7455 2000	152
153	2.1449 0197	2.4349 0308	2.5941 8944	2.7638 2347	153
154	2.1556 2648	2.4491 0668	2.6104 0312	2.7822 4896	154
155	2.1664 0462	2.4633 9314	2.6267 1814	2.8007 9729	155
156	2.1772 3664	2.4777 6293	2.6431 3513	2.8194 6927	156
157	2.1881 2282	2.4922 1655	2.6596 5472	2.8382 6573	157
158	2.1990 6344	2.5067 5448	2.6762 7756	2.8571 8750	158
159	2.2100 5875	2.5213 7722	2.6930 0430	2.8762 3542	159
160	2.2211 0905	2.5360 8525	2.7098 3558	2.8954 1032	160
161	2.2322 1459	2.5508 7908	2.7267 7205	2.9147 1306	161
162	2.2433 7566	2.5657 5921	2.7438 1437	2.9341 4448	162
163	2.2545 9254	2.5807 2614	2.7609 6321	2.9537 0544	163
164	2.2658 6551	2.5957 8037	2.7782 1923	2.9733 9681	164
165	2.2771 9483	2.6109 2242	2.7955 8310	2.9932 1945	165
166	2.2885 8081	2.6261 5280	2.8130 5550	3.0131 7425	166
167	2.3000 2371	2.6414 7203	2.8306 3710	3.0332 6208	167
168	2.3115 2383	2.6568 8062	2.8483 2858	3.0534 3883	168
169	2.3230 8145	2.6723 7909	2.8661 3063	3.0738 4038	169
170	2.3346 9686	2.6879 6796	2.8840 4395	3.0943 3265	170
171	2.3463 7034	2.7036 4778	2.9020 6922	3.1149 6154	171
172	2.3581 0219	2.7194 1906	2.9202 0715	3.1357 2795	172
173	2.3698 9270	2.7352 8233	2.9384 5845	3.1566 3280	173
174	2.3817 4217	2.7512 3815	2.9568 2381	3.1776 7702	174
175	2.3936 5088	2.7672 8704	2.9753 0396	3.1988 6153	175
176	2.4056 1913	2.7834 2954	2.9938 9961	3.2201 8728	176
177	2.4176 4723	2.7996 6622	3.0126 1149	3.2416 5519	177
178	2.4297 3546	2.8159 9760	3.0314 4031	3.2632 6623	178
179	2.4418 8414	2.8324 2426	3.0503 8681	3.2850 2134	179
180	2.4540 9356	2.8489 4673	3.0694 5173	3.3069 2148	180
181	2.4663 6403	2.8655 6559	3.0886 3580	3.3289 6762	181
182	2.4786 9585	2.8822 8139	3.1079 3977	3.3511 6074	182
183	2.4910 8933	2.8990 9469	3.1272 6440	3.3735 0181	183
184	2.5035 4478	2.9160 0608	3.1469 1043	3.3959 9182	184
185	2.5160 6250	2.9330 1612	3.1665 7862	3.4186 3177	185
186	2.5286 4281	2.9501 2538	3.1863 6973	3.4414 2265	186
187	2.5412 8603	2.6973 3444	3.2062 8454	3.4643 6546	187
188	2.5539 9246	2.9846 4389	3.2263 2382	3.4874 6123	188
189	2.5667 6242	3.0020 5431	3.2464 8834	3.5107 1097	189
190	2.5795 9623	3.0195 6630	3.2667 7890	3.5341 1571	190
191	2.5924 9421	3.0371 8043	3.2871 9627	3.5576 7049	191
192	2.6054 5668	3.0548 9732	3.3077 4124	3.5813 9433	192
193	2.6184 8397	3.0727 1755	3.3284 1462	3.6052 7029	193
194	2.6315 7639	3.0906 4174	3.3492 1722	3.6293 0543	194
195	2.6447 3427	3.1086 7048	3.3701 4982	3.6535 0080	195
196	2.6579 5794	3.1268 0440	3.3912 1326	3.6778 5747	196
197	2.6712 4773	3.1450 4409	3.4124 0834	3.7023 7652	197
198	2.6846 0397	3.1633 9018	3.4337 3589	3.7270 5903	198
199	2.6980 2699	3.1818 4329	3.4551 9674	3.7519 0609	199
200	2.7115 1712	3.2004 0404	3.4767 9172	3.7769 1880	200

TABLE I.—Amount of 1 at Compound Interest

$$s = (1 + i)^n$$

n	¾%	⅞%	1%	1⅛%	n
1	1.0075 0000	1.0087 5000	1.0100 0000	1.0112 5000	1
2	1.0150 5625	1.0175 7656	1.0201 0000	1.0226 2656	2
3	1.0226 6917	1.0264 8036	1.0303 0100	1.0341 3111	3
4	1.0303 3919	1.0354 6206	1.0406 0401	1.0457 6509	4
5	1.0380 6673	1.0445 2235	1.0510 1005	1.0575 2994	5
6	1.0458 5224	1.0536 6192	1.0615 2015	1.0694 2716	6
7	1.0536 9613	1.0628 8147	1.0721 3535	1.0814 5821	7
8	1.0615 9885	1.0721 8168	1.0828 5671	1.0936 2462	8
9	1.0695 6084	1.0815 6327	1.0936 8527	1.1059 2789	9
10	1.0775 8255	1.0910 2695	1.1046 2213	1.1183 6958	10
11	1.0856 6441	1.1005 7343	1.1156 6835	1.1309 5124	11
12	1.0938 0690	1.1102 0345	1.1268 2503	1.1436 7444	12
13	1.1020 1045	1.1199 1773	1.1380 9328	1.1565 4078	13
14	1.1102 7553	1.1297 1701	1.1494 7421	1.1695 5186	14
15	1.1186 0259	1.1396 0203	1.1609 6896	1.1827 0932	15
16	1.1269 9211	1.1495 7355	1.1725 7864	1.1960 1480	16
17	1.1354 4455	1.1596 3232	1.1843 0443	1.2094 6997	17
18	1.1439 6039	1.1697 7910	1.1961 4748	1.2230 7650	18
19	1.1525 4009	1.1800 1467	1.2081 0895	1.2368 3611	19
20	1.1611 8414	1.1903 3980	1.2201 9004	1.2507 5052	20
21	1.1698 9302	1.2007 5527	1.2323 9194	1.2648 2146	21
22	1.1786 6722	1.2112 6188	1.2447 1586	1.2790 5071	22
23	1.1875 0723	1.2218 6042	1.2571 6302	1.2934 4003	23
24	1.1964 1353	1.2325 5170	1.2697 3465	1.3079 9123	24
25	1.2053 8663	1.2433 3653	1.2824 3200	1.3227 0613	25
26	1.2144 2703	1.2542 1572	1.2952 5631	1.3375 8657	26
27	1.2235 3523	1.2651 9011	1.3082 0888	1.3526 3442	27
28	1.2327 1175	1.2762 6052	1.3212 9097	1.3678 5156	28
29	1.2419 5709	1.2874 2780	1.3345 0388	1.3832 3989	29
30	1.2512 7176	1.2986 9280	1.3478 4892	1.3988 0134	30
31	1.2606 5630	1.3100 5636	1.3613 2740	1.4145 3785	31
32	1.2701 1122	1.3215 1935	1.3749 4068	1.4304 5140	32
33	1.2796 3706	1.3330 8265	1.3886 9009	1.4465 4398	33
34	1.2892 3434	1.3447 4712	1.4025 7699	1.4628 1760	34
35	1.2989 0359	1.3565 1366	1.4166 0276	1.4792 7430	35
36	1.3086 4537	1.3683 8315	1.4307 6878	1.4959 1613	36
37	1.3184 6021	1.3803 5650	1.4450 7647	1.5127 4519	37
38	1.3283 4866	1.3924 3462	1.4595 2724	1.5297 6357	38
39	1.3383 1128	1.4046 1843	1.4741 2251	1.5469 7341	39
40	1.3483 4861	1.4169 0884	1.4888 6373	1.5643 7687	40
41	1.3584 6123	1.4293 0679	1.5037 5237	1.5819 7611	41
42	1.3686 4969	1.4418 1322	1.5187 8989	1.5997 7334	42
43	1.3789 1456	1.4544 2909	1.5339 7779	1.6177 7079	43
44	1.3892 5642	1.4671 5534	1.5493 1757	1.6359 7071	44
45	1.3996 7584	1.4799 9295	1.5648 1075	1.6543 7538	45
46	1.4101 7341	1.4929 4289	1.5804 5885	1.6729 8710	46
47	1.4207 4971	1.5060 0614	1.5962 6344	1.6918 0821	47
48	1.4314 0533	1.5191 8370	1.6122 2608	1.7108 4105	48
49	1.4421 4087	1.5324 7655	1.6283 4834	1.7300 8801	49
50	1.4529 5693	1.5458 8572	1.6446 3182	1.7495 5150	50

TABLE I.—Amount of 1 at Compound Interest

$$s = (1 + i)^n$$

n	$\frac{3}{4}\%$	$\frac{7}{8}\%$	1%	$1\frac{1}{8}\%$	n
51	1.4638 5411	1.5594 1222	1.6610 7814	1.7692 3395	51
52	1.4748 3301	1.5730 5708	1.6776 8892	1.7891 3784	52
53	1.4858 9426	1.5868 2133	1.6944 6581	1.8092 6564	53
54	1.4970 3847	1.6007 0602	1.7114 1047	1.8296 1988	54
55	1.5082 6626	1.6147 1219	1.7285 2457	1.8502 0310	55
56	1.5195 7825	1.6288 4093	1.7458 0982	1.8710 1788	56
57	1.5309 7509	1.6430 9328	1.7632 6792	1.8920 6684	57
58	1.5424 5740	1.6574 7035	1.7809 0060	1.9133 5259	58
59	1.5540 2583	1.6719 7322	1.7987 0960	1.9348 7780	59
60	1.5656 8103	1.6866 0298	1.8166 9670	1.9566 4518	60
61	1.5774 2363	1.7013 6076	1.8348 6367	1.9786 5744	61
62	1.5892 5431	1.7162 4766	1.8532 1230	2.0009 1733	62
63	1.6011 7372	1.7312 6483	1.8717 4443	2.0234 2765	63
64	1.6131 8252	1.7464 1340	1.8904 6187	2.0461 9121	64
65	1.6252 8139	1.7616 9452	1.9093 6649	2.0692 1087	65
66	1.6374 7100	1.7771 0934	1.9284 6015	2.0924 8949	66
67	1.6497 5203	1.7926 5905	1.9477 4475	2.1160 2999	67
68	1.6621 2517	1.8083 4482	1.9672 2220	2.1398 3533	68
69	1.6745 9111	1.8241 6783	1.9868 9442	2.1639 0848	69
70	1.6871 5055	1.8401 2930	2.0067 6337	2.1882 5245	70
71	1.6998 0418	1.8562 3043	2.0268 3100	2.2128 7029	71
72	1.7125 5271	1.8724 7245	2.0470 9931	2.2377 6508	72
73	1.7253 9685	1.8888 5658	2.0675 7031	2.2629 3994	73
74	1.7383 3733	1.9053 8408	2.0882 4601	2.2883 9801	74
75	1.7513 7486	1.9220 5619	2.1091 2847	2.3141 4249	75
76	1.7645 1017	1.9388 7418	2.1302 1975	2.3401 7659	76
77	1.7777 4400	1.9558 3933	2.1515 2195	2.3665 0358	77
78	1.7910 7708	1.9729 5292	2.1730 3717	2.3931 2675	78
79	1.8045 1015	1.9902 1626	2.1947 6754	2.4200 4942	79
80	1.8180 4398	2.0076 3066	2.2167 1522	2.4472 7498	80
81	1.8316 7931	2.0251 9742	2.2388 8237	2.4748 0682	81
82	1.8454 1691	2.0429 1790	2.2612 7119	2.5026 4840	82
83	1.8592 5753	2.0607 9343	2.2838 8390	2.5308 0319	83
84	1.8732 0196	2.0788 2537	2.3067 2274	2.5592 7473	84
85	1.8872 5098	2.0970 1510	2.3297 8997	2.5880 6657	85
86	1.9014 0536	2.1153 6398	2.3530 8787	2.6171 8232	86
87	1.9156 6590	2.1338 7341	2.3766 1875	2.6466 2562	87
88	1.9300 3339	2.1525 4481	2.4003 8494	2.6764 0016	88
89	1.9445 0865	2.1713 7957	2.4243 8879	2.7065 0966	89
90	1.9590 9246	2.1903 7914	2.4486 3267	2.7369 5789	90
91	1.9737 8565	2.2095 4496	2.4731 1900	2.7677 4867	91
92	1.9885 8905	2.2288 7848	2.4978 5019	2.7988 8584	92
93	2.0035 0346	2.2483 8117	2.5228 2869	2.8303 7331	93
94	2.0185 2974	2.2680 5450	2.5480 5698	2.8622 1501	94
95	2.0336 6871	2.2878 9998	2.5735 3755	2.8944 1492	95
96	2.0489 2123	2.3079 1910	2.5992 7293	2.9269 7709	96
97	2.0642 8814	2.3281 1340	2.6252 6565	2.9599 0559	97
98	2.0797 7030	2.3484 8439	2.6515 1831	2.9932 0452	98
99	2.0953 6858	2.3690 3363	2.6780 3349	3.0268 7807	99
100	2.1110 8384	2.3897 6267	2.7048 1383	3.0609 3045	100

TABLE I.—Amount of 1 at Compound Interest

$$s = (1 + i)^n$$

n	$1\frac{1}{4}\%$	$1\frac{3}{8}\%$	$1\frac{1}{2}\%$	$1\frac{3}{4}\%$	n
1	1.0125 0000	1.0137 5000	1.0150 0000	1.0175 0000	1
2	1.0251 5625	1.0276 8906	1.0302 2500	1.0353 0625	2
3	1.0379 7070	1.0418 1979	1.0456 7838	1.0534 2411	3
4	1.0509 4534	1.0561 4481	1.0613 6355	1.0718 5903	4
5	1.0640 8215	1.0706 6680	1.0772 8400	1.0906 1656	5
6	1.0773 8318	1.0853 8847	1.0934 4326	1.1097 0235	6
7	1.0908 5047	1.1003 1256	1.1098 4491	1.1291 2215	7
8	1.1044 8610	1.1154 4186	1.1264 9259	1.1488 8178	8
9	1.1182 9218	1.1307 7918	1.1433 8998	1.1689 8721	9
10	1.1322 7083	1.1463 2740	1.1605 4083	1.1894 4449	10
11	1.1464 2422	1.1620 8940	1.1779 4894	1.2102 5977	11
12	1.1607 5452	1.1780 6813	1.1956 1817	1.2314 3931	12
13	1.1752 6395	1.1942 6656	1.2135 5244	1.2529 8950	13
14	1.1899 5475	1.2106 8773	1.2317 5573	1.2749 1682	14
15	1.2048 2918	1.2273 3469	1.2502 3207	1.2972 2786	15
16	1.2198 8955	1.2442 1054	1.2689 8555	1.3199 2935	16
17	1.2351 3817	1.2613 1843	1.2880 2033	1.3430 2811	17
18	1.2505 7739	1.2786 6156	1.3073 4064	1.3665 3111	18
19	1.2662 0961	1.2962 4316	1.3269 5075	1.3904 4540	19
20	1.2820 3723	1.3140 6650	1.3468 5501	1.4147 7820	20
21	1.2980 6270	1.3321 3492	1.3670 5783	1.4395 3681	21
22	1.3142 8848	1.3504 5177	1.3875 6370	1.4647 2871	22
23	1.3307 1709	1.3690 2048	1.4083 7715	1.4903 6146	23
24	1.3473 5105	1.3878 4451	1.4295 0281	1.5164 4279	24
25	1.3641 9294	1.4069 2738	1.4509 4535	1.5429 8054	25
26	1.3812 4535	1.4262 7263	1.4727 0953	1.5699 8269	26
27	1.3985 1092	1.4458 8388	1.4948 0018	1.5974 5739	27
28	1.4159 9230	1.4657 6478	1.5172 2218	1.6254 1290	28
29	1.4336 9221	1.4859 1905	1.5399 8051	1.6538 5762	29
30	1.4516 1336	1.5063 5043	1.5630 8022	1.6828 0013	30
31	1.4697 5853	1.5270 6275	1.5865 2642	1.7122 4913	31
32	1.4881 3051	1.5480 5986	1.6103 2432	1.7422 1349	32
33	1.5067 3214	1.5693 4569	1.6344 7918	1.7727 0223	33
34	1.5255 6629	1.5909 2419	1.6589 9637	1.8037 2452	34
35	1.5446 3587	1.6127 9940	1.6838 8132	1.8352 8970	35
36	1.5639 4382	1.6349 7539	1.7091 3954	1.8674 0727	36
37	1.5834 9312	1.6574 5630	1.7347 7663	1.9000 8689	37
38	1.6032 8678	1.6802 4633	1.7607 9828	1.9333 3841	38
39	1.6233 2787	1.7033 4971	1.7872 1025	1.9671 7184	39
40	1.6436 1946	1.7267 7077	1.8140 1841	2.0015 9734	40
41	1.6641 6471	1.7505 1387	1.8412 2868	2.0366 2530	41
42	1.6849 6677	1.7745 8343	1.8688 4712	2.0722 6624	42
43	1.7060 2885	1.7989 8396	1.8968 7982	2.1085 3090	43
44	1.7273 5421	1.8237 1999	1.9253 3302	2.1454 3019	44
45	1.7489 4614	1.8487 9614	1.9542 1301	2.1829 7522	45
46	1.7708 0797	1.8742 1708	1.9835 2621	2.2211 7728	46
47	1.7929 4306	1.8999 8757	2.0132 7910	2.2600 4789	47
48	1.8153 5485	1.9261 1240	2.0434 7829	2.2995 9872	48
49	1.8380 4679	1.9525 9644	2.0741 3046	2.3398 4170	49
50	1.8610 2237	1.9794 4464	2.1052 4242	2.3807 8893	50

TABLE I.—Amount of 1 at Compound Interest

$$s = (1 + i)^n$$

n	$1\frac{1}{4}\%$	$1\frac{3}{8}\%$	$1\frac{1}{2}\%$	$1\frac{3}{4}\%$	n
51	1.8842 8515	2.0066 6201	2.1368 2106	2.4224 5274	51
52	1.9078 3872	2.0342 5361	2.1688 7337	2.4648 4566	52
53	1.9316 8670	2.0622 2460	2.2014 0647	2.5070 8046	53
54	1.9558 3279	2.0905 8019	2.2344 2757	2.5518 7012	54
55	1.9802 8070	2.1193 2566	2.2679 4398	2.5965 2785	55
56	2.0050 3420	2.1484 6639	2.3019 6314	2.6419 6708	56
57	2.0300 9713	2.1780 0780	2.3364 9259	2.6882 0151	57
58	2.0554 7335	2.2079 5541	2.3715 3998	2.7352 4503	58
59	2.0811 6676	2.2383 1480	2.4071 1308	2.7831 1182	59
60	2.1071 8135	2.2690 9163	2.4432 1978	2.8318 1628	60
61	2.1335 2111	2.3002 9164	2.4798 6807	2.8813 7306	61
62	2.1601 9013	2.3319 2065	2.5170 6609	2.9317 9709	62
63	2.1871 9250	2.3639 8456	2.5548 2208	2.9831 0354	63
64	2.2145 3241	2.3964 8934	2.5931 4442	3.0343 0785	64
65	2.2422 1407	2.4294 4107	2.6320 4158	3.0884 2574	65
66	2.2702 4174	2.4628 4589	2.6715 2221	3.1424 7319	66
67	2.2986 1976	2.4967 1002	2.7115 9504	3.1974 6647	67
68	2.3273 5251	2.5310 3978	2.7522 6896	3.2534 2213	68
69	2.3564 4442	2.5658 4158	2.7935 5300	3.3103 5702	69
70	2.3858 9997	2.6011 2190	2.8354 5629	3.3682 8827	70
71	2.4157 2372	2.6368 8732	2.8779 8814	3.4272 3331	71
72	2.4459 2027	2.6731 4453	2.9211 5796	3.4872 0990	72
73	2.4764 9427	2.7099 0026	2.9649 7533	3.5482 3607	73
74	2.5074 5045	2.7471 6139	3.0094 4996	3.6103 3020	74
75	2.5387 9358	2.7849 3486	3.0545 9171	3.6735 1098	75
76	2.5705 2850	2.8232 2771	3.1004 1059	3.7377 9742	76
77	2.6026 6011	2.8620 4710	3.1469 1674	3.8032 0888	77
78	2.6351 9336	2.9014 0024	3.1941 2050	3.8697 6503	78
79	2.6681 3327	2.9412 9450	3.2420 3230	3.9374 8592	79
80	2.7014 8494	2.9817 3730	3.2906 6279	4.0063 9192	80
81	2.7352 5350	3.0227 3618	3.3400 2273	4.0765 0378	81
82	2.7694 4417	3.0642 9881	3.3901 2307	4.1478 4260	82
83	2.8040 6222	3.1064 3291	3.4409 7492	4.2204 2984	83
84	2.8391 1300	3.1491 4637	3.4925 8954	4.2942 8737	84
85	2.8746 0191	3.1924 4713	3.5449 7838	4.3694 3740	85
86	2.9105 3444	3.2363 4328	3.5981 5306	4.4459 0255	86
87	2.9469 1612	3.2808 4300	3.6521 2535	4.5237 0584	87
88	2.9837 5257	3.3259 5459	3.7069 0723	4.6028 7070	88
89	3.0210 4948	3.3716 8646	3.7625 1084	4.6834 2093	89
90	3.0588 1260	3.4180 4715	3.8189 4851	4.7653 8080	90
91	3.0970 4775	3.4650 4530	3.8762 3273	4.8487 7496	91
92	3.1357 6085	3.5120 0967	3.9343 7622	4.9336 2853	92
93	3.1749 5786	3.5609 8916	3.9933 9187	5.0199 6703	93
94	3.2146 4483	3.6099 5276	4.0532 9275	5.1078 1645	94
95	3.2548 2789	3.6595 8961	4.1140 9214	5.1972 0324	95
96	3.2955 1324	3.7099 0897	4.1758 0352	5.2881 5429	96
97	3.3367 0716	3.7609 2021	4.2384 4057	5.3806 9699	97
98	3.3784 1600	3.8126 3287	4.3020 1718	5.4748 5919	98
99	3.4206 4620	3.8650 5657	4.3665 4744	5.5706 6923	99
100	3.4634 0427	3.9182 0110	4.4320 4565	5.6681 5594	100

TABLE I.—Amount of 1 at Compound Interest

$$s = (1 + i)^n$$

n	2%	2¼%	2½%	2¾%	n
1	1.0200 0000	1.0225 0000	1.0250 0000	1.0275 0000	1
2	1.0404 0000	1.0455 0625	1.0506 2500	1.0557 5625	2
3	1.0612 0800	1.0690 3014	1.0768 9063	1.0847 8955	3
4	1.0824 3216	1.0930 8332	1.1038 1289	1.1146 2126	4
5	1.1040 8080	1.1176 7769	1.1314 0821	1.1452 7334	5
6	1.1261 6242	1.1428 2544	1.1596 9342	1.1767 6836	6
7	1.1486 8567	1.1685 3901	1.1886 8575	1.2091 2949	7
8	1.1716 5938	1.1948 3114	1.2184 0290	1.2423 8055	8
9	1.1950 9257	1.2217 1484	1.2488 6297	1.2765 4602	9
10	1.2189 9442	1.2492 0343	1.2800 8454	1.3116 5103	10
11	1.2433 7431	1.2773 1050	1.3120 8666	1.3477 2144	11
12	1.2682 4179	1.3060 4999	1.3448 8882	1.3847 8378	12
13	1.2936 0663	1.3354 3611	1.3785 1104	1.4228 6533	13
14	1.3194 7876	1.3654 8343	1.4129 7382	1.4619 9413	14
15	1.3458 6834	1.3962 0680	1.4482 9817	1.5021 9896	15
16	1.3727 8571	1.4276 2146	1.4845 0562	1.5435 0944	16
17	1.4002 4142	1.4597 4294	1.5216 1826	1.5859 5595	17
18	1.4282 4625	1.4925 8716	1.5596 5872	1.6295 6973	18
19	1.4568 1117	1.5261 7037	1.5986 5019	1.6743 8290	19
20	1.4859 4740	1.5605 0920	1.6386 1644	1.7204 2843	20
21	1.5156 6634	1.5956 2066	1.6795 8185	1.7677 4021	21
22	1.5459 7967	1.6315 2212	1.7215 7140	1.8163 5307	22
23	1.5768 9926	1.6682 3137	1.7646 1068	1.8663 0278	23
24	1.6084 3725	1.7057 6658	1.8087 2595	1.9176 2610	24
25	1.6406 0599	1.7441 4632	1.8539 4410	1.9703 6082	25
26	1.6734 1811	1.7833 8962	1.9002 9270	2.0245 4575	26
27	1.7068 8648	1.8235 1588	1.9478 0002	2.0802 2075	27
28	1.7410 2421	1.8645 4499	1.9964 9502	2.1374 2682	28
29	1.7758 4469	1.9064 9725	2.0464 0739	2.1962 0606	29
30	1.8113 6158	1.9493 9344	2.0975 6758	2.2566 0173	30
31	1.8475 8882	1.9932 5479	2.1500 0677	2.3186 5828	31
32	1.8845 4059	2.0381 0303	2.2037 5694	2.3824 2138	32
33	1.9222 3140	2.0839 6034	2.2588 5086	2.4479 3797	33
34	1.9606 7603	2.1308 4945	2.3153 2213	2.5152 5626	34
35	1.9998 8955	2.1787 9356	2.3732 0519	2.5844 2581	35
36	2.0398 8734	2.2278 1642	2.4325 3532	2.6554 9752	36
37	2.0806 8509	2.2779 4229	2.4933 4870	2.7285 2370	37
38	2.1222 9879	2.3291 9599	2.5556 8242	2.8035 5810	38
39	2.1647 4477	2.3816 0290	2.6195 7448	2.8806 5595	39
40	2.2080 3966	2.4351 8897	2.6850 6384	2.9598 7399	40
41	2.2522 0046	2.4899 8072	2.7521 9043	3.0412 7052	41
42	2.2972 4447	2.5460 0528	2.8209 9520	3.1249 0546	42
43	2.3431 8936	2.6032 9040	2.8915 2008	3.2108 4036	43
44	2.3900 5314	2.6618 6444	2.9638 0808	3.2991 3847	44
45	2.4378 5421	2.7217 5639	3.0379 0328	3.3898 6478	45
46	2.4866 1129	2.7829 9590	3.1138 5086	3.4830 8606	46
47	2.5363 4351	2.8456 1331	3.1916 9713	3.5788 7093	47
48	2.5870 7039	2.9096 3961	3.2714 8956	3.6772 8988	48
49	2.6388 1179	2.9751 0650	3.3532 7680	3.7784 1535	49
50	2.6915 8803	3.0420 4640	3.4371 0872	3.8823 2177	50

TABLE I.—Amount of 1 at Compound Interest

$$s = (1 + i)^n$$

n	2%	2¼%	2½%	2¾%	n
51	2.7454 1979	3.1104 9244	3.5230 3644	3.9890 8562	51
52	2.8003 2819	3.1804 7852	3.6111 1235	4.0987 8547	52
53	2.8563 3475	3.2520 3929	3.7013 9016	4.2115 0208	53
54	2.9134 6144	3.3252 1017	3.7939 2491	4.3273 1838	54
55	2.9717 3067	3.4000 2740	3.8887 7303	4.4463 1964	55
56	3.0311 6529	3.4765 2802	3.9859 9236	4.5685 9343	56
57	3.0917 8859	3.5547 4990	4.0856 4217	4.6942 2975	57
58	3.1536 2436	3.6347 3177	4.1877 8322	4.8233 2107	58
59	3.2166 9685	3.7165 1324	4.2924 7780	4.9559 6239	59
60	3.2810 3079	3.8001 3479	4.3997 8975	5.0922 5136	60
61	3.3466 5140	3.8856 3782	4.5097 8449	5.2322 8827	61
62	3.4135 8443	3.9730 6467	4.6225 2910	5.3761 7620	62
63	3.4818 5612	4.0624 5862	4.7380 9233	5.5240 2105	63
64	3.5514 9324	4.1538 6394	4.8565 4464	5.6759 3162	64
65	3.6225 2311	4.2473 2588	4.9779 5826	5.8320 1974	65
66	3.6949 7357	4.3428 9071	5.1024 0721	5.9924 0029	66
67	3.7688 7304	4.4406 0576	5.2299 6739	6.1571 9130	67
68	3.8442 5050	4.5405 1939	5.3607 1658	6.3265 1406	68
69	3.9211 3551	4.6426 8107	5.4947 3449	6.5004 9319	69
70	3.9995 5822	4.7471 4140	5.6321 0286	6.6792 5676	70
71	4.0795 4939	4.8539 5208	5.7729 0543	6.8629 3632	71
72	4.1611 4038	4.9631 6600	5.9172 2806	7.0516 6706	72
73	4.2443 6318	5.0748 3723	6.0651 5876	7.2455 8791	73
74	4.3292 5045	5.1890 2107	6.2167 8773	7.4448 4158	74
75	4.4158 3546	5.3057 7405	6.3722 0743	7.6495 7472	75
76	4.5041 5216	5.4251 5396	6.5315 1261	7.8599 3802	76
77	4.5942 3521	5.5472 1993	6.6948 0043	8.0760 8632	77
78	4.6861 1991	5.6720 3237	6.8621 7044	8.2981 7869	78
79	4.7798 4231	5.7996 5310	7.0337 2470	8.5263 7861	79
80	4.8754 3916	5.9301 4530	7.2095 6782	8.7608 5402	80
81	4.9729 4794	6.0635 7357	7.3898 0701	9.0017 7751	81
82	5.0724 0690	6.2000 0397	7.5745 5219	9.2493 2639	82
83	5.1738 5504	6.3395 0406	7.7639 1599	9.5036 8286	83
84	5.2773 3214	6.4821 4290	7.9580 1389	9.7650 3414	84
85	5.3828 7878	6.6279 9112	8.1569 6424	10.0335 7258	85
86	5.4905 3636	6.7771 2092	8.3608 8834	10.3094 9583	86
87	5.6003 4708	6.9296 0614	8.5699 1055	10.5930 0696	87
88	5.7123 5402	7.0855 2228	8.7841 5832	10.8843 1465	88
89	5.8266 0110	7.2449 4653	9.0037 6228	11.1836 3331	89
90	5.9431 3313	7.4079 5782	9.2288 5633	11.4911 8322	90
91	6.0619 9579	7.5746 3688	9.4595 7774	11.8071 9076	91
92	6.1832 3570	7.7450 6621	9.6960 6718	12.1318 8851	92
93	6.3069 0042	7.9193 3020	9.9384 6886	12.4655 1544	93
94	6.4330 3843	8.0975 1512	10.1869 3058	12.8083 1711	94
95	6.5616 9920	8.2797 0921	10.4416 0385	13.1605 4584	95
96	6.6929 3318	8.4660 0267	10.7026 4395	13.5224 6085	96
97	6.8267 9184	8.6564 8773	10.9702 1004	13.8943 2852	97
98	6.9633 2768	8.8512 5871	11.2444 6530	14.2764 2255	98
99	7.1025 9423	9.0504 1203	11.5255 7693	14.6690 2417	99
100	7.2446 4612	9.2540 4630	11.8137 1635	15.0724 2234	100

TABLE I.—Amount of 1 at Compound Interest

$$s = (1 + i)^n$$

n	3%	3½%	4%	4½%	n
1	1.0300 0000	1.0350 0000	1.0400 0000	1.0450 0000	1
2	1.0609 0000	1.0712 2500	1.0816 0000	1.0920 2500	2
3	1.0927 2700	1.1087 1788	1.1248 6400	1.1411 6613	3
4	1.1255 0881	1.1475 2300	1.1698 5856	1.1925 1860	4
5	1.1592 7407	1.1876 8631	1.2166 5290	1.2461 8194	5
6	1.1940 5230	1.2292 5533	1.2653 1902	1.3022 6012	6
7	1.2298 7387	1.2722 7926	1.3159 3178	1.3608 6183	7
8	1.2667 7008	1.3168 0904	1.3685 6905	1.4221 0061	8
9	1.3047 7318	1.3628 9735	1.4233 1181	1.4860 9514	9
10	1.3439 1638	1.4105 9876	1.4802 4428	1.5529 6942	10
11	1.3842 3387	1.4599 6972	1.5394 5406	1.6228 5305	11
12	1.4257 6089	1.5110 6866	1.6010 3222	1.6958 8143	12
13	1.4685 3371	1.5639 5606	1.6650 7351	1.7721 9610	13
14	1.5125 8972	1.6186 9452	1.7316 7645	1.8519 4492	14
15	1.5579 6742	1.6753 4883	1.8009 4351	1.9352 8244	15
16	1.6047 0644	1.7339 8604	1.8729 8125	2.0223 7015	16
17	1.6528 4763	1.7946 7555	1.9479 0050	2.1133 7681	17
18	1.7024 3306	1.8574 8920	2.0258 1652	2.2084 7877	18
19	1.7535 0605	1.9225 0132	2.1068 4918	2.3078 6031	19
20	1.8061 1123	1.9897 8886	2.1911 2314	2.4117 1402	20
21	1.8602 9457	2.0594 3147	2.2787 6807	2.5202 4116	21
22	1.9161 0341	2.1315 1158	2.3699 1879	2.6336 5201	22
23	1.9735 8651	2.2061 1448	2.4647 1554	2.7521 6635	23
24	2.0327 9411	2.2833 2849	2.5633 0416	2.8760 1383	24
25	2.0937 7793	2.3632 4498	2.6658 3633	3.0054 3446	25
26	2.1565 9127	2.4459 5856	2.7724 6978	3.1406 7901	26
27	2.2212 8901	2.5315 6711	2.8833 6858	3.2820 0956	27
28	2.2879 2768	2.6201 7196	2.9987 0332	3.4296 9999	28
29	2.3565 6551	2.7118 7798	3.1186 5145	3.5840 3649	29
30	2.4272 6247	2.8067 9370	3.2433 9751	3.7453 1813	30
31	2.5000 8035	2.9050 3148	3.3731 3341	3.9138 5745	31
32	2.5750 8276	3.0067 0759	3.5080 5875	4.0899 8104	32
33	2.6523 3524	3.1119 4235	3.6483 8110	4.2740 3018	33
34	2.7319 0530	3.2208 6033	3.7943 1634	4.4663 6154	34
35	2.8138 6245	3.3335 9045	3.9460 8899	4.6673 4781	35
36	2.8982 7833	3.4502 6611	4.1039 3255	4.8773 7846	36
37	2.9852 2668	3.5710 2543	4.2680 8986	5.0968 6049	37
38	3.0747 8348	3.6960 1132	4.4388 1345	5.3262 1921	38
39	3.1670 2698	3.8253 7171	4.6163 6599	5.5658 9908	39
40	3.2620 3779	3.9592 5972	4.8010 2063	5.8163 6454	40
41	3.3598 9893	4.0978 3381	4.9930 6145	6.0781 0094	41
42	3.4606 9589	4.2412 5799	5.1927 8391	6.3516 1548	42
43	3.5645 1677	4.3897 0202	5.4004 9527	6.6374 3818	43
44	3.6714 5227	4.5433 4160	5.6165 1508	6.9361 2290	44
45	3.7815 9584	4.7023 5855	5.8411 7568	7.2482 4843	45
46	3.8950 4372	4.8669 4110	6.0748 2271	7.5744 1961	46
47	4.0118 9503	5.0372 8404	6.3178 1562	7.9152 6849	47
48	4.1322 5188	5.2135 8898	6.5705 2824	8.2714 5557	48
49	4.2562 1944	5.3960 6459	6.8333 4937	8.6436 7107	49
50	4.3839 0602	5.5849 2686	7.1066 8335	9.0326 3627	50

TABLE I. —Amount of 1 at Compound Interest

$$s = (1 + i)^n$$

n	3%	3½%	4%	4½%	n
51	4.5154 2320	5.7803 9930	7.3909 5068	9.4391 0490	51
52	4.6508 8590	5.9827 1327	7.6865 8871	9.8638 6463	52
53	4.7904 1247	6.1921 0824	7.9940 5226	10.3077 3853	53
54	4.9341 2405	6.4088 3202	8.3138 1435	10.7715 8677	54
55	5.0821 4859	6.6331 4114	8.6463 6692	11.2563 0817	55
56	5.2346 1305	6.8653 0108	8.9922 2160	11.7628 4204	56
57	5.3916 5144	7.1055 8662	9.3519 1046	12.2921 6993	57
58	5.5534 0098	7.3542 8215	9.7259 8688	12.8453 1758	58
59	5.7200 0301	7.6116 8203	10.1150 2635	13.4233 5687	59
60	5.8916 0310	7.8780 9090	10.5196 2741	14.0274 0793	60
61	6.0683 5120	8.1538 2408	10.9404 1250	14.6586 4129	61
62	6.2504 0173	8.4392 0793	11.3780 2900	15.3182 8014	62
63	6.4379 1379	8.7345 8020	11.8331 5016	16.0076 0275	63
64	6.6310 5120	9.0402 9051	12.3064 7617	16.7279 4487	64
65	6.8299 8273	9.3567 0068	12.7987 3522	17.4807 0239	65
66	7.0348 8222	9.6841 8520	13.3106 8463	18.2673 3400	66
67	7.2459 2868	10.0231 3168	13.8431 1201	19.0893 6403	67
68	7.4633 0654	10.3739 4129	14.3968 3649	19.9483 8541	68
69	7.6872 0574	10.7370 2924	14.9727 0995	20.8460 6276	69
70	7.9178 2191	11.1128 2526	15.5716 1835	21.7841 3558	70
71	8.1553 5657	11.5017 7414	16.1944 8308	22.7644 2168	71
72	8.4000 1727	11.9043 3624	16.8422 6241	23.7888 2066	72
73	8.6520 1778	12.3209 8801	17.5159 5290	24.8593 1759	73
74	8.9115 7832	12.7522 2259	18.2165 9102	25.9779 8688	74
75	9.1789 2567	13.1985 5038	18.9452 5466	27.1469 9629	75
76	9.4542 9344	13.6604 9964	19.7030 6485	28.3686 1112	76
77	9.7379 2224	14.1386 1713	20.4911 8744	29.6451 9862	77
78	10.0300 5991	14.6334 6873	21.3108 3494	30.9792 3256	78
79	10.3309 6171	15.1456 4013	22.1632 6834	32.3732 9802	79
80	10.6408 9056	15.6757 3754	23.0497 9907	33.8300 9643	80
81	10.9601 1727	16.2243 8035	23.9717 9103	35.3524 5077	81
82	11.2889 2079	16.7922 4195	24.9306 6267	36.9433 1106	82
83	11.6275 8842	17.3799 7041	25.9278 8918	38.6057 6006	83
84	11.9764 1607	17.9882 6938	26.9650 0475	40.3430 1926	84
85	12.3357 0855	18.6178 5881	28.0436 0494	42.1584 5513	85
86	12.7057 7981	19.2694 8387	29.1653 4914	44.0555 8561	86
87	13.0869 5320	19.9439 1580	30.3319 6310	46.0380 8696	87
88	13.4795 6180	20.6419 5285	31.5452 4163	48.1098 0087	88
89	13.8839 4865	21.3644 2120	32.8070 5129	50.2747 4191	89
90	14.3004 6711	22.1121 7595	34.1193 3334	52.5371 0530	90
91	14.7294 8112	22.8861 0210	35.4841 0668	54.9012 7503	91
92	15.1713 6556	23.6871 1568	36.9034 7094	57.3710 0241	92
93	15.6265 0652	24.5161 6473	38.3796 0978	59.9535 6487	93
94	16.0953 0172	25.3742 3049	39.9147 9417	62.6514 7529	94
95	16.5781 6077	26.2623 2856	41.5113 8594	65.4707 9168	95
96	17.0755 0559	27.1815 1006	43.1718 4138	68.4169 7730	96
97	17.5877 7076	28.1328 6291	44.8987 1503	71.4957 4128	97
98	18.1154 0388	29.1175 1311	46.6946 6363	74.7130 4964	98
99	18.6588 6600	30.1366 2607	48.5624 5018	78.0751 3687	99
100	19.2186 3198	31.1914 0798	50.5049 4818	81.5885 1803	100

TABLE I.—Amount of 1 at Compound Interest

$$s = (1 + i)^n$$

n	5%	5½%	6%	6½%	n
1	1.0500 0000	1.0550 0000	1.0600 0000	1.0650 0000	1
2	1.1025 0000	1.1130 2500	1.1236 0000	1.1342 2500	2
3	1.1576 2500	1.1742 4138	1.1910 1600	1.2079 4963	3
4	1.2155 0625	1.2388 2465	1.2624 7696	1.2864 6635	4
5	1.2762 8156	1.3069 6001	1.3382 2558	1.3700 8666	5
6	1.3400 9564	1.3788 4281	1.4185 1911	1.4591 4230	6
7	1.4071 0042	1.4546 7916	1.5036 3026	1.5539 8655	7
8	1.4774 5544	1.5346 8651	1.5938 4807	1.6549 9567	8
9	1.5513 2822	1.6190 9427	1.6894 7896	1.7625 7039	9
10	1.6288 9463	1.7081 4446	1.7908 4770	1.8771 3747	10
11	1.7103 3936	1.8020 9240	1.8982 9856	1.9991 5140	11
12	1.7958 5633	1.9012 0749	2.0121 9647	2.1290 9624	12
13	1.8856 4914	2.0057 7390	2.1329 2826	2.2674 8750	13
14	1.9799 3160	2.1160 9146	2.2609 0396	2.4148 7418	14
15	2.0789 2818	2.2324 7649	2.3965 5819	2.5718 4101	15
16	2.1828 7459	2.3552 6270	2.5403 5168	2.7390 1067	16
17	2.2920 1832	2.4848 0215	2.6927 7279	2.9170 4637	17
18	2.4066 1923	2.6214 6627	2.8543 3915	3.1066 5438	18
19	2.5269 5020	2.7656 4691	3.0255 9950	3.3085 8691	19
20	2.6532 9771	2.9177 5749	3.2071 3547	3.5236 4506	20
21	2.7859 6259	3.0782 3415	3.3995 6360	3.7526 8199	21
22	2.9252 6072	3.2475 3703	3.6035 3742	3.9966 0632	22
23	3.0715 2376	3.4261 5157	3.8197 4966	4.2563 8573	23
24	3.2250 9994	3.6145 8990	4.0489 3464	4.5330 5081	24
25	3.3863 5494	3.8133 9235	4.2918 7072	4.8276 9911	25
26	3.5556 7269	4.0231 2893	4.5493 8296	5.1414 9955	26
27	3.7334 5632	4.2444 0102	4.8223 4594	5.4756 9702	27
28	3.9201 2914	4.4778 4307	5.1116 8670	5.8316 1733	28
29	4.1161 3560	4.7241 2444	5.4183 8790	6.2106 7245	29
30	4.3219 4238	4.9839 5129	5.7434 9117	6.6143 6616	30
31	4.5380 3949	5.2580 6861	6.0881 0064	7.0442 9996	31
32	4.7649 4147	5.5472 6238	6.4533 8668	7.5021 7946	32
33	5.0031 8854	5.8523 6181	6.8405 8988	7.9898 2113	33
34	5.2533 4797	6.1742 4171	7.2510 2528	8.5091 5950	34
35	5.5160 1537	6.5138 2501	7.6860 8679	9.0622 5487	35
36	5.7918 1614	6.8720 8538	8.1472 5200	9.6513 0143	36
37	6.0814 0694	7.2500 5008	8.6360 8712	10.2786 3603	37
38	6.3854 7729	7.6488 0283	9.1542 5235	10.9467 4737	38
39	6.7047 5115	8.0694 8699	9.7035 0749	11.6582 8595	39
40	7.0399 8871	8.5133 0877	10.2857 1794	12.4160 7453	40
41	7.3919 8815	8.9815 4076	10.9028 6101	13.2231 1938	41
42	7.7615 8756	9.4755 2550	11.5570 3267	14.0826 2214	42
43	8.1496 6693	9.9966 7940	12.2504 5463	14.9979 9258	43
44	8.5571 5028	10.5464 9677	12.9854 8191	15.9728 6209	44
45	8.9850 0779	11.1265 5409	13.7646 1083	17.0110 9813	45
46	9.4342 5818	11.7385 1456	14.5904 8748	18.1168 1951	46
47	9.9059 7109	12.3841 3287	15.4659 1673	19.2944 1278	47
48	10.4012 6965	13.0652 6017	16.3938 7173	20.5485 4961	48
49	10.9213 3313	13.7838 4948	17.3775 0403	21.8842 0533	49
50	11.4673 9979	14.5419 6120	18.4201 5427	23.3066 7868	50

TABLE I.—Amount of 1 at Compound Interest

$$s = (1 + i)^n$$

n	5%	5½%	6%	6½%	n
51	12.0407 6978	15.3417 6907	19.5253 6353	24.8216 1279	51
52	12.6428 0826	16.1855 6637	20.6968 8534	26.4350 1762	52
53	13.2749 4868	17.0757 7252	21.9386 9846	28.1532 9377	53
54	13.9386 9611	18.0149 4001	23.2550 2037	29.9832 5786	54
55	14.6356 3092	19.0057 6171	24.6503 2159	31.9321 6963	55
56	15.3674 1246	20.0510 7860	26.1293 4089	34.0077 6065	56
57	16.1357 8309	21.1538 8793	27.6971 0134	36.2182 6509	57
58	16.9425 7224	22.3173 5176	29.3589 2742	38.5724 5233	58
59	17.7897 0085	23.5448 0611	31.1204 6307	41.0796 6173	59
60	18.6791 8589	24.8397 7045	32.9876 9085	43.7498 3974	60
61	19.6131 4519	26.2059 5782	34.9669 5230	46.5935 7932	61
62	20.5938 0245	27.6472 8550	37.0649 6944	49.6221 6198	62
63	21.6234 9257	29.1678 8620	39.2888 6761	52.8476 0251	63
64	22.7046 6720	30.7721 1994	41.6461 9967	56.2826 9667	64
65	23.8399 0056	32.4645 8654	44.1449 7165	59.9410 7195	65
66	25.0318 9559	34.2501 3880	46.7936 6994	63.8372 4163	66
67	26.2834 9037	36.1338 9643	49.6012 9014	67.9866 6234	67
68	27.5976 6488	38.1212 6074	52.5773 6755	72.4057 9539	68
69	28.9775 4813	40.2179 3008	55.7320 0960	77.1121 7209	69
70	30.4264 2554	42.4299 1623	59.0759 3018	82.1244 6327	70
71	31.9477 4681	44.7635 6163	62.6204 8599	87.4625 5339	71
72	33.5451 3415	47.2255 5751	66.3777 1515	93.1476 1936	72
73	35.2223 9086	49.8229 6318	70.3603 7806	99.2022 1461	73
74	36.9835 1040	52.5632 2615	74.5820 0074	105.6503 5856	74
75	38.8326 8592	55.4542 0359	79.0569 2079	112.5176 3187	75
76	40.7743 2022	58.5041 8479	83.8003 3603	119.8312 7794	76
77	42.8130 3623	61.7219 1495	88.8283 5620	127.6203 1101	77
78	44.9536 8804	65.1166 2027	94.1580 5757	135.9156 3122	78
79	47.2013 7244	68.6980 3439	99.8075 4102	144.7501 4725	79
80	49.5614 4107	72.4764 2628	105.7959 9348	154.1589 0683	80
81	52.0395 1312	76.4626 2973	112.1437 5309	164.1792 3577	81
82	54.6414 8878	80.6680 7436	118.8723 7828	174.8508 8609	82
83	57.3735 6322	85.1048 1845	126.0047 2097	186.2161 9369	83
84	60.2422 4138	89.7855 8347	133.5650 0423	198.3202 4628	84
85	63.2543 5344	94.7237 9056	141.5789 0449	211.2110 6229	85
86	66.4170 7112	99.9335 9904	150.0736 3875	224.9397 8134	86
87	69.7379 2467	105.4299 4698	159.0780 5708	239.5608 6712	87
88	73.2248 2091	111.2285 9407	168.6227 4050	255.1323 2349	88
89	76.8860 6195	117.3461 6674	178.7401 0493	271.7159 2451	89
90	80.7303 6505	123.8002 0591	189.4645 1123	289.3774 5961	90
91	84.7668 8330	130.6092 1724	200.8323 8190	308.1869 9448	91
92	89.0052 2747	137.7927 2419	212.8823 2482	328.2191 4912	92
93	93.4554 8884	145.3713 2402	225.6552 6431	349.5533 9382	93
94	98.1282 6328	153.3667 4684	239.1945 8017	372.2743 6441	94
95	103.0346 7645	161.8019 1791	253.5462 5498	396.4721 9810	95
96	108.1864 1027	170.7010 2340	268.7590 3028	422.2428 9098	96
97	113.5957 3078	180.0895 7969	284.8845 7209	449.6886 7889	97
98	119.2755 1732	189.9945 0657	301.9776 4642	478.9184 4302	98
99	125.2392 9319	200.4442 0443	320.0963 0520	510.0481 4181	99
100	131.5012 5785	211.4686 3567	339.3020 8351	543.2012 7103	100

TABLE I. —Amount of 1 at Compound Interest

$$s = (1 + i)^n$$

n	7%	7½%	8%	8½%	n
1	1.0700 0000	1.0750 0000	1.0800 0000	1.0850 0000	1
2	1.1449 0000	1.1556 2500	1.1664 0000	1.1772 2500	2
3	1.2250 4300	1.2422 9688	1.2597 1200	1.2772 8913	3
4	1.3107 9601	1.3354 6914	1.3604 8896	1.3858 5870	4
5	1.4025 5173	1.4356 2933	1.4693 2808	1.5036 5669	5
6	1.5007 3035	1.5433 0153	1.5868 7432	1.6314 6751	6
7	1.6057 8148	1.6590 4914	1.7138 2427	1.7701 4225	7
8	1.7181 8618	1.7834 7783	1.8509 3021	1.9206 0434	8
9	1.8384 5921	1.9172 3866	1.9990 0463	2.0838 5571	9
10	1.9671 5136	2.0610 3156	2.1589 2500	2.2609 8344	10
11	2.1048 5195	2.2156 0893	2.3316 3900	2.4531 6703	11
12	2.2521 9159	2.3817 7960	2.5181 7012	2.6616 8623	12
13	2.4098 4500	2.5604 1307	2.7196 2373	2.8879 2956	13
14	2.5785 3415	2.7524 4405	2.9371 9362	3.1334 0357	14
15	2.7590 3154	2.9588 7735	3.1721 6911	3.3997 4288	15
16	2.9521 6375	3.1807 9315	3.4259 4264	3.6887 2102	16
17	3.1588 1521	3.4193 5264	3.7000 1805	4.0022 6231	17
18	3.3799 3228	3.6758 0409	3.9960 1950	4.3424 5461	18
19	3.6165 2754	3.9514 8940	4.3157 0106	4.7115 6325	19
20	3.8696 8446	4.2478 5110	4.6609 5714	5.1120 4612	20
21	4.1405 6237	4.5664 3993	5.0338 3372	5.5465 7005	21
22	4.4304 0174	4.9089 2293	5.4365 4041	6.0180 2850	22
23	4.7405 2986	5.2770 9215	5.8714 6365	6.5295 6092	23
24	5.0723 6695	5.6728 7406	6 3411 8074	7.0845 7360	24
25	5.4274 3264	6.0983 3961	6.8484 7520	7.6867 6236	25
26	5.8073 5292	6.5557 1508	7.3963 5321	8.3401 3716	26
27	6.2138 6763	7.0473 9371	7.9880 6147	9.0490 4881	27
28	6.6488 3836	7.5759 4824	8.6271 0639	9.8182 1796	28
29	7.1142 5705	8.1441 4436	9.3172 7490	10.6527 6649	29
30	7.6122 5504	8.7549 5519	10.0626 5689	11.5582 5164	30
31	8.1451 1290	9.4115 7683	10.8676 6944	12.5407 0303	31
32	8.7152 7080	10.1174 4509	11.7370 8300	13.6066 6279	32
33	9.3253 3975	10.8762 5347	12.6760 4964	14.7632 2913	33
34	9.9781 1354	11.6919 7248	13.6901 3361	16.0181 0360	34
35	10.6765 8148	12.5688 7042	14.7853 4429	17.3796 4241	35
36	11.4239 4219	13.5115 3570	15.9681 7184	18.8569 1201	36
37	12.2236 1814	14.5249 0088	17.2456 2558	20.4597 4953	37
38	13.0792 7141	15.6142 6844	18.6252 7563	22.1988 2824	38
39	13.9948 2041	16.7853 3858	20.1152 9768	24.0857 2865	39
40	14.9744 5784	18.0442 3897	21.7245 2150	26.1330 1558	40
41	16.0226 6989	19.3975 5689	23.4624 8322	28.3543 2190	41
42	17.1442 5678	20.8523 7366	25.3394 8187	30.7644 3927	42
43	18.3443 5475	22.4163 0168	27.3666 4042	33.3794 1660	43
44	19.6284 5959	24.0975 2431	29.5559 7166	36.2166 6702	44
45	21 0024 5176	25.9048 3863	3.1 9204 4939	39.2950 8371	45
46	22.4726 2338	27.8477 0153	34.4740 8534	42.6351 6583	46
47	24.0457 0702	29.9362 7915	37.2320 1217	46.2591 5492	47
48	25.7289 0651	32.1815 0008	40.2105 7314	50.1911 8309	48
49	27.5299 2997	34.5951 1259	43.4274 1899	54.4574 3365	49
50	29.4570 2506	37.1897 4603	46.9016 1251	59.0863 1551	50

TABLE I.—Amount of 1 at Compound Interest

$$s = (1 + i)^n$$

n	7%	7½%	8%	8½%	n
51	31.5190 1682	39.9789 7698	50.6537 4151	64.1086 5233	51
52	33.7253 4799	42.9774 0026	54.7060 4084	69.5578 8778	52
53	36.0861 2235	46.2007 0528	59.0825 2410	75.4703 0824	53
54	38.6121 5092	49.6657 5817	63.0091 2603	81.8852 8444	54
55	41.3150 0148	53.3906 9004	68.9138 5611	88.8455 3362	55
56	44.2070 5159	57.3949 9179	74.4269 6460	96.3974 0398	56
57	47.3015 4520	61.6996 1617	80.3811 2177	104.5911 8332	57
58	50.6126 5336	66.3270 8739	86.8116 1151	113.4814 3390	58
59	54.1555 3910	71.3016 1894	93.7565 4043	123.1273 5578	59
60	57.9464 2683	76.6492 4036	01.2570 6367	133.5931 8102	60
61	62.0026 7671	82.3979 3339	109.3576 2876	144.9486 0141	61
62	66.3428 6408	88.5777 7839	118.1062 3906	157.2692 3253	62
63	70.9868 6457	95.2211 1177	127.5547 3819	170.6371 1729	63
64	75.9559 4509	102.3626 9515	137.7591 1724	185.1412 7226	64
65	81.2728 6124	110.0398 9729	148.7798 4662	200.8782 8041	65
66	86.9619 6153	118.2928 8959	160.6822 3435	217.9529 3424	66
67	93.0492 9884	127.1648 5631	173.5368 1310	236.4789 3365	67
68	99.5627 4976	136.7022 2053	187.4197 5815	256.5796 4301	68
69	106.5321 4224	146.9548 8707	202.4133 3880	278.3889 1267	69
70	113.9893 9220	157.9765 0360	218.6064 0590	302.0519 7024	70
71	121.9686 4965	169.8247 4137	236.0949 1837	327.7263 8771	71
72	130.5064 5513	182.5615 9697	254.9825 1104	355.5831 3067	72
73	139.6419 0699	196.2537 1675	275.3811 1279	385.8076 9678	73
74	149.4168 4047	210.9727 4550	297.4116 0181	418.6013 5100	74
75	159.8760 1931	226.7957 0141	321.2045 2996	454.1824 6584	75
76	171.0673 4066	243.8053 7902	346.9008 9236	492.7879 7543	76
77	183.0420 5451	262.0907 8245	374.6529 6374	534.6749 5335	77
78	195.8549 9832	281.7475 9113	404.6252 0084	580.1223 2438	78
79	209.5648 4820	302.8786 6046	436.9952 1691	629.4327 2195	79
80	224.2343 8758	325.5945 6000	471.9548 3426	682.9345 0332	80
81	239.9307 9471	350.0141 5200	509.7112 2101	740.9839 3610	81
82	256.7259 5034	376.2652 1340	550.4881 1869	803.9675 7067	82
83	274.6967 6686	404.4851 0440	594.5271 6818	872.3048 1418	83
84	293.9255 4054	434.8214 8723	642.0893 4164	946.4507 2338	84
85	314.5003 2838	467.4330 9878	693.4564 8897	1026.8990 3487	85
86	336.5153 5137	502.4905 8119	748.9330 0808	1114.1854 5283	86
87	360.0714 2596	540.1773 7477	808.8476 4873	1208.8912 1633	87
88	385.2764 2578	580.6906 7788	873.5554 6063	1311.6469 6971	88
89	412.2457 7558	624.2424 7872	943.4398 9748	1423.1369 6214	89
90	441.1029 7988	671.0606 6463	1018.9150 8928	1544.1036 0392	90
91	471.9801 8847	721.3902 1447	1100.4282 9642	1675.3524 1025	91
92	505.0188 0166	775.4944 8056	1188.4625 6013	1817.7573 6512	92
93	540.3701 1778	833.6565 0660	1283.5395 6494	1972.2667 4116	93
94	578.1960 2602	896.1808 0910	1386.2227 3014	2139.9094 1416	94
95	618.6697 4784	963.3943 6978	1497.1205 4855	2321.8017 1436	95
96	661.9766 3019	1035.6489 4751	1616.8901 9244	2519.1548 6008	96
97	708.3149 9430	1113.3226 1858	1746.2414 0783	2733.2830 2319	97
98	757.8970 4390	1196.8218 1497	1885.9407 2046	2965.6120 8016	98
99	810.9498 3698	1286.5834 5109	2036.8159 7809	3217.6891 0698	99
100	867.7163 2557	1383.0772 0993	2199.7612 5634	3491.1926 8107	100

TABLE II.—Present Value of 1 at Compound Interest

$$v^n = (1 + i)^{-n}$$

n	$\frac{1}{4}\%$	$\frac{7}{24}\%$	$\frac{1}{3}\%$	$\frac{5}{12}\%$	n
1	0.9975 0623	0.9970 9182	0.9966 7774	0.9958 5062	1
2	0.9950 1869	0.9941 9209	0.9933 6652	0.9917 1846	2
3	0.9925 3734	0.9913 0079	0.9900 6630	0.9876 0345	3
4	0.9900 6219	0.9884 1791	0.9867 7704	0.9835 0551	4
5	0.9875 9321	0.9855 4341	0.9834 9871	0.9794 2457	5
6	0.9851 3038	0.9826 7726	0.9802 3127	0.9753 6057	6
7	0.9826 7370	0.9798 1946	0.9769 7469	0.9713 1343	7
8	0.9802 2314	0.9769 6996	0.9737 2893	0.9672 8308	8
9	0.9777 7869	0.9741 2875	0.9704 9395	0.9632 6946	9
10	0.9753 4034	0.9712 9580	0.9672 6972	0.9592 7249	10
11	0.9729 0807	0.9684 7110	0.9640 5620	0.9552 9211	11
12	0.9704 8187	0.9656 5460	0.9608 5335	0.9513 2824	12
13	0.9680 6171	0.9628 4630	0.9576 0115	0.9473 8082	13
14	0.9656 4759	0.9600 4617	0.9544 7955	0.9434 4978	14
15	0.9632 3949	0.9572 5418	0.9513 0852	0.9395 3505	15
16	0.9608 3740	0.9544 7030	0.9481 4803	0.9356 3656	16
17	0.9584 4130	0.9516 9453	0.9449 9803	0.9317 5425	17
18	0.9560 5117	0.9489 2682	0.9418 5851	0.9278 8805	18
19	0.9536 6700	0.9461 6717	0.9387 2941	0.9240 3789	19
20	0.9512 8878	0.9434 1554	0.9356 1071	0.9202 0371	20
21	0.9489 1649	0.9406 7191	0.9325 0236	0.9163 8544	21
22	0.9465 5011	0.9379 3627	0.9294 0435	0.9125 8301	22
23	0.9441 8964	0.9352 0857	0.9263 1663	0.9087 9636	23
24	0.9418 3505	0.9324 8881	0.9232 3916	0.9050 2542	24
25	0.9394 8634	0.9297 7696	0.9201 7192	0.9012 7012	25
26	0.9371 4348	0.9270 7300	0.9171 1487	0.8975 3041	26
27	0.9348 0646	0.9243 7690	0.9140 6798	0.8938 0622	27
28	0.9324 7527	0.9216 8864	0.9110 3121	0.8900 9748	28
29	0.9301 4990	0.9190 0820	0.9080 0453	0.8864 0413	29
30	0.9278 3032	0.9163 3556	0.9049 8790	0.8827 2610	30
31	0.9255 1653	0.9136 7068	0.9019 8130	0.8790 6334	31
32	0.9232 0851	0.9110 1356	0.8989 8468	0.8754 1577	32
33	0.9209 0624	0.9083 6416	0.8959 9802	0.8717 8334	33
34	0.9186 0972	0.9057 2247	0.8930 2128	0.8681 6599	34
35	0.9163 1892	0.9030 8847	0.8900 5444	0.8645 6364	35
36	0.9140 3384	0.9004 6212	0.8870 9745	0.8609 7624	36
37	0.9117 5445	0.8978 4341	0.8841 5028	0.8574 0372	37
38	0.9094 8075	0.8952 3231	0.8812 1290	0.8538 4603	38
39	0.9072 1272	0.8926 2881	0.8782 8528	0.8503 0310	39
40	0.9049 5034	0.8900 3288	0.8753 6739	0.8467 7487	40
41	0.9026 9361	0.8874 4450	0.8724 5920	0.8432 6128	41
42	0.9004 4250	0.8848 6365	0.8695 6066	0.8397 6227	42
43	0.8981 9701	0.8822 9030	0.8666 7175	0.8362 7778	43
44	0.8959 5712	0.8797 2444	0.8637 9245	0.8328 0775	44
45	0.8937 2281	0.8771 6604	0.8609 2270	0.8293 5211	45
46	0.8914 9407	0.8746 1508	0.8580 6249	0.8259 1082	46
47	0.8892 7090	0.8720 7153	0.8552 1179	0.8224 8380	47
48	0.8870 5326	0.8695 3539	0.8523 7055	0.8190 7100	48
49	0.8848 4116	0.8670 0662	0.8495 3876	0.8156 7237	49
50	0.8826 3457	0.8644 8520	0.8467 1637	0.8122 8784	50

TABLE II.—Present Value of 1 at Compound Interest

$$v^n = (1 + i)^{-n}$$

n	$\frac{1}{4}\%$	$\frac{7}{24}\%$	$\frac{1}{3}\%$	$\frac{5}{12}\%$	n
51	0.8804 3349	0.8619 7112	0.8439 0336	0.8089 1735	51
52	0.8782 3790	0.8594 6435	0.8410 9969	0.8055 6084	52
53	0.8760 4778	0.8569 6487	0.8383 0534	0.8022 1827	53
54	0.8738 6312	0.8544 7266	0.8355 2027	0.7988 8956	54
55	0.8716 8391	0.8519 8769	0.8327 4446	0.7955 7467	55
56	0.8695 1013	0.8495 0995	0.8299 7787	0.7922 7353	56
57	0.8673 4178	0.8470 3942	0.8272 2047	0.7889 8608	57
58	0.8651 7883	0.8445 7608	0.8244 7222	0.7857 1228	58
59	0.8630 2128	0.8421 1989	0.8217 3311	0.7824 5207	59
60	0.8608 6911	0.8396 7085	0.8190 0310	0.7792 0538	60
61	0.8587 2230	0.8372 2893	0.8162 8216	0.7759 7216	61
62	0.8565 8085	0.8347 9412	0.8135 7026	0.7727 5236	62
63	0.8544 4474	0.8323 6638	0.8108 6737	0.7695 4591	63
64	0.8523 1395	0.8299 4571	0.8081 7346	0.7663 5278	64
65	0.8501 8848	0.8275 3207	0.8054 8850	0.7631 7289	65
66	0.8480 6831	0.8251 2545	0.8028 1246	0.7600 0620	66
67	0.8459 5343	0.8227 2584	0.8001 4531	0.7568 5265	67
68	0.8438 4382	0.8203 3320	0.7974 8702	0.7537 1218	68
69	0.8417 3947	0.8179 4752	0.7948 3756	0.7505 8474	69
70	0.8396 4037	0.8155 6878	0.7921 9690	0.7474 7028	70
71	0.8375 4650	0.8131 9695	0.7895 6502	0.7443 6874	71
72	0.8354 5786	0.8108 3202	0.7869 4188	0.7412 8008	72
73	0.8333 7442	0.8084 7397	0.7843 2745	0.7382 0423	73
74	0.8312 9618	0.8061 2278	0.7817 2171	0.7351 4114	74
75	0.8292 2312	0.8037 7843	0.7791 2463	0.7320 9076	75
76	0.8271 5523	0.8014 4089	0.7765 3618	0.7290 5304	76
77	0.8250 9250	0.7991 1015	0.7739 5632	0.7260 2792	77
78	0.8230 3491	0.7967 8619	0.7713 8504	0.7230 1536	78
79	0.8209 8246	0.7944 6899	0.7688 2230	0.7200 1529	79
80	0.8189 3512	0.7921 5853	0.7662 6807	0.7170 2768	80
81	0.8168 9289	0.7898 5479	0.7637 2233	0.7140 5246	81
82	0.8148 5575	0.7875 5774	0.7611 8505	0.7110 8959	82
83	0.8128 2369	0.7852 6738	0.7586 5619	0.7081 3901	83
84	0.8107 9670	0.7829 8368	0.7561 3574	0.7052 0067	84
85	0.8087 7476	0.7807 0662	0.7536 2366	0.7022 7453	85
86	0.8067 5787	0.7784 3618	0.7511 1993	0.6993 6052	86
87	0.8047 4600	0.7761 7234	0.7486 2451	0.6964 5861	87
88	0.8027 3915	0.7739 1509	0.7461 3739	0.6935 6874	88
89	0.8007 3731	0.7716 6440	0.7436 5853	0.6906 9086	89
90	0.7987 4046	0.7694 2026	0.7411 8790	0.6878 2493	90
91	0.7967 4859	0.7671 8264	0.7387 2548	0.6849 7088	91
92	0.7947 6168	0.7649 5153	0.7362 7125	0.6821 2868	92
93	0.7927 7973	0.7627 2691	0.7338 2516	0.6792 9827	93
94	0.7908 0273	0.7605 0876	0.7313 8720	0.6764 7960	94
95	0.7888 3065	0.7582 9706	0.7289 5735	0.6736 7263	95
96	0.7868 6349	0.7560 9179	0.7265 3556	0.6708 7731	96
97	0.7849 0124	0.7538 9294	0.7241 2182	0.6680 9359	97
98	0.7829 4388	0.7517 0048	0.7217 1610	0.6653 2141	98
99	0.7809 9140	0.7495 1439	0.7193 1837	0.6625 6074	99
100	0.7790 4379	0.7473 3467	0.7169 2861	0.6598 1153	100

TABLE II.—Present Value of 1 at Compound Interest

$$v^n = (1 + i)^{-n}$$

n	$\frac{1}{4}\%$	$\frac{7}{24}\%$	$\frac{1}{3}\%$	$\frac{5}{12}\%$	n
101	0.7771 0104	0.7451 6128	0.7145 4681	0.6570 7372	101
102	0.7751 6313	0.7429 9421	0.7121 7290	0.6543 4727	102
104	0.7732 3006	0.7408 3345	0.7098 0688	0.6516 3214	103
104	0.7713 0180	0.7386 7897	0.7074 4872	0.6489 2827	104
105	0.7693 7836	0.7365 3075	0.7050 9839	0.6462 3562	105
106	0.7674 5971	0.7343 8879	0.7027 5587	0.6435 5415	106
107	0.7655 4584	0.7322 5305	0.7004 2114	0.6408 8380	107
108	0.7636 3675	0.7301 2352	0.6980 9416	0.6382 2453	108
109	0.7617 3242	0.7280 0019	0.6957 7491	0.6355 7630	109
110	0.7598 3284	0.7258 8303	0.6934 6336	0.6329 3905	110
111	0.7579 3799	0.7237 7203	0.6911 5950	0.6303 1275	111
112	0.7560 4787	0.7216 0716	0.6888 6329	0.6276 9734	112
113	0,7541 6247	0.7195 6842	0.6865 7470	0.6250 9279	113
114	0.7522 8176	0.7174 7578	0.6842 9372	0.6224 9904	114
115	0.7504 0575	0.7153 8923	0.6820 2032	0.6199 1606	115
116	0.7485 3441	0.7133 0875	0.6797 5448	0.6173 4379	116
117	0.7466 6774	0.7112 3431	0.6774 9616	0.6147 8220	117
118	0.7448 0573	0.7091 6591	0.6752 4534	0.6122 3123	118
119	0.7429 4836	0.7071 0353	0.6730 0200	0.6096 9086	119
120	0.7410 9562	0.7050 4714	0.6707 6611	0.6071 6102	120
121	0.7392 4750	0.7029 9673	0.6685 3765	0.6046 4168	121
122	0.7374 0399	0.7009 5229	0.6663 1660	0.6021 3279	122
123	0.7355 6508	0.6989 1379	0.6641 0292	0.5996 3431	123
124	0.7337 3075	0.6968 8122	0.6618 9660	0.5971 4620	124
125	0.7319 0100	0.6948 5456	0.6596 9761	0.5946 6842	125
126	0.7300 7581	0.6928 3379	0.6575 0592	0.5922 0091	126
127	0.7282 5517	0.6908 1890	0.6553 2152	0.5897 4365	127
128	0.7264 3907	0.6888 0988	0.6531 4437	0.5872 9658	128
129	0.7246 2750	0.6868 0669	0.6509 7445	0.5848 5966	129
130	0.7228 2045	0.6848 0933	0.6488 1175	0.5824 3286	130
131	0.7210 1791	0.6828 1778	0.6466 5623	0.5800 1613	131
132	0.7192 1986	0.6808 3202	0.6445 0787	0.5776 0942	132
133	0.7174 2629	0.6788 5203	0.6423 6665	0.5752 1270	133
134	0.7156 3720	0.6768 7780	0.6402 3254	0.5728 2593	134
135	0.7138 5257	0.6749 0932	0.6381 0552	0.5704 4906	135
136	0.7120 7239	0.6729 4656	0.6359 8557	0.5680 8205	136
137	0.7102 9664	0.6709 8950	0.6338 7266	0.5657 2486	137
138	0.7085 2533	0.6690 3814	0.6317 6677	0.5633 7745	138
139	0.7067 5843	0.6670 9246	0.6296 6788	0.5610 3979	139
140	0.7049 9595	0.6651 5243	0.6275 7596	0.5587 1182	140
141	0.7032 3785	0.6632 1804	0.6254 9099	0.5563 9351	141
142	0.7014 8414	0.6612 8928	0.6234 1295	0.5540 8483	142
143	0.6997 3480	0.6593 6613	0.6213 4181	0.5517 8572	143
144	0.6979 8983	0.6574 4857	0.6192 7755	0.5494 9615	144
145	0.6962 4921	0.6555 3659	0.6172 2015	0.5472 1609	145
146	0.6945 1292	0.6536 3017	0.6151 6958	0.5449 4548	146
147	0.6927 8097	0.6517 2929	0.6131 2583	0.5426 8429	147
148	0.6910 5334	0.6498 3394	0.6110 8887	0 5404 3249	148
149	0.6893 3001	0.6479 4410	0.6090 5867	0 5381 9003	149
150	0.6876 1098	0.6460 5976	0.6070 3522	0 5359 5688	150

TABLE II.—Present Value of 1 at Compound Interest

$$v^n = (1 + i)^{-n}$$

n	$\frac{1}{4}\%$	$\frac{7}{24}\%$	$\frac{1}{3}\%$	$\frac{5}{12}\%$	n
151	0.6858 9624	0.6441 8090	0.6050 1849	0.5337 3299	151
152	0.6841 8578	0.6423 0750	0.6030 0847	0.5315 1833	152
153	0.6824 7958	0.6404 3956	0.6010 0512	0.5293 1286	153
154	0.6807 7704	0.6385 7704	0.5990 0842	0.5271 1654	154
155	0.6790 7994	0.6367 1994	0.5970 1836	0.5249 2934	155
156	0.6773 8647	0.6348 6824	0.5950 3491	0.5227 5121	156
157	0.6756 9723	0.6330 2193	0.5930 5805	0.5205 8211	157
158	0.6740 1220	0.6311 8098	0.5910 8776	0.5184 2202	158
159	0.6723 3137	0.6293 4539	0.5891 2401	0.5162 7089	159
160	0.6706 5473	0.6275 1514	0.5871 6679	0.5141 2869	160
161	0.6689 8228	0.6256 9021	0.5852 1607	0.5119 9538	161
162	0.6673 1399	0.6238 7058	0.5832 7183	0.5098 7091	162
163	0.6656 4987	0.6220 5625	0.5813 3405	0.5077 5527	163
164	0.6639 8989	0.6202 4720	0.5794 0271	0.5056 4840	164
165	0.6623 3406	0.6184 4341	0.5774 7778	0.5035 5027	165
166	0.6606 8235	0.6166 4486	0.5755 5925	0.5014 6085	166
167	0.6590 3476	0.6148 5154	0.5736 4710	0.4993 8010	167
168	0.6573 9129	0.6130 6344	0.5717 4129	0.4973 0798	168
169	0.6557 5191	0.6112 8054	0.5698 4182	0.4952 4447	169
170	0.6541 1661	0.6095 0282	0.5679 4866	0.4931 8951	170
171	0.6524 8540	0.6077 3027	0.5660 6178	0.4911 4308	171
172	0.6500 5826	0.6059 6288	0.5641 8118	0.4891 0514	172
173	0.6492 3517	0.6042 0063	0.5623 0682	0.4870 7566	173
174	0.6476 1613	0.6024 4350	0.5604 3870	0.4850 5460	174
175	0.6460 0112	0.6006 9149	0.5585 7677	0.4830 4192	175
176	0.6443 9015	0.5989 4456	0.5567 2104	0.4810 3760	176
177	0.6427 8319	0.5972 0272	0.5548 7147	0.4790 4159	177
178	0.6411 8024	0.5954 6595	0.5530 2804	0.4770 5387	178
179	0.6395 8129	0.5937 3422	0.5511 9074	0.4750 7439	179
180	0.6379 8632	0.5920 0753	0.5493 5954	0.4731 0313	180
181	0.6363 9533	0.5902 8586	0.5475 3442	0.4711 4005	181
182	0.6348 0831	0.5885 6920	0.5457 1537	0.4691 8511	182
183	0.6332 2525	0.5868 5754	0.5439 0237	0.4672 3828	183
184	0.6316 4613	0.5851 5085	0.5420 9538	0.4652 9953	184
185	0.6300 7096	0.5834 4912	0.5402 9440	0.4633 6883	185
186	0.6284 9971	0.5817 5234	0.5384 9940	0.4614 4614	186
187	0.6269 3238	0.5800 6050	0.5367 1037	0.4595 3142	187
188	0.6253 6895	0.5783 7357	0.5349 2728	0.4576 2465	188
189	0.6238 0943	0.5766 9156	0.5331 5011	0.4557 2580	189
190	0.6222 5380	0.5750 1443	0.5313 7885	0.4538 3482	190
191	0.6207 0204	0.5733 4218	0.5296 1347	0.4519 5100	191
192	0.6191 5416	0.5716 7480	0.5278 5396	0.4500 7637	192
193	0.6176 1013	0.5700 1226	0.5261 0029	0.4482 0883	193
194	0.6160 6996	0.5683 5456	0.5243 5245	0.4463 4904	194
195	0.6145 3362	0.5667 0168	0.5226 1041	0.4444 9697	195
196	0.6130 0112	0.5650 5361	0.5208 7417	0.4426 5258	196
197	0.6114 7244	0.5634 1033	0.5191 4369	0.4408 1585	197
198	0.6099 4757	0.5617 7183	0.5174 1896	0.4389 8674	198
199	0.6084 2650	0.5601 3809	0.5156 9996	0.4371 6522	199
200	0.6069 0923	0.5585 0911	0.5139 8667	0.4353 5125	200

TABLE II.—Present Value of 1 at Compound Interest

$$v^n = (1 + i)^{-n}$$

n	$\frac{1}{2}\%$	$\frac{7}{12}\%$	$\frac{5}{8}\%$	$\frac{2}{3}\%$	n
1	0.9950 2488	0.9942 0050	0.9937 8882	0.9933 7748	1
2	0.9900 7450	0.9884 3463	0.9876 1622	0.9867 9882	2
3	0.9851 4876	0.9827 0220	0.9814 8196	0.9802 6373	3
4	0.9802 4752	0.9770 0302	0.9753 8580	0.9737 7192	4
5	0.9753 7067	0.9713 3688	0.9693 2750	0.9673 2310	5
6	0.9705 1808	0.9657 0361	0.9633 0683	0.9609 1699	6
7	0.9656 8963	0.9601 0301	0.9573 2356	0.9545 5330	7
8	0.9608 8520	0.9545 3489	0.9513 7745	0.9482 3175	8
9	0.9561 0468	0.9489 9907	0.9454 6827	0.9419 5207	9
10	0.9513 4794	0.9434 9534	0.9395 9580	0.9357 1398	10
11	0.9466 1489	0.9380 2354	0.9337 5980	0.9295 1720	11
12	0.9419 0534	0.9325 8347	0.9279 6005	0.9233 6145	12
13	0.9372 1924	0.9271 7495	0.9221 9632	0.9172 4648	13
14	0.9325 5646	0.9217 9780	0.9164 6840	0.9111 7200	14
15	0.9279 1688	0.9164 5183	0.9107 7604	0.9051 3775	15
16	0.9233 0037	0.9111 3686	0.9051 1905	0.8991 4346	16
17	0.9187 0684	0.9058 5272	0.8994 9719	0.8931 8886	17
18	0.9141 3616	0.9005 9923	0.8939 1025	0.8872 7371	18
19	0.9095 8822	0.8953 7620	0.8883 5802	0.8813 9772	19
20	0.9050 6290	0.8901 8346	0.8828 4027	0.8755 6065	20
21	0.9005 6010	0.8850 2084	0.8773 5679	0.8697 6224	21
22	0.8960 7971	0.8798 8816	0.8719 0736	0.8640 0222	22
23	0.8916 2160	0.8747 8525	0.8664 9179	0.8582 8035	23
24	0.8871 8567	0.8697 1193	0.8611 0985	0.8525 9638	24
25	0.8827 7181	0.8646 6803	0.8557 6135	0.8469 5004	25
26	0.8783 7991	0.8596 5339	0.8504 4606	0.8413 4110	26
27	0.8740 0986	0.8546 6782	0.8451 6378	0.8357 6931	27
28	0.8696 6155	0.8497 1118	0.8399 1432	0.8302 3441	28
29	0.8653 3488	0.8447 8327	0.8346 9746	0.8247 3617	29
30	0.8610 2973	0.8398 8395	0.8295 1300	0.8192 7434	30
31	0.8567 4600	0.8350 1304	0.8243 6075	0.8138 4868	31
32	0.8524 8358	0.8301 7038	0.8192 4050	0.8084 5896	32
33	0.8482 4237	0.8253 5581	0.8141 5205	0.8031 0492	33
34	0.8440 2226	0.8205 6915	0.8090 9520	0.7977 8635	34
35	0.8398 2314	0.8158 1026	0.8040 6976	0.7925 0299	35
36	0.8356 4492	0.8110 7897	0.7990 7554	0.7872 5463	36
37	0.8314 8748	0.8063 7511	0.7941 1234	0.7820 4102	37
38	0.8273 5073	0.8016 9854	0.7891 7997	0.7768 6194	38
39	0.8232 3455	0.7970 4908	0.7842 7823	0.7717 1716	39
40	0.8191 3886	0.7924 2660	0.7794 0693	0.7666 0645	40
41	0.8150 6354	0.7878 3092	0.7745 6590	0.7615 2959	41
42	0.8110 0850	0.7832 6189	0.7697 5493	0.7564 8635	42
43	0.8069 7363	0.7787 1936	0.7649 7384	0.7514 7650	43
44	0.8029 5884	0.7742 0317	0.7602 2245	0.7464 9984	44
45	0.7989 6402	0.7697 1318	0.7555 0057	0.7415 5613	45
46	0.7949 8907	0.7652 4923	0.7508 0802	0.7366 4516	46
47	0.7910 3390	0.7608 1116	0.7461 4462	0.7317 6672	47
48	0.7870 9841	0.7563 9884	0.7415 1018	0.7269 2058	48
49	0.7831 8250	0.7520 1210	0.7369 0453	0.7221 0654	49
50	0.7792 8607	0.7476 5080	0.7323 2748	0.7173 2437	50

TABLE II.—Present Value of 1 at Compound Interest

$$v^n = (1 + i)^{-n}$$

n	$\frac{1}{2}\%$	$\frac{7}{12}\%$	$\frac{5}{8}\%$	$\frac{2}{3}\%$	n
51	0.7754 0902	0.7433 1480	0.7277 7886	0.7125 7388	51
52	0.7715 5127	0.7390 0394	0.7232 5849	0.7078 5485	52
53	0.7677 1270	0.7347 1809	0.7187 6620	0.7031 6707	53
54	0.7638 9324	0.7304 6709	0.7143 0182	0.6985 1033	54
55	0.7600 9277	0.7262 2080	0.7098 6516	0.6938 8444	55
56	0.7563 1122	0.7220 0908	0.7054 5606	0.6892 8918	56
57	0.7525 4847	0.7178 2179	0.7010 7434	0.6847 2435	57
58	0.7488 0445	0.7136 5878	0.6967 1985	0.6801 8975	58
59	0.7450 7906	0.7095 1991	0.6923 9239	0.6756 8518	59
60	0.7413 7220	0.7054 0505	0.6880 9182	0.6712 1044	60
61	0.7376 8378	0.7013 1405	0.6838 1796	0.6667 6534	61
62	0.7340 1371	0.6972 4678	0.6795 7064	0.6623 4968	62
63	0.7303 6190	0.6932 0310	0.6753 4970	0.6579 6326	63
64	0.7267 2826	0.6891 8286	0.6711 5499	0.6536 0588	64
65	0.7231 1269	0.6851 8594	0.6669 8632	0.6492 7737	65
66	0.7195 1512	0.6812 1221	0.6628 4355	0.6449 7752	66
67	0.7159 3544	0.6772 6151	0.6587 2651	0.6407 0614	67
68	0.7123 7357	0.6733 3373	0.6546 3504	0.6364 6306	68
69	0.7088 2943	0.6694 2873	0.6505 6898	0.6322 4807	69
70	0.7053 0291	0.6655 4638	0.6465 2818	0.6280 6100	70
71	0.7017 9394	0.6616 8654	0.6425 1248	0.6239 0165	71
72	0.6983 0243	0.6578 4909	0.6385 2172	0.6197 6985	72
73	0.6948 2829	0.6540 0009	0.6345 5574	0.6156 6541	73
74	0.6913 7143	0.6502 4082	0.6306 1440	0.6115 8816	74
75	0.6879 3177	0.6464 6975	0.6266 9754	0.6075 3791	75
76	0.6845 0923	0.6427 2054	0.6228 0501	0.6035 1448	76
77	0.6811 0371	0.6389 9308	0.6189 3666	0.5995 1769	77
78	0.6777 1513	0.6352 8724	0.6150 9233	0.5955 4738	78
79	0.6743 4342	0.6316 0289	0.6112 7188	0.5916 0336	79
80	0.6709 8847	0.6279 3991	0.6074 7516	0.5876 8545	80
81	0.6676 5022	0.6242 9817	0.6037 0203	0.5837 9350	81
82	0.6643 2858	0.6206 7755	0.5999 5232	0.5799 2732	82
83	0.6610 2346	0.6170 7793	0.5962 2591	0.5760 8674	83
84	0.6577 3479	0.6134 9919	0.5925 2264	0.5722 7159	84
85	0.6544 6248	0.6099 4120	0.5888 4238	0.5684 8171	85
86	0.6512 0644	0.6064 0384	0.5851 8497	0.5647 1693	86
87	0.6479 6661	0.6028 8700	0.5815 5028	0.5609 7709	87
88	0.6447 4290	0.5993 9056	0.5779 3817	0.5572 6201	88
89	0.6415 3522	0.5959 1439	0.5743 4849	0.5535 7153	89
90	0.6383 4350	0.5924 5838	0.5707 8111	0.5499 0549	90
91	0.6351 6766	0.5890 2242	0.5672 3589	0.5462 6374	91
92	0.6320 0763	0.5856 0638	0.5637 1268	0.5426 4610	92
93	0.6288 6331	0.5822 1015	0.5602 1136	0.5390 5241	93
94	0.6257 3464	0.5788 3363	0.5567 3179	0.5354 8253	94
95	0.6226 2153	0.5754 7668	0.5532 7383	0.5319 3629	95
96	0.6195 2391	0.5721 3920	0.5498 3734	0.5284 1353	96
97	0.6164 4170	0.5688 2108	0.5464 2220	0.5249 1410	97
98	0.6133 7483	0.5655 2220	0.5430 2828	0.5214 3785	98
99	0.6103 2321	0.5622 4245	0.5396 5543	0.5179 8462	99
100	0.6072 8678	0.5589 8172	0.5363 0353	0.5145 5426	100

TABLE II. —Present Value of 1 at Compound Interest

$$v^n = (1 + i)^{-n}$$

n	$\frac{1}{2}\%$	$\frac{7}{12}\%$	$\frac{5}{8}\%$	$\frac{2}{3}\%$	n
101	0.6042 6545	0.5557 3991	0.5329 7246	0.5111 4660	101
102	0.6012 5915	0.5525 1689	0.5296 6207	0.5077 6152	102
103	0.5982 6781	0.5493 1257	0.5263 7225	0.5043 9886	103
104	0.5952 9136	0.5461 2683	0.5231 0285	0.5010 5847	104
105	0.5923 2971	0.5429 5957	0.5198 5377	0.4977 4020	105
106	0.5893 8279	0.5398 1067	0.5166 2486	0.4944 4391	106
107	0.5864 5054	0.5366 8004	0.5134 1601	0.4911 6945	107
108	0.5835 3288	0.5335 6756	0.5102 2709	0.4879 1667	108
109	0.5806 2973	0.5304 7313	0.5070 5798	0.4846 8543	109
110	0.5777 4102	0.5273 9665	0.5039 0855	0.4814 7559	110
111	0.5748 6669	0.5243 3801	0.5007 7868	0.4782 8701	111
112	0.5720 0666	0.5212 9711	0.4976 6826	0.4751 1955	112
113	0.5691 6085	0.5182 7385	0.4945 7715	0.4719 7306	113
114	0.5663 2921	0.5152 6812	0.4915 0524	0.4688 4741	114
115	0.5635 1165	0.5122 7982	0.4884 5242	0.4657 4246	115
116	0.5607 0811	0.5093 0885	0.4854 1855	0.4626 5808	116
117	0.5579 1852	0.5063 5512	0.4824 0353	0.4595 9411	117
118	0.5551 4280	0.5034 1851	0.4794 0723	0.4565 5044	118
119	0.5523 8090	0.5004 9893	0.4764 2955	0.4535 2693	119
120	0.5496 3273	0.4975 9629	0.4734 7036	0.4505 2344	120
121	0.5468 9824	0.4947 1047	0.4705 2955	0.4475 3984	121
122	0.5441 7736	0.4918 4140	0.4676 0700	0.4445 7600	122
123	0.5414 7001	0.4889 8896	0.4647 0261	0.4416 3179	123
124	0.5387 7612	0.4861 5307	0.4618 1626	0.4387 0708	124
125	0.5360 9565	0.4833 3363	0.4589 4784	0.4358 0173	125
126	0.5334 2850	0.4805 3053	0.4560 9723	0.4329 1563	126
127	0.5307 7463	0.4777 4369	0.4532 6433	0.4300 4864	127
128	0.5281 3396	0.4749 7302	0.4504 4902	0.4272 0063	128
129	0.5255 0643	0.4722 1841	0.4476 5120	0.4243 7149	129
130	0.5228 9197	0.4694 7978	0.4448 7076	0.4215 6108	130
131	0.5202 9052	0.4667 5703	0.4421 0759	0.4187 6929	131
132	0.5177 0201	0.4640 5007	0.4393 6158	0.4159 9598	132
133	0.5151 2637	0.4613 5881	0.4366 3262	0.4132 4104	133
134	0.5125 6356	0.4586 8316	0.4339 2062	0.4105 0434	134
135	0.5100 1349	0.4560 2303	0.4312 2546	0.4077 8577	135
136	0.5074 7611	0.4533 7832	0.4285 4704	0.4050 8520	136
137	0.5049 5135	0.4507 4895	0.4258 8526	0.4024 0252	137
138	0.5024 3916	0.4481 3483	0.4232 4001	0.3997 3760	138
139	0.4999 3946	0.4455 3587	0.4206 1119	0.3970 9033	139
140	0.4974 5220	0.4429 5198	0.4179 9870	0.3944 6059	140
141	0.4949 7731	0.4403 8308	0.4154 0243	0.3918 4827	141
142	0.4925 1474	0.4378 2908	0.4128 2229	0.3892 5325	142
143	0.4900 6442	0.4352 8989	0.4102 5818	0.3866 7541	143
144	0.4876 2628	0.4327 6542	0.4077 0999	0.3841 1465	144
145	0.4852 0028	0.4302 5560	0.4051 7763	0.3815 7084	145
146	0.4827 8635	0.4277 6033	0.4026 6100	0.3790 4389	146
147	0.4803 8443	0.4252 7953	0.4001 6000	0.3765 3366	147
148	0.4779 9446	0.4228 1312	0.3976 7453	0.3740 4006	148
149	0.4756 1637	0.4203 6102	0.3952 0451	0.3715 6297	159
150	0.4732 5012	0.4179 2313	0.3927 4982	0.3691 0229	150

TABLE II.—Present Value of 1 at Compound Interest

$$v^n = (1 + i)^{-n}$$

n	½%	7/12%	5/8%	2/3%	n
151	0.4708 9565	0.4154 9939	0.3903 1038	0.3666 5791	151
152	0.4685 5288	0.4130 8970	0.3878 8609	0.3642 2971	152
153	0.4662 2177	0.4106 9399	0.3854 7686	0.3618 1759	153
154	0.4639 0226	0.4083 1216	0.3830 8259	0.3594 2145	154
155	0.4615 9429	0.4059 4416	0.3807 0320	0.3570 4117	155
156	0.4592 9780	0.4035 8988	0.3783 3858	0.3546 7666	156
157	0.4570 1274	0.4012 4926	0.3759 8865	0.3523 2781	157
158	0.4547 3904	0.3989 2221	0.3736 5332	0.3499 9451	158
159	0.4524 7666	0.3966 0866	0.3713 3249	0.3476 7667	159
160	0.4502 2553	0.3943 0853	0.3690 2608	0.3453 7417	160
161	0.4479 8560	0.3920 2174	0.3667 3399	0.3430 8693	161
162	0.4457 5682	0.3897 4821	0.3644 5614	0.3408 1483	162
163	0.4435 3912	0.3874 8786	0.3621 9244	0.3385 5778	163
164	0.4413 3246	0.3852 4062	0.3599 4280	0.3363 1567	164
165	0.4391 3678	0.3830 0642	0.3577 0713	0.3340 8841	165
166	0.4369 5202	0.3807 8517	0.3554 8534	0.3318 7591	166
167	0.4347 7813	0.3785 7681	0.3532 7736	0.3296 7805	167
168	0.4326 1505	0.3763 8125	0.3510 8309	0.3274 9476	168
169	0.4304 6274	0.3741 9843	0.3489 0245	0.3253 2592	169
170	0.4283 2113	0.3720 2826	0.3467 3535	0.3231 7144	170
171	0.4261 9018	0.3698 7068	0.3445 8172	0.3210 3123	171
172	0.4240 6983	0.3677 2562	0.3424 4140	0.3189 0520	172
173	0.4219 6003	0.3655 9299	0.3403 1449	0.3167 9324	173
174	0.4198 6073	0.3634 7273	0.3382 0074	0.3146 9527	174
175	0.4177 7187	0.3613 6477	0.3361 0011	0.3126 1120	175
176	0.4156 9340	0.3592 6904	0.3340 1254	0.3105 4093	176
177	0.4136 2528	0.3571 8546	0.3319 3792	0.3084 8436	177
178	0.4115 6744	0.3551 1396	0.3298 7620	0.3064 4142	178
179	0.4095 1984	0.3530 5447	0.3278 2728	0.3044 1201	179
180	0.4074 8243	0.3510 0693	0.3257 9108	0.3023 9603	180
181	0.4054 5515	0.3489 7127	0.3237 6754	0.3003 9341	181
182	0.4034 3796	0.3469 4741	0.3217 5656	0.2984 0405	182
183	0.4014 3081	0.3449 3529	0.3197 5807	0.2964 2786	183
184	0.3994 3364	0.3429 3483	0.3177 7199	0.2944 6477	184
185	0.3974 4641	0.3409 4598	0.3157 9825	0.2925 1467	185
186	0.3954 6906	0.3389 6866	0.3138 3677	0.2905 7748	186
187	0.3935 0155	0.3370 0281	0.3118 8748	0.2886 5313	187
188	0.3915 4383	0.3350 4837	0.3099 5029	0.2867 4152	188
189	0.3895 9586	0.3331 0525	0.3080 2513	0.2848 4257	189
190	0.3876 5757	0.3311 7341	0.3061 1193	0.2829 5619	190
191	0.3857 2892	0.3292 5277	0.3042 1062	0.2810 8231	191
192	0.3838 0987	0.3273 4326	0.3023 2111	0.2792 2084	192
193	0.3819 0037	0.3254 4484	0.3004 4334	0.2773 7170	193
194	0.3800 0037	0.3235 5742	0.2985 7723	0.2755 3480	194
195	0.3781 0982	0.3216 8095	0.2967 2271	0.2737 1006	195
196	0.3762 2868	0.3198 1536	0.2948 7972	0.2718 9741	196
197	0.3743 5689	0.3179 6059	0.2930 4816	0.2700 9677	197
198	0.3724 9442	0.3161 1657	0.2912 2799	0.2683 0805	198
199	0.3706 4121	0.3142 8325	0.2894 1912	0.2665 3117	199
200	0.3687 9723	0.3124 6057	0.2876 2149	0.2647 6607	200

TABLE II.—Present Value of 1 at Compound Interest

$$v^n = (1 + i)^{-n}$$

n	$\frac{3}{4}\%$	$\frac{7}{8}\%$	1%	$1\frac{1}{8}\%$	n
1	0.9925 5583	0.9913 2590	0.9900 9901	0.9888 7515	1
2	0.9851 6708	0.9827 2704	0.9802 9605	0.9778 7407	2
3	0.9778 3333	0.9742 0276	0.9705 9015	0.9669 9537	3
4	0.9705 5417	0.9657 5243	0.9609 8034	0.9562 3770	4
5	0.9633 2920	0.9573 7539	0.9514 6569	0.9455 9970	5
6	0.9561 5802	0.9490 7102	0.9420 4524	0.9350 8005	6
7	0.9490 4022	0.9408 3868	0.9327 1805	0.9246 7743	7
8	0.9419 7540	0.9326 7775	0.9234 8322	0.9143 9054	8
9	0.9349 6318	0.9245 8761	0.9143 3982	0.9042 1808	9
10	0.9280 0315	0.9165 6765	0.9052 8695	0.8941 5881	10
11	0.9210 9494	0.9086 1724	0.8963 2372	0.8842 1142	11
12	0.9142 3815	0.9007 3581	0.8874 4923	0.8743 7470	12
13	0.9074 3241	0.8929 2273	0.8786 6260	0.8646 4742	13
14	0.9006 7733	0.8851 7743	0.8699 6297	0.8550 2835	14
15	0.8939 7254	0.8774 9931	0.8613 4947	0.8455 1629	15
16	0.8873 1766	0.8698 8779	0.8528 2126	0.8361 1005	16
17	0.8807 1231	0.8623 4230	0.8443 7749	0.8268 0846	17
18	0.8741 5614	0.8548 6225	0.8360 1731	0.8176 1034	18
19	0.8676 4878	0.8474 4709	0.8277 3992	0.8085 1455	19
20	0.8611 8985	0.8400 9624	0.8195 4447	0.7995 1995	20
21	0.8547 7901	0.8328 0917	0.8114 3017	0.7906 2542	21
22	0.8484 1589	0.8255 8530	0.8033 9621	0.7818 2983	22
23	0.8421 0014	0.8184 2409	0.7954 4179	0.7731 3210	23
24	0.8358 3140	0.8113 2499	0.7875 6613	0.7645 3112	24
25	0.8296 0933	0.8042 8748	0.7797 6844	0.7560 2583	25
26	0.8234 3358	0.7973 1101	0.7720 4796	0.7476 1516	26
27	0.8173 0380	0.7903 9505	0.7644 0392	0.7392 9806	27
28	0.8112 1966	0.7835 3908	0.7568 3557	0.7310 7348	28
29	0.8051 8080	0.7767 4258	0.7493 4215	0.7229 4040	29
30	0.7991 8690	0.7700 0504	0.7419 2292	0.7148 9780	30
31	0.7932 3762	0.7633 2594	0.7345 7715	0.7069 4467	31
32	0.7873 3262	0.7567 0477	0.7273 0411	0.6990 8002	32
33	0.7814 7158	0.7501 4104	0.7201 0307	0.6913 0287	33
34	0.7756 5418	0.7436 3424	0.7129 7334	0.6836 1223	34
35	0.7698 8008	0.7371 8388	0.7059 1420	0.6760 0715	35
36	0.7641 4896	0.7307 8947	0.6989 2495	0.6684 8667	36
37	0.7584 6051	0.7244 5053	0.6920 0490	0.6610 4986	37
38	0.7528 1440	0.7181 6657	0.6851 5337	0.6536 9578	38
39	0.7472 1032	0.7119 3712	0.6783 6967	0.6464 2352	39
40	0.7416 4796	0.7057 6171	0.6716 5314	0.6392 3216	40
41	0.7361 2701	0.6996 3986	0.6650 0311	0.6321 2080	41
42	0.7306 4716	0.6935 7111	0.6584 1892	0.6250 8855	42
43	0.7252 0809	0.6875 5500	0.6518 9992	0.6181 3454	43
44	0.7198 0952	0.6815 9108	0.6454 4546	0.6112 5789	44
45	0.7144 5114	0.6756 7889	0.6390 5492	0.6044 5774	45
46	0.7091 3264	0.6698 1798	0.6327 2764	0.5977 3324	46
47	0.7038 5374	0.6640 0792	0.6264 6301	0.5910 8355	47
48	0.6986 1414	0.6582 4824	0.6202 6041	0.5845 0784	48
49	0.6934 1353	0.6525 3853	0.6141 1921	0.5780 0528	49
50	0.6882 5165	0.6468 7835	0.6080 3882	0.5715 7506	50

TABLE II.—Present Value of 1 at Compound Interest

$$v^n = (1 + i)^{-n}$$

n	$\frac{3}{4}\%$	$\frac{7}{8}\%$	1%	$1\frac{1}{8}\%$	n
51	0.6831 2819	0.6412 6726	0.6020 1864	0.5652 1637	51
52	0.6780 4286	0.6357 0484	0.5960 5806	0.5589 2843	52
53	0.6729 9540	0.6301 9067	0.5901 5649	0.5527 1041	53
54	0.6679 8551	0.6247 2433	0.5843 1336	0.5465 6162	54
55	0.6630 1291	0.6193 0541	0.5785 2808	0.5404 8120	55
56	0.6580 7733	0.6139 3349	0.5728 0008	0.5344 6843	56
57	0.6531 7849	0.6086 0817	0.5671 2879	0.5285 2256	57
58	0.6483 1612	0.6033 2904	0.5615 1365	0.5226 4282	58
59	0.6434 8995	0.5980 9571	0.5559 5411	0.5168 2850	59
60	0.6386 9970	0.5929 0776	0.5504 4962	0.5110 7887	60
61	0.6339 4511	0.5877 6482	0.5449 9962	0.5053 9319	61
62	0.6292 2592	0.5826 6649	0.5396 0358	0.4997 7077	62
63	0.6245 4185	0.5776 1238	0.5342 6097	0.4942 1090	63
64	0.6198 9266	0.5726 0211	0.5289 7126	0.4887 1288	64
65	0.6152 7807	0.5676 3530	0.5237 3392	0.4832 7602	65
66	0.6106 9784	0.5627 1158	0.5185 4844	0.4778 9965	66
67	0.6061 5170	0.5578 3056	0.5134 1429	0.4725 8309	67
68	0.6016 3940	0.5529 9188	0.5083 3099	0.4673 2568	68
69	0.5971 6070	0.5481 9517	0.5032 9801	0.4621 2675	69
70	0.5927 1533	0.5434 4007	0.4983 1486	0.4569 8566	70
71	0.5883 0306	0.5387 2622	0.4933 8105	0.4519 0177	71
72	0.5839 2363	0.5340 5325	0.4884 9609	0.4468 7443	72
73	0.5795 7681	0.5294 2082	0.4836 5949	0.4419 0302	73
74	0.5752 6234	0.5248 2857	0.4788 7078	0.4369 8692	74
75	0.5709 7999	0.5202 7615	0.4741 2949	0.4321 2551	75
76	0.5667 2952	0.5157 6322	0.4694 3514	0.4273 1818	76
77	0.5625 1069	0.5112 8944	0.4647 8726	0.4225 6433	77
78	0.5583 2326	0.5068 5447	0.4601 8541	0.4178 6337	78
79	0.5541 6701	0.5024 5796	0.4556 2912	0.4132 1470	79
80	0.5500 4170	0.4980 9959	0.4511 1794	0.4086 1775	80
81	0.5459 4710	0.4937 7902	0.4466 5142	0.4040 7194	81
82	0.5418 8297	0.4894 9593	0.4422 2913	0.3995 7670	82
83	0.5378 4911	0.4852 4999	0.4378 5063	0.3951 3148	83
84	0.5338 4527	0.4810 4089	0.4335 1547	0.3907 3570	84
85	0.5298 7123	0.4768 6829	0.4292 2324	0.3863 8882	85
86	0.5259 2678	0.4727 3188	0.4249 7350	0.3820 9031	86
87	0.5220 1169	0.4686 3136	0.4207 6585	0.3778 3961	87
88	0.5181 2575	0.4645 6640	0.4165 9985	0.3736 3621	88
89	0.5142 6873	0.4605 3671	0.4124 7510	0.3694 7956	89
90	0.5104 4043	0.4565 4197	0.4083 9119	0.3653 6916	90
91	0.5066 4063	0.4525 8187	0.4043 4771	0.3613 0448	91
92	0.5028 6911	0.4486 5613	0.4003 4427	0.3572 8503	92
93	0.4991 2567	0.4447 6444	0.3963 8046	0.3533 1029	93
94	0.4954 1009	0.4409 0651	0.3924 5590	0.3493 7976	94
95	0.4917 2217	0.4370 8204	0.3885 7020	0.3454 9297	95
96	0.4880 6171	0.4332 9075	0.3847 2297	0.3416 4941	96
97	0.4844 2850	0.4295 3234	0.3809 1383	0.3378 4861	97
98	0.4808 2233	0.4258 0654	0.3771 4241	0.3340 9010	98
99	0.4772 4301	0.4221 1305	0.3734 0832	0.3303 7340	99
100	0.4736 9033	0.4184 5159	0.3697 1121	0.3266 9805	100

TABLE II.—Present Value of 1 at Compound Interest

$$v^n = (1 + i)^{-n}$$

n	1¼%	1⅜%	1½%	1¾%	n
1	0.9876 5432	0.9864 3650	0.9852 2167	0.9828 0098	1
2	0.9754 6106	0.9730 5696	0.9706 6175	0.9658 9777	2
3	0.9634 1833	0.9598 5890	0.9563 1699	0.9492 8528	3
4	0.9515 2428	0.9468 3986	0.9421 8423	0.9329 5851	4
5	0.9397 7706	0.9339 9739	0.9282 6033	0.9169 1254	5
6	0.9281 7488	0.9213 2912	0.9145 4219	0.9011 4254	6
7	0.9167 1593	0.9088 3267	0.9010 2679	0.8856 4378	7
8	0.9053 9845	0.8965 0571	0.8877 1112	0.8704 1157	8
9	0.8942 2069	0.8843 4596	0.8745 9224	0.8554 4135	9
10	0.8831 8093	0.8723 5113	0.8616 6723	0.8407 2860	10
11	0.8722 7746	0.8605 1899	0.8489 3323	0.8262 6889	11
12	0.8615 0860	0.8488 4734	0.8363 8742	0.8120 5788	12
13	0.8508 7269	0.8373 3400	0.8240 2702	0.7980 9128	13
14	0.8403 6809	0.8259 7682	0.8118 4928	0.7843 6490	14
15	0.8299 9318	0.8147 7368	0.7998 5150	0.7708 7459	15
16	0.8197 4635	0.8037 2250	0.7880 3104	0.7576 1631	16
17	0.8096 2602	0.7928 2120	0.7763 8526	0.7445 8605	17
18	0.7996 3064	0.7820 6777	0.7649 1159	0.7317 7990	18
19	0.7897 5866	0.7714 6020	0.7536 0747	0.7191 9401	19
20	0.7800 0855	0.7609 9649	0.7424 7042	0.7068 2458	20
21	0.7703 7881	0.7506 7472	0.7314 9795	0.6946 6789	21
22	0.7608 6796	0.7404 9294	0.7206 8763	0.6827 2028	22
23	0.7514 7453	0.7304 4926	0.7100 3708	0.6709 7817	23
24	0.7421 9707	0.7205 4181	0.6995 4392	0.6594 3800	24
25	0.7330 3414	0.7107 6874	0.6892 0583	0.6480 9632	25
26	0.7239 8434	0.7011 2823	0.6790 2052	0.6369 4970	26
27	0.7150 4626	0.6916 1847	0.6689 8574	0.6259 9479	27
28	0.7062 1853	0.6822 3771	0.6590 9925	0.6152 2829	28
29	0.6974 9978	0.6729 8417	0.6493 5887	0.6046 4697	29
30	0.6888 8867	0.6638 5615	0.6397 6243	0.5942 4764	30
31	0.6803 8387	0.6548 5194	0.6303 0781	0.5840 2716	31
32	0.6719 8407	0.6459 6985	0.6209 9292	0.5739 8247	32
33	0.6636 8797	0.6372 0824	0.6118 1568	0.5641 1053	33
34	0.6554 9429	0.6285 6546	0.6027 7407	0.5544 0839	34
35	0.6474 0177	0.6200 3991	0.5938 6608	0.5448 7311	35
36	0.6394 0916	0.6116 3000	0.5850 8974	0.5355 0183	36
37	0.6315 1522	0.6033 3416	0.5764 4309	0.5262 9172	37
38	0.6237 1873	0.5951 5083	0.5679 2423	0.5172 4002	38
39	0.6160 1850	0.5870 7850	0.5595 3126	0.5083 4400	39
40	0.6084 1334	0.5791 1566	0.5512 6232	0.4996 0098	40
41	0.6009 0206	0.5712 6083	0.5431 1559	0.4910 0834	41
42	0.5934 8352	0.5635 1253	0.5350 8925	0.4825 6348	42
43	0.5861 5656	0.5558 6933	0.5271 8153	0.4742 6386	43
44	0.5789 2006	0.5483 2979	0.5193 9067	0.4661 0699	44
45	0.5717 7290	0.5408 9252	0.5117 1494	0.4580 9040	45
46	0.5647 1397	0.5335 5612	0.5041 5265	0.4502 1170	46
47	0.5577 4219	0.5263 1923	0.4967 0212	0.4424 6850	47
48	0.5508 5649	0.5191 8050	0.4893 6170	0.4348 5848	48
49	0.5440 5579	0.5121 3860	0.4821 2975	0.4273 7934	49
50	0.5373 3905	0.5051 9220	0.4750 0468	0.4200 2883	50

TABLE II.—Present Value of 1 at Compound Interest

$$v^n = (1+i)^{-n}$$

n	$1\frac{1}{4}\%$	$1\frac{3}{8}\%$	$1\frac{1}{2}\%$	$1\frac{3}{4}\%$	n
51	0.5307 0524	0.4983 4003	0.4679 8491	0.4128 0475	51
52	0.5241 5332	0.4915 8079	0.4610 6887	0.4057 0492	52
53	0.5176 8229	0.4849 1323	0.4542 5505	0.3987 2719	53
54	0.5112 9115	0.4783 3611	0.4475 4192	0.3918 6947	54
55	0.5049 7892	0.4718 4820	0.4409 2800	0.3851 2970	55
56	0.4987 4461	0.4654 4829	0.4344 1182	0.3785 0585	56
57	0.4925 8727	0.4591 3518	0.4279 9194	0.3719 9592	57
58	0.4865 0594	0.4529 0770	0.4216 6694	0.3655 9796	58
59	0.4804 9970	0.4467 6468	0.4154 3541	0.3593 1003	59
60	0.4745 6760	0.4407 0499	0.4092 9597	0.3531 3025	60
61	0.4687 0874	0.4347 2749	0.4032 4726	0.3470 5676	61
62	0.4629 2222	0.4288 3106	0.3972 8794	0.3410 8772	62
63	0.4572 0713	0.4230 1461	0.3914 1669	0.3352 2135	63
64	0.4515 6259	0.4172 7705	0.3856 3221	0.3294 5587	64
65	0.4459 8775	0.4116 1731	0.3799 3321	0.3237 8956	65
66	0.4404 8173	0.4060 3434	0.3743 1843	0.3182 2069	66
67	0.4350 4368	0.4005 2709	0.3687 8663	0.3127 4761	67
68	0.4296 7277	0.3950 9454	0.3633 3658	0.3073 6866	68
69	0.4243 6817	0.3897 3568	0.3579 6708	0.3020 8222	69
70	0.4191 2905	0.3844 4949	0.3526 7692	0.2968 8670	70
71	0.4139 5462	0.3792 3501	0.3474 6495	0.2917 8054	71
72	0.4088 4407	0.3740 9126	0.3422 9000	0.2867 6221	72
73	0.4037 9661	0.3690 1727	0.3372 7093	0.2818 3018	73
74	0.3988 1147	0.3640 1210	0.3322 8663	0.2769 8298	74
75	0.3938 8787	0.3590 7483	0.3273 7599	0.2722 1914	75
76	0.3890 2506	0.3542 0451	0.3225 3793	0.2675 3724	76
77	0.3842 2228	0.3494 0026	0.3177 7136	0.2629 3586	77
78	0.3794 7879	0.3446 6117	0.3130 7523	0.2584 1362	78
79	0.3747 9387	0.3399 8636	0.3084 4850	0.2539 6916	79
80	0.3701 6679	0.3353 7495	0.3038 9015	0.2496 0114	80
81	0.3655 9683	0.3308 2609	0.2993 9916	0.2453 0825	81
82	0.3610 8329	0.3263 3893	0.2949 7454	0.2410 8919	82
83	0.3566 2547	0.3219 1263	0.2906 1531	0.2369 4269	83
84	0.3522 2268	0.3175 4637	0.2863 2050	0.2328 6751	84
85	0.3478 7426	0.3132 3933	0.2820 8917	0.2288 6242	85
86	0.3435 7951	0.3089 9071	0.2779 2036	0.2249 2621	86
87	0.3393 3779	0.3047 9971	0.2738 1316	0.2210 5770	87
88	0.3351 4843	0.3006 6556	0.2697 6666	0.2172 5572	88
89	0.3310 1080	0.2965 8748	0.2657 7997	0.2135 1914	89
90	0.3269 2425	0.2925 6472	0.2618 5218	0.2098 4682	90
91	0.3228 8814	0.2885 9652	0.2579 8245	0.2062 3766	91
92	0.3189 0187	0.2846 8214	0.2541 6990	0.2026 9057	92
93	0.3149 6481	0.2808 2085	0.2504 1369	0.1992 0450	93
94	0.3110 7636	0.2770 1194	0.2467 1300	0.1957 7837	94
95	0.3072 3591	0.2732 5468	0.2430 6699	0.1924 1118	95
96	0.3034 4287	0.2695 4839	0.2394 7487	0.1891 0190	96
97	0.2996 9666	0.2658 9237	0.2359 3583	0.1858 4953	97
98	0.2959 9670	0.2622 8594	0.2324 4909	0.1826 5310	98
99	0.2923 4242	0.2587 2843	0.2290 1389	0.1795 1165	99
100	0.2887 3326	0.2552 1916	0.2256 2944	0.1764 2422	100

TABLE II.—Present Value of 1 at Compound Interest

$$v^n = (1+i)^{-n}$$

n	2%	2¼%	2½%	2¾%	n
1	0.9803 9216	0.9779 9511	0.9756 0976	0.9732 3601	1
2	0.9611 6878	0.9564 7444	0.9518 1440	0.9471 8833	2
3	0.9423 2233	0.9354 2732	0.9285 9941	0.9218 3779	3
4	0.9238 4543	0.9148 4335	0.9059 5064	0.8971 6573	4
5	0.9057 3081	0.8947 1232	0.8838 5429	0.8731 5400	5
6	0.8879 7138	0.8750 2427	0.8622 9687	0.8497 8491	6
7	0.8705 6018	0.8557 6946	0.8412 6524	0.8270 4128	7
8	0.8534 9037	0.8369 3835	0.8207 4657	0.8049 0635	8
9	0.8367 5527	0.8185 2161	0.8007 2836	0.7833 6385	9
10	0.8203 4830	0.8005 1013	0.7811 9840	0.7623 9791	10
11	0.8042 6304	0.7828 9499	0.7621 4478	0.7419 9310	11
12	0.7884 9318	0.7656 6748	0.7435 5589	0.7221 3440	12
13	0.7730 3253	0.7488 1905	0.7254 2038	0.7028 0720	13
14	0.7578 7502	0.7323 4137	0.7077 2720	0.6839 9728	14
15	0.7430 1473	0.7162 2628	0.6904 6556	0.6656 9078	15
16	0.7284 4581	0.7004 6580	0.6736 2493	0.6478 7424	16
17	0.7141 6256	0.6850 5212	0.6571 9506	0.6305 3454	17
18	0.7001 5937	0.6699 7763	0.6411 6591	0.6136 5892	18
19	0.6864 3076	0.6552 3484	0.6255 2772	0.5972 3496	19
20	0.6729 7133	0.6408 1647	0.6102 7094	0.5812 5057	20
21	0.6597 7582	0.6267 1538	0.5953 8629	0.5656 9398	21
22	0.6468 3904	0.6129 2457	0.5808 6467	0.5505 5375	22
23	0.6341 5592	0.5994 3724	0.5666 9724	0.5358 1874	23
24	0.6217 2149	0.5862 4668	0.5528 7535	0.5214 7809	24
25	0.6095 3087	0.5733 4639	0.5393 9059	0.5075 2126	25
26	0.5975 7928	0.5607 2997	0.5262 3472	0.4939 3796	26
27	0.5858 6204	0.5483 9117	0.5133 9973	0.4807 1821	27
28	0.5743 7455	0.5363 2388	0.5008 7778	0.4678 5227	28
29	0.5631 1231	0.5245 2213	0.4886 6125	0.4553 3068	29
30	0.5520 7089	0.5129 8008	0.4767 4269	0.4431 4421	30
31	0.5412 4597	0.5016 9201	0.4651 1481	0.4312 8391	31
32	0.5306 3330	0.4906 5233	0.4537 7055	0.4197 4103	32
33	0.5202 2873	0.4798 5558	0.4427 0298	0.4085 0708	33
34	0.5100 2817	0.4692 9641	0.4319 0534	0.3975 7380	34
35	0.5000 2761	0.4589 6960	0.4213 7107	0.3869 3314	35
36	0.4902 2315	0.4488 7002	0.4110 9372	0.3765 7727	36
37	0.4806 1093	0.4389 9268	0.4010 6705	0.3664 9856	37
38	0.4711 8719	0.4293 3270	0.3912 8492	0.3566 8959	38
39	0.4619 4822	0.4198 8528	0.3817 4139	0.3471 4316	39
40	0.4528 9042	0.4106 4575	0.3724 3062	0.3378 5222	40
41	0.4440 1021	0.4016 0954	0.3633 4695	0.3288 0995	41
42	0.4353 0413	0.3927 7216	0.3544 8483	0.3200 0968	42
43	0.4267 6875	0.3841 2925	0.3458 3886	0.3114 4495	43
44	0.4184 0074	0.3756 7653	0.3374 0376	0.3031 0944	44
45	0.4101 9680	0.3674 0981	0.3291 7440	0.2949 9702	45
46	0.4021 5373	0.3593 2500	0.3211 4576	0.2871 0172	46
47	0.3942 6836	0.3514 1809	0.3133 1294	0.2794 1773	47
48	0.3865 3761	0.3436 8518	0.3056 7116	0.2719 3940	48
49	0.3789 5844	0.3361 2242	0.2982 1576	0.2646 6122	49
50	0.3715 2788	0.3287 2608	0.2909 4221	0.2575 7783	50

TABLE II.—Present Value of 1 at Compound Interest

$$v^n = (1 + i)^{-n}$$

n	2%	$2\frac{1}{4}$%	$2\frac{1}{2}$%	$2\frac{3}{4}$%	n
51	0.3642 4302	0.3214 9250	0.2838 4606	0.2506 8402	51
52	0.3571 0100	0.3144 1810	0.2769 2298	0.2439 7471	52
53	0.3500 9902	0.3074 9936	0.2701 6876	0.2374 4497	53
54	0.3432 3433	0.3007 3287	0.2635 7928	0.2310 9000	54
55	0.3365 0425	0.2941 1528	0.2571 5052	0.2249 0511	55
56	0.3299 0613	0.2876 4330	0.2508 7855	0.2188 8575	56
57	0.3234 3738	0.2813 1374	0.2447 5956	0.2130 2749	57
58	0.3170 9547	0.2751 2347	0.2387 8982	0.2073 2603	58
59	0.3108 7791	0.2690 6940	0.2329 6568	0.2017 7716	59
60	0.3047 8227	0.2631 4856	0.2272 8359	0.1963 7679	60
61	0.2988 0614	0.2573 5801	0.2217 4009	0.1911 2097	61
62	0.2929 4720	0.2516 9487	0.2163 3179	0.1860 0581	62
63	0.2872 0314	0.2461 5635	0.2110 5541	0.1810 2755	63
64	0.2815 7170	0.2407 3971	0.2059 0771	0.1761 8253	64
65	0.2760 5069	0.2354 4226	0.2008 8557	0.1714 6718	65
66	0.2706 3793	0.2302 6138	0.1959 8593	0.1668 7804	66
67	0.2653 3130	0.2251 9450	0.1912 0578	0.1624 1172	67
68	0.2601 2873	0.2202 3912	0.1865 4223	0.1580 6493	68
69	0.2550 2817	0.2153 9278	0.1819 9241	0.1538 3448	69
70	0.2500 2761	0.2106 5309	0.1775 5358	0.1497 1726	70
71	0.2451 2511	0.2060 1769	0.1732 2300	0.1457 1023	71
72	0.2403 1874	0.2014 0429	0.1689 9803	0.1418 1044	72
73	0.2356 0661	0.1970 5065	0.1648 7615	0.1380 1503	73
74	0.2309 8687	0.1927 1458	0.1608 5478	0.1343 2119	74
75	0.2264 5771	0.1884 7391	0.1569 3149	0.1307 2622	75
76	0.2220 1737	0.1843 2657	0.1531 0389	0.1272 2747	76
77	0.2176 6408	0.1802 7048	0.1493 6965	0.1238 2235	77
78	0.2133 9616	0.1763 0365	0.1457 2649	0.1205 0837	78
79	0.2092 1192	0.1724 2411	0.1421 7218	0.1172 8309	79
80	0.2051 0973	0.1686 2993	0.1387 0457	0.1141 4412	80
81	0.2010 8797	0.1649 1925	0.1353 2153	0.1110 8917	81
82	0.1971 4507	0.1612 9022	0.1320 2101	0.1081 1598	82
83	0.1932 7948	0.1577 4105	0.1288 0098	0.1052 2237	83
84	0.1894 8968	0.1542 6997	0.1256 5949	0.1024 0620	84
85	0.1857 7420	0.1508 7528	0.1225 9463	0.0996 6540	85
86	0.1821 3157	0.1475 5528	0.1196 0452	0.0969 9795	86
87	0.1785 6036	0.1443 0835	0.1166 8733	0.0944 0190	87
88	0.1750 5918	0.1411 3286	0.1138 4130	0.0918 7533	88
89	0.1716 2665	0.1380 2724	0.1110 6468	0.0894 1638	89
90	0.1682 6142	0.1349 8997	0.1083 5579	0.0870 2324	90
91	0.1649 6217	0.1320 1953	0.1057 1296	0.0846 9415	91
92	0.1617 2762	0.1291 1445	0.1031 3460	0.0824 2740	92
93	0.1585 5649	0.1262 7331	0.1006 1912	0.0802 2131	93
94	0.1554 4754	0.1234 9468	0.0981 6500	0.0780 7427	94
95	0.1523 9955	0.1207 7719	0.0957 7073	0.0759 8469	95
96	0.1494 1132	0.1181 1950	0.0934 3486	0.0739 5104	96
97	0.1464 8169	0.1155 2029	0.0911 5596	0.0719 7181	97
98	0.1436 0950	0.1129 7828	0.0889 3264	0.0700 4556	98
99	0.1407 9363	0.1104 9221	0.0867 6355	0.0681 7086	99
100	0.1380 3297	0.1080 6084	0.0846 4737	0.0663 4634	100

TABLE II.—Present Value of 1 at Compound Interest

$$v^n = (1 + i)^{-n}$$

n	3%	3½%	4%	4½%	n
1	0.9708 7379	0.9661 8357	0.9615 3846	0.9569 3780	1
2	0.9425 9591	0.9335 1070	0.9245 5621	0.9157 2995	2
3	0.9151 4166	0.9019 4271	0.8889 9636	0.8762 9660	3
4	0.8884 8705	0.8714 4223	0.8548 0419	0.8385 6134	4
5	0.8626 0878	0.8419 7317	0.8219 2711	0.8024 5105	5
6	0.8374 8426	0.8135 0064	0.7903 1453	0.7678 9574	6
7	0.8130 9151	0.7859 9096	0.7599 1781	0.7348 2846	7
8	0.7894 0923	0.7594 1156	0.7306 9021	0.7031 8513	8
9	0.7664 1673	0.7337 3097	0.7025 8674	0.6729 0443	9
10	0.7440 9391	0.7089 1881	0.6755 6417	0.6439 2768	10
11	0.7224 2128	0.6849 4571	0.6495 8093	0.6161 9874	11
12	0.7013 7988	0.6617 8330	0.6245 9705	0.5896 6386	12
13	0.6809 5134	0.6394 0415	0.6005 7409	0.5642 7164	13
14	0.6611 1781	0.6177 8179	0.5774 7508	0.5399 7286	14
15	0.6418 6195	0.5968 9062	0.5552 6450	0.5167 2044	15
16	0.6231 6694	0.5767 0591	0.5339 0818	0.4944 6932	16
17	0.6050 1645	0.5572 0378	0.5133 7325	0.4731 7639	17
18	0.5873 9461	0.5383 6114	0.4936 2812	0.4528 0037	18
19	0.5702 8603	0.5201 5569	0.4746 4242	0.4333 0179	19
20	0.5536 7575	0.5025 6588	0.4563 8695	0.4146 4286	20
21	0.5375 4928	0.4855 7090	0.4388 3360	0.3967 8743	21
22	0.5218 9250	0.4691 5063	0.4219 5539	0.3797 0089	22
23	0.5066 9175	0.4532 8563	0.4057 2633	0.3633 5013	23
24	0.4919 3374	0.4379 5713	0.3901 2147	0.3477 0347	24
25	0.4776 0557	0.4231 4699	0.3751 1680	0.3327 3060	25
26	0.4636 9473	0.4088 3767	0.3606 8923	0.3184 0248	26
27	0.4501 8906	0.3950 1224	0.3468 1657	0.3046 9137	27
28	0.4370 7675	0.3816 5434	0.3334 7747	0.2915 7069	28
29	0.4243 4636	0.3687 4815	0.3206 5141	0.2790 1502	29
30	0.4119 8676	0.3562 7841	0.3083 1867	0.2670 0002	30
31	0.3999 8715	0.3442 3035	0.2964 6026	0.2555 0241	31
32	0.3883 3703	0.3325 8971	0.2850 5794	0.2444 9991	32
33	0.3770 2625	0.3213 4271	0.2740 9417	0.2339 7121	33
34	0.3660 4490	0.3104 7605	0.2635 5209	0.2238 9589	34
35	0.3553 8340	0.2999 7686	0.2534 1547	0.2142 5444	35
36	0.3450 3243	0.2898 3272	0.2436 6872	0.2050 2817	36
37	0.3349 8294	0.2800 3161	0.2342 9685	0.1961 9921	37
38	0.3252 2615	0.2705 6194	0.2252 8543	0.1877 5044	38
39	0.3157 5355	0.2614 1250	0.2166 2061	0.1796 6549	39
40	0.3065 5684	0.2525 7247	0.2082 8904	0.1719 2870	40
41	0.2976 2800	0.2440 3137	0.2002 7793	0.1645 2507	41
42	0.2889 5922	0.2357 7910	0.1925 7493	0.1574 4026	42
43	0.2805 4294	0.2278 0590	0.1851 6820	0.1506 6054	43
44	0.2723 7178	0.2201 0231	0.1780 4635	0.1441 7276	44
45	0.2644 3862	0.2126 5924	0.1711 9841	0.1379 6437	45
46	0.2567 3653	0.2054 6787	0.1646 1386	0.1320 2332	46
47	0.2492 5876	0.1985 1968	0.1582 8256	0.1263 3810	47
48	0.2419 9880	0.1918 0645	0.1521 9476	0.1208 9771	48
49	0.2349 5029	0.1853 2024	0.1463 4112	0.1156 9158	49
50	0.2281 0708	0.1790 5337	0.1407 1262	0.1107 0965	50

TABLE II.—Present Value of 1 at Compound Interest

$$v^n = (1+i)^{-n}$$

n	3%	3½%	4%	4½%	n
51	0.2214 6318	0.1729 9843	0.1353 0059	0.1059 4225	51
52	0.2150 1280	0.1671 4824	0.1300 9672	0.1013 8014	52
53	0.2087 5029	0.1614 9589	0.1250 9300	0.0970 1449	53
54	0.2026 7019	0.1560 3467	0.1202 8173	0.0928 3683	54
55	0.1967 6717	0.1507 5814	0.1156 5551	0.0888 3907	55
56	0.1910 3609	0.1456 6004	0.1112 0722	0.0850 1347	56
57	0.1854 7193	0.1407 3433	0.1069 3002	0.0813 5260	57
58	0.1800 6984	0.1359 7520	0.1028 1733	0.0778 4938	58
59	0.1748 2508	0.1313 7701	0.0988 6282	0.0744 9701	59
60	0.1697 3309	0.1269 3431	0.0950 6040	0.0712 8901	60
61	0.1647 8941	0.1226 4184	0.0914 0423	0.0682 1915	61
62	0.1599 8972	0.1184 9453	0.0878 8868	0.0652 8148	62
63	0.1553 2982	0.1144 8747	0.0845 0835	0.0624 7032	63
64	0.1508 0565	0.1106 1591	0.0812 5803	0.0597 8021	64
65	0.1464 1325	0.1068 7528	0.0781 3272	0.0572 0594	65
66	0.1421 4879	0.1032 6114	0.0751 2762	0.0547 4253	66
67	0.1380 0853	0.0997 6922	0.0722 3809	0.0523 8519	67
68	0.1339 8887	0.0963 9538	0.0694 5970	0.0501 2937	68
69	0.1300 8628	0.0931 3563	0.0667 8818	0.0479 7069	69
70	0.1262 9736	0.0899 8612	0.0642 1940	0.0459 0497	70
71	0.1226 1880	0.0869 4311	0.0617 4942	0.0439 2820	71
72	0.1190 4737	0.0840 0300	0.0593 7445	0.0420 3655	72
73	0.1155 7998	0.0811 6232	0.0570 9081	0.0402 2637	73
74	0.1122 1357	0.0784 1770	0.0548 9501	0.0384 9413	74
75	0.1089 4521	0.0757 6590	0.0527 8367	0.0368 3649	75
76	0.1057 7205	0.0732 0376	0.0507 5353	0.0352 5023	76
77	0.1026 9131	0.0707 2827	0.0488 0147	0.0337 3228	77
78	0.0997 0030	0.0683 3650	0.0469 2449	0.0322 7969	78
79	0.0967 9641	0.0660 2560	0.0451 1970	0.0308 8965	79
80	0.0939 7710	0.0637 9285	0.0433 8433	0.0295 5948	80
81	0.0912 3990	0.0616 3561	0.0417 1570	0.0282 8658	81
82	0.0885 8243	0.0595 5131	0.0401 1125	0.0270 6850	82
83	0.0860 0236	0.0575 3750	0.0385 6851	0.0259 0287	83
84	0.0834 9743	0.0555 9178	0.0370 8510	0.0247 8744	84
85	0.0810 6547	0.0537 1187	0.0356 5875	0.0237 2003	85
86	0.0787 0434	0.0518 9553	0.0342 8726	0.0226 9860	86
87	0.0764 1198	0.0501 4060	0.0329 6852	0.0217 2115	87
88	0.0741 8639	0.0484 4503	0.0317 0050	0.0207 8579	88
89	0.0720 2562	0.0468 0679	0.0304 8125	0.0198 9070	89
90	0.0699 2779	0.0452 2395	0.0293 0890	0.0190 3417	90
91	0.0678 9105	0.0436 9464	0.0281 8163	0.0182 1451	91
92	0.0659 1364	0.0422 1704	0.0270 9772	0.0174 3016	92
93	0.0639 9383	0.0407 8941	0.0260 5550	0.0166 7958	93
94	0.0621 2993	0.0394 1006	0.0250 5337	0.0159 6132	94
95	0.0603 2032	0.0380 7735	0.0240 8978	0.0152 7399	95
96	0.0585 6342	0.0367 8971	0.0231 6325	0.0146 1626	96
97	0.0568 5769	0.0355 4562	0.0222 7235	0.0139 8685	97
98	0.0552 0164	0.0343 4359	0.0214 1572	0.0133 8454	98
99	0.0535 9383	0.0331 8221	0.0205 9204	0.0128 0817	99
100	0.0520 3284	0.0320 6011	0.0198 0004	0.0122 5663	100

TABLE II.—Present Value of 1 at Compound Interest

$$v^n = (1+i)^{-n}$$

n	5%	5½%	6%	6½%	n
1	0.9523 8095	0.9478 6730	0.9433 9623	0.9389 6714	1
2	0.9070 2948	0.8984 5242	0.8899 9644	0.8816 5928	2
3	0.8638 3760	0.8516 1366	0.8396 1928	0.8278 4909	3
4	0.8227 0247	0.8072 1674	0.7920 9366	0.7773 2309	4
5	0.7835 2617	0.7651 3435	0.7472 5817	0.7298 8084	5
6	0.7462 1540	0.7252 4583	0.7049 6054	0.6853 3412	6
7	0.7106 8133	0.6874 3681	0.6650 5711	0.6435 0621	7
8	0.6768 3936	0.6515 9887	0.6274 1237	0.6042 3119	8
9	0.6446 0892	0.6176 2926	0.5918 9846	0.5673 5323	9
10	0.6139 1325	0.5854 3058	0.5583 9478	0.5327 2604	10
11	0.5846 7929	0.5549 1050	0.5267 8753	0.5002 1224	11
12	0.5568 3742	0.5259 8152	0.4969 6936	0.4696 8285	12
13	0.5303 2135	0.4985 6068	0.4688 3902	0.4410 1676	13
14	0.5050 6795	0.4725 6937	0.4423 0096	0.4141 0025	14
15	0.4810 1710	0.4479 3305	0.4172 6506	0.3888 2652	15
16	0.4581 1152	0.4245 8109	0.3936 4628	0.3650 9533	16
17	0.4362 9669	0.4024 4653	0.3713 6442	0.3428 1251	17
18	0.4155 2065	0.3814 6590	0.3503 4379	0.3218 8969	18
19	0.3957 3396	0.3615 7906	0.3305 1301	0.3022 4384	19
20	0.3768 8948	0.3427 2896	0.3118 0473	0.2837 9703	20
21	0.3589 4236	0.3248 6158	0.2941 5540	0.2664 7608	21
22	0.3418 4987	0.3079 2567	0.2775 0510	0.2502 1228	22
23	0.3255 7131	0.2918 7267	0.2617 9726	0.2349 4111	23
24	0.3100 6791	0.2766 5656	0.2469 7855	0.2206 0198	24
25	0.2953 0277	0.2622 3370	0.2329 9863	0.2071 3801	25
26	0.2812 4073	0.2485 6275	0.2198 1003	0.1944 9579	26
27	0.2678 4832	0.2356 0450	0.2073 6795	0.1826 2515	27
28	0.2550 9364	0.2233 2181	0.1956 3014	0.1714 7902	28
29	0.2429 4632	0.2116 7944	0.1845 5674	0.1610 1316	29
30	0.2313 7745	0.2006 4402	0.1741 1013	0.1511 8607	30
31	0.2203 5947	0.1901 8390	0.1642 5484	0.1419 5875	31
32	0.2098 6617	0.1802 6910	0.1549 5740	0.1332 9460	32
33	0.1998 7254	0.1708 7119	0.1461 8622	0.1251 5925	33
34	0.1903 5480	0.1619 6321	0.1379 1153	0.1175 2042	34
35	0.1812 9029	0.1535 1963	0.1301 0522	0.1103 4781	35
36	0.1726 5741	0.1455 1624	0.1227 4077	0.1036 1297	36
37	0.1644 3563	0.1379 3008	0.1157 9318	0.0972 8917	37
38	0.1566 0536	0.1307 3941	0.1092 3885	0.0913 5134	38
39	0.1491 4797	0.1239 2362	0.1030 5552	0.0857 7590	39
40	0.1420 4568	0.1174 6314	0.0972 2219	0.0805 4075	40
41	0.1352 8160	0.1113 3947	0.0917 1905	0.0756 2512	41
42	0.1288 3962	0.1055 3504	0.0865 2740	0.0710 0950	42
43	0.1227 0440	0.1000 3322	0.0816 2962	0.0666 7559	43
44	0.1168 6133	0.0948 1822	0.0770 0908	0.0626 0619	44
45	0.1112 9651	0.0898 7509	0.0726 5007	0.0587 8515	45
46	0.1059 9668	0.0851 8965	0.0685 3781	0.0551 9733	46
47	0.1009 4921	0.0807 4849	0.0646 5831	0.0518 2848	47
48	0.0961 4211	0.0765 3885	0.0609 9840	0.0486 6524	48
49	0.0915 6391	0.0725 4867	0.0575 4566	0.0456 9506	49
50	0.0872 0373	0.0687 6652	0.0542 8836	0.0429 0616	50

TABLE II.—Present Value of 1 at Compound Interest

$$v^n = (1+i)^{-n}$$

n	5%	5½%	6%	6½%	n
51	0.0830 5117	0.0651 8153	0.0512 1544	0.0402 8747	51
52	0.0790 9635	0.0617 8344	0.0483 1645	0.0378 2861	52
53	0.0753 2986	0.0585 6250	0.0455 8156	0.0355 1982	53
54	0.0717 4272	0.0555 0948	0.0430 0147	0.0333 5195	54
55	0.0683 2640	0.0526 1562	0.0405 6742	0.0313 1638	55
56	0.0650 7276	0.0498 7263	0.0382 7115	0.0294 0505	56
57	0.0619 7406	0.0472 7263	0.0361 0486	0.0276 1038	57
58	0.0590 2291	0.0448 0818	0.0340 6119	0.0259 2524	58
59	0.0562 1230	0.0424 7221	0.0321 3320	0.0243 4295	59
60	0.0535 3552	0.0402 5802	0.0303 1434	0.0228 5723	60
61	0.0509 8621	0.0381 5926	0.0285 9843	0.0214 6218	61
62	0.0485 5830	0.0361 6992	0.0269 7965	0.0201 5229	62
63	0.0462 4600	0.0342 8428	0.0254 5250	0.0189 2233	63
64	0.0440 4381	0.0324 9695	0.0240 1179	0.0177 6745	64
65	0.0419 4648	0.0308 0279	0.0226 5264	0.0166 8305	65
66	0.0399 4903	0.0291 9696	0.0213 7041	0.0156 6484	66
67	0.0380 4670	0.0276 7485	0.0201 6077	0.0147 0877	67
68	0.0362 3495	0.0262 3208	0.0190 1959	0.0138 1105	68
69	0.0345 0948	0.0248 6453	0.0179 4301	0.0129 6812	69
70	0.0328 6617	0.0235 6828	0.0169 2737	0.0121 7664	70
71	0.0313 0111	0.0223 3960	0.0159 6921	0.0114 3346	71
72	0.0298 1058	0.0211 7498	0.0150 6530	0.0107 3565	72
73	0.0283 9103	0.0200 7107	0.0142 1254	0.0100 8042	73
74	0.0270 3908	0.0190 2471	0.0134 0806	0.0094 6518	74
75	0.0257 5150	0.0180 3290	0.0126 4911	0.0088 8750	75
76	0.0245 2524	0.0170 9279	0.0119 3313	0.0083 4507	76
77	0.0233 5737	0.0162 0170	0.0112 5767	0.0078 3574	77
78	0.0222 4512	0.0153 5706	0.0106 2044	0.0073 5751	78
79	0.0211 8582	0.0145 5646	0.0100 1928	0.0069 0846	79
80	0.0201 7698	0.0137 9759	0.0094 5215	0.0064 8681	80
81	0.0192 1617	0.0130 7828	0.0089 1713	0.0060 9090	81
82	0.0183 0111	0.0123 9648	0.0084 1238	0.0057 1916	82
83	0.0174 2963	0.0117 5022	0.0079 3621	0.0053 7010	83
84	0.0165 9965	0.0111 3765	0.0074 8699	0.0050 4235	84
85	0.0158 0919	0.0105 5701	0.0070 6320	0.0047 3460	85
86	0.0150 5637	0.0100 0664	0.0066 6340	0.0044 4563	86
87	0.0143 3940	0.0094 8497	0.0062 8622	0.0041 7430	87
88	0.0136 5657	0.0089 9049	0.0059 3040	0.0039 1953	88
89	0.0130 0626	0.0085 2180	0.0055 9472	0.0036 8031	89
90	0.0123 8691	0.0080 7753	0.0052 7803	0.0034 5569	90
91	0.0117 9706	0.0076 5643	0.0049 7928	0.0032 4478	91
92	0.0112 3530	0.0072 5728	0.0046 9743	0.0030 4674	92
93	0.0107 0028	0.0068 7894	0.0044 3154	0.0028 6079	93
94	0.0101 9074	0.0065 2032	0.0041 8070	0.0026 8619	94
95	0.0097 0547	0.0061 8040	0.0039 4405	0.0025 2224	95
96	0.0092 4331	0.0058 5820	0.0037 2081	0.0023 6831	96
97	0.0088 0315	0.0055 5279	0.0035 1019	0.0022 2376	97
98	0.0083 8395	0.0052 6331	0.0033 1150	0.0020 8804	98
99	0.0079 8471	0.0049 8892	0.0031 2406	0.0019 6060	99
100	0.0076 0449	0.0047 2883	0.0029 4723	0.0018 4094	100

TABLE II. —Present Value of 1 at Compound Interest

$$v^n = (1 + i)^{-n}$$

n	7%	7½%	8%	8½%	n
1	0.9345 7944	0.9302 3256	0.9259 2593	0.9216 5899	1
2	0.8734 3873	0.8653 3261	0.8573 3882	0.8494 5529	2
3	0.8162 9788	0.8049 6057	0.7938 3224	0.7829 0810	3
4	0.7628 9521	0.7488 0053	0.7350 2985	0.7215 7428	4
5	0.7129 8618	0.6965 5863	0.6805 8320	0.6650 4542	5
6	0.6663 4222	0.6479 6152	0.6301 6963	0.6129 4509	6
7	0.6227 4974	0.6027 5490	0.5834 9040	0.5649 2635	7
8	0.5820 0910	0.5607 0223	0.5402 6888	0.5206 6945	8
9	0.5439 3374	0.5215 8347	0.5002 4897	0.4798 7968	9
10	0.5083 4929	0.4851 9393	0.4631 9349	0.4422 8542	10
11	0.4750 9280	0.4513 4319	0.4288 8286	0.4076 3633	11
12	0.4440 1196	0.4198 5413	0.3971 1376	0.3757 0168	12
13	0.4149 6445	0.3905 6198	0.3676 9792	0.3462 6883	13
14	0.3878 1724	0.3633 1347	0.3404 6104	0.3191 4178	14
15	0.3624 4602	0.3379 6602	0.3152 4170	0.2941 3989	15
16	0.3387 3460	0.3143 8699	0.2918 9047	0.2710 9667	16
17	0.3165 7439	0.2924 5302	0.2702 6895	0.2498 5869	17
18	0.2958 6392	0.2720 4932	0.2502 4903	0.2302 8450	18
19	0.2765 0832	0.2530 6913	0.2317 1206	0.2122 4378	19
20	0.2584 1900	0.2354 1315	0.2145 4821	0.1956 1639	20
21	0.2415 1309	0.2189 8897	0.1986 5575	0.1802 9160	21
22	0.2257 1317	0.2037 1067	0.1839 4051	0.1661 6738	22
23	0.2109 4688	0.1894 9830	0.1703 1528	0.1531 4965	23
24	0.1971 4662	0.1762 7749	0.1576 9934	0.1411 5176	24
25	0.1842 4918	0.1639 7906	0.1460 1790	0.1300 9378	25
26	0.1721 9549	0.1525 3866	0.1352 0176	0.1199 0210	26
27	0.1609 3037	0.1418 9643	0.1251 8682	0.1105 0885	27
28	0.1504 0221	0.1319 9668	0.1159 1372	0.1018 5148	28
29	0.1405 6282	0.1227 8761	0.1073 2752	0.0938 7233	29
30	0.1313 6712	0.1142 2103	0.0993 7733	0.0865 1828	30
31	0.1227 7301	0.1062 5212	0.0920 1605	0.0797 4035	31
32	0.1147 4113	0.0988 3918	0.0852 0005	0.0734 9341	32
33	0.1072 3470	0.0919 4343	0.0788 8893	0.0677 3586	33
34	0.1002 1934	0.0855 2877	0.0730 4531	0.0624 2936	34
35	0.0936 6294	0.0795 6164	0.0676 3454	0.0575 3858	35
36	0.0875 3546	0.0740 1083	0.0626 2458	0.0530 3095	36
37	0.0818 0884	0.0688 4729	0.0579 8572	0.0488 7645	37
38	0.0764 5686	0.0640 4399	0.0536 9048	0.0450 4742	38
39	0.0714 5501	0.0595 7580	0.0497 1341	0.0415 1836	39
40	0.0667 8038	0.0554 1935	0.0460 3093	0.0382 6577	40
41	0.0624 1157	0.0515 5288	0.0426 2123	0.0352 6799	41
42	0.0583 2857	0.0479 5617	0.0394 6411	0.0325 0506	42
43	0.0545 1268	0.0446 1039	0.0365 4084	0.0299 5858	43
44	0.0509 4643	0.0414 9804	0.0338 3411	0.0276 1160	44
45	0.0476 1349	0.0386 0283	0.0313 2788	0.0254 4848	45
46	0.0444 9859	0.0359 0961	0.0290 0730	0.0234 5482	46
47	0.0415 8747	0.0334 0428	0.0268 5861	0.0216 1734	47
48	0.0388 6679	0.0310 7375	0.0248 6908	0.0199 2382	48
49	0.0363 2410	0.0289 0582	0.0230 2693	0.0183 6297	49
50	0.0339 4776	0.0268 8913	0.0213 2123	0.0169 2439	50

TABLE II.—Present Value of 1 at Compound Interest

$$v^n = (1+i)^{-n}$$

n	7%	7½%	8%	8½%	n
51	0.0317 2688	0.0250 1315	0.0197 4188	0.0155 9852	51
52	0.0296 5129	0.0232 6804	0.0182 7952	0.0143 7651	52
53	0.0277 1140	0.0210 4409	0.0169 2540	0.0132 5024	53
54	0.0258 9858	0.0201 3460	0.0156 7174	0.0122 1221	54
55	0.0242 0428	0.0187 2986	0.0145 1087	0.0112 5549	55
56	0.0226 2083	0.0174 2312	0.0134 3599	0.0103 7372	56
57	0.0211 4096	0.0162 0756	0.0124 4073	0.0095 6104	57
58	0.0197 5791	0.0150 7680	0.0115 1920	0.0088 1201	58
59	0.0184 6533	0.0140 2493	0.0106 6592	0.0081 2167	59
60	0.0172 5732	0.0130 4644	0.0098 7585	0.0074 8541	60
61	0.0161 2834	0.0121 3623	0.0091 4431	0.0068 9900	61
62	0.0150 7321	0.0112 8951	0.0084 6695	0.0063 5852	62
63	0.0140 8711	0.0105 0187	0.0078 3977	0.0058 6039	63
64	0.0131 6553	0.0097 6918	0.0072 5905	0.0054 0128	64
65	0.0123 0423	0.0090 8761	0.0067 2134	0.0049 7814	65
66	0.0114 9928	0.0084 5359	0.0062 2346	0.0045 8815	66
67	0.0107 4699	0.0078 6381	0.0057 6247	0.0042 2871	67
68	0.0100 4392	0.0073 1517	0.0053 3562	0.0038 9743	68
69	0.0093 8684	0.0068 0481	0.0049 4039	0.0035 9210	69
70	0.0087 7275	0.0063 3006	0.0045 7443	0.0033 1069	70
71	0.0081 9883	0.0058 8842	0.0042 3558	0.0030 5133	71
72	0.0076 6246	0.0054 7760	0.0039 2184	0.0028 1228	72
73	0.0071 6117	0.0050 9544	0.0036 3133	0.0025 9196	73
74	0.0066 9269	0.0047 3995	0.0033 6234	0.0023 8891	74
75	0.0062 5485	0.0044 0925	0.0031 1328	0.0022 0176	75
76	0.0058 4565	0.0041 0163	0.0028 8267	0.0020 2927	76
77	0.0054 6323	0.0038 1547	0.0026 6914	0.0018 7030	77
78	0.0051 0582	0.0035 4928	0.0024 7142	0.0017 2377	78
79	0.0047 7179	0.0033 0165	0.0022 8835	0.0015 8873	79
80	0.0044 5962	0.0030 7130	0.0021 1885	0.0014 6427	80
81	0.0041 6787	0.0028 5703	0.0019 6190	0.0013 4956	81
82	0.0038 9520	0.0026 5770	0.0018 1657	0.0012 4383	82
83	0.0036 4038	0.0024 7228	0.0016 8201	0.0011 4639	83
84	0.0034 0222	0.0022 9979	0.0015 5742	0.0010 5658	84
85	0.0031 7965	0.0021 3934	0.0014 4205	0.0009 7381	85
86	0.0029 7163	0.0019 9009	0.0013 3523	0.0008 9752	86
87	0.0027 7723	0.0018 5124	0.0012 3633	0.0008 2720	87
88	0.0025 9554	0.0017 2209	0.0011 4475	0.0007 6240	88
89	0.0024 2574	0.0016 0194	0.0010 5995	0.0007 0267	89
90	0.0022 6704	0.0014 9018	0.0009 8144	0.0006 4762	90
91	0.0021 1873	0.0013 8621	0.0009 0874	0.0005 9689	91
92	0.0019 8012	0.0012 8950	0.0008 4142	0.0005 5013	92
93	0.0018 5058	0.0011 9953	0.0007 7910	0.0005 0703	93
94	0.0017 2952	0.0011 1585	0.0007 2138	0.0004 6731	94
95	0.0016 1637	0.0010 3800	0.0006 6795	0.0004 3070	95
96	0.0015 1063	0.0009 6558	0.0006 1847	0.0003 9696	96
97	0.0014 1180	0.0008 9821	0.0005 7266	0.0003 6586	97
98	0.0013 1944	0.0008 3555	0.0005 3024	0.0003 3720	98
99	0.0012 3312	0.0007 7725	0.0004 9096	0.0003 1078	99
100	0.0011 5245	0.0007 2303	0.0004 5459	0.0002 8644	100

TABLE III.—Amount of Annuity of 1 per Period

$$s_{\overline{n}|i} = \frac{(1+i)^n - 1}{i}$$

n	$\frac{1}{4}\%$	$\frac{7}{24}\%$	$\frac{1}{3}\%$	$\frac{5}{12}\%$	n
1	1.0000 0000	1.0000 0000	1.0000 0000	1.0000 0000	1
2	2.0025 0000	2.0029 1667	2.0033 3333	2.0041 6667	2
3	3.0075 0625	3.0087 5851	3.0100 1111	3.0125 1736	3
4	4.0150 2502	4.0175 3405	4.0200 4448	4.0250 6952	4
5	5.0250 6258	5.0292 5186	5.0334 4463	5.0418 4064	5
6	6.0376 2523	6.0439 2051	6.0502 2278	6.0628 4831	6
7	7.0527 1930	7.0615 4861	7.0703 9019	7.0881 1018	7
8	8.0703 5110	8.0821 4480	8.0939 5816	8.1176 4397	8
9	9.0905 2697	9.1057 1772	9.1209 3802	9.1514 6749	9
10	10.1132 5329	10.1322 7606	10.1513 4114	10.1895 9860	10
11	11.1385 3642	11.1618 2853	11.1851 7895	11.2320 5526	11
12	12.1663 8277	12.1943 8387	12.2224 6288	12.2788 5549	12
13	13.1967 9872	13.2299 5082	13.2632 0442	13.3300 1739	13
14	14.2297 9072	14.2685 3818	14.3074 1510	14.3855 5913	14
15	15.2653 6520	15.3101 5475	15.3551 0648	15.4454 9896	15
16	16.3035 2861	16.3548 0936	16.4062 9017	16.5098 5520	16
17	17.3442 8743	17.4025 1089	17.4609 7781	17.5786 4627	17
18	18.3876 4815	18.4532 6822	18.5191 8107	18.6518 9063	18
19	19.4336 1727	19.5070 9025	19.5809 1167	19.7296 0684	19
20	20.4822 0131	20.5639 8593	20.6461 8137	20.8118 1353	20
21	21.5334 0682	21.6239 6422	21.7150 0198	21.8985 2942	21
22	22.5872 4033	22.6870 3412	22.7873 8532	22.9897 7330	22
23	23.6437 0843	23.7532 0463	23.8633 4327	24.0855 6402	23
24	24.7028 1770	24.8224 8481	24.9428 8775	25.1859 2054	24
25	25.7645 7475	25.8948 8373	26.0260 3071	26.2908 6187	25
26	26.8289 8619	26.9704 1047	27.1127 8414	27.4004 0713	26
27	27.8960 5865	28.0490 7417	28.2031 6009	28.5145 7549	27
28	28.9657 9880	29.1308 8397	29.2971 7062	29.6333 8622	28
29	30.0382 1330	30.2158 4904	30.3948 2786	30.7568 5867	29
30	31.1133 0883	31.3039 7860	31.4961 4395	31.8850 1224	30
31	32.1910 9210	32.3952 8188	32.6011 3110	33.0178 6646	31
32	33.2715 6983	33.4897 6811	33.7098 0154	34.1554 4090	32
33	34.3547 4876	34.5874 4660	34.8221 6754	35.2977 5524	33
34	35.4406 3563	35.6883 2666	35.9382 4143	36.4448 2922	34
35	36.5292 3722	36.7924 1761	37.0580 3557	37.5966 8268	35
36	37.6205 6031	37.8997 2883	38.1815 6236	38.7533 3552	36
37	38.7146 1171	39.0102 6970	39.3088 3423	39.9148 0775	37
38	39.8113 9824	40.1240 4966	40.4398 6368	41.0811 1945	38
39	40.9109 2673	41.2410 7813	41.5746 6322	42.2522 9078	39
40	42.0132 0405	42.3613 6461	42.7132 4543	43.4283 4199	40
41	43.1182 3706	43.4849 1859	43.8556 2292	44.6092 9342	41
42	44.2260 3265	44.6117 4961	45.0018 0833	45.7951 6548	42
43	45.3365 9774	45.7418 6721	46.1518 1436	46.9859 7866	43
44	46.4499 3923	46,8752 8099	47.3056 5374	48.1817 5358	44
45	47.5660 6408	48.0120 0056	48.4633 3925	49.3825 1088	45
46	48.6849 7924	49.1520 3556	49.6248 8371	50.5882 7134	46
47	49.8066 9169	50.2953 9566	50.7902 9999	51.7990 5581	47
48	50.9312 0842	51.4420 9057	51.9596 0099	53.0148 8521	48
49	52.0585 3644	52.5921 3000	53.1327 9966	54.2357 8056	49
50	53.1886 8278	53.7455 2371	54.3099 0899	55.4617 6298	50

TABLE III.—Amount of Annuity of 1 per Period

$$s_{\overline{n}|i} = \frac{(1+i)^n - 1}{i}$$

n	$\frac{1}{4}\%$	$\frac{7}{24}\%$	$\frac{1}{3}\%$	$\frac{5}{12}\%$	n
51	54.3216 5449	54.9022 8149	55.4909 4202	56.6928 5366	51
52	55.4574 5862	56.0624 1314	56.6759 1183	57.9290 7388	52
53	56.5961 0227	57.2259 2851	57.8648 3154	59.1704 4503	53
54	57.7375 9252	58.3928 3747	59.0577 1431	60.4169 8855	54
55	58.8819 3650	59.5631 4991	60.2545 7336	61.6687 2600	55
56	60.0291 4135	60.7368 7577	61.4554 2194	62.9256 7902	56
57	61.1792 1420	61.9140 2499	62.6602 7334	64.1878 6935	57
58	62.3321 6223	63.0946 0756	63.8691 4092	65.4553 1881	58
59	63.4879 9264	64.2786 3350	65.0820 3806	66.7280 4930	59
60	64.6467 1262	65.4661 1285	66.2989 7818	68.0060 8284	60
61	65.8083 2940	66.6570 5568	67.5199 7478	69.2894 4152	61
62	66.9728 5023	67.8514 7209	68.7450 4136	70.5781 4753	62
63	68.1402 8235	69.0493 7222	69.9741 9150	71.8722 2314	63
64	69.3106 3306	70.2507 6622	71.2074 3880	73.1716 9074	64
65	70.4839 0964	71.4556 6429	72.4447 9693	74.4765 7278	65
66	71.6601 1942	72.6640 7664	73.6862 7959	75.7868 9184	66
67	72.8392 6971	73.8760 1353	74.9319 0052	77.1026 7055	67
68	74.0213 6789	75.0914 8524	76.1816 7352	78.4239 3168	68
69	75.2064 2131	76.3105 0207	77.4356 1243	79.7506 9806	69
70	76.3944 3736	77.5330 7437	78.6937 3114	81.0829 9264	70
71	77.5854 2345	78.7592 1250	79.9560 4358	82.4208 3844	71
72	78.7793 8701	79.9889 2687	81.2225 6372	83.7642 5860	72
73	79.9763 3548	81.2222 2791	82.4933 0560	85.1132 7634	73
74	81.1762 7632	82.4591 2607	83.7682 8329	86.4679 1500	74
75	82.3792 1701	83.6996 3186	85.0475 1090	87.8281 9797	75
76	83.5851 6505	84.9437 5578	86.3310 0260	89.1941 4880	76
77	84.7941 2797	86.1915 0840	87.6187 7261	90.5657 9109	77
78	86.0061 1329	87.4429 0030	88.9108 3519	91.9431 4855	78
79	87.2211 2857	88.6979 4209	90.2072 0464	93.3262 4500	79
80	88.4391 8139	89.9566 4443	91.5078 9532	94.7151 0436	80
81	89.6602 7934	91.2190 1797	92.8129 2164	96.1097 5062	81
82	90.8844 3004	92.4850 7344	94.1222 9804	97.5102 0792	82
83	92.1116 4112	93.7548 2157	95.4360 3904	98.9165 0045	83
84	93.3419 2022	95.0282 7313	96.7541 5917	100.3286 5254	84
85	94.5752 7502	96.3054 3893	98.0766 7303	101.7466 8859	85
86	95.8117 1321	97.5863 2980	99.4035 9527	103.1706 3312	86
87	97.0512 4249	98.8709 5659	100.7349 4059	104.6005 1076	87
88	98.2938 7060	100.1593 3021	102.0707 2373	106.0363 4622	88
89	99.5396 0527	101.4514 6159	103.4109 5947	107.4781 6433	89
90	100.7884 5429	102.7473 6169	104.7556 6267	108.9259 9002	90
91	102.0404 2542	104.0470 4149	106.1048 4821	110.3798 4831	91
92	103.2955 2649	105.3505 1203	107.4585 3104	111.8397 6434	92
93	104.5537 6530	106.6577 8436	108.8167 2614	113.3057 6336	93
94	105.8151 4972	107.9688 6956	110.1794 4856	114.7778 7071	94
95	107.0796 8759	109.2837 7877	111.5467 1339	116.2561 1184	95
96	108.3473 8681	110.6025 2312	112.9185 3577	117.7405 1230	96
97	109.6182 5528	111.9251 1381	114.2949 3089	119.2310 9777	97
98	110.8923 0091	113.2515 6206	115.6759 1399	120.7278 9401	98
99	112.1695 3167	114.5818 7912	117.0615 0037	122.2309 2690	99
100	113.4499 5550	115.9160 7626	118.4517 0537	123.7402 2243	100

TABLE III.—Amount of Annuity of 1 per Period

$$s_{\overline{n}|i} = \frac{(1+i)^n - 1}{i}$$

n	¼%	7/24%	⅓%	5/12%	n
101	114.7335 8038	117.2541 6482	119.8465 4439	125.2558 0669	101
102	116.0204 1434	118.5961 5613	121.2460 3287	126.7777 0589	102
103	117.3104 6537	119.9420 6159	122.6501 8632	128.3059 4633	103
104	118.6037 4153	121.2918 9260	124.0590 2027	129.8405 5444	104
105	119.9002 5089	122.6456 6062	125.4725 5034	131.3815 5675	105
106	121.2000 0152	124.0033 7713	126.8907 9217	132.9289 7990	106
107	122.5030 0152	125.3650 5365	128.3137 6148	134.4828 5065	107
108	123.8092 5902	126.7307 0172	129.7414 7402	136.0431 9586	108
109	125.1187 8217	128.1003 3294	131.1739 4560	137.6100 4251	109
110	126.4315 7913	129.4739 5891	132.6111 9208	139.1834 1769	110
111	127.7476 5807	130.8515 9129	134.0532 2939	140.7633 4860	111
112	129.0670 2722	132.2332 4176	135.5000 7349	142.3498 6255	112
113	130.3896 9479	133.6189 2205	136.9517 4040	143.9429 8698	113
114	131.7156 6902	135.0086 4391	138.4082 4620	145.5427 4942	114
115	133.0449 5820	136.4024 1912	139.8696 0702	147.1491 7754	115
116	134.3775 7059	137.8002 5951	141.3358 3905	148.7622 9912	116
117	135.7135 1452	139.2021 7693	142.8069 5851	150.3821 4203	117
118	137.0527 9830	140.6081 8328	144.2829 8170	152.0087 3429	118
119	138.3954 3030	142.0182 9048	145.7639 2498	153.6421 0401	119
120	139.7414 1888	143.4325 1049	147.2498 0477	155.2822 7945	120
121	141.0907 7242	144.8508 5532	148.7406 3745	156.9292 8895	121
122	142.4434 9935	146.2733 3698	150.2364 3958	158.5831 6098	122
123	143.7996 0810	147.6999 6754	151.7372 2771	160.2439 2415	123
124	145.1591 0712	149.1307 5912	153.2430 1847	161.9116 0717	124
125	146.5220 0489	150.5657 2383	154.7538 2853	163.5862 3887	125
126	147.8883 0990	152.0048 7386	156.2696 7463	165.2678 4819	126
127	149.2580 3068	153.4482 2141	157.7905 7354	166.9564 6423	127
128	150.6311 7575	154.8957 7872	159.3165 4212	168.6521 1616	128
129	152.0077 5369	156.3475 5807	160.8475 9726	170.3548 3331	129
130	153.3877 7308	157.8035 7178	162.3837 5592	172.0646 4512	130
131	154.7712 4251	159.2638 3220	163.9250 3510	173.7815 8114	131
132	156.1581 7062	160.7283 5171	165.4714 5189	175.5056 7106	132
133	157.5485 6604	162.1971 4274	167.0230 2339	177.2369 4469	133
134	158.9424 3746	163.6702 1774	168.5797 6680	178.9754 3196	134
135	160.3397 9355	165.1475 8920	170.1416 9936	180.7211 6293	135
136	161.7406 4304	166.6292 6967	171.7088 3836	182.4741 6777	136
137	163.1449 9464	168.1152 7171	173.2812 0115	184.2344 7681	137
138	164.5528 5713	169.6056 0792	174.8588 0516	186.0021 2046	138
139	165.9642 3927	171.1002 9094	176.4416 6784	187.7771 2929	139
140	167.3791 4987	172.5993 3346	178.0298 0673	189.5595 3400	140
141	168.7975 9775	174.1027 4818	179.6232 3942	191.3493 6539	141
142	170.2195 9174	175.6105 4786	181.2219 8355	193.1466 5441	142
143	171.6451 4072	177.1227 4529	182.8260 5683	194.9514 3214	143
144	173.0742 5357	178.6393 5330	184.4354 7702	196.7637 2977	144
145	174.5069 3921	180.1603 8475	186.0502 6194	198.5835 7865	145
146	175.9432 0655	181.6858 5254	187.6704 2948	200.4110 1023	146
147	177.3830 6457	183.2157 6961	189.2959 9758	202.2460 5610	147
148	178.8265 2223	184.7501 4893	190.9269 8424	204.0887 4800	148
149	180.2735 8854	186.2890 0353	192.5634 0752	205.9391 1779	149
150	181.7242 7251	187.8323 4646	194.2052 8554	207.7971 9744	150

TABLE III. —Amount of Annuity of 1 per Period

$$s_{\overline{n}|i} = \frac{(1+i)^n - 1}{i}$$

n	$\frac{1}{4}\%$	$\frac{7}{24}\%$	$\frac{1}{3}\%$	$\frac{5}{12}\%$	n
151	183.1785 8319	189.3801 9080	195.8526 3650	209.6630 1910	151
152	184.6365 2965	190.9325 4969	197.5054 7862	211.5366 1501	152
153	186.0981 2097	192.4894 3630	199.1638 3021	213.4180 1758	153
154	187.5633 6627	194.0508 6382	200.8277 0965	215.3072 5932	154
155	189.0322 7469	195.6168 4551	202.4971 3534	217.2043 7290	155
156	190.5048 5538	197.1873 9464	204.1721 2580	219.1093 9112	156
157	191.9811 1752	198.7625 2454	205.8526 9955	221.0223 4691	157
158	193.4610 7031	200.3422 4857	207.5388 7521	222.9432 7336	158
159	194.9447 2298	201.9265 8013	209.2306 7146	224.8722 0366	159
160	196.4320 8479	203.5155 3265	210.9281 0704	226.8091 7118	160
161	197.9231 6500	205.1091 1962	212.6312 0073	228.7542 0939	161
162	199.4179 7292	206.7073 5455	214.3399 7139	230.7073 5193	162
163	200.9165 1785	208.3102 5101	216.0544 3797	232.6686 3256	163
164	202.4188 0914	209.9178 2257	217.7746 1942	234.6380 8520	164
165	203.9248 5617	211.5300 8289	219.5005 3482	236.6157 4389	165
166	205.4346 6831	213.1470 4563	221.2322 0327	238.6016 4282	166
167	206.9482 5498	214.7687 2451	222.9696 4395	240.5958 1633	167
168	208.4656 2562	216.3951 3329	224.7128 7610	242.5982 9890	168
169	209.9867 8968	218.0262 8576	226.4619 1902	244.6091 2515	169
170	211.5117 5665	219.6621 9576	228.2167 9208	246.6283 2983	170
171	213.0405 3605	221.3028 7717	229.9775 1472	248.6559 4788	171
172	214.5731 3739	222.9483 4389	231.7441 0643	250.6920 1433	172
173	216.1095 7023	224.5986 0989	233.5165 8679	252.7365 6439	173
174	217.6498 4415	226.2536 8917	235.2949 7541	254.7896 3340	174
175	219.1939 6876	227.9135 9577	237.0792 9200	256.8512 5688	175
176	220.7419 5369	229.5783 4375	238.8695 5630	258.9214 7045	176
177	222.2938 0857	231.2479 4726	240.6657 8816	261.0003 0991	177
178	223.8495 4309	232.9224 2044	242.4680 0745	263.0878 1120	178
179	225.4091 6695	234.6017 7750	244.2762 3414	265.1840 1041	179
180	226.9726 8987	236.2860 3268	246.0904 8826	267.2889 4379	180
181	228.5401 2159	237.9752 0028	247.9107 8988	269.4026 4772	181
182	230.1114 7190	239.6692 9461	249.7371 5918	271.5251 5875	182
183	231.6867 5058	241.3683 3005	251.5696 1638	273.6565 1358	183
184	233.2659 6745	243.0723 2101	253.4081 8177	275.7967 4905	184
185	234.8491 3237	244.7812 8195	255.2528 7571	277.9459 0218	185
186	236.4362 5520	246.4952 2736	257.1037 1863	280.1040 1010	186
187	238.0273 4584	248.2141 7177	258.9607 3102	282.2711 1014	187
188	239.6224 1420	249.9381 2977	260.8239 3346	284.4472 3977	188
189	241.2214 7024	251.6671 1598	262.6933 4657	286.6324 3660	189
190	242.8245 2392	253.4011 4507	264.5689 9106	288.8267 3842	190
191	244.4315 8523	255.1402 3174	266.4508 8769	291.0301 8316	191
192	246.0426 6419	256.8843 9075	268.3390 5732	293.2428 0892	192
193	247.6577 7085	258.6336 3689	270.2335 2084	295.4646 5396	193
194	249.2769 1528	260.3879 8500	272.1342 9925	297.6957 5669	194
195	250.9001 0756	262.1474 4995	274.0414 1358	299.9361 5568	195
196	252.5273 5783	263.9120 4668	275.9548 8495	302.1858 8966	196
197	254.1586 7623	265.6817 9015	277.8747 3457	304.4449 9753	197
198	255.7940 7292	267.4566 9537	279.8009 8369	306.7135 1835	198
199	257.4335 5810	269.2367 7740	281.7336 5363	308.9914 9135	199
200	259.0771 4200	271.0220 5134	283.6727 6581	311.2789 5589	200

TABLE III.—Amount of Annuity of 1 per Period

$$s_{\overline{n}|i} = \frac{(1+i)^n - 1}{i}$$

n	½%	7/12%	⅝%	⅔%	n
1	1.0000 0000	1.0000 0000	1.0000 0000	1.0000 0000	1
2	2.0050 0000	2.0058 3333	2.0062 5000	2.0066 6667	2
3	3.0150 2500	3.0175 3403	3.1087 8906	3.0200 4444	3
4	4.0301 0013	4.0351 3631	4.0376 5649	4.0401 7807	4
5	5.0502 5063	5.0586 7460	5.0628 9185	5.0671 1259	5
6	6.0755 0188	6.0881 8354	6.0945 3492	6.1008 9335	6
7	7.1058 7939	7.1236 9794	7.1326 2576	7.1415 6597	7
8	8.1414 0879	8.1652 5284	8.1772 0468	8.1891 7641	8
9	9.1821 1583	9.2128 8349	9.2283 1220	9.2437 7092	9
10	10.2280 2641	10.2666 2531	10.2859 8916	10.3053 9606	10
11	11.2791 6654	11.3265 1396	11.3502 7659	11.3740 9870	11
12	12.3355 6237	12.3925 8529	12.4212 1582	12.4499 2602	12
13	13.3972 4018	13.4648 7537	13.4988 4842	13.5329 2553	13
14	14.4642 2639	14.5434 2048	14.5832 1622	14.6231 4503	14
15	15.5365 4752	15.6282 5710	15.6743 6132	15.7206 3266	15
16	16.6142 3026	16.7194 2193	16.7723 2608	16.8254 3688	16
17	17.6973 0141	17.8169 5189	17.8771 5312	17.9376 0646	17
18	18.7857 8791	18.9208 8411	18.9888 8532	19.0571 9051	18
19	19.8797 1685	20.0312 5593	20.1075 6586	20.1842 3844	19
20	20.9791 1544	21.1481 0493	21.2332 3814	21.3188 0003	20
21	22.0840 1101	22.2714 6887	22.3659 4588	22.4609 2536	21
22	23.1944 3107	23.4013 8577	23.5057 3304	23.6106 6487	22
23	24.3104 0322	24.5378 9386	24.6526 4387	24.7680 6930	23
24	25.4319 5524	25.6810 3157	25.8067 2290	25.9331 8976	24
25	26.5591 1502	26.8308 3759	26.9680 1492	27.1060 7769	25
26	27.6919 1059	27.9873 5081	28.1365 6501	28.2867 8488	26
27	28.8303 7015	29.1506 1035	29.3124 1854	29.4753 6344	27
28	29.9745 2200	30.3206 5558	30.4956 2116	30.6718 6586	28
29	31.1243 9461	31.4975 2607	31.6862 1879	31.8763 4497	29
30	32.2800 1658	32.6812 6164	32.8842 5766	33.0888 5394	30
31	33.4414 1666	33.8719 0233	34.0897 8427	34.3094 4630	31
32	34.6086 2375	35.0694 8843	35.3028 4542	35.5381 7594	32
33	35.7816 6686	36.2740 6045	36.5234 8820	36.7750 9711	33
34	36.9605 7520	37.4856 5913	37.7517 6000	38.0202 6443	34
35	38.1453 7807	38.7043 2548	38.9877 0850	39.2737 3286	35
36	39.3361 0496	39.9301 0071	40.2313 8168	40.5355 5774	36
37	40.5327 8549	41.1630 2630	41.4828 2782	41.8057 9479	37
38	41.7354 4942	42.4031 4395	42.7420 9549	43.0845 0009	38
39	42.9441 2666	43.6504 9562	44.0092 3359	44.3717 3009	39
40	44.1588 4730	44.9051 2352	45,2842 9130	45.6675 4163	40
41	45.3796 4153	46.1670 7007	46.5673 1812	46.9719 9191	41
42	46.6065 3974	47.4363 7798	47.8583 6386	48.2851 3852	42
43	47.8395 7244	48.7130 9018	49.1574 7863	49.6070 3944	43
44	49.0787 7030	49.9972 4988	50.4647 1287	50.9377 5304	44
45	50.3241 6415	51.2889 0050	51.7801 1733	52.2773 3806	45
46	51.5757 8497	52.5880 6575	53.1037 4306	53.6258 5365	46
47	52.8336 6390	53.8948 4959	54.4356 4146	54.9833 5934	47
48	54.0978 3222	55.2092 3621	55.7758 6421	56.3499 1507	48
49	55.3683 2138	56.5312 9009	57.1244 6337	57.7255 8117	49
50	56.6451 6299	57.8610 5595	58.4814 9126	59.1104 1837	50

TABLE III.—Amount of Annuity of 1 per Period

$$s_{\overline{n}|i} = \frac{(1+i)^n - 1}{i}$$

n	½%	7/12%	⅝%	⅔%	n
51	57.9283 8880	59.1985 7877	59.8470 0058	60.5044 8783	51
52	59.2180 3075	60.5439 0381	61.2210 4434	61.9078 5108	52
53	60.5141 2090	61.8970 7659	62.6036 7586	63.3205 7009	53
54	61.8166 9150	63.2581 4287	63.9949 4884	64.7427 0722	54
55	63.1257 7496	64.6271 4870	65.3949 1727	66.1743 2527	55
56	64.4414 0384	66.0041 4040	66.8036 3550	67.6154 8744	56
57	65.7636 1086	67.3891 6455	68.2211 5822	69.0662 5736	57
58	67.0924 2891	68.7822 6801	69.6475 4046	70.5266 9907	58
59	68.4278 9105	70.1834 9791	71.0828 3759	71.9968 7706	59
60	69.7700 3051	71.5929 0165	72.5271 0532	73.4768 5625	60
61	71.1188 8066	73.0105 2691	73.9803 9973	74.9667 0195	61
62	72.4744 7507	74.4364 2165	75.4427 7723	76.4664 7997	62
63	73.8368 4744	75.8706 3411	76.9142 9459	77.9762 5650	63
64	75.2060 3168	77.3132 1281	78.3950 0893	79.4960 9821	64
65	76.5820 6184	78.7642 0655	79.8849 7774	81.0260 7220	65
66	77.9649 7215	80.2236 6442	81.3842 5885	82.5662 4601	66
67	79.3547 9701	81.6916 3579	82.8929 1046	84.1166 8765	67
68	80.7515 7099	83.1681 7034	84.4109 9115	85.6774 6557	68
69	82.1553 2885	84.6533 1800	85.9385 5985	87.2486 4867	69
70	83.5661 0549	86.1471 2902	87.4756 7585	88.8303 0633	70
71	84.9839 3602	87.6496 5394	89.0223 9882	90.4225 0837	71
72	86.4088 5570	89.1609 4359	90.5787 8882	92.0253 2510	72
73	87.8408 9998	90.6810 4909	92.1449 0625	93.6388 2726	73
74	89.2801 0448	92.2100 2188	93.7208 1191	95.2630 8611	74
75	90.7265 0500	93.7479 1367	95.3065 6698	96.8981 7335	75
76	92.1801 3752	95.2947 7650	96.9022 3303	98.5441 6118	76
77	93.6410 3821	96.8506 6270	98.5078 7198	100.2011 2225	77
78	95.1092 4340	98.4156 2490	100.1235 4618	101.8691 2973	78
79	96.5847 8962	99.9897 1604	101.7493 1835	103.5482 5726	79
80	98.0677 1357	101.5729 8938	103.3852 5159	105.2385 7898	80
81	99.5580 5214	103.1654 9849	105.0314 0941	106.9401 6950	81
82	101.0558 4240	104.7672 9723	106.6878 5572	108.6531 0397	82
83	102.5611 2161	106.3784 3980	108.3546 5482	110.3774 5799	83
84	104.0739 2722	107.9989 8070	110.0318 7141	112.1133 0771	84
85	105.5942 9685	109.6289 7475	111.7195 7061	113.8607 2977	85
86	107.1222 6834	111.2684 7710	113.4178 1792	115.6198 0130	86
87	108.6578 7968	112.9175 4322	115.1266 7928	117.3905 9997	87
88	110.2011 6908	114.5762 2889	116.8462 2103	119.1732 0397	88
89	111.7521 7492	116.2445 9022	118.5765 0991	120.9676 9200	89
90	113.3109 3580	117.9226 8367	120.3176 1310	122.7741 4328	90
91	114.8774 9048	119.6105 6599	122.0695 9818	124.5926 3757	91
92	116.4518 7793	121.3082 9429	123.8325 3317	126.4232 5515	92
93	118.0341 3732	123.0159 2601	125.6064 8650	128.2660 7685	93
94	119.6243 0800	124.7335 1891	127.3915 2704	130.1211 8403	94
95	121.2224 2954	126.4611 3110	129.1877 2408	131.9886 5859	95
96	122.8285 4169	128.1988 2103	130.9951 4736	133.8685 8298	96
97	124.4426 8440	129.9466 4749	132.8138 6703	135.7610 4020	97
98	126.0648 9782	131.7046 6960	134.6439 5370	137.6661 1380	98
99	127.6952 2231	133.4729 4684	136.4854 7841	139.5838 8790	99
100	129.3336 9842	135.2515 3903	138.3385 1265	141.5144 4715	100

TABLE III. —Amount of Annuity of 1 per Period

$$s_{\overline{n}|i} = \frac{(1+i)^n - 1}{i}$$

n	½%	7/12%	⅝%	⅔%	n
101	130.9803 6692	137.0405 0634	140.2031 2836	143.4578 7680	101
102	132.6352 6875	138.8399 0929	142.0793 9791	145.4142 6264	102
103	134.2984 4509	140.6498 0876	143.9673 9414	147.3836 9106	103
104	135.9699 3732	142.4702 6598	145.8671 9036	149.3662 4900	104
105	137.6497 8701	144.3013 4253	147.7788 6030	151.3620 2399	105
106	139.3380 3594	146.1431 0036	149.7024 7817	153.3711 0415	106
107	141.0347 2612	147.9956 0178	151.6381 1866	155.3935 7818	107
108	142.7398 9975	149.8589 0946	153.5858 5690	157.4295 3537	108
109	144.4535 9925	151.7330 8643	155.5457 6851	159.4790 6560	109
110	146.1758 6725	153.6181 9610	157.5179 2956	161.5422 5937	110
111	147.9067 4658	155.5143 0225	159.5024 1662	163.6192 0777	111
112	149.6462 8032	157.4214 6901	161.4993 0673	165.7100 0249	112
113	151.3945 1172	159.3397 6091	163.5086 7739	167.8147 3584	113
114	153.1514 8428	161.2692 4285	165.5306 0663	169.9335 0074	114
115	154.9172 4170	163.2099 8010	167.5651 7292	172.0663 9075	115
116	156.6918 2791	165.1620 3832	169.6124 5525	174.2135 0002	116
117	158.4752 8704	167.1254 8354	171.6725 3310	176.3749 2335	117
118	160.2676 6348	169.1003 8219	173.7454 8643	178.5507 5618	118
119	162.0690 0180	171.0868 0109	175.8313 9572	180.7410 9455	119
120	163.8793 4681	173.0848 0743	177.9303 4194	182.9460 3518	120
121	165.6987 4354	175.0944 6881	180.0424 0658	185.1656 7542	121
122	167.5272 3726	177.1158 5321	182.1676 7162	187.4001 1325	122
123	169.3648 7344	179.1490 2902	184.3062 1957	189.6494 4734	123
124	171.2116 9781	181.1940 6502	186.4581 3344	191.9137 7699	124
125	173.0677 5630	183.2510 3040	188.6234 9677	194.1932 0217	125
126	174.9330 9508	185.3199 9474	190.8023 9363	196.4878 2352	126
127	176.8077 6056	187.4010 2805	192.9949 0859	198.7977 4234	127
128	178.6917 9936	189.4942 0071	195.2011 2677	201.1230 6062	128
129	180.5852 5836	191.5995 8355	197.4211 3381	203.4638 8103	129
130	182.4881 8465	193.7172 4778	199.6550 1589	205.8203 0690	130
131	184.4006 2557	195.8472 6506	201.9028 5974	208.1924 4228	131
132	186.3226 2870	197.9897 0744	204.1647 5262	210.5803 9189	132
133	188.2542 4184	200.1446 4740	206.4407 8232	212.9842 6117	133
134	190.1955 1305	202.3121 5785	208.7310 3721	215.4041 5625	134
135	192.1464 9062	204.4923 1210	211.0356 0619	217.8401 8396	135
136	194.1072 2307	206.6851 8392	213.3545 7873	220.2924 5185	136
137	196.0777 5919	208.8908 4749	215.6880 4485	222.7610 6820	137
138	198.0581 4798	211.1093 7744	218.0360 9513	225.2461 4198	138
139	200.0484 3872	213.3408 4881	220.3988 2072	227.7477 8293	139
140	202.0486 8092	215.5853 3709	222.7763 1335	230.2661 0148	140
141	204.0589 2432	217.8429 1822	225.1686 6531	232.8012 0883	141
142	206.0792 1894	220.1136 6858	227.5759 6947	235.3532 1688	142
143	208.1096 1504	222.3976 6498	229.9983 1928	237.9222 3833	143
144	210.1501 6311	224.6949 8469	232.4358 0878	240.5083 8659	144
145	212.2009 1393	227.0057 0544	234.8885 3258	243.1117 7583	145
146	214.2619 1850	229.3299 0538	237.3565 8591	245.7325 2100	146
147	216.3332 2809	231.6676 6317	239.8400 6457	248.3707 3781	147
148	218.4148 9423	234.0190 5787	242.3390 6497	251.0265 4273	148
149	220.5069 6870	236.3841 6904	244.8536 8413	253.7000 5301	149
150	222.6095 0354	238.7630 7669	247.3840 1966	256.3913 8670	150

TABLE III.—Amount of Annuity of 1 per Period

$$s_{\overline{n}|i} = \frac{(1+i)^n - 1}{i}$$

n	½%	7⁄12%	⅝%	⅔%	n
151	224.7225 5106	241.1558 6130	249.9301 6978	259.1006 6261	151
152	226.8461 6382	243.5626 0383	252.4922 3334	261.8280 0036	152
153	228.9803 9464	245.9833 8568	255.0703 0980	264.5735 2036	153
154	231.1252 9661	248.4182 8877	257.6644 9923	267.3373 4383	154
155	233.2809 2309	250.8673 9545	260.2749 0235	270.1195 9279	155
156	235.4473 2771	253.3307 8859	262.9016 2049	272.9203 9008	156
157	237.6245 6435	255.8085 5153	265.5447 5562	275.7398 5934	157
158	239.8126 8717	258.3007 6808	268.2044 1035	278.5781 2507	158
159	242.0117 5060	260.8075 2256	270.8806 8791	281.4353 1257	159
160	244.2218 0936	263.3288 9977	273.5736 9221	284.3115 4799	160
161	246.4429 1840	265.8649 8502	276.2835 2779	287.2069 5831	161
162	248.6751 3300	268.4158 6410	279.0102 9983	290.1216 7136	162
163	250.9185 0866	270.9816 2331	281.7541 1421	293.0558 1584	163
164	253.1731 0121	273.5623 4944	284.5150 7742	296.0095 2128	164
165	255.4389 6671	276.1581 2982	287.2932 9666	298.9829 1809	165
166	257.7161 6154	278.7690 5224	290.0888 7976	301.9761 3754	166
167	260.0047 4235	281.3952 0504	292.9019 3526	304.9893 1179	167
168	262.3047 6606	284.0366 7707	295.7325 7235	308.0225 7387	168
169	264.6162 8989	286.6935 5769	298.5809 0093	311.0760 5770	169
170	266.9393 7134	289.3659 3678	301.4470 3156	314.1498 9808	170
171	269.2740 6820	292.0539 0474	304.3310 7551	317.2442 3073	171
172	271.6204 3854	294.7575 5252	307.2331 4473	320.3591 9227	172
173	273.9785 4073	297.4769 7158	310.1533 5189	323.4949 2022	173
174	276.3484 3344	300.2122 5391	313.0918 1033	326.6515 5302	174
175	278.7301 7561	302.9634 9206	316.0486 3415	329.8292 3004	175
176	281.1238 2648	305.7307 7910	319.0239 3811	333.0280 9158	176
177	283.5294 4562	308.5142 0864	322.0178 3773	336.2482 7885	177
178	285.9470 9284	311.3138 7486	325.0304 4921	339.4899 3405	178
179	288.3768 2831	314.1298 7246	328.0618 8952	342.7532 0027	179
180	290.8187 1245	316.9622 9672	331.1122 7633	346.0382 2161	180
181	293.2728 0601	319.8112 4345	334.1817 2806	349.3451 4309	181
182	295.7391 7004	322.6768 0904	337.2703 6386	352.6741 1071	182
183	298.2178 6589	325.5590 9042	340.3783 0363	356.0252 7144	183
184	300.7089 5522	328.4581 8512	343.5056 6803	359.3987 7325	184
185	303.2125 0000	331.3741 9120	346.6525 7845	362.7947 6508	185
186	305.7285 6250	334.3072 0731	349.8191 5707	366.2133 9684	186
187	308.2572 0531	337.2573 3269	353.0055 2680	369.6548 1949	187
188	310.7984 9134	340.2246 6713	356.2118 1134	373.1191 8495	188
189	313.3524 8379	343.2093 1102	359.4381 3516	376.6066 4618	189
190	315.9192 4621	346.2113 6533	362.6846 2351	380.1173 5716	190
191	318.4988 4244	349.2309 3163	365.9514 0241	383.6514 7287	191
192	321.0913 3666	352.2681 1207	369.2385 9867	387.2091 4936	192
193	323.6967 9334	355.3230 0939	372.5463 3991	390.7905 4369	193
194	326.3152 7731	358.3957 2694	375.8747 5454	394.3958 1398	194
195	328.9468 5369	361.4863 6868	379.2239 7175	398.0251 1941	195
196	331.5915 8796	364.5950 3917	382.5941 2158	401.6786 2020	196
197	334.2495 4590	367.7218 4356	385.9853 3484	405.3564 7767	197
198	336.9207 9363	370.8668 8765	389.3977 4318	409.0588 5419	198
199	339.6053 9760	374.0302 7783	392.8314 7907	412.7859 1322	199
200	342.3034 2450	377.2121 2111	396.2866 7582	416.5378 1930	200

TABLE III. —Amount of Annuity of 1 per Period

$$s_{\overline{n}|i} = \frac{(1+i)^n - 1}{i}$$

n	¾%	⅞%	1%	1⅛%	n
1	1.0000 0000	1.0000 0000	1.0000 0000	1.0000 0000	1
2	2.0075 0000	2.0087 5000	2.0100 0000	2.0112 5000	2
3	3.0225 5625	3.0263 2656	3.0301 0000	3.0338 7656	3
4	4.0452 2542	4.0528 0692	4.0604 0100	4.0680 0767	4
5	5.0755 6461	5.0882 6898	5.1010 0501	5.1137 7276	5
6	6.1136 3135	6.1327 9133	6.1520 1506	6.1713 0270	6
7	7.1594 8358	7.1864 5326	7.2135 3521	7.2407 2986	7
8	8.2131 7971	8.2493 3472	8.2856 7056	8.3221 8807	8
9	9.2747 7856	9.3215 1640	9.3685 2727	9.4158 1269	9
10	10.3443 3940	10.4030 7967	10.4622 1254	10.5217 4058	10
11	11.4219 2194	11.4941 0662	11.5668 3467	11.6401 1016	11
12	12.5075 8636	12.5946 8005	12.6825 0301	12.7710 6140	12
13	13.6013 9325	13.7048 8350	13.8093 2804	13.9147 3584	13
14	14.7034 0370	14.8248 0123	14.9474 2132	15.0712 7662	14
15	15.8136 7923	15.9545 1824	16.0968 9554	16.2408 2848	15
16	16.9322 8183	17.0941 2028	17.2578 6449	17.4235 3780	16
17	18.0592 7394	18.2436 9383	18.4304 4314	18.6195 5260	17
18	19.1947 1849	19.4033 2615	19.6147 4757	19.8290 2257	18
19	20.3386 7888	20.5731 0526	20.8108 9504	21.0520 9907	19
20	21.4912 1897	21.7531 1993	22.0190 0399	22.2889 3519	20
21	22.6524 0312	22.9434 5973	23.2391 9403	23.5396 8571	21
22	23.8222 9614	24.1442 1500	24.4715 8598	24.8045 0717	22
23	25.0009 6336	25.3554 7688	25.7163 0183	26.0835 5788	23
24	26.1884 7059	26.5773 3730	26.9734 6485	27.3769 9790	24
25	27.3848 8412	27.8098 8900	28.2431 9950	28.6849 8913	25
26	28.5902 7075	29.0532 2553	29.5256 3150	30.0076 9526	26
27	29.8046 9778	30.3074 4126	30.8208 8781	31.3452 8183	27
28	31.0282 3301	31.5726 3137	32.1290 9669	32.6979 1625	28
29	32.2609 4476	32.8488 9189	33.4503 8766	34.0657 6781	29
30	33.5029 0184	34.1363 1970	34.7848 9153	35.4490 0769	30
31	34.7541 7361	35.4350 1249	36.1327 4045	36.8478 0903	31
32	36.0148 2991	36.7450 6885	37.4940 6785	38.2623 4688	32
33	37.2849 4113	38.0665 8820	38.8690 0853	39.6927 9829	33
34	38.5645 7819	39.3996 7085	40.2576 9862	41.1393 4227	34
35	39.8538 1253	40.7444 1797	41.6602 7560	42.6021 5987	35
36	41.1527 1612	42.1009 3163	43.0768 7836	44.0814 3417	36
37	42.4613 6149	43.4693 1478	44.5076 4714	45.5773 5030	37
38	43.7798 2170	44.8496 7128	45.9527 2361	47.0900 9549	38
39	45.1081 7037	46.2421 0591	47.4122 5085	48.6198 5906	39
40	46.4464 8164	47.6467 2433	48.8863 7336	50.1668 3248	40
41	47.7948 3026	49.0636 3317	50.3752 3709	51.7312 0934	41
42	49.1532 9148	50.4929 3996	51.8789 8946	53.3131 8545	42
43	50.5219 4117	51.9347 5319	53.3977 7936	54.9129 5879	43
44	51.9008 5573	53.3891 8228	54.9317 5715	56.5307 2957	44
45	53.2901 1215	54.8563 3762	56.4810 7472	58.1667 0028	45
46	54.6897 8799	56.3363 3058	58.0458 8547	59.8210 7566	46
47	56.0999 6140	57.8292 7347	59.6263 4432	61.4940 6276	47
48	57.5207 1111	59.3352 7961	61.2226 0777	63.1858 7097	48
49	58.9521 1644	60.8544 6331	62.8348 3385	64.8967 1201	49
50	60.3942 5732	62.3869 3986	64.4631 8218	66.6268 0002	50

TABLE III. —Amount of Annuity of 1 per Period

$$s_{\overline{n}|i} = \frac{(1+i)^n - 1}{i}$$

n	$\frac{3}{4}\%$	$\frac{7}{8}\%$	1%	$1\frac{1}{8}\%$	n
51	61.8472 1424	63.9328 2559	66.1078 1401	68.3763 5152	51
52	63.3110 6835	65.4922 3781	67.7688 9215	70.1455 8548	52
53	64.7859 0136	67.0652 9489	69.4465 8107	71.9347 2332	53
54	66.2717 9562	68.6521 1622	71.1410 4688	73.7439 8895	54
55	67.7688 3409	70.2528 2224	72.8524 5735	75.5736 0883	55
56	69.2771 0035	71.8675 3443	74.5809 8192	77.4238 1193	56
57	70.7966 7860	73.4963 7536	76.3267 9174	79.2948 2981	57
58	72.3276 5369	75.1394 6864	78.0900 5966	81.1868 9665	58
59	73.8701 1109	76.7969 3900	79.8709 6025	83.1002 4923	59
60	75.4241 3693	78.4689 1221	81.6696 6986	85.0351 2704	60
61	76.9898 1795	80.1555 1519	83.4863 6655	86.9917 7222	61
62	78.5672 4159	81.8568 7595	85.3212 3022	88.9704 2966	62
63	80.1564 9590	83.5731 2362	87.1744 4252	90.9713 4699	63
64	81.7576 6962	85.3043 8845	89.0461 8695	92.9947 7464	64
65	83.3708 5214	87.0508 0185	90.9366 4882	95.0409 6586	65
66	84.9961 3353	88.8124 9636	92.8460 1531	97.1101 7672	66
67	86.6336 0453	90.5896 0571	94.7744 7546	99.2026 6621	67
68	88.2833 5657	92.3822 6476	96.7222 2021	101.3186 9621	68
69	89.9454 8174	94.1906 0957	98.6894 4242	103.4585 3154	69
70	91.6200 7285	96.0147 7741	100.6763 3684	105.6224 4002	70
71	93.3072 2340	97.8549 0671	102.6831 0021	107.8106 9247	71
72	95.0070 2758	99.7111 3714	104.7099 3121	110.0235 6276	72
73	96.7195 8028	101.5836 0959	106.7570 3052	112.2613 2784	73
74	98.4449 7714	103.4724 6618	108.8246 0083	114.5242 6778	74
75	100.1833 1446	105.3778 5025	110.9128 4684	116.8126 6579	75
76	101.9346 8932	107.2999 0644	113.0219 7530	119.1268 0828	76
77	103.6991 9949	109.2387 8063	115.1521 9506	121.4669 8487	77
78	105.4769 4349	111.1946 1996	117.3037 1701	123.8334 8845	78
79	107.2680 2056	113.1675 7288	119.4767 5418	126.2266 1520	79
80	109.0725 3072	115.1577 8914	121.6715 2172	128.6466 6462	80
81	110.8905 7470	117.1654 1980	123.8882 3694	131.0939 3960	81
82	112.7222 5401	119.1906 1722	126.1271 1931	133.5687 4642	82
83	114.5676 7091	121.2335 3512	128.3883 9050	136.0713 9481	83
84	116.4269 2845	123.2943 2855	130.6722 7440	138.6021 9801	84
85	118.3001 3041	125.3731 5393	132.9789 9715	141.1614 7273	85
86	120.1873 8139	127.4701 6903	135.3087 8712	143.7495 3930	86
87	122.0887 8675	129.5855 3301	137.6618 7499	146.3667 2162	87
88	124.0044 5265	131.7194 0642	140.0384 9374	149.0133 4724	88
89	125.9344 8604	133.8719 5123	142.4388 7868	151.6897 4739	89
90	127.8789 9469	136.0433 3080	144.8632 6746	154.3962 5705	90
91	129.8380 8715	138.2337 0994	147.3119 0014	157.1332 1494	91
92	131.8118 7280	140.4432 5491	149.7850 1914	159.9009 6361	92
93	133.8004 6185	142.6721 3339	152.2828 6933	162.6998 4945	93
94	135.8039 6531	144.9205 1455	154.8056 9803	165.5302 2276	94
95	137.8224 9505	147.1885 6906	157.3537 5501	168.3924 3776	95
96	139.8561 6377	149.4764 6903	159.9272 9256	171.2868 5269	96
97	141.9050 8499	151.7843 8813	162.5265 6548	174.2138 2978	97
98	143.9693 7313	154.1125 0153	165.1518 3114	177.1737 3537	98
99	146.0491 4343	156.4609 8592	167.8033 4945	180.1669 3989	99
100	148.1445 1201	158.8300 1955	170.4813 8294	183.1938 1796	100

TABLE III. —Amount of Annuity of 1 per Period

$$s_{\overline{n}|i} = \frac{(1+i)^n - 1}{i}$$

n	1¼%	1⅜%	1½%	1¾%	n
1	1.0000 0000	1.0000 0000	1.0000 0000	1.0000 0000	1
2	2.0125 0000	2.0137 5000	2.0150 0000	2.0175 0000	2
3	3.0376 5625	3.0414 3906	3.0452 2500	3.0528 0625	3
4	4.0756 2695	4.0832 5885	4.0909 0338	4.1062 3036	4
5	5.1265 7229	5.1394 0366	5.1522 6693	5.1780 8938	5
6	6.1906 5444	6.2100 7046	6.2295 5093	6.2687 0596	6
7	7.2680 3762	7.2954 5893	7.3229 9419	7.3784 0831	7
8	8.3588 8809	8.3957 7149	8.4328 3911	8.5075 3045	8
9	9.4633 7420	9.5112 1335	9.5593 3169	9.6564 1224	9
10	10.5816 6637	10.6419 9253	10.7027 2167	10.8253 9945	10
11	11.7139 3720	11.7883 1993	11.8632 6249	12.0148 4394	11
12	12.8603 6142	12.9504 0933	13.0412 1143	13.2251 0371	12
13	14.0211 1594	14.1284 7745	14.2368 2960	14.4565 4303	13
14	15.1963 7988	15.3227 4402	15.4503 8205	15.7095 3253	14
15	16.3863 3463	16.5334 3175	16.6821 3778	16.9844 4935	15
16	17.5911 6382	17.7607 6644	17.9323 6984	18.2816 7721	16
17	18.8110 5336	19.0049 7697	19.2013 5539	19.6016 0656	17
18	20.0461 9153	20.2662 9541	20.4893 7572	20.9446 3468	18
19	21.2967 6893	21.5449 5697	21.7967 1636	22.3111 6578	19
20	22.5629 7854	22.8412 0013	23.1236 6710	23.7016 1119	20
21	23.8450 1577	24.1552 6663	24.4705 2211	25.1163 8938	21
22	25.1430 7847	25.4874 0155	25.8375 7994	26.5559 2620	22
23	26.4573 6695	26.8378 5332	27.2251 4364	28.0206 5490	23
24	27.7880 8403	28.2068 7380	28.6335 2080	29.5110 1637	24
25	29.1354 3508	29.5947 1832	30.0630 2361	31.0274 5915	25
26	30.4996 2802	31.0016 4569	31.5139 6896	32.5704 3969	26
27	31.8808 7337	32.4279 1832	32.9866 7850	34.1404 2238	27
28	33.2793 8429	33.8738 0220	34.4814 7867	35.7378 7977	28
29	34.6953 7659	35.3395 6698	35.9987 0085	37.3632 9267	29
30	36.1290 6880	36.8254 8602	37.5386 8137	39.0171 5029	30
31	37.5806 8216	38.3318 3646	39.1017 6159	40.6999 5042	31
32	39.0504 4069	39.8588 9921	40.6882 8801	42.4121 9955	32
33	40.5385 7120	41.4069 5907	42.2986 1233	44.1544 1305	33
34	42.0453 0334	42.9763 0476	43.9330 9152	45.9271 1527	34
35	43.5708 6963	44.5672 2895	45.5920 8789	47.7308 3979	35
36	45.1155 0550	46.1800 2835	47.2759 6921	49.5661 2949	36
37	46.6794 4932	47.8150 0374	48.9851 0874	51.4335 3675	37
38	48.2926 4243	49.4724 6004	50.7198 8538	53.3336 2365	38
39	49.8862 2921	51.1527 0636	52.4806 8366	55.2669 6206	39
40	51.4895 5708	52.8560 5608	54.2678 9391	57.2341 3390	40
41	53.1331 7654	54.5828 2685	56.0819 1232	59.2357 3124	41
42	54.7973 4125	56.3333 4072	57.9231 4100	61.2723 5654	42
43	56.4823 0801	58.1079 2415	59.7919 8812	63.3446 2278	43
44	58.1883 3687	59.9069 0811	61.6888 6794	65.4531 5367	44
45	59.9156 9108	61.7306 2810	63.6142 0096	67.5985 8386	45
46	61.6646 3721	63.5794 2423	65.5684 1398	69.7815 5908	46
47	63.4354 4518	65.4536 4131	67.5519 4018	72.0027 3637	47
48	65.2283 8824	67.3536 2888	69.5652 1929	74.2627 8425	48
49	67.0437 4310	69.2797 4128	71.6086 9758	76.5623 8298	49
50	68.8817 8989	71.2323 3772	73.6828 2804	78.9022 2468	50

TABLE III. —Amount of Annuity of 1 per Period

$$s_{\overline{n}|i} = \frac{(1+i)^n - 1}{i}$$

n	1¼%	1⅜%	1½%	1¾%	n
51	70.7428 1226	73.2117 8237	75.7880 7046	81.2830 1361	51
52	72.6270 9741	75.2184 4437	77.9248 9152	83.7054 6635	52
53	74.5349 3613	77.2526 9798	80.0937 6489	86.1703 1201	53
54	76.4666 2283	79.3149 2258	82.2951 7136	88.6782 9247	54
55	78.4224 5562	81.4055 0277	84.5295 9893	91.2301 6259	55
56	80.4027 3631	83.5248 2843	86.7975 4292	93.8266 9043	56
57	82.4077 7052	85.6732 9482	89.0995 0606	96.4686 5752	57
58	84.4378 6765	87.8513 0262	91.4359 9865	99.1568 5902	58
59	86.4933 4099	90.0592 5804	93.8075 3863	101.8921 0405	59
60	88.5745 0776	92.2975 7283	96.2146 5171	104.6752 1588	60
61	90.6816 8910	94.5666 6446	98.6578 7149	107.5070 3215	61
62	92.8152 1022	96.8669 5610	101.1377 3956	110.3884 0522	62
63	94.9754 0034	99.1988 7674	103.6548 0565	113.3202 0231	63
64	97.1625 9285	101.5628 6130	106.2096 2774	116.3033 0585	64
65	99.3771 2526	103.9593 5064	108.8027 7215	119.3386 1370	65
66	101.6193 3933	106.3887 9171	111.4348 1374	122.4270 3944	66
67	103.8895 8107	108.8516 3760	114.1063 3594	125.5695 1263	67
68	106.1882 0083	111.3483 4761	116.8179 3098	128.7669 7910	68
69	108.5155 5334	113.8793 8739	119.5701 9995	132.0204 0124	69
70	110.8719 9776	116.4452 2897	122.3637 5295	135.3307 5826	70
71	113.2578 9773	119.0463 5087	125.1992 0924	138.6990 4653	71
72	115.6736 2145	121.6832 3819	128.0771 9738	142.1262 7984	72
73	118.1195 4172	124.3563 8272	130.9983 5534	145.6134 8974	73
74	120.5960 3599	127.0662 8298	133.9633 3067	149.1617 2581	74
75	123.1034 8644	129.8134 4437	136.9727 8063	152.7720 5601	75
76	125.6422 8002	132.5983 7923	140.0273 7234	156.4455 6699	76
77	128.2128 0852	135.4216 0695	143.1277 8292	160.1833 6441	77
78	130.8154 6863	138.2836 5404	146.2746 9967	163.9865 7329	78
79	133.4506 6199	141.1850 5429	149.4688 2016	167.8563 3832	79
80	136.1187 9526	144.1263 4878	152.7108 5247	171.7938 2424	80
81	138.8202 8020	147.1080 8608	156.0015 1525	175.8002 1617	81
82	141.5555 3370	150.1308 2226	159.3415 3798	179.8767 1995	82
83	144.3249 7787	153.1951 2107	162.7316 6105	184.0245 6255	83
84	147.1290 4010	156.3015 5398	166.1726 3597	188.2449 9239	84
85	149.9681 5310	159.4507 0035	169.6652 2551	192.5392 7976	85
86	152.8427 5501	162.6431 4748	173.2102 0389	196.9087 1716	86
87	155.7532 8945	165.8794 9076	176.8083 5695	201.3546 1971	87
88	158.7002 0557	169.1603 3375	180.4604 8230	205.8783 2555	88
89	161.6839 5814	172.4862 8834	184.1673 8954	210.4811 9625	89
90	164.7050 0762	175.8579 7481	187.9299 0038	215.1646 1718	90
91	167.7638 2021	179.2760 2196	191.7488 4889	219.9299 9798	91
92	170.8608 6796	182.7410 6726	195.6250 8162	224.7787 7295	92
93	173.9966 2881	186.2537 5694	199.5594 5784	229.7124 0148	93
94	177.1715 8667	189.8147 4610	203.5528 4971	234.7323 6850	94
95	180.3862 3151	193.4246 9886	207.6061 4246	239.8401 8495	95
96	183.6410 5940	197.0842 8847	211.7202 3459	245.0373 8819	96
97	186.9365 7264	200.7941 9743	215.8960 3811	250.3255 4248	97
98	190.2732 7980	204.5551 1765	220.1344 7868	255.7062 3947	98
99	193.6516 9580	208.3677 5051	224.4364 9586	261.1810 9866	99
100	197.0723 4200	212.2328 0708	228.8030 4330	266.7517 6789	100

TABLE III.—Amount of Annuity of 1 per Period

$$s_{\overline{n}|i} = \frac{(1+i)^n - 1}{i}$$

n	2%	2¼%	2½%	2¾%	n
1	1.0000 0000	1.0000 0000	1.0000 0000	1.0000 0000	1
2	2.0200 0000	2.0225 0000	2.0250 0000	2.0275 0000	2
3	3.0604 0000	3.0680 0625	3.0756 2500	3.0832 5625	3
4	4.1216 0800	4.1370 3639	4.1525 1563	4.1680 4580	4
5	5.2040 4016	5.2301 1971	5.2563 2852	5.2826 6706	5
6	6.3081 2096	6.3477 9740	6.3877 3673	6.4279 4040	6
7	7.4342 8338	7.4906 2284	7.5474 3015	7.6047 0876	7
8	8.5829 6905	8.6591 6186	8.7361 1590	8.8138 3825	8
9	9.7546 2843	9.8539 9300	9.9545 1880	10.0562 1880	9
10	10.9497 2100	11.0757 0784	11.2033 8177	11.3327 6482	10
11	12.1687 1542	12.3249 1127	12.4834 6631	12.6444 1585	11
12	13.4120 8973	13.6022 2177	13.7955 5297	13.9921 3729	12
13	14.6803 3152	14.9082 7176	15.1404 4179	15.3769 2107	13
14	15.9739 3815	16.2437 0788	16.5189 5284	16.7997 8639	14
15	17.2934 1692	17.6091 9130	17.9319 2666	18.2617 8052	15
16	18.6392 8525	19.0053 9811	19.3802 2483	19.7639 7948	16
17	20.0120 7096	20.4330 1957	20.8647 3045	21.3074 8892	17
18	21.4123 1238	21.8927 6251	22.3863 4871	22.8934 4487	18
19	22.8405 5863	23.3853 4966	23.9460 0743	24.5230 1460	19
20	24.2973 6980	24.9115 2003	25.5446 5761	26.1973 9750	20
21	25.7833 1719	26.4720 2923	27.1832 7405	27.9178 2593	21
22	27.2989 8354	28.0676 4989	28.8628 5590	29.6855 6615	22
23	28.8449 6321	29.6991 7201	30.5844 2730	31.5019 1921	23
24	30.4218 6247	31.3674 0338	32.3490 3798	33.3682 2199	24
25	32.0302 9972	33.0731 6996	34.1577 6393	35.2858 4810	25
26	33.6709 0572	34.8173 1628	36.0117 0803	37.2562 0892	26
27	35.3443 2383	36.6007 0590	37.9120 0073	39.2807 5467	27
28	37.0512 1031	38.4242 2178	39.8598 0075	41.3609 7542	28
29	38.7922 3451	40.2887 6677	41.8562 9577	43.4984 0224	29
30	40.5680 7921	42.1952 6402	43.9027 0316	45.6946 0830	30
31	42.3794 4079	44.1446 5746	46.0002 7074	47.9512 1003	31
32	44.2270 2961	46.1379 1226	48.1502 7751	50.2698 6831	32
33	46.1115 7020	48.1760 1528	50.3540 3445	52.6522 8969	33
34	48.0338 0160	50.2599 7563	52.6128 8531	55.1002 2765	34
35	49.9944 7763	52.3908 2508	54.9282 0744	57.6154 8391	35
36	51.9943 6719	54.5696 1864	57.3014 1263	60.1999 0972	36
37	54.0342 5453	56.7974 3506	59.7339 4794	62.8554 0724	37
38	56.1149 3962	59.0753 7735	62.2272 9664	65.5839 3094	38
39	58.2372 3841	61.4045 7334	64.7829 7906	68.3874 8904	39
40	60.4019 8318	63.7861 7624	67.4025 5354	71.2681 4499	40
41	62.6100 2284	66.2213 6521	70.0876 1737	74.2280 1898	41
42	64.8622 2330	68.7113 4592	72.8398 0781	77.2692 8950	42
43	67.1594 6777	71.2573 5121	75.6608 0300	80.3941 9496	43
44	69.5026 5712	73.8606 4161	78.5523 2308	83.6050 3532	44
45	71.8927 1027	76.5225 0605	81.5161 3116	86.9041 7379	45
46	74.3305 6447	79.2442 6243	84.5540 3443	90.2940 3857	46
47	76.8171 7576	82.0272 5834	87.6678 8530	93.7771 2463	47
48	79.3535 1927	84.8728 7165	90.8595 8243	97.3559 9556	48
49	81.9405 8966	87.7825 1126	94.1310 7199	101.0332 8544	49
50	84.5794 0145	90.7576 1776	97.4843 4879	104.8117 0079	50

TABLE III. —Amount of Annuity of 1 per Period

$$s_{\overline{n}|i} = \frac{(1+i)^n - 1}{i}$$

n	2%	2¼%	2½%	2¾%	n
51	07.0700 0040	03.7006 6416	100.9214 5751	108.6940 2256	51
52	90.0164 0927	96.9101 5661	104.4444 9395	112.6831 0818	52
53	92.8167 3746	100.0906 3513	108.0556 0629	116.7818 9365	53
54	95.6730 7221	103.3426 7442	111.7569 9645	120.9933 9573	54
55	98.5865 3365	106.6678 8460	115.5509 2136	125.3207 1411	55
56	101.5582 6432	110.0679 1200	119.4396 9440	129.7670 3375	56
57	104.5894 2961	113.5444 4002	123.4256 8676	134.3356 2718	57
58	107.6812 1820	117.0991 8992	127.5113 2893	139.0298 5692	58
59	110.8348 4257	120.7339 2169	131.6991 1215	143.8531 7799	59
60	114.0515 3942	124.4504 3493	135.9915 8995	148.8091 4038	60
61	117.3325 7021	128.2505 6972	140.3913 7970	153.9013 9174	61
62	120.6792 2161	132.1362 0754	144.9011 6419	159.1336 8002	62
63	124.0928 0604	136.1092 7221	149.5236 9330	164.5098 5622	63
64	127.5746 6216	140.1717 3083	154.2617 8563	170.0338 7726	64
65	131.1261 5541	144.3255 9477	159.1183 3027	175.7098 0889	65
66	134.7486 7852	148.5729 2066	164.0962 8853	181.5418 2863	66
67	138.4436 5209	152.9158 1137	169.1986 9574	187.5342 2892	67
68	142.2125 2513	157.3564 1713	174.4286 6314	193.6914 2021	68
69	146.0567 7563	161.8969 3651	179.7893 7971	200.0179 3427	69
70	149.9779 1114	166.5396 1758	185.2841 1421	206.5184 2746	70
71	153.9774 6937	171.2867 5898	190.9162 1706	213.1976 8422	71
72	158.0570 1875	176.1407 1106	196.6891 2249	220.0606 2054	72
73	162.2181 5913	181.1038 7705	202.6063 5055	227.1122 8760	73
74	166.4625 2231	186.1787 1429	208.6715 0931	234.3578 7551	74
75	170.7917 7276	191.3677 3536	214.8882 9705	241.8027 1709	75
76	175.2076 0821	196.6735 0941	221.2605 0447	249.4522 9181	76
77	179.7117 6038	202.0986 6337	227.7920 1709	257.3122 2983	77
78	184.3059 9558	207.6458 8329	234.4868 1751	265.3883 1615	78
79	188.9921 1549	213.3179 1567	241.3489 8795	273.6864 9485	79
80	193.7719 5780	219.1175 6877	248.3827 1265	282.2128 7345	80
81	198.6473 9696	225.0477 1407	255.5922 8047	290.9737 2747	81
82	203.6203 4490	231.1112 8763	262.9820 8748	299.9755 0498	82
83	208.6927 5180	237.3112 9160	270.5566 3966	309.2248 3137	83
84	213.8666 0683	243.6507 9567	278.3205 5566	318.7285 1423	84
85	219.1439 3897	250.1329 3857	286.2785 6955	328.4935 4837	85
86	224.5268 1775	256.7609 2969	294.4355 3379	338.5271 2095	86
87	230.0173 5411	263.5380 5060	302.7964 2213	348.8366 1678	87
88	235.6177 0119	270.4676 5674	311.3663 3268	359.4296 2374	88
89	241.3300 5521	277.5531 7902	320.1504 9100	370.3139 3839	89
90	247.1566 5632	284.7981 2555	329.1542 5328	381.4975 7170	90
91	253.0997 8944	292.2060 8337	338.3831 0961	392.9887 5492	91
92	259.1617 8523	299.7807 2025	347.8426 8735	404.7959 4568	92
93	265.3450 2094	307.5257 8645	357.5387 5453	416.9278 3418	93
94	271.6519 2135	315.4451 1665	367.4772 2339	429.3933 4962	94
95	278.0849 5978	323.5426 3177	377.6641 5398	442.2016 6674	95
96	284.6466 5898	331.8223 4099	388.1057 5783	455.3622 1257	96
97	291.3395 9216	340.2883 4366	398.8084 0177	468.8846 7342	97
98	298.1663 8400	348.9448 3139	409.7786 1182	482.7790 0194	98
99	305.1297 1168	357.7960 9010	421.0230 7711	497.0554 2449	99
100	312.2323 0591	366.8465 0213	432.5486 5404	511.7244 4867	100

TABLE III.—Amount of Annuity of 1 per Period

$$s_{\overline{n}|i} = \frac{(1+i)^n - 1}{i}$$

n	3%	3½%	4%	4½%	n
1	1.0000 0000	1.0000 0000	1.0000 0000	1.0000 0000	1
2	2.0300 0000	2.0350 0000	2.0400 0000	2.0450 0000	2
3	3.0909 0000	3.1062 2500	3.1216 0000	3.1370 2500	3
4	4.1836 2700	4.2149 4288	4.2464 6400	4.2781 9113	4
5	5.3091 3581	5.3624 6588	5.4163 2256	5.4707 0973	5
6	6.4684 0988	6.5501 5218	6.6329 7546	6.7168 9166	6
7	7.6624 6218	7.7794 0751	7.8982 9448	8.0191 5179	7
8	8.8923 3605	9.0516 8677	9.2142 2626	9.3800 1362	8
9	10.1591 0613	10.3684 9581	10.5827 9531	10.8021 1423	9
10	11.4638 7931	11.7313 9316	12.0061 0712	12.2882 0937	10
11	12.8077 9569	13.1419 9192	13.4863 5141	13.8411 7879	11
12	14.1920 2956	14.6019 6164	15.0258 0546	15.4640 3184	12
13	15.6177 9045	16.1130 3030	16.6268 3768	17.1599 1327	13
14	17.0863 2416	17.6769 8636	18.2919 1119	18.9321 0937	14
15	18.5989 1389	19.2956 8088	20.0235 8764	20.7840 5429	15
16	20.1568 8130	20.9710 2971	21.8245 3114	22.7193 3673	16
17	21.7615 8774	22.7050 1575	23.6975 1239	24.7417 0689	17
18	23.4144 3537	24.4996 9130	25.6454 1288	26.8550 8370	18
19	25.1168 6844	26.3571 8050	27.6712 2940	29.0635 6246	19
20	26.8703 7449	28.2796 8181	29.7780 7858	31.3714 2277	20
21	28.6764 8572	30.2694 7068	31.9692 0172	33.7831 3680	21
22	30.5367 8030	32.3289 0215	34.2479 6979	36.3033 7795	22
23	32.4528 8370	34.4604 1373	36.6178 8858	38.9370 2996	23
24	34.4264 7022	36.6665 2821	39.0826 0412	41.6891 9631	24
25	36.4592 6432	38.9498 5669	41.6459 0829	44.5652 1015	25
26	38.5530 4225	41.3131 0168	44.3117 4462	47.5706 4460	26
27	40.7096 3352	43.7590 6024	47.0842 1440	50.7113 2361	27
28	42.9309 2252	46.2906 2734	49.9675 8298	53.9933 3317	28
29	45.2188 5020	48.9107 9930	52.9662 8630	57.4230 3316	29
30	47.5754 1571	51.6226 7728	56.0849 3775	61.0070 6966	30
31	50.0026 7818	54.4294 7098	59.3283 3526	64.7523 8779	31
32	52.5027 5852	57.3345 0247	62.7014 6867	68.6662 4524	32
33	55.0778 4128	60.3412 1005	66.2095 2742	72.7562 2628	33
34	57.7301 7652	63.4531 5240	69.8579 0851	77.0302 5646	34
35	60.4620 8181	66.6740 1274	73.6522 2486	81.4966 1800	35
36	63.2759 4427	70.0076 0318	77.5983 1385	86.1639 6581	36
37	66.1742 2259	73.4578 6930	81.7022 4640	91.0413 4427	37
38	69.1594 4927	77.0288 9472	85.9703 3626	96.1382 0476	38
39	72.2342 3275	80.7249 0604	90.4091 4971	101.4644 2398	39
40	75.4012 5973	84.5502 7775	95.0255 1570	107.0303 2306	40
41	78.6632 9753	88.5095 3747	99.8265 3633	112.8466 8760	41
42	82.0231 9645	92.6073 7128	104.8195 9778	118.9247 8854	42
43	85.4838 9234	96.8486 2928	110.0123 8169	125.2764 0402	43
44	89.0484 0911	101.2383 3130	115.4128 7696	131.9138 4220	44
45	92.7198 6139	105.7816 7290	121.0293 9204	138.8499 6510	45
46	96.5014 5723	110.4840 3145	126.8705 6772	146.0982 1353	46
47	100.3965 0095	115.3509 7255	132.9453 9043	153.6726 3314	47
48	104.4083 9598	120.3882 5659	139.2632 0604	161.5879 0163	48
49	108.5406 4785	125.6018 4557	145.8337 3429	169.8593 5720	49
50	112.7968 6729	130.9979 1016	152.6670 8366	178.5030 2828	50

TABLE III. —Amount of Annuity of 1 per Period

$$s_{\overline{n}|i} = \frac{(1+i)^n - 1}{i}$$

n	3%	3½%	4%	4½%	n
51	117.1807 7331	136.5828 3702	159.7737 6700	187.5356 6455	51
52	121.6961 9651	142.3632 3631	167.1647 1768	196.9747 6946	52
53	126.3470 8240	148.3459 4958	174.8513 0639	206.8386 3408	53
54	131.1374 9488	154.5380 5782	182.8453 5865	217.1463 7262	54
55	136.0716 1972	160.9468 8984	191.1591 7299	227.9179 5938	55
56	141.1537 6831	167.5800 3099	199.8055 3991	239.1742 6756	56
57	146.3883 8136	174.4453 3207	208.7977 6151	250.9371 0960	57
58	151.7800 3280	181.5509 1869	218.1496 7197	263.2292 7953	58
59	157.3334 3379	188.9052 0085	227.8756 5885	276.0745 9711	59
60	163.0534 3680	196.5168 8288	237.9906 8520	289.4979 5398	60
61	168.9450 3991	204.3949 7378	248.5103 1261	303.5253 6190	61
62	175.0133 9110	212.5487 9786	259.4507 2511	318.1840 0319	62
63	181.2637 9284	220.9880 0579	270.8287 5412	333.5022 8333	63
64	187.7017 0662	229.7225 8599	282.6619 0428	349.5098 8608	64
65	194.3327 5782	238.7628 7650	294.9683 8045	366.2378 3096	65
66	201.1627 4055	248.1195 7718	307.7671 1567	383.7185 3335	66
67	208.1976 2277	257.8037 6238	321.0778 0030	401.9858 6735	67
68	215.4435 5145	267.8268 9406	334.9209 1231	421.0752 3138	68
69	222.9068 5800	278.2008 3535	349.3177 4880	441.0236 1679	69
70	230.5940 6374	288.9378 6459	364.2904 5876	461.8696 7955	70
71	238.5118 8565	300.0506 8985	379.8620 7711	483.6538 1513	71
72	246.6672 4222	311.5524 6400	396.0565 6019	506.4182 3681	72
73	255.0672 5949	323.4568 0024	412.8988 2260	530.2070 5747	73
74	263.7192 7727	335.7777 8824	430.4147 7550	555.0663 7505	74
75	272.6308 5559	348.5300 1083	448.6313 6652	581.0443 6193	75
76	281.8097 8126	361.7285 6121	467.5766 2118	608.1913 5822	76
77	291.2640 7469	375.3890 6085	487.2796 8603	636.5599 6934	77
78	301.0019 9693	389.5276 7798	507.7708 7347	666.2051 6796	78
79	311.0320 5684	404.1611 4671	529.0817 0841	697.1844 0052	79
80	321.3630 1855	419.3067 8685	551.2449 7675	729.5576 9854	80
81	332.0039 0910	434.9825 2439	574.2947 7582	763.3877 9497	81
82	342.9640 2638	451.2069 1274	598.2665 6685	798.7402 4575	82
83	354.2529 4717	467.9991 5469	623.1972 2952	835.6835 5680	83
84	365.8805 3558	485.3791 2510	649.1251 1870	874.2893 1686	84
85	377.8569 5165	503.3673 9448	676.0901 2345	914.6323 3612	85
86	390.1926 6020	521.9852 5329	704.1337 2839	956.7907 9125	86
87	402.8984 4001	541.2547 3715	733.2990 7753	1000.8463 7685	87
88	415.9853 9321	561.1986 5295	763.6310 4063	1046.8844 6381	88
89	429.4649 5500	581.8406 0581	795.1762 8225	1094.9942 6468	89
90	443.3489 0365	603.2050 2701	827.9833 3354	1145.2690 0659	90
91	457.6493 7076	625.3172 0295	862.1026 6688	1197.8061 1189	91
92	472.3788 5189	648.2033 0506	897.5867 7356	1252.7073 8692	92
93	487.5502 1744	671.8904 2073	934.4902 4450	1310.0792 1933	93
94	503.1767 2397	696.4065 8546	972.8698 5428	1370.0327 8420	94
95	519.2720 2569	721.7808 1595	1012.7846 4845	1432.6842 5949	95
96	535.8501 8645	748.0431 4451	1054.2960 3439	1498.1550 5117	96
97	552.9256 9205	775.2246 5457	1097.4678 7577	1566.5720 2847	97
98	570.5134 6281	803.3575 1748	1142.3665 9080	1638.0677 6976	98
99	588.6288 6669	832.4750 3059	1189.0612 5443	1712.7808 1939	99
100	607.2877 3270	862.6116 5666	1237.6237 0461	1790.8559 5627	100

TABLE III. —Amount of Annuity of 1 per Period

$$s_{\overline{n}|i} = \frac{(1+i)^n - 1}{i}$$

n	5%	5½%	6%	6½%	n
1	1.0000 0000	1.0000 0000	1.0000 0000	1.0000 0000	1
2	2.0500 0000	2.0550 0000	2.0600 0000	2.0650 0000	2
3	3.1525 0000	3.1680 2500	3.1836 0000	3.1992 2500	3
4	4.3101 2500	4.3422 6638	4.3746 1600	4.4071 7463	4
5	5.5256 3125	5.5810 9103	5.6370 9296	5.6936 4098	5
6	6.8019 1281	6.8880 5103	6.9753 1854	7.0637 2764	6
7	8.1420 0845	8.2668 9384	8.3938 3765	8.5228 6994	7
8	9.5491 0888	9.7215 7300	9.8974 6791	10.0768 5648	8
9	11.0265 6432	11.2562 5951	11.4913 1598	11.7318 5215	9
10	12.5778 9254	12.8753 5379	13.1807 9494	13.4944 2254	10
11	14.2067 8716	14.5834 9825	14.9716 4264	15.3715 6001	11
12	15.9171 2652	16.3855 9065	16.8699 4120	17.3707 1141	12
13	17.7129 8235	18.2867 9814	18.8821 3767	19.4998 0765	13
14	19.5986 3199	20.2925 7203	21.0150 6593	21.7672 9515	14
15	21.5785 6359	22.4086 6350	23.2759 6988	24.1821 6933	15
16	23.6574 9177	24.6411 3999	25.6725 2808	26.7540 1034	16
17	25.8403 6636	26.9964 0269	28.2128 7976	29.4930 2101	17
18	28.1323 8467	29.4812 0483	30.9056 5255	32.4100 6738	18
19	30.5390 0391	32.1026 7110	33.7599 9170	35.5167 2176	19
20	33.0659 5410	34.8683 1801	36.7855 9120	38.8253 0867	20
21	35.7192 5181	37.7860 7550	39.9927 2668	42.3489 5373	21
22	38.5052 1440	40.8643 0965	43.3922 9028	46.1016 3573	22
23	41.4304 7512	44.1118 4669	46.9958 2769	50.0982 4205	23
24	44.5019 9887	47.5379 9825	50.8155 7735	54.3546 2778	24
25	47.7270 9882	51.1525 8816	54.8645 1200	58.8876 7859	25
26	51.1134 5376	54.9659 8051	59.1563 8272	63.7153 7769	26
27	54.6691 2645	58.9891 0943	63.7057 6568	68.8568 7725	27
28	58.4025 8277	63.2335 1045	68.5281 1162	74.3325 7427	28
29	62.3227 1191	67.7113 5353	73.6397 9832	80.1641 9159	29
30	66.4388 4750	72.4354 7797	79.0581 8622	86.3748 6405	30
31	70.7607 8988	77.4194 2926	84.8016 7739	92.9892 3021	31
32	75.2988 2937	82.6774 9787	90.8897 7803	100.0335 3017	32
33	80.0637 7084	88.2247 6025	97.3431 6471	107.5357 0963	33
34	85.0659 5938	94.0771 2207	104.1837 5460	115.5255 3076	34
35	90.3203 0735	100.2513 6378	111.4347 7987	124.0346 9026	35
36	95.8363 2272	106.7651 8879	119.1208 6666	133.0969 4513	36
37	101.6281 3886	113.6372 7417	127.2681 1866	142.7482 4656	37
38	107.7095 4580	120.8873 2425	135.9042 0578	153.0268 8259	38
39	114.0950 2309	128.5361 2708	145.0584 5813	163.9736 2995	39
40	120.7997 7424	136.6056 1407	154.7619 6562	175.6319 1590	40
41	127.8397 6295	145.1189 2285	165.0476 8356	188.0479 9044	41
42	135.2317 5110	154.1004 6360	175.9505 4457	201.2711 0981	42
43	142.9933 3866	163.5759 8910	187.5075 7724	215.3537 3195	43
44	151.1430 0559	173.5726 6850	199.7580 3188	230.3517 2453	44
45	159.7001 5587	184.1191 6527	212.7435 1379	246.3245 8662	45
46	168.6851 6366	195.2457 1936	226.5081 2462	263.3356 8475	46
47	178.1194 2185	206.9842 3392	241.0986 1210	281.4525 0426	47
48	188.0253 9294	219.3683 6679	256.5645 2882	300.7469 1704	48
49	198.4266 6259	232.4336 2696	272.9584 0055	321.2954 6665	49
50	209.3479 9572	246.2174 7645	290.3359 0458	343.1796 7198	50

TABLE III.—Amount of Annuity of 1 per Period

$$s_{\overline{n}|i} = \frac{(1+i)^n - 1}{i}$$

n	5%	5½%	6%	6½%	n
51	220.8153 9550	260.7594 3765	308.7560 5886	366.4863 5066	51
52	232.8561 6528	276.1012 0672	328.2814 2239	391.3079 6345	52
53	245.4989 7354	292.2867 7309	348.9783 0773	417.7429 8108	53
54	258.7739 2222	309.3625 4561	370.9170 0620	445.8962 7485	54
55	272.7126 1833	327.3774 8562	394.1720 2657	475.8795 3271	55
56	287.3482 4924	346.3832 4733	418.8223 4816	507.8117 0234	56
57	302.7156 6171	366.4343 2593	444.9516 8905	541.8194 6299	57
58	318.8514 4479	387.5882 1386	472.6487 9040	578.0377 2808	58
59	335.7940 1703	409.9055 6562	502.0077 1782	616.6101 8041	59
60	353.5837 1788	433.4503 7173	533.1281 8089	657.6898 4214	60
61	372.2629 0378	458.2901 4217	566.1158 7174	701.4396 8187	61
62	391.8760 4897	484.4960 9999	601.0828 2405	748.0332 6120	62
63	412.4698 5141	512.1433 8549	638.1477 9349	797.6554 2317	63
64	434.0933 4398	541.3112 7170	677.4366 6110	850.5030 2568	64
65	456.7980 1118	572.0833 9164	719.0828 6076	906.7857 2235	65
66	480.6379 1174	604.5479 7818	763.2278 3241	966.7267 9430	66
67	505.6698 0733	638.7981 1698	810.0215 0236	1030.5640 3593	67
68	531.9532 9770	674.9320 1341	859.6227 9250	1098.5506 9827	68
69	559.5509 6258	713.0532 7415	912.2001 6005	1170.9564 9365	69
70	588.5285 1071	753.2712 0423	967.9321 6965	1248.0686 6574	70
71	618.9549 3625	795.7011 2046	1027.0080 9983	1330.1931 2901	71
72	650.9026 8306	840.4646 8209	1089.6285 8582	1417.6556 8240	72
73	684.4478 1721	887.6902 3960	1156.0063 0097	1510.8033 0176	73
74	719.6702 0807	937.5132 0278	1226.3666 7903	1610.0055 1637	74
75	756.6537 1848	990.0764 2893	1300.9486 7977	1715.6558 7493	75
76	795.4864 0440	1045.5306 3252	1380.0056 0055	1828.1735 0681	76
77	836.2607 2462	1104.0348 1731	1463.8059 3659	1948.0047 8475	77
78	879.0737 6085	1165.7567 3226	1552.6342 9278	2075.6250 9576	78
79	924.0274 4889	1230.8733 5254	1646.7923 5035	2211.5407 2698	79
80	971.2288 2134	1299.5713 8693	1746.5998 9137	2356.2908 7423	80
81	1020.7902 6240	1372.0478 1321	1852.3958 8485	2510.4497 8106	81
82	1072.8297 7552	1448.5104 4294	1964.5396 3794	2674.6290 1683	82
83	1127.4712 6430	1529.1785 1730	2083.4120 1622	2849.4799 0292	83
84	1184.8448 2752	1614.2833 3575	2209.4167 3719	3035.6960 9661	84
85	1245.0870 6889	1704.0689 1921	2342.9817 4142	3234.0163 4289	85
86	1308.3414 2234	1798.7927 0977	2484.5606 4591	3445.2274 0518	86
87	1374.7584 9345	1898.7263 0881	2634.6342 8466	3670.1671 8652	87
88	1444.4964 1812	2004.1562 5579	2793.7123 4174	3909.7280 5364	88
89	1517.7212 3903	2115.3848 4986	2962.3350 8225	4164.8603 7713	89
90	1594.6073 0098	2232.7310 1660	3141.0751 8718	4436.5763 0164	90
91	1675.3376 6603	2356.5312 2252	3330.5396 9841	4725.9537 6125	91
92	1760.1045 4933	2487.1404 3976	3531.3720 8032	5034.1407 5573	92
93	1849.1097 7680	2624.9331 6394	3744.2544 0514	5362.3599 0485	93
94	1942.5652 6564	2770.3044 8796	3969.9096 6944	5711.9132 9867	94
95	2040.6935 2892	2923.6712 3480	4209.1042 4961	6084.1876 6308	95
96	2143.7282 0537	3085.4731 5271	4462.6505 0459	6480.6598 6118	96
97	2251.9146 1564	3256.1741 7611	4731.4095 3486	6902.9027 5216	97
98	2365.5103 4642	3436.2637 5580	5016.2941 0696	7352.5914 3105	98
99	2484.7858 6374	3626.2582 6237	5318.2717 5337	7831.5098 7406	99
100	2610.0251 5693	3826.7024 6680	5638.3680 5857	8341.5580 1588	100

TABLE III. —Amount of Annuity of 1 per Period

$$s_{\overline{n}|i} = \frac{(1+i)^n - 1}{i}$$

n	7%	7½%	8%	8½%	n
1	1.0000 0000	1.0000 0000	1.0000 0000	1.0000 0000	1
2	2.0700 0000	2.0750 0000	2.0800 0000	2.0850 0000	2
3	3.2149 0000	3.2306 2500	3.2464 0000	3.2622 2500	3
4	4.4399 4300	4.4729 2188	4.5061 1200	4.5395 1413	4
5	5.7507 3901	5.8083 9102	5.8666 0096	5.9253 7283	5
6	7.1532 9074	7.2440 2034	7.3359 2904	7.4290 2952	6
7	8.6540 2109	8.7873 2187	8.9228 0336	9.0604 9702	7
8	10.2598 0257	10.4463 7101	10.6366 2763	10.8306 3927	8
9	11.9779 8875	12.2298 4883	12.4875 5784	12.7512 4361	9
10	13.8164 4796	14.1470 8750	14.4865 6247	14.8350 9932	10
11	15.7835 9932	16.2081 1906	16.6454 8746	17.0960 8276	11
12	17.8884 5127	18.4237 2799	18.9771 2646	19.5492 4979	12
13	20.1406 4286	20.8055 0759	21.4952 9658	22.2109 3603	13
14	22.5504 8786	23.3659 2066	24.2149 2030	25.0988 6559	14
15	25.1290 2201	26.1183 6470	27.1521 1393	28.2322 6916	15
16	27.8880 5355	29.0772 4206	30.3242 8304	31.6320 1204	16
17	30.8402 1730	32.2580 3521	33.7502 2569	35.3207 3306	17
18	33.9990 3251	35.6773 8785	37.4502 4374	39.3229 9538	18
19	37.3789 6479	39.3531 9194	41.4462 6324	43.6654 4998	19
20	40.9954 9232	43.3046 8134	45.7619 6430	48.3770 1323	20
21	44.8651 7678	47.5525 3244	50.4229 2144	53.4890 5936	21
22	49.0057 3916	52.1189 7237	55.4567 5516	59.0356 2940	22
23	53.4361 4090	57.0278 9530	60.8932 9557	65.0536 5790	23
24	58.1766 7076	62.3049 8744	66.7647 5922	71.5832 1882	24
25	63.2490 3772	67.9778 6150	73.1059 3995	78.6677 9242	25
26	68.6764 7036	74.0762 0112	79.9544 1515	86.3545 5478	26
27	74.4838 2328	80.6319 1620	87.3507 6836	94.6946 9193	27
28	80.6976 9091	87.6793 0991	95.3388 2983	103.7437 4075	28
29	87.3465 2927	95.2552 5816	103.9659 3622	113.5619 5871	29
30	94.4607 8632	103.3994 0252	113.2832 1111	124.2147 2520	30
31	102.0730 4137	112.1543 5771	123.3458 6800	135.7729 7684	31
32	110.2181 5426	121.5659 3454	134.2135 3744	148.3136 7987	32
33	118.9334 2506	131.6833 7963	145.9506 2044	161.9203 4266	33
34	128.2587 6481	142.5596 3310	158.6266 7007	176.6835 7179	34
35	138.2368 7835	154.2516 0558	172.3168 0368	192.7016 7539	35
36	148.9134 5984	166.8204 7600	187.1021 4797	210.0813 1780	36
37	160.3374 0202	180.3320 1170	203.0703 1981	228.9382 2981	37
38	172.5610 2017	194.8569 1258	220.3159 4540	249.3979 7935	38
39	185.6402 9158	210.4711 8102	238.9412 2103	271.5968 0759	39
40	199.6351 1199	227.2565 1960	259.0565 1871	295.6825 3624	40
41	214.6095 6983	245.3007 5857	280.7810 4021	321.8155 5182	41
42	230.6322 3972	264.6983 1546	304.2435 2342	350.1698 7372	42
43	247.7764 9650	285.5506 8912	329.5830 0530	380.9343 1299	43
44	266.1208 5125	307.9669 9080	356.9496 4572	414.3137 2959	44
45	285.7493 1084	332.0645 1511	386.5056 1738	450.5303 9661	45
46	306.7517 6260	357.9693 5375	418.4260 6677	489.8254 8032	46
47	329.2243 8598	385.8170 5528	452.9001 5211	532.4606 4615	47
48	353.2700 9300	415.7533 3442	490.1321 6428	578.7198 0107	48
49	378.9989 9951	447.9348 3451	530.3427 3742	628.9109 8416	49
50	406.5289 2947	482.5299 4709	573.7701 5642	683.3684 1782	50

TABLE III.—Amount of Annuity of 1 per Period

$$s_{\overline{n}|i} = \frac{(1+i)^n - 1}{i}$$

n	7%	7½%	8%	8½%	n
51	435.9859 5454	519.7196 9313	620.6717 6893	742.4547 3333	51
52	467.5049 7135	559.6986 7011	671.3255 1044	806.5633 8566	52
53	501.2303 1935	602.6760 7037	726.0315 5128	876.1212 7345	53
54	537.3164 4170	648.8767 7565	785.1140 7538	951.5915 8169	54
55	575.9285 9262	698.5425 3382	848.9232 0141	1033.4768 6613	55
56	617.2435 9410	751.9332 2386	917.8370 5752	1122.3223 9975	56
57	661.4506 4569	809.3282 1564	992.2640 2213	1218.7198 0373	57
58	708.7521 9089	871.0278 3182	1072.6451 4390	1323.3109 8705	58
59	759.3648 4425	937.3549 1920	1159.4567 5541	1436.7924 2095	59
60	813.5203 8335	1008.6565 3814	1253.2132 9584	1559.9197 7673	60
61	871.4668 1019	1085.3057 7851	1354.4703 5951	1693.5129 5775	61
62	933.4694 8690	1167.7037 1189	1463.8279 8827	1838.4615 5916	62
63	999.8123 5098	1256.2814 9029	1581.9342 2733	1995.7307 9169	63
64	1070.7992 1555	1351.5026 0206	1709.4889 6552	2166.3679 0898	64
65	1146.7551 6064	1453.8652 9721	1847.2480 8276	2351.5091 8125	65
66	1228.0280 2188	1563.9051 9450	1996.0279 2938	2552.3874 6165	66
67	1314.9899 8341	1682.1980 8409	2156.7101 6373	2770.3403 9589	67
68	1408.0392 8225	1809.3629 4040	2330.2469 7683	3006.8193 2954	68
69	1507.6020 3201	1946.0651 6093	2517.6667 3497	3263.3989 7255	69
70	1614.1341 7425	2093.0200 4800	2720.0800 7377	3541.7878 8522	70
71	1728.1235 6645	2250.9965 5160	2938.6864 7967	3843.8398 5546	71
72	1850.0922 1610	2420.8212 9296	3174.7813 9805	4171.5662 4318	72
73	1980.5986 7123	2603.3828 8994	3429.7639 0989	4527.1493 7385	73
74	2120.2405 7821	2799.6366 0668	3705.1450 2268	4912.9570 7063	74
75	2269.6574 1869	3010.6093 5218	4002.5566 2449	5331.5584 2163	75
76	2429.5334 3800	3237.4050 5360	4323.7611 5445	5785.7408 8747	76
77	2600.6007 7866	3481.2104 3262	4670.6620 4681	6278.5288 6290	77
78	2783.6428 3316	3743.3012 1506	5045.3150 1056	6813.2038 1625	78
79	2979.4978 3148	4025.0488 0619	5449.9402 1140	7393.3261 4063	79
80	3189.0626 7969	4327.9274 6666	5886.9354 2831	8022.7588 6259	80
81	3413.2970 6727	4653.5220 2666	6358.8902 6258	8705.6933 6591	81
82	3653.2278 6198	5003.5361 7866	6868.6014 8358	9446.6773 0201	82
83	3909.9538 1231	5379.8013 9206	7419.0896 0227	10250.6448 7268	83
84	4184.6505 7918	5784.2864 9646	8013.6167 7045	11122.9496 8686	84
85	4478.5761 1972	6219.1079 8369	8655.7061 1209	12069.4004 1024	85
86	4793.0764 4810	6686.5410 8247	9349.1626 0105	13096.2994 4511	86
87	5129.5917 9946	7189.0316 6366	10098.0956 0914	14210.4848 9794	87
88	5489.6632 2543	7729.2090 3843	10906.9432 5787	15419.3761 1427	88
89	5874.9396 5121	8309.8997 1631	11780.4987 1850	16731.0230 8398	89
90	6287.1854 2679	8934.1421 9504	12723.9386 1598	18154.1600 4612	90
91	6728.2884 0667	9605.2028 5966	13742.8537 0526	19698.2636 5004	91
92	7200.2685 9513	10326.5930 7414	14843.2820 0168	21373.6160 6029	92
93	7705.2873 9679	11102.0875 5470	16031.7445 6181	23191.3734 2542	93
94	8245.6575 1457	11935.7441 2130	17315.2841 2676	25163.6401 6658	94
95	8823.8535 4059	12831.9249 3040	18701.5068 5690	27303.5495 8074	95
96	9442.5232 8843	13795.3193 0018	20198.6274 0545	29625.3512 9510	96
97	10104.4999 1862	14830.9682 4769	21815.5175 9788	32144.5061 5518	97
98	10812.8149 1292	15944.2908 6627	23561.7590 0572	34877.7891 7837	98
99	11570.7119 5683	17141.1126 8124	25447.6997 2617	37843.4012 5853	99
100	12381.6617 9381	18427.6961 3233	27484.5157 0427	41061.0903 6551	100

TABLE IV. —Present Value of Annuity of 1 per Period

$$a_{\overline{n}|i} = \frac{1 - (1+i)^{-n}}{i}$$

n	¼%	7/24%	⅓%	5/12%	n
1	0.9975 0623	0.9970 9182	0.9966 7774	0.9958 5062	1
2	1.9925 2492	1.9912 8390	1.9900 4426	1.9875 6908	2
3	2.9850 6227	2.9825 8470	2.9801 1056	2.9751 7253	3
4	3.9751 2446	3.9710 0260	3.9668 8760	3.9586 7804	4
5	4.9627 1766	4.9565 4601	4.9503 8631	4.9381 0261	5
6	5.9478 4804	5.9392 2327	5.9306 1759	5.9134 6318	6
7	6.9305 2174	6.9190 4273	6.9075 9228	6.8847 7661	7
8	7.9107 4487	7.8960 1269	7.8813 2121	7.8520 5969	8
9	8.8885 2357	8.8701 4144	8.8518 1516	8.8153 2915	9
10	9.8638 6391	9.8414 3725	9.8190 8487	9.7746 0164	10
11	10.8367 7198	10.8099 0834	10.7831 4107	10.7298 9374	11
12	11.8072 5384	11.7755 6295	11.7439 9442	11.6812 2198	12
13	12.7753 1555	12.7384 0915	12.7016 5557	12.6286 0280	13
14	13.7409 6314	13.6984 5542	13.6561 3512	13.5720 5257	14
15	14.7042 0264	14.6557 0959	14.6074 4364	14.5115 8762	15
16	15.6650 4004	15.6101 7990	15.5555 9167	15.4472 2418	16
17	16.6234 8133	16.5618 7442	16.5005 8970	16.3789 7843	17
18	17.5795 3250	17.5108 0125	17.4424 4821	17.3068 6648	18
19	18.5331 9950	18.4569 6842	18.3811 7762	18.2309 0438	19
20	19.4844 8828	19.4003 8396	19.3167 8832	19.1511 0809	20
21	20.4334 0477	20.3410 5587	20.2492 9069	20.0674 9352	21
22	21.3799 5488	21.2789 9213	21.1786 9504	20.9800 7653	22
23	22.3241 4452	22.2142 0071	22.1050 1167	21.8888 7289	23
24	23.2659 7957	23.1466 8952	23.0282 5083	22.7938 9831	24
25	24.2054 6591	24.0764 6648	23.9484 2275	23.6951 6843	25
26	25.1426 0939	25.0035 3949	24.8655 3763	24.5926 9884	26
27	26.0774 1585	25.9279 1639	25.7796 0561	25.4865 0506	27
28	27.0098 9112	26.8496 0503	26.6906 3682	26.3766 0254	28
29	27.9400 4102	27.7686 1324	27.5986 4135	27.2630 0668	29
30	28.8678 7134	28.6849 4879	28.5036 2925	28.1457 3278	30
31	29.7933 8787	29.5986 1947	29.4056 1055	29.0247 9612	31
32	30.7165 9638	30.5096 3303	30.3045 9523	29.9002 1189	32
33	31.6375 0262	31.4179 9720	31.2005 9325	30.7719 9524	33
34	32.5561 1234	32.3237 1967	32.0936 1454	31.6401 6122	34
35	33.4724 3126	33.2268 0814	32.9836 6898	32.5047 2486	35
36	34.3864 6510	34.1272 7025	33.8707 6642	33.3657 0109	36
37	35.2982 1955	35.0251 1366	34.7549 1670	34.2231 0481	37
38	36.2077 0030	35.9203 4597	35.6361 2960	35.0769 5084	38
39	37.1149 1302	36.8129 7478	36.5144 1488	35.9272 5394	39
40	38.0198 6336	37.7030 0767	37.3897 8228	36.7740 2881	40
41	38.9225 5697	38.5904 5217	38.2622 4147	37.6172 9009	41
42	39.8229 9947	39.4753 1582	39.1318 0213	38.4570 5236	42
43	40.7211 9648	40.3576 0612	39.9984 7388	39.2933 3013	43
44	41.6171 5359	41.2373 3056	40.8622 6633	40.1261 3788	44
45	42.5108 7640	42.1144 9659	41.7231 8903	40.9554 8999	45
46	43.4023 7047	42.9891 1167	42.5812 5153	41.7814 0081	46
47	44.2916 4137	43.8611 8320	43.4364 6332	42.6038 8461	47
48	45.1786 9463	44.7307 1859	44.2888 3387	43.4229 5562	48
49	46.0635 3580	45.5977 2521	45.1383 7263	44.2386 2799	49
50	46.9461 7037	46.4622 1042	45.9850 8900	45.0509 1582	50

TABLE IV.—Present Value of Annuity of 1 per Period

$$a_{\overline{n}|i} = \frac{1-(1+i)^{-n}}{i}$$

n	¼%	7/24%	⅜%	5/12%	n
51	47.8266 0386	47.3241 8154	46.8289 9236	45.8598 3317	51
52	48.7048 4176	48.1836 4589	47.6700 9205	46.6653 9401	52
53	49.5808 8953	49.0406 1076	48.5083 9739	47.4676 1228	53
54	50.4547 5265	49.8950 8341	49.3439 1767	48.2665 0184	54
55	51.3264 3656	50.7470 7110	50.1766 6213	49.0620 7651	55
56	52.1959 4669	51.5965 8106	51.0066 3999	49.8543 5003	56
57	53.0632 8847	52.4436 2048	51.8338 6046	50.6433 3612	57
58	53.9284 6730	53.2881 9656	52.6583 3268	51.4290 4840	58
59	54.7914 8858	54.1303 1645	53.4800 6580	52.2115 0046	59
60	55.6523 5769	54.9699 8730	54.2990 6890	52.9907 0584	60
61	56.5110 7999	55.8072 1623	55.1153 5106	53.7666 7800	61
62	57.3676 6083	56.6420 1035	55.9289 2133	54.5394 3035	62
63	58.2221 0557	57.4743 7673	56.7397 8870	55.3089 7627	63
64	59.0744 1952	58.3043 2244	57.5479 6216	56.0753 2905	64
65	59.9246 0800	59.1318 5451	58.3534 5065	56.8385 0194	65
66	60.7726 7631	59.9569 7996	59.1562 6311	57.5985 0814	66
67	61.6186 2974	60.7797 0580	59.9564 0842	58.3553 6078	67
68	62.4624 7355	61.6000 3900	60.7538 9543	59.1090 7296	68
69	63.3042 1302	62.4179 8652	61.5487 3299	59.8596 5770	69
70	64.1438 5339	63.2335 5529	62.3409 2989	60.6071 2798	70
71	64.9813 9989	64.0467 5224	63.1304 9490	61.3514 9672	71
72	65.8168 5774	64.8575 8427	63.9174 3678	62.0927 7680	72
73	66.6502 3216	65.6660 5824	64.7017 6423	62.8309 8103	73
74	67.4815 2834	66.4721 8103	65.4834 8595	63.5661 2216	74
75	68.3107 5146	67.2759 5945	66.2626 1058	64.2982 1292	75
76	69.1379 0670	68.0774 0035	67.0391 4676	65.0272 6596	76
77	69.9629 9920	68.8765 1050	67.8131 0308	65.7532 9388	77
78	70.7860 3411	69.6732 9670	68.5844 8812	66.4763 0924	78
79	71.6070 1657	70.4677 6569	69.3533 1042	67.1963 2453	79
80	72.4259 5169	71.2599 2422	70.1195 7849	67.9133 5221	80
81	73.2428 4458	72.0497 7901	70.8833 0082	68.6274 0467	81
82	74.0577 0033	72.8373 3675	71.6444 8587	69.3384 9426	82
83	74.8705 2402	73.6226 0413	72.4031 4206	70.0466 3326	83
84	75.6813 2072	74.4055 8781	73.1592 7780	70.7518 3393	84
85	76.4900 9548	75.1862 9442	73.9129 0146	71.4541 0846	85
86	77.2968 5335	75.9647 3060	74.6640 2139	72.1534 6898	86
87	78.1015 9935	76.7409 0294	75.4126 4591	72.8499 2759	87
88	78.9043 3850	77.5148 1803	76.1587 8329	73.5434 9633	88
89	79.7050 7581	78.2864 8243	76.9024 4182	74.2341 8720	89
90	80.5038 1627	79.0559 0268	77.6436 2972	74.9220 1212	90
91	81.3005 6486	79.8230 8532	78.3823 5520	75.6069 8300	91
92	82.0953 2654	80.5880 3685	79.1186 2645	76.2891 1168	92
93	82.8881 0628	81.3507 6377	79.8524 5161	76.9684 0995	93
94	83.6789 0900	82.1112 7253	80.5838 3882	77.6448 8955	94
95	84.4677 3966	82.8695 6959	81.3127 9616	78.3185 6218	95
96	85.2546 0315	83.6256 6138	82.0393 3172	78.9894 3950	96
97	86.0395 0439	84.3795 5432	82.7634 5354	79.6575 3308	97
98	86.8224 4827	85.1312 5480	83.4851 6964	80.3228 5450	98
99	87.6034 3967	85.8807 6919	84.2044 8802	80.9854 1524	99
100	88.3824 8346	86.6281 0386	84.9214 1663	81.6452 2677	100

TABLE IV. —Present Value of Annuity of 1 per Period

$$a_{\overline{n}|i} = \frac{1 - (1 + i)^{-n}}{i}$$

n	$\frac{1}{4}\%$	$\frac{7}{24}\%$	$\frac{1}{3}\%$	$\frac{5}{12}\%$	n
101	89.1595 8450	87.3732 6514	85.6359 6344	82.3023 0049	101
102	89.9347 4763	88.1162 5935	86.3481 3635	82.9566 4777	102
103	90.7079 7768	88.8570 9280	87.0579 4323	83.6082 7991	103
104	91.4792 7948	89.5957 7177	87.7653 9195	84.2572 0818	104
105	92.2486 5784	90.3323 0252	88.4704 9034	84.9034 4381	105
106	93.0161 1755	91.0666 9131	89.1732 4621	85.5469 9795	106
107	93.7816 6339	91.7989 4436	89.8736 6735	86.1878 8175	107
108	94.5453 0014	92.5290 6788	90.5717 6150	86.8261 0628	108
109	95.3070 3256	93.2570 6806	91.2675 3641	87.4616 8258	109
110	96.0668 6539	93.9829 5109	91.9609 9977	88.0946 2163	110
111	96.8248 0338	94.7067 2312	92.6521 5927	88.7249 3437	111
112	97.5808 5126	95.4283 9028	93.3410 2255	89.3526 3171	112
113	98.3350 1372	96.1479 5870	94.0275 9726	89.9777 2450	113
114	99.0872 9548	96.8654 3448	94.7118 9098	90.6002 2354	114
115	99.8377 0123	97.5808 2372	95.3939 1131	91.2201 3959	115
116	100.5862 3564	98.2941 3246	96.0736 6578	91.8374 8338	116
117	101.3329 0338	99.0053 6678	96.7511 6194	92.4522 6558	117
118	102.0777 0911	99.7145 3269	97.4264 0727	93.0644 9681	118
119	102.8206 5747	100.4216 3621	98.0994 0927	93.6741 8767	119
120	103.5617 5308	101.1266 8335	98.7701 7538	94.2813 4869	120
121	104.3010 0058	101.8296 8009	99.4387 1304	94.8859 9036	121
122	105.0384 0457	102.5306 3237	100.1050 2964	95.4881 2315	122
123	105.7739 6965	103.2295 4616	100.7691 3256	96.0877 5747	123
124	106.5077 0040	103.9264 2738	101.4310 2916	96.6849 0367	124
125	107.2396 0139	104.6212 8194	102.0907 2677	97.2795 7209	125
126	107.9696 7720	105.3141 1573	102.7482 3269	97.8717 7301	126
127	108.6979 3237	106.0049 3464	103.4035 5420	98.4615 1666	127
128	109.4243 7144	106.6937 4451	104.0566 9857	99.0488 1324	128
129	110.1489 9894	107.3805 5120	104.7076 7303	99.6336 7290	129
130	110.8718 1939	108.0653 6053	105.3564 8478	100.2161 0576	130
131	111.5928 3730	108.7481 7831	106.0031 4101	100.7961 2189	131
132	112.3120 5716	109.4290 1032	106.6476 4888	101.3737 3131	132
133	113.0294 8345	110.1078 6235	107.2900 1552	101.9489 4401	133
134	113.7451 2065	110.7847 4016	107.9302 4806	102.5217 6994	134
135	114.4589 7321	111.4596 4947	108.5683 5358	103.0922 1899	135
136	115.1710 4560	112.1325 9603	109.2043 3915	103.6603 0104	136
137	115.8813 4224	112.8035 8553	109.8382 1181	104.2260 2590	137
138	116.5898 6758	113.4726 2368	110.4699 7859	104.7894 0335	138
139	117.2966 2601	114.1397 1613	111.0996 4646	105.3504 4314	139
140	118.0016 2196	114.8048 6856	111.7272 2242	105.9091 5496	140
141	118.7048 5981	115.4680 8660	112.3527 1341	106.4655 4847	141
142	119.4063 4395	116.1293 7588	112.9761 2636	107.0196 3330	142
143	120.1060 7875	116.7887 4201	113.5974 6817	107.5714 1902	143
144	120.8040 6858	117.4461 9058	114.2167 4572	108.1209 1517	144
145	121.5003 1778	118.1017 2717	114.8339 6586	108.6681 3126	145
146	122.1948 3071	118.7553 5734	115.4491 3545	109.2130 7674	146
147	122.8876 1168	119.4070 8663	116.0622 6128	109.7557 6103	147
148	123.5786 6502	120.0569 2057	116.6733 5015	110.2961 9353	148
149	124.2679 9503	120.7048 6467	117.2824 0882	110.8343 8356	149
150	124.9556 0601	121.3509 2444	117.8894 4404	111.3703 4044	150

TABLE IV.—Present Value of Annuity of 1 per Period

$$a_{\overline{n}|i} = \frac{1 - (1+i)^{-n}}{i}$$

n	$\frac{1}{4}\%$	$\frac{7}{24}\%$	$\frac{1}{3}\%$	$\frac{5}{12}\%$	n
151	125.6415 0226	121.9951 0534	118.4944 6254	111.9040 7343	151
152	126.3256 8804	122.6374 1284	119.0974 7100	112.4355 9176	152
153	127.0081 6762	123.2778 5240	119.6984 7612	112.9649 0463	153
154	127.6889 4525	123.9164 2944	120.2974 8454	113.4920 2117	154
155	128.3680 2519	124.5531 4937	120.8945 0290	114.0169 5051	155
156	129.0454 1166	125.1880 1761	121.4895 3781	114.5397 0171	156
157	129.7211 0889	125.8210 3954	122.0825 9587	115.0602 8383	157
158	130.3951 2109	126.4522 2052	122.6736 8363	115.5787 0585	158
159	131.0674 5246	127.0815 6591	123.2628 0764	116.0949 7674	159
160	131.7381 0719	127.7090 8105	123.8499 7443	116.6091 0543	160
161	132.4070 8946	128.3347 7125	124.4351 9050	117.1211 0081	161
162	133.0744 0346	128.9586 4184	125.0184 6233	117.6309 7172	162
163	133.7400 5332	129.5806 9809	125.5997 9638	118.1387 2699	163
164	134.4040 4321	130.2009 4529	126.1791 9909	118.6443 7539	164
165	135.0663 7727	130.8193 8870	126.7566 7687	119.1479 2566	165
166	135.7270 5962	131.4360 3355	127.3322 3612	119.6493 8641	166
167	136.3860 9439	132.0508 8509	127.9058 8322	120.1487 6662	167
168	137.0434 8567	132.6639 4853	128.4776 2451	120.6460 7460	168
169	137.6992 3758	133.2752 2907	129.0474 6633	121.1413 1907	169
170	138.3533 5419	133.8847 3189	129.6154 1499	121.6345 0858	170
171	139.0058 3959	134.4924 6216	130.1814 7677	122.1256 5166	171
172	139.6566 9785	135.0984 2504	130.7456 5795	122.6147 5680	172
173	140.3059 3302	135.7026 2567	131.3079 6478	123.1018 3246	173
174	140.9535 4914	136.3050 6917	131.8684 0347	123.5868 8705	174
175	141.5995 5027	136.9057 6066	132.4269 8025	124.0699 2898	175
176	142.2439 4042	137.5047 0522	132.9837 0128	124.5509 6658	176
177	142.8867 2361	138.1019 0794	133.5385 7275	125.0300 0817	177
178	143.5279 0385	138.6973 7389	134.0916 0079	125.5070 6204	178
179	144.1674 8514	139.2911 0811	134.6427 9152	125.9821 3643	179
180	144.8054 7146	139.8831 1564	135.1921 5106	126.4552 3956	180
181	145.4418 6679	140.4734 0151	135.7396 8549	126.9263 7961	181
182	146.0766 7510	141.0619 7071	136.2854 0086	127.3955 6471	182
183	146.7099 0035	141.6488 2825	136.8293 0322	127.8628 0299	183
184	147.3415 4649	142.2339 7909	137.3713 9860	128.3281 0253	184
185	147.9716 1744	142.8174 2821	137.9116 9300	128.7914 7136	185
186	148.6001 1715	143.3991 8055	138.4501 9241	129.2529 1749	186
187	149.2270 4952	143.9792 4105	138.9869 0277	129.7124 4891	187
188	149.8524 1848	144.5576 1463	139.5218 3005	130.1700 7357	188
189	150.4762 2791	145.1343 0618	140.0549 8016	130.6257 9936	189
190	151.0984 8170	145.7093 2062	140.5863 5901	131.0796 3418	190
191	151.7191 8375	146.2826 6280	141.1159 7248	131.5315 8586	191
192	152.3383 3790	146.8543 3760	141.6438 2643	131.9816 6223	192
193	152.9559 4803	147.4243 4986	142.1699 2672	132.4298 7106	193
194	153.5720 1799	147.9927 0442	142.6942 7917	132.8762 2010	194
195	154.1865 5161	148.5594 0611	143.2168 8958	133.3207 1707	195
196	154.7995 5272	149.1244 5971	143.7377 6375	133.7633 6965	196
197	155.4110 2516	149.6878 7004	144.2569 0743	134.2041 8550	197
198	156.0209 7273	150.2496 4187	144.7743 2639	134.6431 7224	198
199	156.6293 9923	150.8097 7996	145.2900 2635	135.0803 3746	199
200	157.2363 0846	151.3682 8907	145.8040 1302	135.5156 8872	200

TABLE IV. —Present Value of Annuity of 1 per Period

$$a_{\overline{n}|i} = \frac{1 - (1 + i)^{-n}}{i}$$

n	½%	7/12%	⅝%	⅔%	n
1	0.9950 2488	0.9942 0050	0.9937 8882	0.9933 7748	1
2	1.9850 9938	1.9826 3513	1.9814 0504	1.9801 7631	2
3	2.9702 4814	2.9653 3733	2.9628 8699	2.9604 4004	3
4	3.9504 9566	3.9423 4034	3.9382 7279	3.9342 1196	4
5	4.9258 6633	4.9136 7723	4.9076 0029	4.9015 3506	5
6	5.8963 8441	5.8793 8084	5.8709 0712	5.8624 5205	6
7	6.8620 7404	6.8394 8385	6.8282 3068	6.8170 0535	7
8	7.8229 5924	7.7940 1875	7.7796 0813	7.7652 3710	8
9	8.7790 6392	8.7430 1781	8.7250 7640	8.7071 8917	9
10	9.7304 1186	9.6865 1315	9.6646 7220	9.6429 0315	10
11	10.6770 2673	10.6245 3669	10.5984 3200	10.5724 2035	11
12	11.6189 3207	11.5571 2016	11.5263 9205	11.4957 8180	12
13	12.5561 5131	12.4842 9511	12.4485 8837	12.4130 2828	13
14	13.4887 0777	13.4060 9291	13.3650 5676	13.3242 0028	14
15	14.4166 2465	14.3225 4473	14.2758 3281	14.2293 3802	15
16	15.3399 2502	15.2336 8160	15.1809 5186	15.1284 8148	16
17	16.2586 3186	16.1395 3432	16.0804 4905	16.0216 7035	17
18	17.1727 6802	17.0401 3354	16.9743 5931	16.9089 4405	18
19	18.0823 5624	17.9355 0974	17.8627 1733	17.7903 4177	19
20	18.9874 1915	18.8256 9320	18.7455 5759	18.6659 0242	20
21	19.8879 7925	19.7107 1404	19.6229 1438	19.5356 6466	21
22	20.7840 5896	20.5906 0220	20.4948 2174	20.3996 6688	22
23	21.6756 8055	21.4653 8745	21.3613 1353	21.2579 4723	23
24	22.5628 6622	22.3350 9938	22.2224 2338	22.1105 4361	24
25	23.4456 3803	23.1997 6741	23.0781 8473	22.9574 9365	25
26	24.3240 1794	24.0594 2079	23.9286 3079	23.7988 3475	26
27	25.1980 2780	24.9140 8862	24.7737 9457	24.6346 0406	27
28	26.0676 8936	25.7637 9979	25.6137 0889	25.4648 3847	28
29	26.9330 2423	26.6085 8307	26.4484 0635	26.2895 7464	29
30	27.7940 5397	27.4484 6702	27.2779 1935	27.1088 4898	30
31	28.6507 9997	28.2834 8006	28.1022 8010	27.9226 9766	31
32	29.5032 8355	29.1136 5044	28.9215 2060	28.7311 5662	32
33	30.3515 2592	29.9390 0625	29.7356 7265	29.5342 6154	33
34	31.1955 4818	30.7595 7540	30.5447 6785	30.3320 4789	34
35	32.0353 7132	31.5753 8566	31.3488 3761	31.1245 5088	35
36	32.8710 1624	32.3864 6463	32.1479 1315	31.9118 0551	36
37	33.7025 0372	33.1928 3974	32.9420 2550	32.6938 4653	37
38	34.5298 5445	33.9945 3828	33.7312 0546	33.4707 0848	38
39	35.3530 8900	34.7915 8736	34.5154 8369	34.2424 2564	39
40	36.1722 2786	35.5840 1396	35.2948 9062	35.0090 3209	40
41	36.9872 9141	36.3718 4487	36.0694 5652	35.7705 6168	41
42	37.7982 9991	37.1551 0676	36.8392 1145	36.5270 4803	42
43	38.6052 7354	37.9338 2612	37.6041 8529	37.2785 2453	43
44	39.4082 3238	38.7080 2929	38.3644 0774	38.0250 2437	44
45	40.2071 9640	39.4777 4248	39.1199 0831	38.7665 8050	45
46	41.0021 8547	40.2429 9170	39.8707 1634	39.5032 2566	46
47	41.7932 1937	41.0038 0287	40.6168 6096	40.2349 9238	47
48	42.5803 1778	41.7602 0170	41.3583 7114	40.9619 1296	48
49	43.3635 0028	42.5122 1380	42.0952 7566	41.6840 1949	49
50	44.1427 8635	43.2598 6460	42.8276 0314	42.4013 4387	50

TABLE IV. —Present Value of Annuity of 1 per Period

$$a_{\overline{n}|i} = \frac{1 - (1+i)^{-n}}{i}$$

n	½%	7/12%	⅝%	⅔%	n
51	44.9181 9537	44.0031 7940	43.5553 8201	43.1139 1775	51
52	45.6897 4664	44.7421 8335	44.2786 4050	43.8217 7260	52
53	46.4574 5934	45.4769 0144	44.9974 0671	44.5249 3967	53
54	47.2213 5258	46.2073 5853	45.7117 0853	45.2234 5000	54
55	47.9814 4535	46.9335 7933	46.4215 7370	45.9173 3444	55
56	48.7377 5657	47.6555 8841	47.1270 2976	46.6066 2362	56
57	49.4903 0505	48.3734 1020	47.8281 0410	47.2913 4796	57
58	50.2391 0950	49.0870 6898	48.5248 2396	47.9715 3771	58
59	50.9841 8855	49.7965 8889	49.2172 1636	48.6472 2289	59
60	51.7255 6075	50.5019 9394	49.9053 0818	49.3184 3334	60
61	52.4632 4453	51.2033 0800	50.5891 2614	49.9851 9868	61
62	53.1972 5824	51.9005 5478	51.2686 9679	50.6475 4835	62
63	53.9276 2014	52.5937 5787	51.9440 4650	51.3055 1161	63
64	54.6543 4839	53.2829 4073	52.6152 0149	51.9591 1749	64
65	55.3774 6109	53.9681 2668	53.2821 8781	52.6083 9486	65
66	56.0969 7621	54.6493 3888	53.9450 3137	53.2533 7238	66
67	56.8129 1165	55.3266 0040	54.6037 5788	53.8940 7852	67
68	57.5252 8522	55.9999 3413	55.2583 9293	54.5305 4158	68
69	58.2341 1465	56.6693 6287	55.9089 6191	55.1627 8965	69
70	58.9394 1756	57.3349 0925	56.5554 9010	55.7908 5064	70
71	59.6412 1151	57.9965 9579	57.1980 0258	56.4147 5229	71
72	60.3395 1394	58.6544 4488	57.8365 2431	57.0345 2215	72
73	61.0343 4222	59.3084 7877	58.4710 8006	57.6501 8756	73
74	61.7257 1366	59.9587 1959	59.1016 9447	58.2617 7572	74
75	62.4136 4543	60.6051 8934	59.7283 9201	58.8693 1363	75
76	63.0981 5466	61.2479 0988	60.3511 9703	59.4728 2811	76
77	63.7792 5836	61.8869 0297	60.9701 3370	60.0723 4581	77
78	64.4569 7350	62.5221 9021	61.5852 2604	60.6678 9319	78
79	65.1313 1691	63.1537 9310	62.1964 9792	61.2594 9654	79
80	65.8023 0538	63.7817 3301	62.8039 7309	61.8471 8200	80
81	66.4699 5561	64.4060 3118	63.4076 7512	62.4309 7549	81
82	67.1342 8419	65.0267 0874	64.0076 2745	63.0109 0281	82
83	67.7953 0765	65.6437 8667	64.6038 5337	63.5869 8954	83
84	68.4530 4244	66.2572 8585	65.1963 7602	64.1592 6114	84
85	69.1075 0491	66.8672 2705	65.7852 1840	64.7277 4285	85
86	69.7587 1135	67.4736 3089	66.3704 0338	65.2924 5979	86
87	70.4066 7796	68.0765 1789	66.9519 5367	65.8534 3687	87
88	71.0514 2086	68.6759 0845	67.5298 9185	66.4106 9888	88
89	71.6929 5608	69.2718 2283	68.1042 4034	66.9642 7041	89
90	72.3312 9958	69.8642 8121	68.6750 2146	67.5141 7590	90
91	72.9664 6725	70.4533 0363	69.2422 5735	68.0604 3964	91
92	73.5984 7487	71.0389 1001	69.8059 7004	68.6030 8574	92
93	74.2273 3818	71.6211 2017	70.3661 8141	69.1421 3815	93
94	74.8530 7282	72.1999 5379	70.9229 1320	69.6776 2068	94
95	75.4756 9434	72.7754 3047	71.4761 8703	70.2095 5696	95
96	76.0952 1825	73.3475 6967	72.0260 2438	70.7379 7049	96
97	76.7116 5995	73.9163 9075	72.5724 4658	71.2628 8460	97
98	77.3250 3478	74.4819 1294	73.1154 7487	71.7843 2245	98
99	77.9353 5799	75.0441 5539	73.6551 3030	72.3023 0707	99
100	78.5426 4477	75.6031 3712	74.1914 3384	72.8168 6132	100

TABLE IV. —Present Value of Annuity of 1 per Period

$$a_{\overline{n}|i} = \frac{1 - (1 + i)^{-n}}{i}$$

n	½%	$\frac{7}{12}$%	⅝%	⅔%	n
101	79.1469 1021	76.1588 7702	74.7244 0630	73.3280 0792	101
102	79.7481 6937	76.7113 9392	75.2540 6838	73.8357 6944	102
103	80.3464 3718	77.2607 0648	75.7804 4062	74.3401 6830	103
104	80.9417 2854	77.8068 3331	76.3035 4348	74.8412 2677	104
105	81.5340 5825	78.3497 9288	76.8233 9724	75.3389 6697	105
106	82.1234 4104	78.8896 0355	77.3400 2210	75.8334 1088	106
107	82.7098 9158	79.4262 8359	77.8534 3812	76.3245 8032	107
108	83.2934 2446	79.9598 5115	78.3636 6521	76.8124 9699	108
109	83.8740 5419	80.4903 2428	78.8707 2319	77.2971 8242	109
110	84.4517 9522	81.0177 2093	79.3746 3174	77.7786 5801	110
111	85.0266 6191	81.5420 5895	79.8754 1043	78.2569 4503	111
112	85.5986 6856	82.0633 5606	80.3730 7868	78.7320 6458	112
113	86.1678 2942	82.5816 2991	80.8676 5583	79.2040 3764	113
114	86.7341 5862	83.0968 9803	81.3591 6108	79.6728 8505	114
115	87.2976 7027	83.6091 7785	81.8476 1349	80.1386 2751	115
116	87.8583 7838	84.1184 8671	82.3330 3204	80.6012 8559	116
117	88.4162 9690	84.6248 4182	82.8154 3557	81.0608 7970	117
118	88.9714 3970	85.1282 6033	83.2948 4280	81.5174 3015	118
119	89.5238 2059	85.6287 5926	83.7712 7235	81.9709 5708	119
120	90.0734 5333	86.1263 5554	84.2447 4271	82.4214 8052	120
121	90.6203 5157	86.6210 6602	84.7152 7226	82.8690 2036	121
122	91.1645 2892	87.1129 0742	85.1828 7926	83.3135 9636	122
123	91.7059 9893	87.6018 9638	85.6475 8188	83.7552 2815	123
124	92.2447 7505	88.0880 4946	86.1093 9814	84.1939 3523	124
125	92.7808 7070	88.5713 8308	86.5683 4597	84.6297 3696	125
126	93.3142 9920	89.0519 1361	87.0244 4320	85.0626 5259	126
127	93.8450 7384	89.5296 5731	87.4777 0753	85.4927 0122	127
128	94.3732 0780	90.0046 3032	87.9281 5655	85.9199 0185	128
129	94.8987 1422	90.4768 4873	88.3758 0776	86.3442 7334	129
130	95.4216 0619	90.9463 2851	88.8206 7852	86.7658 3442	130
131	95.9418 9671	91.4130 8554	89.2627 8610	87.1846 0371	131
132	96.4595 9872	91.8771 3561	89.7021 4768	87.6005 9969	132
133	96.9747 2509	92.3384 9442	90.1387 8030	88.0138 4072	133
134	97.4872 8865	92.7971 7758	90.5727 0092	88.4243 4507	134
135	97.9973 0214	93.2532 0060	91.0039 2638	88.8321 3084	135
136	98.5047 7825	93.7065 7892	91.4324 7342	89.2372 1604	136
137	99.0097 2960	94.1573 2787	91.8583 5868	89.6396 1856	137
138	99.5121 6875	94.6054 6270	92.2815 9869	90.0393 5616	138
139	100.0121 0821	95.0509 9857	92.7022 0988	90.4364 4649	139
140	100.5095 6041	95.4939 5056	93.1202 0857	90.8309 0709	140
141	101.0045 3772	95.9343 3364	93.5356 1100	91.2227 5536	141
142	101.4970 5246	96.3721 6272	93.9484 3330	91.6120 0861	142
143	101.9871 1688	96.8074 5261	94.3586 9148	91.9986 8402	143
144	102.4747 4316	97.2402 1804	94.7664 0147	92.3827 9867	144
145	102.9599 4344	97.6704 7364	95.1715 7910	92.7643 6952	145
146	103.4427 2979	98.0982 3397	95.5742 4010	93.1434 1340	146
147	103.9231 1422	98.5235 1350	95.9744 0010	93.5199 4706	147
148	104.4011 0868	98.9463 2663	96.3720 7463	93.8939 8712	148
149	104.8767 2505	99.3666 8765	96.7672 7913	94.2655 5010	149
150	105.3499 7518	99.7846 1078	97.1600 2895	94.6346 5239	150

TABLE IV.—Present Value of Annuity of 1 per Period

$$a_{\overline{n}|i} = \frac{1 - (1 + i)^{-n}}{i}$$

n	$\frac{1}{2}\%$	$\frac{7}{12}\%$	$\frac{5}{8}\%$	$\frac{2}{3}\%$	n
151	105.8208 7082	100.2001 1017	97.5503 3933	95.0013 1029	151
152	106.2894 2371	100.6131 9987	97.9382 2542	95.3655 4000	152
153	106.7556 4548	101.0238 9385	98.3237 0228	95.7273 5759	153
154	107.2195 4774	101.4322 0601	98.7067 8488	96.0867 7904	154
155	107.6811 4203	101.8381 5017	99.0874 8808	96.4438 2021	155
156	108.1404 3983	102.2417 4005	99.4658 2666	96.7984 9687	156
157	108.5974 5257	102.6429 8931	99.8418 1532	97.1508 2468	157
158	109.0521 9161	103.0419 1152	100.2154 6864	97.5008 1919	158
159	109.5046 6827	103.4385 2019	100.5868 0113	97.8484 9586	159
160	109.9548 9380	103.8328 2872	100.9558 2721	98.1938 7003	160
161	110.4028 7940	104.2248 5046	101.3225 6120	98.5369 5695	161
162	110.8486 3622	104.6145 9866	101.6870 1734	98.8777 7178	162
163	111.2921 7534	105.0020 8652	102.0492 0978	99.2163 2956	163
164	111.7335 0780	105.3873 2715	102.4091 5258	99.5526 4523	164
165	112.1726 4458	105.7703 3357	102.7668 5971	99.8867 3364	165
166	112.6095 9660	106.1511 1874	103.1223 4505	100.2186 0955	166
167	113.0443 7473	106.5296 9555	103.4756 2241	100.5482 8760	167
168	113.4769 8978	106.9060 7680	103.8267 0550	100.8757 8236	168
169	113.9074 5251	107.2802 7523	104.1756 0795	101.2011 0828	169
170	114.3357 7365	107.6523 0349	104.5223 4330	101.5242 7972	170
171	114.7619 6383	108.0221 7417	104.8669 2502	101.8453 1095	171
172	115.1860 3366	108.3898 9979	105.2093 6648	102.1642 1614	172
173	115.6079 9369	108.7554 9278	105.5496 8098	102.4810 0939	173
174	116.0278 5442	109.1189 6552	105.8878 8172	102.7957 0466	174
175	116.4456 2629	109.4803 3029	106.2239 8183	103.1083 1586	175
176	116.8613 1969	109.8395 9933	106.5579 9436	103.4188 5678	176
177	117.2749 4496	110.1967 8478	106.8899 3229	103.7273 4115	177
178	117.6865 1240	110.5518 9874	107.2198 0848	104.0337 8257	178
179	118.0960 3224	110.9049 5322	107.5476 3576	104.3381 9457	179
180	118.5035 1467	111.2559 6015	107.8734 2684	104.6405 9061	180
181	118.9089 6982	111.6049 3142	108.1971 9438	104.9409 8402	181
182	119.3124 0778	111.9518 7882	108.5189 5094	105.2393 8807	182
183	119.7138 3859	112.2968 1411	108.8387 0900	105.5358 1593	183
184	120.1132 7222	112.6397 4894	109.1564 8100	105.8302 8070	184
185	120.5107 1863	112.9806 9492	109.4722 7925	106.1227 9536	185
186	120.9061 8769	113.3196 6359	109.7861 1603	106.4133 7285	186
187	121.2996 8925	113.6566 6640	110.0980 0351	106.7020 2598	187
188	121.6912 3308	113.9917 1477	110.4079 5379	106.9887 6750	188
189	122.0808 2894	114.3248 2002	110.7159 7893	107.2736 1007	189
190	122.4684 8650	114.6559 9342	111.0220 9086	107.5565 6626	190
191	122.8542 1543	114.9852 4619	111.3263 0147	107.8376 4857	191
192	123.2380 2530	115.3125 8945	111.6286 2258	108.1168 6941	192
193	123.6199 2567	115.6380 3429	111.9290 6592	108.3942 4111	193
194	123.9999 2604	115.9615 9171	112.2276 4315	108.6697 7590	194
195	124.3780 3586	116.2832 7265	112.5243 6586	108.9434 8597	195
196	124.7542 6454	116.6030 8801	112.8192 4558	109.2153 8338	196
197	125.1286 2143	116.9210 4859	113.1122 9374	109.4854 8015	197
198	125.5011 1585	117.2371 6516	113.4035 2173	109.7537 8819	198
199	125.8717 5707	117.5514 4842	113.6929 4085	110.0203 1937	199
200	126.2405 5430	117.8639 0899	113.9805 6234	110.2850 8543	200

TABLE IV.—Present Value of Annuity of 1 per Period

$$a_{\overline{n}|i} = \frac{1 - (1 + i)^{-n}}{i}$$

n	¾%	⅞%	1%	1⅛%	n
1	0.9925 5583	0.9913 2590	0.9900 9901	0.9888 7515	1
2	1.9777 2291	1.9740 5294	1.9703 9506	1.9667 4923	2
3	2.9555 5624	2.9482 5570	2.9409 8521	2.9337 4460	3
4	3.9261 1041	3.9140 0813	3.9019 6555	3.8899 8230	4
5	4.8894 3961	4.8713 8352	4.8534 3124	4.8355 8200	5
6	5.8455 9763	5.8204 5454	5.7954 7647	5.7706 6205	6
7	6.7946 3785	6.7612 9323	6.7281 9453	6.6953 3948	7
8	7.7366 1325	7.6939 7098	7.6516 7775	7.6097 3002	8
9	8.6715 7642	8.6185 5859	8.5660 1758	8.5139 4810	9
10	9.5995 7958	9.5351 2624	9.4713 0453	9.4081 0690	10
11	10.5206 7452	10.4437 4348	10.3676 2825	10.2923 1832	11
12	11.4349 1267	11.3444 7929	11.2550 7747	11.1666 9302	12
13	12.3423 4508	12.2374 0202	12.1337 4007	12.0313 4044	13
14	13.2430 2242	13.1225 7945	13.0037 0304	12.8863 6880	14
15	14.1369 9495	14.0000 7876	13.8650 5252	13.7318 8509	15
16	15.0243 1261	14.8699 6656	14.7178 7378	14.5679 9514	16
17	15.9050 2492	15.7323 0885	15.5622 5127	15.3948 0360	17
18	16.7791 8107	16.5871 7111	16.3982 6858	16.2124 1395	18
19	17.6468 2984	17.4346 1820	17.2260 0850	17.0209 2850	19
20	18.5080 1969	18.2747 1445	18.0455 5297	17.8204 4845	20
21	19.3627 9870	19.1075 2361	18.8569 8313	18.6110 7387	21
22	20.2112 1459	19.9331 0891	19.6603 7934	19.3929 0371	22
23	21.0533 1473	20.7515 3300	20.4558 2113	20.1660 3580	23
24	21.8891 4614	21.5628 5799	21.2433 8726	20.9305 6693	24
25	22.7187 5547	22.3671 4547	22.0231 5570	21.6865 9276	25
26	23.5421 8905	23.1644 5647	22.7952 0366	22.4342 0792	26
27	24.3594 9286	23.9548 5152	23.5596 0759	23.1735 0598	27
28	25.1707 1251	24.7383 9060	24.3164 4316	23.9045 7946	28
29	25.9758 9331	25.5151 3319	25.0657 8530	24.6275 1986	29
30	26.7750 8021	26.2851 3823	25.8077 0822	25.3424 1766	30
31	27.5683 1783	27.0484 6417	26.5422 8537	26.0493 6233	31
32	28.3556 5045	27.8051 6894	27.2695 8947	26.7484 4236	32
33	29.1371 2203	28.5553 0998	27.9896 9255	27.4397 4522	33
34	29.9127 7621	29.2989 4422	28.7026 6589	28.1233 5745	34
35	30.6826 5629	30.0361 2809	29.4085 8009	28.7993 6460	35
36	31.4468 0525	30.7669 1757	30.1075 0504	29.4678 5127	36
37	32.2052 6576	31.4913 6810	30.7995 0994	30.1289 0114	37
38	32.9580 8016	32.2095 3467	31.4846 6330	30.7825 9692	38
39	33.7052 9048	32.9214 7179	32.1630 3298	31.4290 2044	39
40	34.4469 3844	33.6272 3350	32.8346 8611	32.0682 5260	40
41	35.1830 6545	34.3268 7335	33.4996 8922	32.7903 7340	41
42	35.9137 1260	35.0204 4446	34.1581 0814	33.3254 6195	42
43	36.6389 2070	35.7079 9947	34.8100 0806	33.9435 9649	43
44	37.3587 3022	36.3895 9055	35.4554 5352	34.5548 5438	44
45	38.0731 8136	37.0652 6944	36.0945 0844	35.1593 1212	45
46	38.7823 1401	37.7350 8743	36.7272 3608	35.7570 4536	46
47	39.4861 6774	38.3990 9535	37.3536 9909	36.3481 2891	47
48	40.1847 8189	39.0573 4359	37.9739 5949	36.9326 3674	48
49	40.8781 9542	39.7098 8212	38.5880 7871	37.5106 4202	49
50	41.5664 4707	40.3567 6047	39.1961 1753	38.0822 1708	50

TABLE IV.—Present Value of Annuity of 1 per Period

$$a_{\overline{n}|i} = \frac{1 - (1 + i)^{-n}}{i}$$

n	¾%	⅞%	1%	1⅛%	n
51	42.2495 7525	40.9980 2772	39.7981 3617	38.6474 3345	51
52	42.9276 1812	41.6337 3256	40.3941 9423	39.2063 6188	52
53	43.6006 1351	42.2639 2324	40.9843 5072	39.7590 7232	53
54	44.2685 9902	42.8886 4757	41.5686 6408	40.3056 3394	54
55	44.9316 1193	43.5079 5298	42.1471 9216	40.8461 1514	55
56	45.5896 8926	44.1218 8647	42.7199 9224	41.3805 8358	56
57	46.2428 6776	44.7304 9465	43.2871 2102	41.9091 0613	57
58	46.8911 8388	45.3338 2369	43.8486 3468	42.4317 4896	58
59	47.5346 7382	45.9319 1939	44.4045 8879	42.9485 7746	59
60	48.1733 7352	46.5248 2716	44.9550 3841	43.4596 5633	60
61	48.8073 1863	47.1125 9198	45.5000 3803	43.9650 4952	61
62	49.4365 4455	47.6952 5847	46.0396 4161	44.4648 2029	62
63	50.0610 8640	48.2728 7085	46.5739 0258	44.9590 3119	63
64	50.6809 7906	48.8454 7296	47.1028 7385	45.4477 4407	64
65	51.2962 5713	49.4131 0826	47.6266 0777	45.9310 2009	65
66	51.9069 5497	49.9758 1984	48.1451 5621	46.4089 1975	66
67	52.5131 0667	50.5336 5040	48.6585 7050	46.8815 0284	67
68	53.1147 4607	51.0866 4228	49.1669 0149	47.3488 2852	68
69	53.7119 0677	51.6348 3745	49.6701 9949	47.8109 5527	69
70	54.3046 2210	52.1782 7752	50.1685 1435	48.2679 4094	70
71	54.8929 2516	52.7170 0374	50.6618 9539	48.7198 4270	71
72	55.4768 4880	53.2510 5699	51.1503 9148	49.1667 1714	72
73	56.0564 2561	53.7804 7781	51.6340 5097	49.6086 2016	73
74	56.6316 8795	54.3053 0638	52.1129 2175	50.0456 0708	74
75	57.2026 6794	54.8255 8253	52.5870 5124	50.4777 3259	75
76	57.7693 9746	55.3413 4575	53.0564 8637	50.9050 5077	76
77	58.3319 0815	55.8526 3520	53.5212 7364	51.3276 1510	77
78	58.8902 3141	56.3594 8966	53.9814 5905	51.7454 7847	78
79	59.4443 9842	56.8619 4762	54.4370 8817	52.1586 9317	79
80	59.9944 4012	57.3600 4721	54.8882 0611	52.5673 1092	80
81	60.5403 8722	57.8538 2623	55.3348 5753	52.9713 8286	81
82	61.0822 7019	58.3433 2216	55.7770 8666	53.3709 5957	82
83	61.6201 1930	58.8285 7215	56.2149 3729	53.7660 9104	83
84	62.1539 6456	59.3096 1304	56.6484 5276	54.1568 2674	84
85	62.6838 3579	59.7864 8133	57.0776 7600	54.5432 1557	85
86	63.2097 6257	60.2592 1321	57.5026 4951	54.9253 0588	86
87	63.7317 7427	60.7278 4457	57.9234 1535	55.3031 4549	87
88	64.2499 0002	61.1924 1097	58.3400 1520	55.6767 8169	88
89	64.7641 6875	61.6529 4768	58.7524 9030	56.0462 6126	89
90	65.2746 0918	62.1094 8965	59.1608 8148	56.4116 3041	90
91	65.7812 4981	62.5620 7152	59.5652 2919	56.7729 3490	91
92	66.2841 1892	63.0107 2765	59.9655 7346	57.1302 1992	92
93	66.7832 4458	63.4554 9210	60.3619 5392	57.4835 3021	93
94	67.2786 5467	63.8963 9861	60.7544 0982	57.8329 0997	94
95	67.7703 7685	64.3334 8065	61.1429 8002	58.1784 0294	95
96	68.2584 3856	64.7667 7140	61.5277 0299	58.5200 5235	96
97	68.7428 6705	65.1963 0375	61.9086 1682	58.8579 0096	97
98	69.2236 8938	65.6221 1028	62.2857 5923	59.1919 9106	98
99	69.7009 3239	66.0442 2333	62.6591 6755	59.5223 6446	99
100	70.1746 2272	66.4626 7492	63.0288 7877	59.8490 6251	100

TABLE IV.—Present Value of Annuity of 1 per Period

$$a_{\overline{n}|i} = \frac{1 - (1+i)^{-n}}{i}$$

n	1¼%	1⅜%	1½%	1¾%	n
1	0.9876 5432	0.9864 3650	0.9852 2167	0.9828 0098	1
2	1.9631 1538	1.9594 9346	1.9558 8342	1.9486 9875	2
3	2.9265 3371	2.9193 5237	2.9122 0042	2.8979 8403	3
4	3.8780 5798	3.8661 9222	3.8543 8465	3.8309 4254	4
5	4.8178 3504	4.8001 8962	4.7826 4497	4.7478 5508	5
6	5.7460 0992	5.7215 1874	5.6971 8717	5.6489 9762	6
7	6.6627 2585	6.6303 5140	6.5982 1396	6.5346 4139	7
8	7.5681 2429	7.5268 5712	7.4859 2508	7.4050 5297	8
9	8.4623 4498	8.4112 0308	8.3605 1732	8.2604 9432	9
10	9.3455 2591	9.2835 5421	9.2221 8455	9.1012 2291	10
11	10.2178 0337	10.1440 7320	10.0711 1779	9.9274 9181	11
12	11.0793 1197	10.9929 2054	10.9075 0521	10.7395 4969	12
13	11.9301 8466	11.8302 5454	11.7315 3222	11.5376 4097	13
14	12.7705 5275	12.6562 3136	12.5433 8150	12.3220 0587	14
15	13.6005 4592	13.4710 0504	13.3432 3301	13.0928 8046	15
16	14.4202 9227	14.2747 2754	14.1312 6405	13.8504 9677	16
17	15.2299 1829	15.0675 4874	14.9076 4931	14.5950 8282	17
18	16.0295 4893	15.8496 1651	15.6725 6089	15.3268 6272	18
19	16.8193 0759	16.6210 7671	16.4261 6837	16.0460 5673	19
20	17.5993 1613	17.3820 7320	17.1686 3879	16.7528 8130	20
21	18.3696 9495	18.1327 4792	17.9001 3673	17.4475 4919	21
22	19.1305 6291	18.8732 4086	18.6208 2437	18.1302 6948	22
23	19.8820 3744	19.6036 9012	19.3308 6145	18.8012 4764	23
24	20.6242 3451	20.3242 3193	20.0304 0537	19.4606 8565	24
25	21.3572 6865	21.0350 0067	20.7196 1120	20.1087 8196	25
26	22.0812 5299	21.7361 2890	21.3986 3172	20.7457 3166	26
27	22.7962 9925	22.4277 4737	22.0676 1746	21.3717 2644	27
28	23.5025 1778	23.1099 8508	22.7267 1671	21.9869 5474	28
29	24.2000 1756	23.7829 6925	23.3760 7558	22.5916 0171	29
30	24.8889 0623	24.4468 2540	24.0158 3801	23.1858 4934	30
31	25.5692 9010	25.1016 7734	24.6461 4582	23.7698 7650	31
32	26.2412 7418	25.7476 4719	25.2671 3874	24.3438 5897	32
33	26.9049 6215	26.3848 5543	25.8789 5442	24.9079 6951	33
34	27.5604 5644	27.0134 2089	26.4817 2849	25.4623 7789	34
35	28.2078 5822	27.6334 6080	27.0755 9458	26.0072 5100	35
36	28.8472 6737	28.2450 9080	27.6606 8431	26.5427 5283	36
37	29.4787 8259	28.8484 2496	28.2371 2740	27.0690 4455	37
38	30.1025 0133	29.4435 7579	28.8050 5163	27.5862 8457	38
39	30.7185 1983	30.0306 5430	29.3645 8288	28.0946 2857	39
40	31.3269 3316	30.6097 6996	29.9158 4520	28.5942 2955	40
41	31.9278 3522	31.1810 3079	30.4589 6079	29.0852 3789	41
42	32.5213 1874	31.7445 4332	30.9940 5004	29.5678 0135	42
43	33.1074 7530	32.3004 1264	31.5212 3157	30.0420 6522	43
44	33.6863 9536	32.8487 4243	32.0406 2223	30.5081 7221	44
45	34.2581 6825	33.3896 3495	32.5523 3718	30.9662 6261	45
46	34.8228 8222	33.9231 9108	33.0564 8983	31.4164 7431	46
47	35.3806 2442	34.4495 1031	33.5531 9195	31.8589 4281	47
48	35.9314 8091	34.9686 9081	34.0425 5365	32.2938 0129	48
49	36.4755 3670	35.4808 2941	34.5246 8339	32.7211 8063	49
50	37.0128 7574	35.9860 2161	34.9996 8807	33.1412 0946	50

TABLE IV.—Present Value of Annuity of 1 per Period

$$a_{\overline{n}|i} = \frac{1 - (1 + i)^{-n}}{i}$$

n	$1\frac{1}{4}\%$	$1\frac{3}{8}\%$	$1\frac{1}{2}\%$	$1\frac{3}{4}\%$	n
51	37.5435 8099	36.4843 6164	35.4676 7298	33.5540 1421	51
52	38.0677 3431	36.9759 4243	35.9287 4185	33.9597 1913	52
53	38.5854 1660	37.4608 5566	36.3829 9690	34.3584 4633	53
54	39.0967 0776	37.9391 9178	36.8305 3882	34.7503 1579	54
55	39.6016 8667	38.4110 3998	37.2714 6681	35.1354 4550	55
56	40.1004 3128	38.8764 8826	37.7058 7863	35.5139 5135	56
57	40.5930 1855	39.3356 2344	38.1338 7058	35.8859 4727	57
58	41.0795 2449	39.7885 3114	38.5555 3751	36.2515 4523	58
59	41.5600 2419	40.2352 9582	38.9709 7292	36.6108 5526	59
60	42.0345 9179	40.6760 0081	39.3802 6889	36.9639 8552	60
61	42.5033 0054	41.1107 2829	39.7835 1614	37.3110 4228	61
62	42.9662 2275	41.5395 5935	40.1808 0408	37.6521 3000	62
63	43.4234 2988	41.9625 7396	40.5722 2077	37.9873 5135	63
64	43.8749 9247	42.3798 5101	40.9578 5298	38.3168 0723	64
65	44.3209 8022	42.7914 6832	41.3377 8618	38.6405 9678	65
66	44.7614 6195	43.1975 0266	41.7121 0461	38.9588 1748	66
67	45.1965 0563	43.5980 2975	42.0808 9125	39.2715 6509	67
68	45.6261 7840	43.9931 2429	42.4442 2783	39.5789 3375	68
69	46.0505 4656	44.3828 5997	42.8021 9490	39.8810 1597	69
70	46.4696 7562	44.7673 0946	43.1548 7183	40.1779 0267	70
71	46.8836 3024	45.1465 4448	43.5023 3678	40.4696 8321	71
72	47.2924 7431	45.5206 3573	43.8446 6677	40.7564 4542	72
73	47.6962 7093	45.8896 5300	44.1819 3771	41.0382 7560	73
74	48.0950 8240	46.2536 6511	44.5142 2434	41.3152 5857	74
75	48.4889 7027	46.6127 3994	44.8416 0034	41.5874 7771	75
76	48.8779 9533	46.9669 4445	45.1641 3826	41.8550 1495	76
77	49.2622 1761	47.3163 4471	45.4819 0962	42.1179 5081	77
78	49.6416 9640	47.6610 0588	45.7949 8485	42.3763 6443	78
79	50.0164 9027	48.0009 9224	46.1034 3335	42.6303 3359	79
80	50.3866 5706	48.3363 6719	46.4073 2349	42.8799 3474	80
81	50.7522 5389	48.6671 9328	46.7067 2265	43.1252 4298	81
82	51.1133 3717	48.9935 3221	47.0016 9720	43.3663 3217	82
83	51.4699 6264	49.3154 4484	47.2923 1251	43.6032 7486	83
84	51.8221 8532	49.6329 9122	47.5786 3301	43.8361 4237	84
85	52.1700 5958	49.9462 3055	47.8607 2218	44.0650 0479	85
86	52.5136 3909	50.2552 2125	48.1386 4254	44.2899 3099	86
87	52.8529 7688	50.5600 2096	48.4124 5571	44.5109 8869	87
88	53.1881 2531	50.8606 8653	48.6822 2237	44.7282 4441	88
89	53.5191 3611	51.1572 7401	48.9480 0234	44.9417 6355	89
90	53.8460 6035	51.4498 3873	49.2098 5452	45.1516 1037	90
91	54.1689 4850	51.7384 3524	49.4678 3696	45.3578 4803	91
92	54.4878 5037	52.0231 1738	49.7220 0686	45.5605 3860	92
93	54.8028 1518	52.3039 3823	49.9724 2055	45.7597 4310	93
94	55.1138 9154	52.5809 5016	50.2191 3355	45.9555 2147	94
95	55.4211 2744	52.8542 0484	50.4622 0054	46.1479 3265	95
96	55.7245 7031	53.1237 5324	50.7016 7541	46.3370 3455	96
97	56.0242 6698	53.3896 4561	50.9376 1124	46.5228 8408	97
98	56.3202 6368	53.6519 3155	51.1700 6034	46.7055 3718	98
99	56.6126 0610	53.9106 5998	51.3990 7422	46.8850 4882	99
100	56.9013 3936	54.1658 7914	51.6247 0367	47.0614 7304	100

TABLE IV. —Present Value of Annuity of 1 per Period

$$a_{\overline{n}|i} = \frac{1 - (1+i)^{-n}}{i}$$

n	2%	$2\frac{1}{4}$%	$2\frac{1}{2}$%	$2\frac{3}{4}$%	n
1	0.9803 9216	0.9779 9511	0.9756 0976	0.9732 3601	1
2	1.9415 6094	1.9344 6955	1.9274 2415	1.9204 2434	2
3	2.8838 8327	2.8698 9687	2.8560 2356	2.8422 6213	3
4	3.8077 2870	3.7847 4021	3.7619 7421	3.7394 2787	4
5	4.7134 5951	4.6794 5253	4.6458 2850	4.6125 8186	5
6	5.6014 3089	5.5544 7680	5.5081 2536	5.4623 6678	6
7	6.4719 9107	6.4102 4626	6.3493 9060	6.2894 0806	7
8	7.3254 8144	7.2471 8461	7.1701 3717	7.0943 1441	8
9	8.1622 3671	8.0657 0622	7.9708 6553	7.8776 7826	9
10	8.9825 8501	8.8662 1635	8.7520 6393	8.6400 7616	10
11	9.7868 4805	9.6491 1134	9.5142 0871	9.3820 6926	11
12	10.5753 4122	10.4147 7882	10.2577 6460	10.1042 0366	12
13	11.3483 7375	11.1635 9787	10.9831 8497	10.8070 1086	13
14	12.1062 4877	11.8959 3924	11.6909 1217	11.4910 0814	14
15	12.8492 6350	12.6121 6551	12.3813 7773	12.1566 9892	15
16	13.5777 0931	13.3126 3131	13.0550 0266	12.8045 7315	16
17	14.2918 7188	13.9976 8343	13.7121 9772	13.4351 0769	17
18	14.9920 3125	14.6676 6106	14.3533 6363	14.0487 6661	18
19	15.6784 6201	15.3228 9590	14.9788 9134	14.6460 0157	19
20	16.3514 3334	15.9637 1237	15.5891 6229	15.2272 5213	20
21	17.0112 0916	16.5904 2775	16.1845 4857	15.7929 4612	21
22	17.6580 4820	17.2033 5232	16.7654 1324	16.3434 9987	22
23	18.2922 0412	17.8027 8955	17.3321 1048	16.8793 1861	23
24	18.9139 2560	18.3890 3624	17.8849 8583	17.4007 9670	24
25	19.5234 5647	18.9623 8263	18.4243 7642	17.9083 1795	25
26	20.1210 3576	19.5231 1260	18.9506 1114	18.4022 5592	26
27	20.7068 9780	20.0715 0376	19.4640 1087	18.8829 7413	27
28	21.2812 7236	20.6078 2764	19.9648 8866	19.3508 2640	28
29	21.8443 8466	21.1323 4977	20.4535 4991	19.8061 5708	29
30	22.3964 5555	21.6453 2985	20.9302 9259	20.2493 0130	30
31	22.9377 0152	22.1470 2186	21.3954 0741	20.6805 8520	31
32	23.4683 3482	22.6376 7419	21.8491 7796	21.1003 2623	32
33	23.9885 6355	23.1175 2977	22.2918 8094	21.5088 3332	33
34	24.4985 9172	23.5868 2618	22.7237 8628	21.9064 0712	34
35	24.9986 1933	24.0457 9577	23.1451 5734	22.2933 4026	35
36	25.4888 4248	24.4946 6579	23.5562 5107	22.6699 1753	36
37	25.9694 5341	24.9336 5848	23.9573 1812	23.0364 1609	37
38	26.4406 4060	25.3629 9118	24.3486 0304	23.3931 0568	38
39	26.9025 8883	25.7828 7646	24.7303 4443	23.7402 4884	39
40	27.3554 7924	26.1935 2221	25.1027 7505	24.0781 0106	40
41	27.7994 8945	26.5951 3174	25.4661 2200	24.4069 1101	41
42	28.2347 9358	26.9879 0390	25.8206 0683	24.7269 2069	42
43	28.6615 6233	27.3720 3316	26.1664 4569	25.0383 6563	43
44	29.0799 6307	27.7477 0969	26.5038 4945	25.3414 7507	44
45	29.4901 5987	28.1151 1950	26.8330 2386	25.6364 7209	45
46	29.8923 1360	28.4744 4450	27.1541 6962	25.9235 7381	46
47	30.2865 8196	28.8258 6259	27.4674 8255	26.2029 9154	47
48	30.6731 1957	29.1695 4777	27.7731 5371	26.4749 3094	48
49	31.0520 7801	29.5056 7019	28.0713 6947	26.7395 9215	49
50	31.4236 0589	29.8343 9627	28.3623 1168	26.9971 6998	50

TABLE IV.—Present Value of Annuity of 1 per Period

$$a_{\overline{n}|i} = \frac{1 - (1 + i)^{-n}}{i}$$

n	2%	2¼%	2½%	2¾%	n
51	31.7878 4892	30.1568 8877	28.6461 5774	27.2478 5400	51
52	32.1449 4992	30.4703 0687	28.9230 8072	27.4918 2871	52
53	32.4950 4894	30.7778 0623	29.1932 4948	27.7292 7368	53
54	32.8382 8327	31.0785 3910	29.4568 2876	27.9603 6368	54
55	33.1747 8752	31.3726 5438	29.7139 7928	28.1852 6879	55
56	33.5046 9365	31.6602 9768	29.9648 5784	28.4041 5454	56
57	33.8281 3103	31.9416 1142	30.2096 1740	28.6171 8203	57
58	34.1452 2650	32.2167 3489	30.4484 0722	28.8245 0806	58
59	34.4561 0441	32.4858 0429	30.6813 7290	29.0262 8522	59
60	34.7608 8668	32.7489 5285	30.9086 5649	29.2226 6201	60
61	35.0596 9282	33.0063 1086	31.1303 9657	29.4137 8298	61
62	35.3526 4002	33.2580 0573	31.3467 2836	29.5997 8879	62
63	35.6398 4316	33.5041 6208	31.5577 8377	29.7808 1634	63
64	35.9214 1486	33.7449 0179	31.7636 9148	29.9569 9887	64
65	36.1974 6555	33.9803 4405	31.9645 7705	30.1284 6605	65
66	36.4681 0348	34.2106 0543	32.1605 6298	30.2953 4409	66
67	36.7334 3478	34.4357 9993	32.3517 6876	30.4577 5581	67
68	36.9935 6351	34.6560 3905	32.5383 1099	30.6158 2074	68
69	37.2485 9168	34.8714 3183	32.7203 0340	30.7696 5522	69
70	37.4986 1929	35.0820 8492	32.8978 5698	30.9193 7247	70
71	37.7437 4441	35.2881 0261	33.0710 7998	31.0650 8270	71
72	37.9840 6314	35.4895 8691	33.2400 7803	31.2068 9314	72
73	38.2196 6975	35.6866 3756	33.4049 5417	31.3449 0816	73
74	38.4506 5662	35.8793 5214	33.5658 0895	31.4792 2936	74
75	38.6771 1433	36.0678 2605	33.7227 4044	31.6099 5558	75
76	38.8991 3170	36.2521 5262	33.8758 4433	31.7371 8304	76
77	39.1167 9578	36.4324 2310	34.0252 1398	31.8610 0540	77
78	39.3301 9194	36.6087 2675	34.1709 4047	31.9815 1377	78
79	39.5394 0386	36.7811 5085	34.3131 1265	32.0987 9685	79
80	39.7445 1359	36.9497 8079	34.4518 1722	32.2129 4098	80
81	39.9456 0156	37.1147 0004	34.5871 3875	32.3240 3015	81
82	40.1427 4663	37.2759 9026	34.7191 5976	32.4321 4613	82
83	40.3360 2611	37.4337 3130	34.8479 6074	32.5373 6850	83
84	40.5255 1579	37.5880 0127	34.9736 2023	32.6397 7469	84
85	40.7112 8999	37.7388 7655	35.0962 1486	32.7394 4009	85
86	40.8934 2156	37.8864 3183	35.2158 1938	32.8364 3804	86
87	41.0719 8192	38.0307 4018	35.3325 0671	32.9308 3994	87
88	41.2470 4110	38.1718 7304	35.4463 4801	33.0227 1527	88
89	41.4186 6774	38.3099 0028	35.5574 1269	33.1121 3165	89
90	41.5869 2916	38.4448 9025	35.6657 6848	33.1991 5489	90
91	41.7518 9133	38.5769 0978	35.7714 8144	33.2838 4905	91
92	41.9136 1895	38.7060 2423	35.8746 1604	33.3662 7644	92
93	42.0721 7545	38.8322 9754	35.9752 3516	33.4464 9776	93
94	42.2276 2299	38.9557 9221	36.0734 0016	33.5245 7202	94
95	42.3800 2254	39.0765 6940	36.1691 7089	33.6005 5671	95
96	42.5294 3386	39.1946 8890	36.2626 0574	33.6745 0775	96
97	42.6759 1555	39.3102 0920	36.3537 6170	33.7464 7956	97
98	42.8195 2505	39.4231 8748	36.4426 9434	33.8165 2512	98
99	42.9603 1867	39.5336 7968	36.5294 5790	33.8846 9598	99
100	43.0983 5164	39.6417 4052	36.6141 0526	33.9510 4232	100

TABLE IV.—Present Value of Annuity of 1 per Period

$$a_{\overline{n}|i} = \frac{1-(1+i)^{-n}}{i}$$

n	3%	3½%	4%	4½%	n
1	0.9708 7379	0.9661 8357	0.9615 3846	0.9569 3780	1
2	1.9134 6970	1.8996 9428	1.8860 9467	1.8726 6775	2
3	2.8286 1135	2.8016 3698	2.7750 9103	2.7489 6435	3
4	3.7170 9840	3.6730 7921	3.6298 9522	3.5875 2570	4
5	4.5797 0719	4.5150 5238	4.4518 2233	4.3899 7674	5
6	5.4171 9144	5.3285 5302	5.2421 3686	5.1578 7248	6
7	6.2302 8296	6.1145 4398	6.0020 5467	5.8927 0094	7
8	7.0196 9219	6.8739 5554	6.7327 4487	6.5958 8607	8
9	7.7861 0892	7.6076 8651	7.4353 3161	7.2687 9050	9
10	8.5302 0284	8.3166 0532	8.1108 9578	7.9127 1818	10
11	9.2526 2411	9.0015 5104	8.7604 7671	8.5289 1692	11
12	9.9540 0399	9.6633 3433	9.3850 7376	9.1185 8078	12
13	10.6349 5533	10.3027 3849	9.9856 4785	9.6828 5242	13
14	11.2960 7314	10.9205 2028	10.5631 2293	10.2228 2528	14
15	11.9379 3509	11.5174 1090	11.1183 8743	10.7395 4573	15
16	12.5611 0203	12.0941 1681	11.6522 9561	11.2340 1505	16
17	13.1661 1847	12.6513 2059	12.1656 6885	11.7071 9143	17
18	13.7535 1308	13.1896 8173	12.6592 9697	12.1599 9180	18
19	14.3237 9911	13.7098 3742	13.1339 3940	12.5932 9359	19
20	14.8774 7486	14.2124 0330	13.5903 2634	13.0079 3645	20
21	15.4150 2414	14.6979 7420	14.0291 5995	13.4047 2388	21
22	15.9369 1664	15.1671 2484	14.4511 1533	13.7844 2476	22
23	16.4436 0839	15.6204 1047	14.8568 4167	14.1477 7489	23
24	16.9355 4212	16.0583 6760	15.2469 6314	14.4954 7837	24
25	17.4131 4769	16.4815 1459	15.6220 7994	14.8282 0896	25
26	17.8768 4242	16.8903 5226	15.9827 6918	15.1466 1145	26
27	18.3270 3147	17.2853 6451	16.3295 8575	15.4513 0282	27
28	18.7641 0823	17.6670 1885	16.6630 6322	15.7428 7351	28
29	19.1884 5459	18.0357 6700	16.9837 1463	16.0218 8853	29
30	19.6004 4135	18.3920 4541	17.2920 3330	16.2888 8854	30
31	20.0004 2849	18.7362 7576	17.5884 9356	16.5443 9095	31
32	20.3887 6553	19.0688 6547	17.8735 5150	16.7888 9086	32
33	20.7657 9178	19.3902 0818	18.1476 4567	17.0228 6207	33
34	21.1318 3668	19.7006 8423	18.4111 9776	17.2467 5796	34
35	21.4872 2007	20.0006 6110	18.6646 1323	17.4610 1240	35
36	21.8322 5250	20.2904 9381	18.9082 8195	17.6660 4058	36
37	22.1672 3544	20.5705 2542	19.1425 7880	17.8622 3979	37
38	22.4924 6159	20.8410 8736	19.3678 6423	18.0499 9023	38
39	22.8082 1513	21.1024 9987	19.5844 8484	18.2296 5572	39
40	23.1147 7197	21.3550 7234	19.7927 7388	18.4015 8442	40
41	23.4123 9997	21.5991 0371	19.9930 5181	18.5661 0949	41
42	23.7013 5920	21.8348 8281	20.1856 2674	18.7235 4975	42
43	23.9819 0213	22.0626 8870	20.3707 9494	18.8742 1029	43
44	24.2542 7392	22.2827 9102	20.5488 4129	19.0183 8305	44
45	24.5187 1254	22.4954 5026	20.7200 3970	19.1563 4742	45
46	24.7754 4907	22.7009 1813	20.8846 5356	19.2883 7074	46
47	25.0247 0783	22.8994 3780	21.0429 3612	19.4147 0884	47
48	25.2667 0664	23.0912 4425	21.1951 3088	19.5356 0654	48
49	25.5016 5693	23.2765 6450	21.3414 7200	19.6512 9813	49
50	25.7297 6401	23.4556 1787	21.4821 8462	19.7620 0778	50

TABLE IV.—Present Value of Annuity of 1 per Period

$$a_{\overline{n}|i} = \frac{1 - (1 + i)^{-n}}{i}$$

n	3%	3½%	4%	4½%	*n*
51	25.9512 2719	23.6286 1630	21.6174 8521	19.8679 5003	51
52	26.1662 3999	23.7957 6454	21.7475 8193	19.9693 3017	52
53	26.3749 9028	23.9572 6043	21.8726 7493	20.0663 4466	53
54	26.5776 6047	24.1132 9510	21.9929 5667	20.1591 8149	54
55	26.7744 2764	24.2640 5323	22.1086 1218	20.2480 2057	55
56	26.9654 6373	24.4097 1327	22.2189 1940	20.3330 3404	56
57	27.1509 3566	24.5504 4760	22.3267 4943	20.4143 8664	57
58	27.3310 0549	24.6864 2281	22.4295 6676	20.4922 3602	58
59	27.5058 3058	24.8177 9981	22.5284 2957	20.5667 3303	59
60	27.6755 6367	24.9447 3412	22.6234 8997	20.6380 2204	60
61	27.8403 5307	25.0673 7596	22.7148 9421	20.7062 4118	61
62	28.0003 4279	25.1858 7049	22.8027 8289	20.7715 2266	62
63	28.1556 7261	25.3003 5796	22.8872 9124	20.8339 9298	63
64	28.3064 7826	25.4109 7388	22.9685 4927	20.8937 7319	64
65	28.4528 9152	25.5178 4916	23.0466 8199	20.9509 7913	65
66	28.5950 4031	25.6211 1030	23.1218 0961	21.0057 2165	66
67	28.7330 4884	25.7208 7951	23.1940 4770	21.0581 0684	67
68	28.8670 3771	25.8172 7489	23.2635 0740	21.1082 3621	68
69	28.9971 2399	25.9104 1052	23.3302 9558	21.1562 0690	69
70	29.1234 2135	26.0003 9664	23.3945 1498	21.2021 1187	70
71	29.2460 4015	26.0873 3975	23.4562 6440	21.2460 4007	71
72	29.3650 8752	26.1713 4275	23.5156 3885	21.2880 7662	72
73	29.4806 6750	26.2525 0508	23.5727 2966	21.3283 0298	73
74	29.5928 8106	26.3309 2278	23.6276 2468	21.3667 9711	74
75	29.7018 2628	26.4066 8868	23.6804 0834	21.4036 3360	75
76	29.8075 9833	26.4798 9244	23.7311 6187	21.4388 8383	76
77	29.9102 8964	26.5506 2072	23.7799 6333	21.4726 1611	77
78	30.0099 8994	26.6189 5721	23.8268 8782	21.5048 9579	78
79	30.1067 8635	26.6849 8281	23.8720 0752	21.5357 8545	79
80	30.2007 6345	26.7487 7567	23.9153 9185	21.5653 4493	80
81	30.2920 0335	26.8104 1127	23.9571 0754	21.5936 3151	81
82	30.3805 8577	26.8699 6258	23.9972 1879	21.6207 0001	82
83	30.4665 8813	26.9275 0008	24.0357 8730	21.6466 0288	83
84	30.5500 8556	26.9830 9186	24.0728 7240	21.6713 9032	84
85	30.6311 5103	27.0368 0373	24.1085 3116	21.6951 1035	85
86	30.7098 5537	27.0886 9926	24.1428 1842	21.7178 0895	86
87	30.7862 6735	27.1388 3986	24.1757 8694	21.7395 3009	87
88	30.8604 5374	27.1872 8489	24.2074 8745	21.7603 1588	88
89	30.9324 7936	27.2340 9168	24.2379 6870	21.7802 0658	89
90	31.0024 0714	27.2793 1564	24.2672 7759	21.7992 4075	90
91	31.0702 9820	27.3230 1028	24.2954 5923	21.8174 5526	91
92	31.1362 1184	27.3652 2732	24.3225 5695	21.8348 8542	92
93	31.2002 0567	27.4060 1673	24.3486 1245	21.8515 6499	93
94	31.2623 3560	27.4454 2680	24.3736 6582	21.8675 2631	94
95	31.3226 5592	27.4835 0415	24.3977 5559	21.8828 0030	95
96	31.3812 1934	27.5202 9387	24.4209 1884	21.8974 1655	96
97	31.4380 7703	27.5558 3948	24.4431 9119	21.9114 0340	97
98	31.4932 7867	27.5901 8308	24.4646 0692	21.9247 8794	98
99	31.5468 7250	27.6233 6529	24.4851 9896	21.9375 9612	99
100	31.5989 0534	27.6554 2540	24.5049 9900	21.9498 5274	100

TABLE IV.—Present Value of Annuity of 1 per Period

$$a_{\overline{n}|i} = \frac{1 - (1 + i)^{-n}}{i}$$

n	5%	5½%	6%	6½%	n
1	0.9523 8095	0.9478 6730	0.9433 9623	0.9389 6714	1
2	1.8594 1043	1.8463 1971	1.8333 9267	1.8206 2642	2
3	2.7232 4803	2.6979 3338	2.6730 1195	2.6484 7551	3
4	3.5459 5050	3.5051 5012	3.4651 0561	3.4257 9860	4
5	4.3294 7667	4.2702 8448	4.2123 6379	4.1556 7944	5
6	5.0756 9206	4.9955 3031	4.9173 2433	4.8410 1356	6
7	5.7863 7340	5.6829 6712	5.5823 8144	5.4845 1977	7
8	6.4632 1276	6.3345 6599	6.2097 9381	6.0887 5096	8
9	7.1078 2168	6.9521 9525	6.8016 9227	6.6561 0419	9
10	7.7217 3493	7.5376 2583	7.3600 8705	7.1888 3022	10
11	8.3064 1422	8.0925 3633	7.8868 7458	7.6890 4246	11
12	8.8632 5164	8.6185 1785	8.3838 4394	8.1587 2532	12
13	9.3935 7299	9.1170 7853	8.8526 8296	8.5997 4208	13
14	9.8986 4094	9.5896 4790	9.2949 8393	9.0138 4233	14
15	10.3796 5804	10.0375 8094	9.7122 4899	9.4026 6885	15
16	10.8377 6956	10.4621 6203	10.1058 9527	9.7677 6418	16
17	11.2740 6625	10.8646 0856	10.4772 5969	10.1105 7670	17
18	11.6895 8690	11.2460 7447	10.8276 0348	10.4324 6638	18
19	12.0853 2086	11.6076 5352	11.1581 1649	10.7347 1022	19
20	12.4622 1034	11.9503 8249	11.4699 2122	11.0185 0725	20
21	12.8211 5271	12.2752 4406	11.7640 7662	11.2849 8333	21
22	13.1630 0258	12.5831 6973	12.0415 8172	11.5351 9562	22
23	13.4885 7388	12.8750 4240	12.3033 7898	11.7701 3673	23
24	13.7986 4179	13.1516 9895	12.5503 5753	11.9907 3871	24
25	14.0939 4457	13.4139 3266	12.7833 5616	12.1978 7672	25
26	14.3751 8530	13.6624 9541	13.0031 6619	12.3923 7251	26
27	14.6430 3362	13.8980 9991	13.2105 3414	12.5749 9766	27
28	14.8981 2726	14.1214 2172	13.4061 6428	12.7464 7668	28
29	15.1410 7358	14.3331 0116	13.5907 2102	12.9074 8984	29
30	15.3724 5103	14.5337 4517	13.7648 3115	13.0586 7591	30
31	15.5928 1050	14.7239 2907	13.9290 8599	13.2006 3465	31
32	15.8026 7667	14.9041 9817	14.0840 4339	13.3339 2925	32
33	16.0025 4921	15.0750 6936	14.2302 2961	13.4590 8850	33
34	16.1929 0401	15.2370 3257	14.3681 4114	13.5766 0892	34
35	16.3741 9429	15.3905 5220	14.4982 4636	13.6869 5673	35
36	16.5468 5171	15.5360 6843	14.6209 8713	13.7905 6970	36
37	16.7112 8734	15.6739 9851	14.7367 8031	13.8878 5887	37
38	16.8678 9271	15.8047 3793	14.8460 1916	13.9792 1021	38
39	17.0170 4067	15.9286 6154	14.9490 7468	14.0649 8611	39
40	17.1590 8635	16.0461 2469	15.0462 9687	14.1455 2687	40
41	17.2943 6796	16.1574 6416	15.1380 1592	14.2211 5199	41
42	17.4232 0758	16.2629 9920	15.2245 4332	14.2921 6149	42
43	17.5459 1198	16.3630 3242	15.3061 7294	14.3588 3708	43
44	17.6627 7331	16.4578 5063	15.3831 8202	14.4214 4327	44
45	17.7740 6982	16.5477 2572	15.4558 3209	14.4802 2842	45
46	17.8800 6650	16.6329 1537	15.5243 6990	14.5354 2575	46
47	17.9810 1571	16.7136 6386	15.5890 2821	14.5872 5422	47
48	18.0771 5782	16.7902 0271	15.6500 2661	14.6359 1946	48
49	18.1687 2173	16.8627 5139	15.7075 7227	14.6816 1451	49
50	18.2559 2546	16.9315 1790	15.7618 6064	14.7245 2067	50

TABLE IV.—Present Value of Annuity of 1 per Period

$$a_{\overline{n}|i} = \frac{1 - (1+i)^{-n}}{i}$$

n	5%	5½%	6%	6½%	n
51	18.3389 7663	16.9966 9943	15.8130 7607	14.7648 0814	51
52	18.4180 7298	17.0584 8287	15.8613 9252	14.8026 3675	52
53	18.4934 0284	17.1170 4538	15.9069 7408	14.8381 5658	53
54	18.5651 4556	17.1725 5486	15.9499 7554	14.8715 0852	54
55	18.6334 7196	17.2251 7048	15.9905 4297	14.9028 2490	55
56	18.6985 4473	17.2750 4311	16.0288 1412	14.9322 2996	56
57	18.7605 1879	17.3223 1575	16.0649 1898	14.9598 4033	57
58	18.8195 4170	17.3671 2393	16.0989 8017	14.9857 6557	58
59	18.8757 5400	17.4095 9614	16.1311 1337	15.0101 0852	59
60	18.9292 8952	17.4498 5416	16.1614 2771	15.0329 6574	60
61	18.9802 7574	17.4880 1343	16.1900 2614	15.0544 2793	61
62	19.0288 3404	17.5241 8334	16.2170 0579	15.0745 8021	62
63	19.0750 8003	17.5584 6762	16.2424 5829	15.0935 0255	63
64	19.1191 2384	17.5909 6457	16.2664 7009	15.1112 7000	64
65	19.1610 7033	17.6217 6737	16.2891 2272	15.1279 5305	65
66	19.2010 1936	17.6509 6433	16.3104 9314	15.1436 1789	66
67	19.2390 6606	17.6786 3917	16.3306 5390	15.1583 2666	67
68	19.2753 0101	17.7048 7125	16.3496 7349	15.1721 3770	68
69	19.3098 1048	17.7297 3579	16.3676 1650	15.1851 0583	69
70	19.3426 7665	17.7533 0406	16.3845 4387	15.1972 8247	70
71	19.3739 7776	17.7756 4366	16.4005 1308	15.2087 1593	71
72	19.4037 8834	17.7968 1864	16.4155 7838	15.2194 5158	72
73	19.4321 7937	17.8168 8970	16.4297 9093	15.2295 3200	73
74	19.4592 1845	17.8359 1441	16.4431 9899	15.2389 9718	74
75	19.4849 6995	17.8539 4731	16.4558 4810	15.2478 8468	75
76	19.5094 9519	17.8710 4010	16.4677 8123	15.2562 2974	76
77	19.5328 5257	17.8872 4180	16.4790 3889	15.2640 6549	77
78	19.5550 9768	17.9025 9887	16.4896 5933	15.2714 2299	78
79	19.5762 8351	17.9171 5532	16.4996 7862	15.2783 3145	79
80	19.5964 6048	17.9309 5291	16.5091 3077	15.2848 1826	80
81	19.6156 7665	17.9440 3120	16.5180 4790	15.2909 0917	81
82	19.6339 7776	17.9564 2768	16.5264 6028	15.2966 2832	82
83	19.6514 0739	17.9681 7789	16.5343 9649	15.3019 9843	83
84	19.6680 0704	17.9793 1554	16.5418 8348	15.3070 4078	84
85	19.6838 1623	17.9898 7255	16.5489 4668	15.3117 7538	85
86	19.6988 7260	17.9998 7919	16.5556 1008	15.3162 2101	86
87	19.7132 1200	18.0093 6416	16.5618 9630	15.3203 9531	87
88	19.7268 6857	18.0183 5466	16.5678 2670	15.3243 1485	88
89	19.7398 7483	18.0268 7645	16.5734 2141	15.3279 9516	89
90	19.7522 6174	18.0349 5398	16.5786 9944	15.3314 5086	90
91	19.7640 5880	18.0426 1041	16.5836 7872	15.3346 9564	91
92	19.7752 9410	18.0498 6769	16.5883 7615	15.3377 4239	92
93	19.7859 9438	18.0567 4662	16.5928 0769	15.3406 0318	93
94	19.7961 8512	18.0632 6694	16.5969 8839	15.3432 8937	94
95	19.8058 9059	18.0694 4734	16.6009 3244	15.3458 1161	95
96	19.8151 3390	18.0753 0553	16.6046 5325	15.3481 7992	96
97	19.8239 3705	18.0808 5833	16.6081 6344	15.3504 0368	97
98	19.8323 2100	18.0861 2164	16.6114 7494	15.3524 9172	98
99	19.8403 0571	18.0911 1055	16.6145 9900	15.3544 5232	99
100	19.8479 1020	18.0958 3939	16.6175 4623	15.3562 9326	100

TABLE IV.—Present Value of Annuity of 1 per Period

$$a_{\overline{n}|i} = \frac{1 - (1 + i)^{-n}}{i}$$

n	7%	7½%	8%	8½%	n
1	0.9345 7944	0.9302 3256	0.9259 2593	0.9216 5899	1
2	1.8080 1817	1.7955 6517	1.7832 6475	1.7711 1427	2
3	2.6243 1604	2.6005 2574	2.5770 9699	2.5540 2237	3
4	3.3872 1126	3.3493 2627	3.3121 2684	3.2755 9666	4
5	4.1001 9744	4.0458 8490	3.9927 1004	3.9406 4208	5
6	4.7665 3966	4.6938 4642	4.6228 7966	4.5535 8717	6
7	5.3892 8940	5.2966 0132	5.2063 7006	5.1185 1352	7
8	5.9712 9851	5.8573 0355	5.7466 3894	5.6391 8297	8
9	6.5152 3225	6.3788 8703	6.2468 8791	6.1190 6264	9
10	7.0235 8154	6.8640 8096	6.7100 8140	6.5613 4806	10
11	7.4986 7434	7.3154 2415	7.1389 6426	6.9689 8439	11
12	7.9426 8630	7.7352 7827	7.5360 7802	7.3446 8607	12
13	8.3576 5074	8.1258 4026	7.9037 7594	7.6909 5490	13
14	8.7454 6799	8.4891 5373	8.2442 3698	8.0100 9668	14
15	9.1079 1401	8.8271 1974	8.5594 7869	8.3042 3658	15
16	9.4466 4860	9.1415 0674	8.8513 6916	8.5753 3325	16
17	9.7632 2299	9.4339 5976	9.1216 3811	8.8251 9194	17
18	10.0590 8691	9.7060 0908	9.3718 8714	9.0554 7644	18
19	10.3355 9524	9.9590 7821	9.6035 9920	9.2677 2022	19
20	10.5940 1425	10.1944 9136	9.8181 4741	9.4633 3661	20
21	10.8355 2733	10.4134 8033	10.0168 0316	9.6436 2821	21
22	11.0612 4050	10.6171 9101	10.2007 4366	9.8097 9559	22
23	11.2721 8738	10.8066 8931	10.3710 5895	9.9629 4524	23
24	11.4693 3400	10.9829 6680	10.5287 5828	10.1040 9700	24
25	11.6535 8318	11.1469 4586	10.6747 7619	10.2341 9078	25
26	11.8257 7867	11.2994 8452	10.8099 7795	10.3540 9288	26
27	11.9867 0904	11.4413 8095	10.9351 6477	10.4646 0174	27
28	12.1371 1125	11.5733 7763	11.0510 7849	10.5664 5321	28
29	12.2776 7407	11.6961 6524	11.1584 0601	10.6603 2554	29
30	12.4090 4118	11.8103 8627	11.2577 8334	10.7468 4382	30
31	12.5318 1419	11.9166 3839	11.3497 9939	10.8265 8416	31
32	12.6465 5532	12.0154 7757	11.4349 9944	10.9000 7757	32
33	12.7537 9002	12.1074 2099	11.5138 8837	10.9678 1343	33
34	12.8540 0936	12.1929 4976	11.5869 3367	11.0302 4279	34
35	12.9476 7230	12.2725 1141	11.6545 6822	11.0877 8137	35
36	13.0352 0776	12.3465 2224	11.7171 9279	11.1408 1233	36
37	13.1170 1660	12.4153 6953	11.7751 7851	11.1896 8878	37
38	13.1934 7345	12.4794 1351	11.8288 6899	11.2347 3620	38
39	13.2649 2846	12.5389 8931	11.8785 8240	11.2762 5457	39
40	13.3317 0884	12.5944 0866	11.9246 1333	11.3145 2034	40
41	13.3941 2041	12.6459 6155	11.9672 3457	11.3497 8833	41
42	13.4524 4898	12.6939 1772	12.0066 9867	11.3822 9339	42
43	13.5069 6167	12.7385 2811	12.0432 3951	11.4122 5197	43
44	13.5579 0810	12.7800 2615	12.0770 7362	11.4398 6357	44
45	13.6055 2159	12.8186 2898	12.1084 0150	11.4653 1205	45
46	13.6500 2018	12.8545 3858	12.1374 0880	11.4887 6686	46
47	13.6916 0764	12.8879 4287	12.1642 6741	11.5103 8420	47
48	13.7304 7443	12.9190 1662	12.1891 3649	11.5303 0802	48
49	13.7667 9853	12.9479 2244	12.2121 6341	11.5486 7099	49
50	13.8007 4629	12.9748 1157	12.2334 8464	11.5655 9538	50

TABLE IV. —Present Value of Annuity of 1 per Period

$$a_{\overline{n}|i} = \frac{1 - (1 + i)^{-n}}{i}$$

n	7%	7½%	8%	8½%	n
51	13.8324 7317	12.9998 2472	12.2532 2652	11.5811 9390	51
52	13.8621 2446	13.0230 9276	12.2715 0604	11.5955 7041	52
53	13.8898 3594	13.0447 3745	12.2884 3152	11.6088 2066	53
54	13.9157 3453	13.0648 7205	12.3041 0326	11.6210 3287	54
55	13.9399 3881	13.0836 0191	12.3186 1413	11.6322 8835	55
56	13.9625 5964	13.1010 2503	12.3320 5012	11.6426 6208	56
57	13.9837 0059	13.1172 3258	12.3444 9085	11.6522 2311	57
58	14.0034 5850	13.1323 0938	12.3560 1005	11.6610 3513	58
59	14.0219 2383	13.1463 3431	12.3666 7597	11.6691 5680	59
60	14.0391 8115	13.1593 8075	12.3765 5182	11.6766 4221	60
61	14.0553 0949	13.1715 1698	12.3856 9613	11.6835 4121	61
62	14.0703 8270	13.1828 0649	12.3941 6309	11.6898 9973	62
63	14.0844 6981	13.1933 0836	12.4020 0286	11.6957 6012	63
64	14.0976 3534	13.2030 7755	12.4092 6190	11.7011 6140	64
65	14.1099 3957	13 2121 6516	12.4159 8324	11.7061 3954	65
66	14.1214 3885	13.2206 1875	12.4222 0671	11.7107 2769	66
67	14.1321 8584	13.2284 8256	12.4279 6917	11.7149 5639	67
68	14.1422 2976	13.2357 9773	12.4333 0479	11.7188 5382	68
69	14.1516 1660	13.2426 0254	12.4382 4518	11.7224 4592	69
70	14.1603 8934	13.2489 3260	12.4428 1961	11.7257 5661	70
71	14.1685 8817	13.2548 2102	12.4470 5519	11.7288 0793	71
72	14.1762 5063	13.2602 9862	12.4509 7703	11.7316 2021	72
73	14.1834 1180	13.2653 9407	12.4546 0836	11.7342 1218	73
74	14.1901 0449	13.2701 3402	12.4579 7071	11.7366 0109	74
75	14.1963 5933	13.2745 4327	12.4610 8399	11.7388 0284	75
76	14.2022 0498	13.2786 4490	12.4639 6665	11.7408 3211	76
77	14.2076 6821	13.2824 6038	12.4666 3579	11.7427 0241	77
78	14.2127 7403	13.2860 0965	12.4691 0721	11.7444 2618	78
79	14.2175 4582	13.2893 1130	12.4713 9557	11.7460 1492	79
80	14.2220 0544	13.2923 8261	12.4735 1441	11.7474 7919	80
81	14.2261 7331	13.2952 3964	12.4754 7631	11.7488 2874	81
82	14.2300 6851	13.2978 9734	12.4772 9288	11.7500 7257	82
83	14.2337 0889	13.3003 6962	12.4789 7489	11.7512 1896	83
84	14.2371 1111	13.3026 6941	12.4805 3230	11.7522 7554	84
85	14.2402 9076	13.3048 0875	12.4819 7436	11.7532 4935	85
86	14.2432 6239	13.3067 9884	12.4833 0959	11.7541 4686	86
87	14.2460 3962	13.3086 5008	12.4845 4592	11.7549 7407	87
88	14.2486 3516	13.3103 7217	12.4856 9066	11.7557 3647	88
89	14.2510 6089	13.3119 7411	12.4867 5061	11.7564 3914	89
90	14.2533 2794	13.3134 6429	12.4877 3205	11.7570 8677	90
91	14.2554 4667	13.3148 5050	12.4886 4079	11.7576 8365	91
92	14.2574 2680	13.3161 4000	12.4894 8221	11.7582 3378	92
93	14.2592 7738	13.3173 3954	12.4902 6131	11.7587 4081	93
94	14.2610 0690	13.3184 5538	12.4909 8269	11.7592 0812	94
95	14.2626 2327	13.3194 9338	12.4916 5064	11.7596 3882	95
96	14.2641 3390	13.3204 5896	12.4922 6911	11.7600 3578	96
97	14.2655 4570	13.3213 5717	12.4928 4177	11.7604 0164	97
98	14.2668 6514	13.3221 9272	12.4933 7201	11.7607 3884	98
99	14.2680 9826	13.3229 6997	12.4938 6297	11.7610 4962	99
100	14.2692 5071	13.3236 9290	12.4943 1757	11.7613 3606	100

TABLE V. —Periodic Rent of Annuity Whose Present Value is 1

$$\frac{1}{a_{\overline{n}|i}} = \frac{i}{1-(1+i)^{-n}} \qquad \left[\frac{1}{s_{\overline{n}|i}} = \frac{1}{a_{\overline{n}|i}} - i\right]$$

n	¼%	7/24%	⅓%	5/12%	n
1	1.0025 0000	1.0029 1667	1.0033 3333	1.0041 6667	1
2	0.5018 7578	0.5021 8856	0.5025 0139	0.5031 2717	2
3	0.3350 0139	0.3352 7967	0.3355 5802	0.3361 1496	3
4	0.2515 6445	0.2518 2557	0.2520 8680	0.2526 0958	4
5	0.2015 0250	0.2017 5340	0.2020 0444	0.2025 0693	5
6	0.1681 2803	0.1683 7219	0.1686 1650	0.1691 0564	6
7	0.1442 8928	0.1445 2866	0.1447 6824	0.1452 4800	7
8	0.1264 1035	0.1266 4620	0.1268 8228	0.1273 5512	8
9	0.1125 0462	0.1127 3777	0.1129 7118	0.1134 3876	9
10	0.1013 8015	0.1016 1117	0.1018 4248	0.1023 0596	10
11	0.0922 7840	0.0925 0772	0.0927 3736	0.0931 9757	11
12	0.0846 9370	0.0849 2163	0.0851 4990	0.0856 0748	12
13	0.0782 7595	0.0785 0274	0.0787 2989	0.0791 8532	13
14	0.0727 7510	0.0730 0093	0.0732 2716	0.0736 8082	14
15	0.0680 0777	0.0682 3279	0.0684 5825	0.0689 1045	15
16	0.0638 3642	0.0640 6076	0.0642 8557	0.0647 3655	16
17	0.0601 5587	0.0603 7964	0.0606 0389	0.0610 5387	17
18	0.0568 8433	0.0571 0761	0.0573 3140	0.0577 8053	18
19	0.0539 5722	0.0541 8008	0.0544 0348	0.0548 5191	19
20	0.0513 2288	0.0515 4537	0.0517 6844	0.0522 1630	20
21	0.0489 3947	0.0491 6166	0.0493 8445	0.0498 3183	21
22	0.0467 7278	0.0469 9471	0.0472 1726	0.0476 6427	22
23	0.0447 9455	0.0450 1625	0.0452 3861	0.0456 8531	23
24	0.0429 8121	0.0432 0272	0.0434 2492	0.0438 7139	24
25	0.0413 1298	0.0415 3433	0.0417 5640	0.0422 0270	25
26	0.0397 7312	0.0399 9434	0.0402 1630	0.0406 6247	26
27	0.0383 4736	0.0385 6847	0.0387 9035	0.0392 3645	27
28	0.0370 2347	0.0372 4450	0.0374 6632	0.0379 1239	28
29	0.0357 9093	0.0360 1188	0.0362 3367	0.0366 7974	29
30	0.0346 4059	0.0348 6149	0.0350 8325	0.0355 2936	30
31	0.0335 6449	0.0337 8536	0.0340 0712	0.0344 5330	31
32	0.0325 5569	0.0327 7653	0.0329 9830	0.0334 4458	32
33	0.0316 0806	0.0318 2889	0.0320 5067	0.0324 9708	33
34	0.0307 1620	0.0309 3703	0.0311 5885	0.0316 0540	34
35	0.0298 7533	0.0300 9618	0.0303 1803	0.0307 6476	35
36	0.0290 8121	0.0293 0208	0.0295 2399	0.0299 7090	36
37	0.0283 3004	0.0285 5094	0.0287 7291	0.0292 2003	37
38	0.0276 1843	0.0278 3938	0.0280 6141	0.0285 0875	38
39	0.0269 4335	0.0271 6434	0.0273 8644	0.0278 3402	39
40	0.0263 0204	0.0265 2308	0.0267 4527	0.0271 9310	40
41	0.0256 9204	0.0259 1315	0.0261 3543	0.0263 8352	41
42	0.0251 1112	0.0253 3229	0.0255 5466	0.0260 0303	42
43	0.0245 5724	0.0247 7848	0.0250 0095	0.0254 4961	43
44	0.0240 2855	0.0242 4987	0.0244 7246	0.0249 2141	44
45	0.0235 2339	0.0237 4479	0.0239 6749	0.0244 1675	45
46	0.0230 4022	0.0232 6170	0.0234 8451	0.0239 3409	46
47	0.0225 7762	0.0227 9920	0.0230 2213	0.0234 7204	47
48	0.0221 3433	0.0223 5600	0.0225 7905	0.0230 2929	48
49	0.0217 0915	0.0219 3092	0.0221 5410	0.0226 0468	49
50	0.0213 0099	0.0215 2287	0.0217 4618	0.0221 9711	50

TABLE V.—Periodic Rent of Annuity Whose Present Value is 1

$$\frac{1}{a_{\overline{n}|i}} = \frac{i}{1-(1+i)^{-n}} \qquad \left[\frac{1}{s_{\overline{n}|i}} = \frac{1}{a_{\overline{n}|i}} - i\right]$$

n	$\frac{1}{4}\%$	$\frac{7}{24}\%$	$\frac{1}{3}\%$	$\frac{5}{12}\%$	n
51	0.0209 0886	0.0211 3085	0.0213 5429	0.0218 0557	51
52	0.0205 3184	0.0207 5393	0.0209 7751	0.0214 2916	52
53	0.0201 6906	0.0203 9126	0.0206 1499	0.0210 6700	53
54	0.0198 1974	0.0200 4205	0.0202 6592	0.0207 1830	54
55	0.0194 8314	0.0197 0557	0.0199 2958	0.0203 8234	55
56	0.0191 5858	0.0193 8113	0.0196 0529	0.0200 5843	56
57	0.0188 4542	0.0190 6810	0.0192 9241	0.0197 4593	57
58	0.0185 4308	0.0187 6588	0.0189 9035	0.0194 4426	58
59	0.0182 5101	0.0184 7394	0.0186 9856	0.0191 5287	59
60	0.0179 6869	0.0181 9175	0.0184 1652	0.0188 7123	60
61	0.0176 9564	0.0179 1883	0.0181 4377	0.0185 9888	61
62	0.0174 3142	0.0176 5474	0.0178 7984	0.0183 3536	62
63	0.0171 7561	0.0173 9906	0.0176 2432	0.0180 8025	63
64	0.0169 2780	0.0171 5139	0.0173 7681	0.0178 3315	64
65	0.0166 8764	0.0169 1136	0.0171 3695	0.0175 9371	65
66	0.0164 5476	0.0166 7863	0.0169 0438	0.0173 6156	66
67	0.0162 2886	0.0164 5286	0.0166 7878	0.0171 3639	67
68	0.0160 0961	0.0162 3376	0.0164 5985	0.0169 1788	68
69	0.0157 9674	0.0160 2102	0.0162 4729	0.0167 0574	69
70	0.0155 8996	0.0158 1439	0.0160 4083	0.0164 9971	70
71	0.0153 8902	0.0156 1359	0.0158 4021	0.0162 9952	71
72	0.0151 9368	0.0154 1840	0.0156 4518	0.0161 0493	72
73	0.0150 0370	0.0152 2857	0.0154 5553	0.0159 1572	73
74	0.0148 1887	0.0150 4389	0.0152 7103	0.0157 3165	74
75	0.0146 3898	0.0148 6415	0.0150 9147	0.0155 5253	75
76	0.0144 6385	0.0146 8916	0.0149 1666	0.0153 7816	76
77	0.0142 9327	0.0145 1974	0.0147 4641	0.0152 0836	77
78	0.0141 2708	0.0143 5270	0.0145 8056	0.0150 4295	78
79	0.0139 6511	0.0141 9089	0.0144 1892	0.0148 8177	79
80	0.0138 0721	0.0140 3313	0.0142 6135	0.0147 2464	80
81	0.0136 5321	0.0138 7929	0.0141 0770	0.0145 7144	81
82	0.0135 0298	0.0137 2922	0.0139 5781	0.0144 2200	82
83	0.0133 5639	0.0135 8278	0.0138 1156	0.0142 7620	83
84	0.0132 1330	0.0134 3985	0.0136 6881	0.0141 3391	84
85	0.0130 7359	0.0133 0030	0.0135 2944	0.0139 9500	85
86	0.0129 3714	0.0131 6400	0.0133 9333	0.0138 5935	86
87	0.0128 0384	0.0130 3086	0.0132 6038	0.0137 2685	87
88	0.0126 7357	0.0129 0076	0.0131 3046	0.0135 9740	88
89	0.0125 4625	0.0127 7360	0.0130 0349	0.0134 7088	89
90	0.0124 2177	0.0126 4928	0.0128 7036	0.0133 4731	90
91	0.0123 0004	0.0125 2770	0.0127 5797	0.0132 2629	91
92	0.0121 8096	0.0124 0879	0.0126 3925	0.0131 0803	92
93	0.0120 6446	0.0122 9245	0.0125 2310	0.0129 9234	93
94	0.0119 5044	0.0121 7860	0.0124 0944	0.0128 7915	94
95	0.0118 3884	0.0120 6716	0.0122 9819	0.0127 6837	95
96	0.0117 2957	0.0119 5805	0.0121 8928	0.0126 5992	96
97	0.0116 2257	0.0118 5121	0.0120 8263	0.0125 5374	97
98	0.0115 1776	0.0117 4657	0.0119 7818	0.0124 4976	98
99	0.0114 1508	0.0116 4405	0.0118 7585	0.0123 4790	99
100	0.0113 1446	0.0115 4360	0.0117 7559	0.0122 4811	100

TABLE V.—Periodic Rent of Annuity Whose Present Value is 1

$$\frac{1}{a_{\overline{n}|i}} = \frac{i}{1-(1+i)^{-n}} \qquad \left[\frac{1}{s_{\overline{n}|i}} = \frac{1}{a_{\overline{n}|i}} - i\right]$$

n	¼%	7/24%	⅓%	5/12%	n
101	0.0112 1584	0.0114 4515	0.0116 7734	0.0121 5033	101
102	0.0111 1917	0.0113 4864	0.0115 8103	0.0120 5449	102
103	0.0110 2439	0.0112 5403	0.0114 8660	0.0119 6054	103
104	0.0109 3144	0.0111 6124	0.0113 9401	0.0118 6842	104
105	0.0108 4027	0.0110 7024	0.0113 0320	0.0117 7809	105
106	0.0107 5083	0.0109 8096	0.0112 1413	0.0116 8948	106
107	0.0106 6307	0.0108 9337	0.0111 2673	0.0116 0256	107
108	0.0105 7694	0.0108 0741	0.0110 4097	0.0115 1727	108
109	0.0104 9241	0.0107 2305	0.0109 5680	0.0114 3358	109
110	0.0104 0942	0.0106 4023	0.0108 7417	0.0113 5143	110
111	0.0103 2793	0.0105 5891	0.0107 9306	0.0112 7079	111
112	0.0102 4791	0.0104 7906	0.0107 1340	0.0111 9161	112
113	0.0101 6932	0.0104 0064	0.0106 3518	0.0111 1386	113
114	0.0100 9211	0.0103 2360	0.0105 5834	0.0110 3750	114
115	0.0100 1625	0.0102 4792	0.0104 8285	0.0109 6249	115
116	0.0099 4172	0.0101 7355	0.0104 0868	0.0108 8880	116
117	0.0098 6846	0.0101 0046	0.0103 3579	0.0108 1639	117
118	0.0097 9646	0.0100 2863	0.0102 6416	0.0107 4524	118
119	0.0097 2567	0.0099 5801	0.0101 9374	0.0106 7530	119
120	0.0096 5608	0.0098 8859	0.0101 2451	0.0106 0655	120
121	0.0095 8764	0.0098 2032	0.0100 5645	0.0105 3896	121
122	0.0095 2033	0.0097 5318	0.0099 8951	0.0104 7251	122
123	0.0094 5412	0.0096 8715	0.0099 2367	0.0104 0715	123
124	0.0093 8899	0.0096 2219	0.0098 5892	0.0103 4288	124
125	0.0093 2491	0.0095 5828	0.0097 9521	0.0102 7965	125
126	0.0092 6186	0.0094 9540	0.0097 3253	0.0102 1745	126
127	0.0091 9981	0.0094 3352	0.0096 7085	0.0101 5625	127
128	0.0091 3873	0.0093 7262	0.0096 1015	0.0100 9603	128
129	0.0090 7861	0.0093 1267	0.0095 5040	0.0100 3677	129
130	0.0090 1942	0.0092 5366	0.0094 9159	0.0099 7844	130
131	0.0089 6115	0.0091 9556	0.0094 3368	0.0099 2102	131
132	0.0089 0376	0.0091 3834	0.0093 7667	0.0098 6449	132
133	0.0088 4725	0.0090 8200	0.0093 2053	0.0098 0883	133
134	0.0087 9159	0.0090 2651	0.0092 6524	0.0097 5403	134
135	0.0087 3675	0.0089 7186	0.0092 1079	0.0097 0005	135
136	0.0086 8274	0.0089 1801	0.0091 5715	0.0096 4689	136
137	0.0086 2952	0.0088 6497	0.0091 0430	0.0095 9453	137
138	0.0085 7707	0.0088 1270	0.0090 5223	0.0095 4295	138
139	0.0085 2539	0.0087 6119	0.0090 0093	0.0094 9213	139
140	0.0084 7446	0.0087 1043	0.0089 5037	0.0094 4205	140
141	0.0084 2425	0.0086 6040	0.0089 0054	0.0093 9271	141
142	0.0083 7476	0.0086 1109	0.0088 5143	0.0093 4408	142
143	0.0083 2597	0.0085 6247	0.0088 0301	0.0092 9615	143
144	0.0082 7787	0.0085 1454	0.0087 5528	0.0092 4890	144
145	0.0082 3043	0.0084 6728	0.0087 0822	0.0092 0233	145
146	0.0081 8365	0.0084 2067	0.0086 6182	0.0091 5641	146
147	0.0081 3752	0.0083 7471	0.0086 1607	0.0091 1114	147
148	0.0080 9201	0.0083 2938	0.0085 7094	0.0090 6650	148
149	0.0080 4712	0.0082 8467	0.0085 2643	0.0090 2247	149
150	0.0080 0284	0.0082 4056	0.0084 8252	0.0089 7905	150

TABLE V.—Periodic Rent of Annuity Whose Present Value is 1

$$\frac{1}{a_{\overline{n}|i}} = \frac{i}{1-(1+i)^{-n}} \qquad \left[\frac{1}{s_{\overline{n}|i}} = \frac{1}{a_{\overline{n}|i}} - i\right]$$

n	1/4%	7/24%	1/3%	5/12%	n
151	0.0079 5915	0.0081 9705	0.0084 3921	0.0089 3623	151
152	0.0079 1605	0.0081 5412	0.0083 9648	0.0088 9398	152
153	0.0078 7351	0.0081 1176	0.0083 5432	0.0088 5231	153
154	0.0078 3153	0.0080 6995	0.0083 1273	0.0088 1119	154
155	0.0077 9010	0.0080 2870	0.0082 7167	0.0087 7063	155
156	0.0077 4921	0.0079 8798	0.0082 3116	0.0087 3060	156
157	0.0077 0885	0.0079 4780	0.0081 9118	0.0086 9110	157
158	0.0076 6900	0.0079 0813	0.0081 5171	0.0086 5211	158
159	0.0076 2966	0.0078 6896	0.0081 1275	0.0086 1364	159
160	0.0075 9082	0.0078 3030	0.0080 7429	0.0085 7566	160
161	0.0075 5246	0.0077 9212	0.0080 3631	0.0085 3817	161
162	0.0075 1459	0.0077 5442	0.0079 9882	0.0085 0116	162
163	0.0074 7719	0.0077 1720	0.0079 6180	0.0084 6462	163
164	0.0074 4025	0.0076 0844	0.0079 2524	0.0084 2855	164
165	0.0074 0377	0.0076 4413	0.0078 8913	0.0083 9293	165
166	0.0073 6773	0.0076 0826	0.0078 5347	0.0083 5775	166
167	0.0073 3213	0.0075 7284	0.0078 1825	0.0083 2302	167
168	0.0072 9695	0.0075 3784	0.0077 8346	0.0082 8871	168
169	0.0072 6220	0.0075 0327	0.0077 4909	0.0082 5482	169
170	0.0072 2787	0.0074 6911	0.0077 1513	0.0082 2135	170
171	0.0071 9394	0.0074 3536	0.0076 8158	0.0081 8829	171
172	0.0071 6042	0.0074 0201	0.0076 4844	0.0081 5563	172
173	0.0071 2728	0.0073 6905	0.0076 1568	0.0081 2336	173
174	0.0070 9454	0.0073 3648	0.0075 8332	0.0080 9147	174
175	0.0070 6217	0.0073 0429	0.0075 5133	0.0080 5997	175
176	0.0070 3018	0.0072 7248	0.0075 1972	0.0080 2884	176
177	0.0069 9855	0.0072 4103	0.0074 8847	0.0079 9808	177
178	0.0069 6729	0.0072 0994	0.0074 5759	0.0079 6768	178
179	0.0069 3638	0.0071 7921	0.0074 2706	0.0079 3763	179
180	0.0069 0582	0.0071 4883	0.0073 9688	0.0079 0794	180
181	0.0068 7560	0.0071 1879	0.0073 6704	0.0078 7858	181
182	0.0068 4572	0.0070 8908	0.0073 3754	0.0078 4957	182
183	0.0068 1617	0.0070 5971	0.0073 0838	0.0078 2088	183
184	0.0067 8695	0.0070 3067	0.0072 7954	0.0077 9253	184
185	0.0067 5805	0.0070 0195	0.0072 5102	0.0077 6449	185
186	0.0067 2947	0.0069 7354	0.0072 2281	0.0077 3677	186
187	0.0067 0120	0.0069 4545	0.0071 9492	0.0077 0936	187
188	0.0066 7323	0.0069 1766	0.0071 6734	0.0076 8226	188
189	0.0066 4557	0.0068 9017	0.0071 4005	0.0076 5546	189
190	0.0066 1820	0.0068 6298	0.0071 1307	0.0076 2895	190
191	0.0065 9112	0.0068 3608	0.0070 8637	0.0076 0274	191
192	0.0065 6434	0.0068 0947	0.0070 5996	0.0075 7681	192
193	0.0065 3783	0.0067 8314	0.0070 3384	0.0075 5117	193
194	0.0065 1160	0.0067 5708	0.0070 0799	0.0075 2580	194
195	0.0064 8565	0.0067 3131	0.0069 8242	0.0075 0071	195
196	0.0064 5997	0.0067 0581	0.0069 5711	0.0074 7589	196
197	0.0064 3455	0.0066 8057	0.0069 3208	0.0074 5133	197
198	0.0064 0939	0.0066 5559	0.0069 0730	0.0074 2704	198
199	0.0063 8450	0.0066 3087	0.0068 8278	0.0074 0300	199
200	0.0063 5985	0.0066 0640	0.0068 5852	0.0073 7922	200

TABLE V.—Periodic Rent of Annuity Whose Present Value is 1

$$\frac{1}{a_{\overline{n}|i}} = \frac{i}{1-(1+i)^{-n}} \qquad \left[\frac{1}{s_{\overline{n}|i}} = \frac{1}{a_{\overline{n}|i}} - i\right]$$

n	½%	7/12%	5/8%	2/3%	n
1	1.0050 0000	1.0058 3333	1.0062 5000	1.0066 6667	1
2	0.5037 5312	0.5043 7924	0.5046 9237	0.5050 0554	2
3	0.3366 7221	0.3372 2976	0.3375 0865	0.3377 8762	3
4	0.2531 3279	0.2536 5644	0.2539 1842	0.2541 8051	4
5	0.2030 0997	0.2035 1357	0.2037 6558	0.2040 1772	5
6	0.1695 9546	0.1700 8594	0.1703 3143	0.1705 7709	6
7	0.1457 2854	0.1462 0986	0.1464 5082	0.1466 9198	7
8	0.1278 2886	0.1283 0351	0.1285 4118	0.1287 7907	8
9	0.1139 0736	0.1143 7698	0.1146 1218	0.1148 4763	9
10	0.1027 7057	0.1032 3632	0.1034 6963	0.1037 0321	10
11	0.0936 5903	0.0941 2175	0.0943 5358	0.0945 8572	11
12	0.0860 6643	0.0865 2675	0.0867 5742	0.0869 8843	12
13	0.0796 4224	0.0801 0064	0.0803 3039	0.0805 6052	13
14	0.0741 3609	0.0745 9295	0.0748 2198	0.0750 5141	14
15	0.0693 6436	0.0698 1999	0.0700 4845	0.0702 7734	15
16	0.0651 8937	0.0656 4401	0.0658 7202	0.0661 0049	16
17	0.0615 0579	0.0619 5966	0.0621 8732	0.0624 1546	17
18	0.0582 3173	0.0586 8499	0.0589 1239	0.0591 4030	18
19	0.0553 0253	0.0557 5532	0.0559 8252	0.0562 1027	19
20	0.0526 6645	0.0531 1889	0.0533 4597	0.0535 7362	20
21	0.0502 8163	0.0507 3383	0.0509 6083	0.0511 8843	21
22	0.0481 1380	0.0485 6585	0.0487 9281	0.0490 2041	22
23	0.0461 3465	0.0465 8663	0.0468 1360	0.0470 4123	23
24	0.0443 2061	0.0447 7258	0.0449 9959	0.0452 2729	24
25	0.0426 5186	0.0431 0388	0.0433 3096	0.0435 5876	25
26	0.0411 1163	0.0415 6376	0.0417 9094	0.0420 1886	26
27	0.0396 8565	0.0401 3793	0.0403 6523	0.0405 9331	27
28	0.0383 6167	0.0388 1415	0.0390 4159	0.0392 6983	28
29	0.0371 2914	0.0375 8186	0.0378 0946	0.0380 3789	29
30	0.0359 7892	0.0364 3191	0.0366 5969	0.0368 8832	30
31	0.0349 0304	0.0353 5633	0.0355 8430	0.0358 1316	31
32	0.0338 9453	0.0343 4815	0.0345 7633	0.0348 0542	32
33	0.0329 4727	0.0334 0124	0.0336 2964	0.0338 5898	33
34	0.0320 5586	0.0325 1020	0.0327 3883	0.0329 6843	34
35	0.0312 1550	0.0316 7024	0.0318 9911	0.0321 2898	35
36	0.0304 2194	0.0308 7710	0.0311 0622	0.0313 3637	36
37	0.0296 7139	0.0301 2698	0.0303 5636	0.0305 8680	37
38	0.0289 6045	0.0294 1649	0.0296 4614	0.0298 7687	38
39	0.0282 8607	0.0287 4258	0.0289 7250	0.0292 0354	39
40	0.0276 4552	0.0281 0251	0.0283 3271	0.0285 6406	40
41	0.0270 3631	0.0274 9379	0.0277 2429	0.0279 5595	41
42	0.0264 5622	0.0269 1420	0.0271 4499	0.0273 7697	42
43	0.0259 0320	0.0263 6170	0.0265 9278	0.0268 2509	43
44	0.0253 7541	0.0258 3443	0.0260 6583	0.0262 9847	44
45	0.0248 7117	0.0253 3073	0.0255 6243	0.0257 9541	45
46	0.0243 8894	0.0248 4905	0.0250 8106	0.0253 1439	46
47	0.0239 2733	0.0243 8798	0.0246 2032	0.0248 5399	47
48	0.0234 8503	0.0239 4624	0.0241 7890	0.0244 1292	48
49	0.0230 6087	0.0235 2265	0.0237 5563	0.0239 9001	49
50	0.0226 5376	0.0231 1611	0.0233 4943	0.0235 8416	50

TABLE V.—Periodic Rent of Annuity Whose Present Value is 1

$$\frac{1}{a_{\overline{n}|i}} = \frac{i}{1-(1+i)^{-n}} \qquad \left[\frac{1}{s_{\overline{n}|i}} = \frac{1}{a_{\overline{n}|i}} - i\right]$$

n	$\frac{1}{2}$%	$\frac{7}{12}$%	$\frac{5}{8}$%	$\frac{2}{3}$%	n
51	0.0222 6269	0.0227 2563	0.0229 5928	0.0231 9437	51
52	0.0218 8675	0.0223 5027	0.0225 8425	0.0228 1971	52
53	0.0215 2507	0.0219 8919	0.0222 2350	0.0224 5932	53
54	0.0211 7686	0.0216 4157	0.0218 7623	0.0221 1242	54
55	0.0208 4139	0.0213 0671	0.0215 4171	0.0217 7827	55
56	0.0205 1797	0.0209 8390	0.0212 1925	0.0214 5618	56
57	0.0202 0598	0.0206 7251	0.0209 0821	0.0211 4552	57
58	0.0199 0481	0.0203 7196	0.0206 0801	0.0208 4569	58
59	0.0196 1392	0.0200 8170	0.0203 1809	0.0205 5616	59
60	0.0193 3280	0.0198 0120	0.0200 3795	0.0202 7639	60
61	0.0190 6096	0.0195 2999	0.0197 6709	0.0200 0592	61
62	0.0187 9796	0.0192 6762	0.0195 0508	0.0197 4429	62
63	0.0185 4337	0.0190 1366	0.0192 5148	0.0194 9108	63
64	0.0182 9681	0.0187 6773	0.0190 0591	0.0192 4590	64
65	0.0180 5789	0.0185 2946	0.0187 6800	0.0190 0837	65
66	0.0178 2627	0.0182 9848	0.0185 3739	0.0187 7815	66
67	0.0176 0163	0.0180 7449	0.0183 1376	0.0185 5491	67
68	0.0173 8366	0.0178 5716	0.0180 9680	0.0183 3835	68
69	0.0171 7206	0.0176 4622	0.0178 8622	0.0181 2816	69
70	0.0169 6657	0.0174 4138	0.0176 8175	0.0179 2409	70
71	0.0167 6693	0.0172 4239	0.0174 8313	0.0177 2586	71
72	0.0165 7289	0.0170 4901	0.0172 9011	0.0175 3324	72
73	0.0163 8422	0.0168 6100	0.0171 0247	0.0173 4600	73
74	0.0162 0070	0.0166 7814	0.0169 1999	0.0171 6391	74
75	0.0160 2214	0.0165 0024	0.0167 4246	0.0169 8678	75
76	0.0158 4832	0.0163 2709	0.0165 6968	0.0168 1440	76
77	0.0156 7908	0.0161 5851	0.0164 0147	0.0166 4659	77
78	0.0155 1423	0.0159 9432	0.0162 3766	0.0164 8318	78
79	0.0153 5360	0.0158 3436	0.0160 7808	0.0163 2400	79
80	0.0151 9704	0.0156 7847	0.0159 2256	0.0161 6889	80
81	0.0150 4439	0.0155 2650	0.0157 7096	0.0160 1769	81
82	0.0148 9552	0.0153 7830	0.0156 2314	0.0158 7027	82
83	0.0147 5028	0.0152 3373	0.0154 7895	0.0157 2649	83
84	0.0146 0855	0.0150 9268	0.0153 3828	0.0155 8621	84
85	0.0144 7021	0.0149 5501	0.0152 0098	0.0154 4933	85
86	0.0143 3513	0.0148 2060	0.0150 6696	0.0153 1570	86
87	0.0142 0320	0.0146 8935	0.0149 3608	0.0151 8524	87
88	0.0140 7431	0.0145 6115	0.0148 0826	0.0150 5781	88
89	0.0139 4837	0.0144 3588	0.0146 8337	0.0149 3334	89
90	0.0138 2527	0.0143 1347	0.0145 6134	0.0148 1170	90
91	0.0137 0493	0.0141 9380	0.0144 4205	0.0146 9282	91
92	0.0135 8724	0.0140 7679	0.0143 2542	0.0145 7660	92
93	0.0134 7213	0.0139 6236	0.0142 1137	0.0144 6296	93
94	0.0133 5950	0.0138 5042	0.0140 9982	0.0143 5181	94
95	0.0132 4930	0.0137 4090	0.0139 9067	0.0142 4308	95
96	0.0131 4143	0.0136 3372	0.0138 8387	0.0141 3668	96
97	0.0130 3583	0.0135 2880	0.0137 7933	0.0140 3255	97
98	0.0129 3242	0.0134 2608	0.0136 7700	0.0139 3062	98
99	0.0128 3115	0.0133 2549	0.0135 7679	0.0138 3082	99
100	0.0127 3194	0.0132 2696	0.0134 7865	0.0137 3308	100

TABLE V.—Periodic Rent of Annuity Whose Present Value is 1

$$\frac{1}{a_{\overline{n}|i}} = \frac{i}{1-(1+i)^{-n}} \qquad \left[\frac{1}{s_{\overline{n}|i}} = \frac{1}{a_{\overline{n}|i}} - i\right]$$

n	½%	7/12%	⅝%	⅔%	n
101	0.0126 3473	0.0131 3045	0.0133 8251	0.0136 3735	101
102	0.0125 3947	0.0130 3587	0.0132 8832	0.0135 4357	102
103	0.0124 4611	0.0129 4319	0.0131 9602	0.0134 5168	103
104	0.0123 5457	0.0128 5234	0.0131 0555	0.0133 6162	104
105	0.0122 6481	0.0127 6238	0.0130 1687	0.0132 7334	105
106	0.0121 7679	0.0126 7594	0.0129 2992	0.0131 8680	106
107	0.0120 9045	0.0125 9029	0.0128 4465	0.0131 0194	107
108	0.0120 0575	0.0125 0628	0.0127 6102	0.0130 1871	108
109	0.0119 2264	0.0124 2385	0.0126 7897	0.0129 3708	109
110	0.0118 4107	0.0123 4298	0.0125 9848	0.0128 5700	110
111	0.0117 6102	0.0122 6361	0.0125 1950	0.0127 7842	111
112	0.0116 8242	0.0121 8571	0.0124 4198	0.0127 0131	112
113	0.0116 0526	0.0121 0923	0.0123 6588	0.0126 2562	113
114	0.0115 2948	0.0120 3414	0.0122 9118	0.0125 5132	114
115	0.0114 5506	0.0119 6041	0.0122 1783	0.0124 7838	115
116	0.0113 8195	0.0118 8799	0.0121 4579	0.0124 0675	116
117	0.0113 1013	0.0118 1686	0.0120 7504	0.0123 3641	117
118	0.0112 3956	0.0117 4698	0.0120 0555	0.0122 6732	118
119	0.0111 7021	0.0116 7832	0.0119 3727	0.0121 9944	119
120	0.0111 0205	0.0116 1085	0.0118 7018	0.0121 3276	120
121	0.0110 3505	0.0115 4454	0.0118 0425	0.0120 6724	121
122	0.0109 6918	0.0114 7936	0.0117 3945	0.0120 0284	122
123	0.0109 0441	0.0114 1528	0.0116 7575	0.0119 3955	123
124	0.0108 4072	0.0113 5228	0.0116 1314	0.0118 7734	124
125	0.0107 7808	0.0112 9033	0.0115 5157	0.0118 1618	125
126	0.0107 1647	0.0112 2940	0.0114 9102	0.0117 5604	126
127	0.0106 5586	0.0111 6948	0.0114 3148	0.0116 9690	127
128	0.0105 9623	0.0111 1054	0.0113 7292	0.0116 3875	128
129	0.0105 3755	0.0110 5255	0.0113 1531	0.0115 8154	129
130	0.0104 7981	0.0109 9550	0.0112 5864	0.0115 2527	130
131	0.0104 2298	0.0109 3935	0.0112 0288	0.0114 6992	131
132	0.0103 6704	0.0108 8410	0.0111 4800	0.0114 1545	132
133	0.0103 1197	0.0108 2972	0.0110 9400	0.0113 6185	133
134	0.0102 5775	0.0107 7619	0.0110 4086	0.0113 0910	134
135	0.0102 0436	0.0107 2349	0.0109 8854	0.0112 5719	135
136	0.0101 5179	0.0106 7161	0.0109 3703	0.0112 0609	136
137	0.0101 0002	0.0106 2052	0.0108 8633	0.0111 5578	137
138	0.0100 4902	0.0105 7021	0.0108 3640	0.0111 0625	138
139	0.0099 9879	0.0105 2067	0.0107 8723	0.0110 5749	139
140	0.0099 4930	0.0104 7187	0.0107 3881	0.0110 0947	140
141	0.0099 0055	0.0104 2380	0.0106 9111	0.0109 6218	141
142	0.0098 5250	0.0103 7644	0.0106 4414	0.0109 1560	142
143	0.0098 0516	0.0103 2978	0.0105 9786	0.0108 6972	143
144	0.0097 5850	0.0102 8381	0.0105 5226	0.0108 2453	144
145	0.0097 1252	0.0102 3851	0.0105 0734	0.0107 8000	145
146	0.0096 6719	0.0101 9386	0.0104 6307	0.0107 3613	146
147	0.0096 2250	0.0101 4986	0.0104 1944	0.0106 9291	147
148	0.0095 7844	0.0101 0649	0.0103 7645	0.0106 5031	148
149	0.0095 3500	0.0100 6373	0.0103 3407	0.0106 0833	149
150	0.0094 9217	0.0100 2159	0.0102 9230	0.0105 6695	150

TABLE V.—Periodic Rent of Annuity Whose Present Value is 1

$$\frac{1}{a_{\overline{n}|i}} = \frac{i}{1-(1+i)^{-n}} \qquad \left[\frac{1}{s_{\overline{n}|i}} = \frac{1}{a_{\overline{n}|i}} - i\right]$$

n	½%	7/12%	5/8%	2/3%	n
151	0.0094 4993	0.0099 8003	0.0102 5112	0.0105 2617	151
152	0.0094 0827	0.0099 3905	0.0102 1052	0.0104 8597	152
153	0.0093 6719	0.0098 9865	0.0101 7049	0.0104 4633	153
154	0.0093 2666	0.0098 5880	0.0101 3102	0.0104 0726	154
155	0.0092 8668	0.0098 1950	0.0100 9209	0.0103 6873	155
156	0.0092 4723	0.0097 8074	0.0100 5370	0.0103 3074	156
157	0.0092 0832	0.0097 4251	0.0100 1584	0.0102 9327	157
158	0.0091 6992	0.0097 0479	0.0099 7850	0.0102 5632	158
159	0.0091 3203	0.0096 6758	0.0099 4166	0.0102 1988	159
160	0.0090 9464	0.0096 3087	0.0099 0532	0.0101 8394	160
161	0.0090 5774	0.0095 9464	0.0098 6947	0.0101 4848	161
162	0.0090 2131	0.0095 5890	0.0098 3410	0.0101 1350	162
163	0.0089 8536	0.0095 2362	0.0097 9919	0.0100 7899	163
164	0.0089 4987	0.0094 8881	0.0097 6475	0.0100 4494	164
165	0.0089 1483	0.0094 5445	0.0097 3076	0.0100 1134	165
166	0.0088 8024	0.0094 2053	0.0096 9722	0.0099 7819	166
167	0.0088 4608	0.0093 8705	0.0096 6411	0.0099 4547	167
168	0.0088 1236	0.0093 5400	0.0096 3143	0.0099 1318	168
169	0.0087 7906	0.0093 2138	0.0095 9918	0.0098 8131	169
170	0.0087 4617	0.0092 8917	0.0095 6733	0.0098 4986	170
171	0.0087 1369	0.0092 5736	0.0095 3589	0.0098 1881	171
172	0.0086 8161	0.0092 2595	0.0095 0486	0.0097 8816	172
173	0.0086 4992	0.0091 9494	0.0094 7421	0.0097 5791	173
174	0.0086 1862	0.0091 6431	0.0094 4395	0.0097 2803	174
175	0.0085 8770	0.0091 3406	0.0094 1407	0.0096 9854	175
176	0.0085 5715	0.0091 0418	0.0093 8456	0.0096 6942	176
177	0.0085 2697	0.0090 7468	0.0093 5542	0.0096 4066	177
178	0.0084 9715	0.0090 4553	0.0093 2664	0.0096 1226	178
179	0.0084 6769	0.0090 1673	0.0092 9821	0.0095 8422	179
180	0.0084 3857	0.0089 8828	0.0092 7012	0.0095 5652	180
181	0.0084 0979	0.0089 6018	0.0092 4238	0.0095 2917	181
182	0.0083 8136	0.0089 3241	0.0092 1498	0.0095 0215	182
183	0.0083 5325	0.0089 0497	0.0091 8791	0.0094 7546	183
184	0.0083 2547	0.0088 7786	0.0091 6116	0.0094 4909	184
185	0.0082 9802	0.0088 5107	0.0091 3473	0.0094 2305	185
186	0.0082 7087	0.0088 2459	0.0091 0862	0.0093 9732	186
187	0.0082 4404	0.0087 9843	0.0090 8282	0.0093 7189	187
188	0.0082 1752	0.0087 7257	0.0090 5732	0.0093 4678	188
189	0.0081 9129	0.0087 4701	0.0090 3212	0.0093 2196	189
190	0.0081 6537	0.0087 2174	0.0090 0722	0.0092 9743	190
191	0.0081 3973	0.0086 9677	0.0089 8260	0.0092 7320	191
192	0.0081 1438	0.0086 7208	0.0089 5828	0.0092 4925	192
193	0.0080 8931	0.0086 4767	0.0089 3423	0.0092 2558	193
194	0.0080 6452	0.0086 2355	0.0089 1046	0.0092 0219	194
195	0.0080 4000	0.0085 9969	0.0088 8696	0.0091 7907	195
196	0.0080 1576	0.0085 7610	0.0088 6374	0.0091 5622	196
197	0.0079 9178	0.0085 5278	0.0088 4077	0.0091 3363	197
198	0.0079 6806	0.0085 2972	0.0088 1807	0.0091 1130	198
199	0.0079 4459	0.0085 0691	0.0087 9562	0.0090 8923	199
200	0.0079 2138	0.0084 8436	0.0087 7343	0.0090 6741	200

TABLE V. —Periodic Rent of Annuity Whose Present Value is 1

$$\frac{1}{a_{\overline{n}|i}} = \frac{i}{1-(1+i)^{-n}} \qquad \left[\frac{1}{s_{\overline{n}|i}} = \frac{1}{a_{\overline{n}|i}} - i\right]$$

n	¾%	⅞%	1%	1⅛%	n
1	1.0075 0000	1.0087 5000	1.0100 0000	1.0112 5000	1
2	0.5056 3200	0.5065 7203	0.5075 1244	0.5084 5323	2
3	0.3383 4579	0.3391 8361	0.3400 2211	0.3408 6130	3
4	0.2547 0501	0.2554 9257	0.2562 8109	0.2570 7058	4
5	0.2045 2242	0.2052 8049	0.2060 3980	0.2068 0034	5
6	0.1710 6891	0.1718 0789	0.1725 4837	0.1732 9034	6
7	0.1471 7488	0.1479 0070	0.1486 2828	0.1493 5762	7
8	0.1292 5552	0.1299 7190	0.1306 9029	0.1314 1071	8
9	0.1153 1929	0.1160 2868	0.1167 4037	0.1174 5432	9
10	0.1041 7123	0.1048 7538	0.1055 8208	0.1062 9131	10
11	0.0950 5094	0.0957 5111	0.0964 5408	0.0971 5984	11
12	0.0874 5148	0.0881 4860	0.0888 4879	0.0895 5203	12
13	0.0810 2188	0.0817 1669	0.0824 1482	0.0831 1626	13
14	0.0755 1146	0.0762 0453	0.0769 0117	0.0776 0138	14
15	0.0707 3639	0.0714 2817	0.0721 2378	0.0728 2321	15
16	0.0665 5879	0.0672 4965	0.0679 4460	0.0686 4363	16
17	0.0628 7321	0.0635 6346	0.0642 5806	0.0649 5698	17
18	0.0595 9766	0.0602 8756	0.0609 8205	0.0616 8113	18
19	0.0566 6740	0.0573 5715	0.0580 5175	0.0587 5120	19
20	0.0540 3063	0.0547 2042	0.0554 1532	0.0561 1531	20
21	0.0516 4543	0.0523 3541	0.0530 3075	0.0537 3145	21
22	0.0494 7748	0.0501 6779	0.0508 6371	0.0515 6525	22
23	0.0474 9846	0.0481 8921	0.0488 8584	0.0495 8833	23
24	0.0456 8474	0.0463 7604	0.0470 7347	0.0477 7701	24
25	0.0440 1650	0.0447 0843	0.0454 0675	0.0461 1144	25
26	0.0424 7693	0.0431 6959	0.0438 6888	0.0445 7479	26
27	0.0410 5176	0.0417 4520	0.0424 4553	0.0431 5273	27
28	0.0397 2871	0.0404 2300	0.0411 2444	0.0418 3299	28
29	0.0384 9723	0.0391 9243	0.0398 9502	0.0406 0498	29
30	0.0373 4816	0.0380 4431	0.0387 4811	0.0394 5953	30
31	0.0362 7352	0.0369 7068	0.0376 7573	0.0383 8866	31
32	0.0352 6634	0.0359 6454	0.0366 7089	0.0373 8535	32
33	0.0343 2048	0.0350 1976	0.0357 2744	0.0364 4349	33
34	0.0334 3053	0.0341 3092	0.0348 3997	0.0355 5763	34
35	0.0325 9170	0.0332 9324	0.0340 0368	0.0347 2299	35
36	0.0317 9973	0.0325 0244	0.0332 1431	0.0339 3529	36
37	0.0310 5082	0.0317 5473	0.0324 6805	0.0331 9072	37
38	0.0303 4157	0.0310 4671	0.0317 6150	0.0324 8589	38
39	0.0296 6893	0.0303 7531	0.0310 9160	0.0318 1773	39
40	0.0290 3016	0.0297 3780	0.0304 5560	0.0311 8349	40
41	0.0284 2276	0.0291 3169	0.0298 5102	0.0305 8069	41
42	0.0278 4452	0.0285 5475	0.0292 7563	0.0300 0709	42
43	0.0272 9338	0.0280 0493	0.0287 2737	0.0294 6064	43
44	0.0267 6751	0.0274 8039	0.0282 0441	0.0289 3949	44
45	0.0262 6521	0.0269 7943	0.0277 0505	0.0284 4197	45
46	0.0257 8495	0.0265 0053	0 0272 2775	0.0279 6652	46
47	0.0253 2532	0.0260 4228	0.0267 7111	0.0275 1173	47
48	0.0248 8504	0.0256 0338	0.0263 3384	0.0270 7632	48
49	0.0244 6292	0.0251 8265	0.0259 1474	0.0266 5910	49
50	0.0240 5787	0.0247 7900	0.0255 1273	0.0262 5898	50

TABLE V. —Periodic Rent of Annuity Whose Present Value is 1

$$\frac{1}{a_{\overline{n}|i}} = \frac{i}{1-(1+i)^{-n}} \qquad \left[\frac{1}{s_{\overline{n}|i}} = \frac{1}{a_{\overline{n}|i}} - i\right]$$

n	¾%	⅞%	1%	1⅛%	n
51	0.0236 6888	0.0243 9142	0 0251 2680	0.0258 7494	51
52	0.0232 9503	0.0240 1899	0.0247 5603	0.0255 0606	52
53	0.0229 3546	0.0236 6084	0 0243 9956	0.0251 5149	53
54	0.0225 8938	0.0233 1619	0.0240 5658	0.0248 1043	54
55	0 0222 5605	0.0229 8430	0 0237 2637	0.0244 8213	55
56	0 0219 3478	0.0226 6449	0 0234 0823	0.0241 6592	56
57	0.0216 2496	0 0223 5611	0.0231 0156	0.0238 6116	57
58	0.0213 2597	0.0220 5858	0.0228 0573	0.0235 6726	58
59	0.0210 3727	0 0217 7135	0.0225 2020	0.0232 8366	59
60	0.0207 5836	0.0214 9390	0.0222 4445	0.0230 0985	60
61	0.0204 8873	0.0212 2575	0.0219 7800	0.0227 4534	61
62	0.0202 2795	0.0209 6644	0.0217 2041	0.0224 8969	62
63	0 0199 7560	0.0207 1557	0.0214 7125	0.0222 4247	63
64	0.0197 3127	0.0204 7273	0.0212 3013	0.0220 0329	64
65	0.0194 9460	0.0202 3754	0 0209 9667	0.0217 7178	65
66	0.0192 6524	0.0200 0968	0.0207 7052	0.0215 4758	66
67	0.0190 4286	0.0197 8879	0.0205 5136	0.0213 3037	67
68	0 0188 2716	0.0195 7459	0.0203 3888	0.0211 1985	68
69	0.0186 1785	0.0193 6677	0.0201 3280	0.0209 1571	69
70	0 0184 1464	0 0191 6506	0.0199 3282	0.0207 1769	70
71	0.0182 1728	0.0189 6921	0.0197 3870	0.0205 2552	71
72	0.0180 2554	0 0187 7897	0.0195 5019	0.0203 3896	72
73	0.0178 3917	0.0185 9411	0.0193 6706	0.0201 5779	73
74	0.0176 5796	0.0184 1441	0.0191 8910	0.0199 8177	74
75	0.0174 8170	0.0182 3966	0.0190 1609	0.0198 1072	75
76	0.0173 1020	0.0180 6967	0.0188 4784	0.0196 4442	76
77	0.0171 4328	0.0179 0426	0.0186 8416	0.0194 8269	77
78	0.0169 8074	0.0177 4324	0.0185 2488	0.0193 2536	78
79	0.0168 2244	0.0175 8645	0.0183 6984	0.0191 7226	79
80	0.0166 6821	0.0174 3374	0.0182 1885	0.0190 2323	80
81	0.0165 1790	0.0172 8494	0.0180 7180	0.0188 7812	81
82	0.0163 7136	0.0171 3992	0.0179 2851	0.0187 3678	82
83	0.0162 2847	0.0169 9854	0.0177 8886	0.0185 9908	83
84	0.0160 8908	0.0168 6067	0.0176 5273	0.0184 6489	84
85	0.0159 5308	0.0167 2619	0.0175 1998	0.0183 3409	85
86	0.0158 2034	0.0165 9497	0.0173 9050	0.0182 0654	86
87	0.0156 9076	0.0164 6691	0.0172 6417	0.0180 8215	87
88	0.0155 6423	0.0163 4190	0.0171 4089	0.0179 6081	88
89	0.0154 4064	0.0162 1982	0.0170 2056	0.0178 4240	89
90	0.0153 1989	0.0161 0060	0.0169 0306	0.0177 2684	90
91	0.0152 0190	0.0159 8413	0.0167 8832	0.0176 1403	91
92	0.0150 8657	0.0158 7031	0.0166 7624	0.0175 0387	92
93	0.0149 7382	0.0157 5908	0.0165 6673	0.0173 9629	93
94	0.0148 6356	0.0156 5033	0.0164 5971	0.0172 9119	94
95	0.0147 5571	0.0155 4401	0.0163 5511	0.0171 8851	95
96	0.0146 5020	0.0154 4002	0.0162 5284	0.0170 8816	96
97	0.0145 4696	0.0153 3829	0.0161 5284	0.0169 9007	97
98	0.0144 4592	0.0152 3877	0.0160 5503	0.0168 9418	98
99	0.0143 4701	0.0151 4137	0.0159 5936	0.0168 0041	99
100	0.0142 5017	0.0150 4604	0.0158 6574	0.0167 0870	100

TABLE V.—Periodic Rent of Annuity Whose Present Value is 1

$$\frac{1}{a_{\overline{n}|i}} = \frac{i}{1-(1+i)^{-n}} \qquad \left[\frac{1}{s_{\overline{n}|i}} = \frac{1}{a_{\overline{n}|i}} - i\right]$$

n	1¼%	1⅜%	1½%	1¾%	n
1	1.0125 0000	1.0137 5000	1.0150 0000	1.0175 0000	1
2	0.5093 9441	0.5103 3597	0.5112 7792	0.5131 6295	2
3	0.3417 0117	0.3425 4173	0.3433 8296	0.3450 6746	3
4	0.2578 6102	0.2586 5243	0.2594 4478	0.2610 3237	4
5	0.2075 6211	0.2083 2510	0.2090 8932	0.2106 2142	5
6	0.1740 3381	0.1747 7877	0.1755 2521	0.1770 2256	6
7	0.1500 8872	0.1508 2157	0.1515 5616	0.1530 3059	7
8	0.1321 3314	0.1328 5758	0.1335 8402	0.1350 4292	8
9	0.1181 7055	0.1188 8906	0.1196 0982	0.1210 5813	9
10	0.1070 0307	0.1077 1737	0.1084 3418	0.1098 7534	10
11	0.0978 6839	0.0985 7973	0.0992 9384	0.1007 3038	11
12	0.0902 5831	0.0909 6764	0.0916 7999	0.0931 1377	12
13	0.0838 2100	0.0845 2903	0.0852 4036	0.0866 7283	13
14	0.0783 0515	0.0790 1246	0.0797 2332	0.0811 5562	14
15	0.0735 2646	0.0742 3351	0.0749 4436	0.0763 7739	15
16	0.0693 4672	0.0700 5388	0.0707 6508	0.0721 9958	16
17	0.0656 6023	0.0663 6780	0.0670 7966	0.0685 1623	17
18	0.0623 8479	0.0630 9301	0.0638 0578	0.0652 4492	18
19	0.0594 5548	0.0601 6457	0.0608 7847	0.0623 2061	19
20	0.0568 2039	0.0575 3054	0.0582 4574	0.0596 9122	20
21	0.0544 3748	0.0551 4884	0.0558 6550	0.0573 1464	21
22	0.0522 7238	0.0529 8507	0.0537 0331	0.0551 5638	22
23	0.0502 9666	0.0510 1080	0.0517 3075	0.0531 8796	23
24	0.0484 8665	0.0492 0235	0.0499 2410	0.0513 8565	24
25	0.0468 2247	0.0475 3981	0.0482 6345	0.0497 2952	25
26	0.0452 8729	0.0460 0635	0.0467 3196	0.0482 0269	26
27	0.0438 6677	0.0445 8763	0.0453 1527	0.0467 9079	27
28	0.0425 4863	0.0432 7134	0.0440 0108	0.0454 8151	28
29	0.0413 2228	0.0420 4689	0.0427 7878	0.0442 6424	29
30	0.0401 7854	0.0409 0511	0.0416 3919	0.0431 2975	30
31	0.0391 0942	0.0398 3798	0.0405 7430	0.0420 7005	31
32	0.0381 0791	0.0388 3850	0.0395 7710	0.0410 7812	32
33	0.0371 6786	0.0379 0053	0.0386 4144	0.0401 4779	33
34	0.0362 8387	0.0370 1864	0.0377 6189	0.0392 7363	34
35	0.0354 5111	0.0361 8801	0.0369 3363	0.0384 5082	35
36	0.0346 6533	0.0354 0438	0.0361 5240	0.0376 7507	36
37	0.0339 2270	0.0346 6394	0.0354 1437	0.0369 4257	37
38	0.0332 1983	0.0339 6327	0.0347 1613	0.0362 4990	38
39	0.0325 5365	0.0332 9931	0.0340 5463	0.0355 9399	39
40	0.0319 2141	0.0326 6931	0.0334 2710	0.0349 7209	40
41	0.0313 2063	0.0320 7078	0.0328 3106	0.0343 8170	41
42	0.0307 4906	0.0315 0148	0.0322 6426	0.0338 2057	42
43	0.0302 0466	0.0309 5936	0.0317 2465	0.0332 8666	43
44	0.0296 8557	9.0304 4257	0.0312 1038	0.0327 7810	44
45	0.0291 9012	0.0299 4941	0.0307 1976	0.0322 9321	45
46	0.0287 1675	0.0294 7836	0.0302 5125	0.0318 3043	46
47	0.0282 6406	0.0290 2799	0.0298 0342	0.0313 8836	47
48	0.0278 3075	0.0285 9701	0.0293 7500	0.0309 6569	48
49	0.0274 1563	0.0281 8424	0.0289 6478	0.0305 6124	49
50	0.0270 1763	0.0277 8857	0.0285 7168	0.0301 7391	50

TABLE V. —Periodic Rent of Annuity Whose Present Value is 1

$$\frac{1}{a_{\overline{n}|i}} = \frac{i}{1-(1+i)^{-n}} \qquad \left[\frac{1}{s_{\overline{n}|i}} = \frac{1}{a_{\overline{n}|i}} - i\right]$$

n	$1\frac{1}{4}\%$	$1\frac{3}{8}\%$	$1\frac{1}{2}\%$	$1\frac{3}{4}\%$	n
51	0.0266 3571	0.0274 0900	0.0281 0460	0.0290 0209	51
52	0.0262 6897	0.0270 4461	0.0278 3287	0.0294 4665	52
53	0.0259 1653	0.0266 9453	0.0274 8537	0.0291 0492	53
54	0.0255 7760	0.0263 5797	0.0271 5138	0.0287 7672	54
55	0.0252 5145	0.0260 3418	0.0268 3018	0.0284 6129	55
56	0.0249 3739	0.0257 2249	0.0265 2106	0.0281 5795	56
57	0.0246 3478	0.0254 2225	0.0262 2341	0.0278 6606	57
58	0.0243 4303	0.0251 3287	0.0259 3661	0.0275 8503	58
59	0.0240 6158	0.0248 5380	0.0256 6012	0.0273 1430	59
60	0.0237 8993	0.0245 8452	0.0253 9343	0.0270 5336	60
61	0.0235 2758	0.0243 2455	0.0251 3604	0.0268 0172	61
62	0.0232 7410	0.0240 7344	0.0248 8751	0.0265 5892	62
63	0.0230 2904	0.0238 3076	0.0246 4741	0.0263 2455	63
64	0.0227 9203	0.0235 9612	0.0244 1534	0.0260 9821	64
65	0.0225 6268	0.0233 6914	0.0241 9094	0.0258 7952	65
66	0.0223 4065	0.0231 4949	0.0239 7386	0.0256 6813	66
67	0.0221 2560	0.0229 3682	0.0237 6376	0.0254 6372	67
68	0.0219 1724	0.0227 3082	0.0235 6033	0.0252 6596	68
69	0.0217 1527	0.0225 3122	0.0233 6329	0.0250 7459	69
70	0.0215 1941	0.0223 3773	0.0231 7235	0.0248 8930	70
71	0.0213 2941	0.0221 5009	0.0229 8727	0.0247 0985	71
72	0.0211 4501	0.0219 6806	0.0228 0779	0.0245 3600	72
73	0.0209 6600	0.0217 9140	0.0226 3368	0.0243 6750	73
74	0.0207 9215	0.0216 1991	0.0224 6473	0.0242 0413	74
75	0.0206 2325	0.0214 5336	0.0223 0072	0.0240 4570	75
76	0.0204 5910	0.0212 9157	0.0221 4146	0.0238 9200	76
77	0.0202 9953	0.0211 3435	0.0219 8676	0.0237 4284	77
78	0.0201 4435	0.0209 8151	0.0218 3645	0.0235 9806	78
79	0.0199 9341	0.0208 3290	0.0216 9036	0.0234 5748	79
80	0.0198 4652	0.0206 8836	0.0215 4832	0.0233 2093	80
81	0.0197 0356	0.0205 4772	0.0214 1019	0.0231 8828	81
82	0.0195 6437	0.0204 1086	0.0212 7583	0.0230 5936	82
83	0.0194 2881	0.0202 7762	0.0211 4509	0.0229 3406	83
84	0.0192 9675	0.0201 4789	0.0210 1784	0.0228 1223	84
85	0.0191 6808	0.0200 2153	0.0208 9396	0.0226 9375	85
86	0.0190 4267	0.0198 9843	0.0207 7333	0.0225 7850	86
87	0.0189 2041	0.0197 7847	0.0206 5584	0.0224 6636	87
88	0.0188 0119	0.0196 6155	0.0205 4138	0.0223 5724	88
89	0.0186 8490	0.0195 4756	0.0204 2984	0.0222 5102	89
90	0.0185 7146	0.0194 3641	0.0203 2113	0.0221 4760	90
91	0.0184 6076	0.0193 2799	0.0202 1516	0.0220 4690	91
92	0.0183 5271	0.0192 2222	0.0201 1182	0.0219 4882	92
93	0.0182 4724	0.0191 1902	0.0200 1104	0.0218 5327	93
94	0.0181 4425	0.0190 1829	0.0199 1273	0.0217 6017	94
95	0.0180 4366	0.0189 1997	0.0198 1681	0.0216 6944	95
96	0.0179 4540	0.0188 2397	0.0197 2321	0.0215 8101	96
97	0.0178 4941	0.0187 3022	0.0196 3186	0.0214 9480	97
98	0.0177 5560	0.0186 3866	0.0195 4268	0.0214 1074	98
99	0.0176 6391	0.0185 4921	0.0194 5560	0.0213 2876	99
100	0.0175 7428	0.0184 6181	0.0193 7057	0.0212 4880	100

TABLE V. —Periodic Rent of Annuity Whose Present Value is 1

$$\frac{1}{a_{\overline{n}|i}} = \frac{i}{1-(1+i)^{-n}} \qquad \left[\frac{1}{s_{\overline{n}|i}} = \frac{1}{a_{\overline{n}|i}} - i\right]$$

n	2%	2¼%	2½%	2¾%	n
1	1.0200 0000	1.0225 0000	1.0250 0000	1.0275 0000	1
2	0.5150 4950	0.5169 3758	0.5188 2716	0.5207 1825	2
3	0.3467 5467	0.3484 4458	0.3501 3717	0.3518 3243	3
4	0.2626 2375	0.2642 1893	0.2658 1788	0.2674 2059	4
5	0.2121 5839	0.2137 0021	0.2152 4686	0.2167 9832	5
6	0.1785 2581	0.1800 3496	0.1815 4997	0.1830 7083	6
7	0.1545 1196	0.1560 0025	0.1574 9543	0.1589 9747	7
8	0.1365 0980	0.1379 8462	0.1394 6735	0.1409 5795	8
9	0.1225 1544	0.1239 8170	0.1254 5689	0.1269 4095	9
10	0.1113 2653	0.1127 8768	0.1142 5876	0.1157 3972	10
11	0.1021 7794	0.1036 3649	0.1051 0596	0.1065 8629	11
12	0.0945 5960	0.0960 1740	0.0974 8713	0.0989 6871	12
13	0.0881 1835	0.0895 7686	0.0910 4827	0.0925 3252	13
14	0.0826 0197	0.0840 6230	0.0855 3653	0.0870 2457	14
15	0.0778 2547	0.0792 8852	0.0807 6646	0.0822 5917	15
16	0.0736 5013	0.0751 1663	0.0765 9899	0.0780 9710	16
17	0.0699 6984	0.0714 4039	0.0729 2777	0.0744 3186	17
18	0.0667 0210	0.0681 7720	0.0696 7008	0.0711 8063	18
19	0.0637 8177	0.0652 6182	0.0667 6062	0.0682 7802	19
20	0.0611 5672	0.0626 4207	0.0641 4713	0.0656 7173	20
21	0.0587 8477	0.0602 7572	0.0617 8733	0.0633 1941	21
22	0.0566 3140	0.0581 2821	0.0596 4661	0.0611 8640	22
23	0.0546 6810	0.0561 7097	0.0576 9638	0.0592 4410	23
24	0.0528 7110	0.0543 8023	0.0559 1282	0.0574 6863	24
25	0.0512 2044	0.0527 3599	0.0542 7592	0.0558 3997	25
26	0.0496 9923	0.0512 2134	0.0527 6875	0.0543 4116	26
27	0.0482 9309	0.0498 2188	0.0513 7687	0.0529 5776	27
28	0.0469 8967	0.0485 2525	0.0500 8793	0.0516 7738	28
29	0.0457 7836	0.0473 2081	0.0488 9127	0.0504 8935	29
30	0.0446 4992	0.0461 9934	0.0477 7764	0.0493 8442	30
31	0.0435 9635	0.0451 5280	0.0467 3900	0.0483 5453	31
32	0.0426 1061	0.0441 7415	0.0457 6831	0.0473 9263	32
33	0.0416 8653	0.0432 5722	0.0448 5938	0.0464 9253	33
34	0.0408 1867	0.0423 9655	0.0440 0675	0.0456 4875	34
35	0.0400 0221	0.0415 8731	0.0432 0558	0.0448 5645	35
36	0.0392 3285	0.0408 2522	0.0424 5158	0.0441 1132	36
37	0.0385 0678	0.0401 0643	0.0417 4090	0.0434 0953	37
38	0.0378 2057	0.0394 2753	0.0410 7012	0.0427 4764	38
39	0.0371 7114	0.0387 8543	0.0404 3615	0.0421 2256	39
40	0.0365 5575	0.0381 7738	0.0398 3623	0.0415 3151	40
41	0.0359 7188	0.0376 0087	0.0392 6786	0.0409 7200	41
42	0.0354 1729	0.0370 5364	0.0387 2876	0.0404 4175	42
43	0.0348 8993	0.0365 3364	0.0382 1688	0.0399 3871	43
44	0.0343 8794	0.0360 3901	0.0377 3037	0.0394 6100	44
45	0.0339 0962	0.0355 6805	0.0372 6752	0.0390 0693	45
46	0.0334 5342	0.0351 1921	0.0368 2676	0.0385 7493	46
47	0.0330 1792	0.0346 9107	0.0364 0669	0.0381 6358	47
48	0.0326 0184	0.0342 8233	0.0360 0599	0.0377 7158	48
49	0.0322 0396	0.0338 9179	0.0356 2348	0.0373 9773	49
50	0.0318 2321	0.0335 1836	0.0352 5806	0.0370 4092	50

TABLE V.—Periodic Rent of Annuity Whose Present Value is 1

$$\frac{1}{a_{\overline{n}|i}} = \frac{i}{1-(1+i)^{-n}} \qquad \left[\frac{1}{s_{\overline{n}|i}} = \frac{1}{a_{\overline{n}|i}} - i\right]$$

n	2%	2¼%	2½%	2¾%	n
51	0.0314 5356	0.0331 6102	0.0349 0870	0.0367 0014	51
52	0.0311 0909	0.0328 1884	0.0345 7446	0.0363 7444	52
53	0.0307 7392	0.0324 9094	0.0342 5449	0.0360 6297	53
54	0.0304 5226	0.0321 7654	0.0339 4799	0.0357 6491	54
55	0.0301 4337	0.0318 7489	0.0336 5419	0.0354 7953	55
56	0.0298 4656	0.0315 8530	0.0333 7243	0.0352 0612	56
57	0.0295 6120	0.0313 0712	0.0331 0204	0.0349 4404	57
58	0.0292 8667	0.0310 3977	0.0328 4244	0.0346 9270	58
59	0.0290 2243	0.0307 8268	0.0325 9307	0.0344 5153	59
60	0.0287 6797	0.0305 3533	0.0323 5340	0.0342 2002	60
61	0.0285 2278	0.0302 9724	0.0321 2294	0.0339 9767	61
62	0.0282 8643	0.0300 6795	0.0319 0126	0.0337 8402	62
63	0.0280 5848	0.0298 4704	0.0316 8790	0.0335 7866	63
64	0.0278 3855	0.0296 3411	0.0314 8249	0.0333 8118	64
65	0.0276 2624	0.0294 2878	0.0312 8463	0.0331 9120	65
66	0.0274 2122	0.0292 3070	0.0310 9398	0.0330 0837	66
67	0.0272 2316	0.0290 3955	0.0309 1021	0.0328 3236	67
68	0.0270 3173	0.0288 5500	0.0307 3300	0.0326 6285	68
69	0.0268 4665	0.0286 7677	0.0305 6206	0.0324 9955	69
70	0.0266 6765	0.0285 0458	0.0303 9712	0.0323 4218	70
71	0.0264 9446	0.0283 3816	0.0302 3790	0.0321 9048	71
72	0.0263 2683	0.0281 7728	0.0300 8417	0.0320 4420	72
73	0.0261 6454	0.0280 2169	0.0299 3568	0.0319 0311	73
74	0.0260 0736	0.0278 7118	0.0297 9222	0.0317 6698	74
75	0.0258 5508	0.0277 2554	0.0296 5358	0.0316 3560	75
76	0.0257 0751	0.0275 8457	0.0295 1956	0.0315 0878	76
77	0.0255 6447	0.0274 4808	0.0293 8997	0.0313 8633	77
78	0.0254 2576	0.0273 1589	0.0292 6463	0.0312 6806	78
79	0.0252 9123	0.0271 8784	0.0291 4338	0.0311 5382	79
80	0.0251 6071	0.0270 6376	0.0290 2605	0.0310 4342	80
81	0.0250 3405	0.0269 4350	0.0289 1248	0.0309 3674	81
82	0.0249 1110	0.0268 2692	0.0288 0254	0.0308 3361	82
83	0.0247 9173	0.0267 1387	0.0286 9608	0.0307 3389	83
84	0.0246 7581	0.0266 0423	0.0285 9298	0.0306 3747	84
85	0.0245 6321	0.0264 9787	0.0284 9310	0.0305 4420	85
86	0.0244 5381	0.0263 9467	0.0283 9633	0.0304 5397	86
87	0.0243 4750	0.0262 9452	0.0283 0255	0.0303 6667	87
88	0.0242 4416	0.0261 9730	0.0282 1165	0.0302 8219	88
89	0.0241 4370	0.0261 0291	0.0281 2353	0.0302 0041	89
90	0.0240 4602	0.0260 1126	0.0280 3809	0.0301 2125	90
91	0.0239 5101	0.0259 2224	0.0279 5523	0.0300 4460	91
92	0.0238 5859	0.0258 3577	0.0278 7486	0.0299 7038	92
93	0.0237 6868	0.0257 5176	0.0277 9690	0.0298 9850	93
94	0.0236 8118	0.0256 7012	0.0277 2126	0.0298 2887	94
95	0.0235 9602	0.0255 9078	0.0276 4786	0.0297 6141	95
96	0.0235 1313	0.0255 1366	0.0275 7662	0.0296 9605	96
97	0.0234 3242	0.0254 3868	0.0275 0747	0.0296 3272	97
98	0.0233 5383	0.0253 6578	0.0274 4034	0.0295 7134	98
99	0.0232 7729	0.0252 9489	0.0273 7517	0.0295 1185	99
100	0.0232 0274	0.0252 2594	0.0273 1188	0.0294 5418	100

TABLE V.—Periodic Rent of Annuity Whose Present Value is 1

$$\frac{1}{a_{\overline{n}|i}} = \frac{i}{1-(1+i)^{-n}} \qquad \left[\frac{1}{s_{\overline{n}|i}} = \frac{1}{a_{\overline{n}|i}} - i\right]$$

n	3%	3½%	4%	4½%	n
1	1.0300 0000	1.0350 0000	1.0400 0000	1.0450 0000	1
2	0.5226 1084	0.5264 0049	0.5301 9608	0.5339 9756	2
3	0.3535 3036	0.3569 3418	0.3603 4854	0.3637 7336	3
4	0.2690 2705	0.2722 5114	0.2754 9005	0.2787 4365	4
5	0.2183 5457	0.2214 8137	0.2246 2711	0.2277 9164	5
6	0.1845 9750	0.1876 6821	0.1907 6190	0.1938 7839	6
7	0.1605 0635	0.1635 4449	0.1666 0961	0.1697 0147	7
8	0.1424 5639	0.1454 7665	0.1485 2783	0.1516 0965	8
9	0.1284 3386	0.1314 4601	0.1344 9299	0.1375 7447	9
10	0.1172 3051	0.1202 4137	0.1232 9094	0.1263 7882	10
11	0.1080 7745	0.1110 9197	0.1141 4904	0.1172 4818	11
12	0.1004 6209	0.1034 8395	0.1065 5217	0.1096 6619	12
13	0.0940 2954	0.0970 6157	0.1001 4373	0.1032 7535	13
14	0.0885 2634	0.0915 7073	0.0946 6897	0.0978 2032	14
15	0.0837 6658	0.0868 2507	0.0899 4110	0.0931 1381	15
16	0.0796 1085	0.0826 8483	0.0858 2000	0.0890 1537	16
17	0.0759 5253	0.0790 4313	0.0821 9852	0.0854 1758	17
18	0.0727 0870	0.0758 1684	0.0789 9333	0.0822 3690	18
19	0.0698 1388	0.0729 4033	0.0761 3862	0.0794 0734	19
20	0.0672 1571	0.0703 6108	0.0735 8175	0.0768 7614	20
21	0.0648 7178	0.0680 3659	0.0712 8011	0.0746 0057	21
22	0.0627 4739	0.0659 3207	0.0691 9881	0.0725 4565	22
23	0.0608 1390	0.0640 1880	0.0673 0906	0.0706 8249	23
24	0.0590 4742	0.0622 7283	0.0655 8683	0.0689 8703	24
25	0.0574 2787	0.0606 7404	0.0640 1196	0.0674 3903	25
26	0.0559 3829	0.0592 0540	0.0625 6738	0.0660 2137	26
27	0.0545 6421	0.0578 5241	0.0612 3854	0.0647 1946	27
28	0.0532 9323	0.0566 0265	0.0600 1298	0.0635 2081	28
29	0.0521 1467	0.0554 4538	0.0588 7993	0.0624 1461	29
30	0.0510 1926	0.0543 7133	0.0578 3010	0.0613 9154	30
31	0.0499 9893	0.0533 7240	0.0568 5535	0.0604 4345	31
32	0.0490 4662	0.0524 4150	0.0559 4859	0.0595 6320	32
33	0.0481 5612	0.0515 7242	0.0551 0357	0.0587 4453	33
34	0.0473 2196	0.0507 5966	0.0543 1477	0.0579 8191	34
35	0.0465 3929	0.0499 9835	0.0535 7732	0.0572 7045	35
36	0.0458 0379	0.0492 8416	0.0528 8688	0.0566 0578	36
37	0.0451 1162	0.0486 1325	0.0522 3957	0.0559 8402	37
38	0.0444 5934	0.0479 8214	0.0516 3192	0.0554 0169	38
39	0.0438 4385	0.0473 8775	0.0510 6083	0.0548 5567	39
40	0.0432 6238	0.0468 2728	0.0505 2349	0.0543 4315	40
41	0.0427 1241	0.0462 9822	0.0500 1738	0.0538 6158	41
42	0.0421 9167	0.0457 9828	0.0495 4020	0.0534 0868	42
43	0.0416 9811	0.0453 2539	0.0490 8989	0.0529 8235	43
44	0.0412 2985	0.0448 7768	0.0486 6454	0.0525 8071	44
45	0.0407 8518	0.0444 5343	0.0482 6246	0.0522 0202	45
46	0.0403 6254	0.0440 5108	0.0478 8205	0.0518 4471	46
47	0.0399 6051	0.0436 6919	0.0475 2189	0.0515 0734	47
48	0.0395 7777	0.0433 0646	0.0471 8065	0.0511 8858	48
49	0.0392 1314	0.0429 6167	0.0468 5712	0.0508 8722	49
50	0.0388 6550	0.0426 3371	0.0465 5020	0.0506 0215	50

TABLE V.—Periodic Rent of Annuity Whose Present Value is 1

$$\frac{1}{a_{\overline{n}|i}} = \frac{i}{1-(1+i)^{-n}} \qquad \left[\frac{1}{s_{\overline{n}|i}} = \frac{1}{a_{\overline{n}|i}} - i\right]$$

n	3%	3½%	4%	4½%	n
51	0.0385 3382	0.0423 2156	0.0462 5885	0.0503 3232	51
52	0.0382 1718	0.0420 2429	0.0459 8212	0.0500 7679	52
53	0.0379 1471	0.0417 4100	0.0457 1915	0.0498 3469	53
54	0.0376 2558	0.0414 7090	0.0454 6910	0.0496 0519	54
55	0.0373 4907	0.0412 1323	0.0452 3124	0.0493 8754	55
56	0.0370 8447	0.0409 6730	0.0450 0487	0.0491 8105	56
57	0.0368 3114	0.0407 3245	0.0447 8932	0.0489 8506	57
58	0.0365 8848	0.0405 0810	0.0445 8401	0.0487 9897	58
59	0.0363 5593	0.0402 9366	0.0443 8836	0.0486 2221	59
60	0.0361 3296	0.0400 8862	0.0442 0185	0.0484 5426	60
61	0.0359 1908	0.0398 9249	0.0440 2398	0.0482 9462	61
62	0.0357 1385	0.0397 0480	0.0438 5430	0.0481 4284	62
63	0.0355 1682	0.0395 2513	0.0436 9237	0.0479 9848	63
64	0.0353 2760	0.0393 5308	0.0435 3780	0.0478 6115	64
65	0.0351 4581	0.0391 8826	0.0433 9019	0.0477 3047	65
66	0.0349 7110	0.0390 3031	0.0432 4921	0.0476 0608	66
67	0.0348 0313	0.0388 7892	0.0431 1451	0.0474 8765	67
68	0.0346 4159	0.0387 3375	0.0429 8578	0.0473 7487	68
69	0.0344 8618	0.0385 9453	0.0428 6272	0.0472 6745	69
70	0.0343 3663	0.0384 6095	0.0427 4506	0.0471 6511	70
71	0.0341 9266	0.0383 3277	0.0426 3253	0.0470 6759	71
72	0.0340 5404	0.0382 0973	0.0425 2489	0.0469 7465	72
73	0.0339 2053	0.0380 9160	0.0424 2190	0.0468 8606	73
74	0.0337 9191	0.0379 7816	0.0423 2334	0.0468 0159	74
75	0.0336 6796	0.0378 6919	0.0422 2900	0.0467 2104	75
76	0.0335 4849	0.0377 6450	0.0421 3869	0.0466 4422	76
77	0.0334 3331	0.0376 6390	0.0420 5221	0.0465 7094	77
78	0.0333 2224	0.0375 6721	0.0419 6939	0.0465 0104	78
79	0.0332 1510	0.0374 7426	0.0418 9007	0.0464 3434	79
80	0.0331 1175	0.0373 8489	0.0418 1408	0.0463 7069	80
81	0.0330 1201	0.0372 9894	0.0417 4127	0.0463 0995	81
82	0.0329 1576	0.0372 1628	0.0416 7150	0.0462 5197	82
83	0.0328 2284	0.0371 3676	0.0416 0463	0.0461 9663	83
84	0.0327 3313	0.0370 6025	0.0415 4054	0.0461 4379	84
85	0.0326 4650	0.0369 8662	0.0414 7909	0.0460 9334	85
86	0.0325 6284	0.0369 1576	0.0414 2018	0.0460 4516	86
87	0.0324 8202	0.0368 4756	0.0413 6370	0.0459 9915	87
88	0.0324 0393	0.0367 8190	0.0413 0953	0.0459 5522	88
89	0.0323 2848	0.0367 1868	0.0412 5758	0.0459 1325	89
90	0.0322 5556	0.0366 5781	0.0412 0776	0.0458 7316	90
91	0.0321 8508	0.0365 9919	0.0411 5995	0.0458 3486	91
92	0.0321 1694	0.0365 4273	0.0411 1410	0.0457 9827	92
93	0.0320 5107	0.0364 8834	0.0410 7010	0.0457 6331	93
94	0.0319 8737	0.0364 3594	0.0410 2789	0.0457 2991	94
95	0.0319 2577	0.0363 8546	0.0409 8738	0.0456 9799	95
96	0.0318 6619	0.0363 3682	0.0409 4850	0.0456 6749	96
97	0.0318 0856	0.0362 8995	0.0409 1119	0.0456 3834	97
98	0.0317 5281	0.0362 4478	0.0408 7538	0.0456 1048	98
99	0.0316 9886	0.0362 0124	0.0408 4100	0.0455 8385	99
100	0.0316 4667	0.0361 5927	0.0408 0800	0.0455 5839	100

TABLE V.—Periodic Rent of Annuity Whose Present Value is 1

$$\frac{1}{a_{\overline{n}|i}} = \frac{i}{1-(1+i)^{-n}} \qquad \left[\frac{1}{s_{\overline{n}|i}} = \frac{1}{a_{\overline{n}|i}} - i\right]$$

n	5%	5½%	6%	6½%	n
1	1.0500 0000	1.0550 0000	1.0600 0000	1.0650 0000	1
2	0.5378 0488	0.5416 1800	0.5454 3689	0.5492 6150	2
3	0.3672 0856	0.3706 5407	0.3741 0981	0.3775 7570	3
4	0.2820 1183	0.2852 9449	0.2885 9149	0.2919 0274	4
5	0.2309 7480	0.2341 7644	0.2373 9640	0.2406 3454	5
6	0.1970 1747	0.2001 7895	0.2033 6263	0.2065 6831	6
7	0.1728 1982	0.1759 6442	0.1791 3502	0.1823 3137	7
8	0.1547 2181	0.1578 6401	0.1610 3594	0.1642 3730	8
9	0.1406 9008	0.1438 3946	0.1470 2224	0.1502 3803	9
10	0.1295 0458	0.1326 6777	0.1358 6796	0.1391 0469	10
11	0.1203 8889	0.1235 7065	0.1267 9294	0.1300 5521	11
12	0.1128 2541	0.1160 2923	0.1192 7703	0.1225 6817	12
13	0.1064 5577	0.1096 8426	0.1129 6011	0.1162 8256	13
14	0.1010 2397	0.1042 7912	0.1075 8491	0.1109 4048	14
15	0.0963 4229	0.0996 2560	0.1029 6276	0.1063 5278	15
16	0.0922 6991	0.0955 8254	0.0989 5214	0.1023 7757	16
17	0.0886 9914	0.0920 4797	0.0954 4480	0.0989 0633	17
18	0.0855 4622	0.0889 1992	0.0923 5654	0.0958 5461	18
19	0.0827 4501	0.0861 5006	0.0896 2086	0.0931 5575	19
20	0.0802 4259	0.0836 7933	0.0871 8456	0.0907 5640	20
21	0.0779 9611	0.0814 6478	0.0850 0455	0.0886 1333	21
22	0.0759 7051	0.0794 7123	0.0830 4557	0.0866 9120	22
23	0.0741 3682	0.0776 6965	0.0812 7848	0.0849 6078	23
24	0.0724 7090	0.0760 3580	0.0796 7900	0.0833 9770	24
25	0.0709 5246	0.0745 4935	0.0782 2672	0.0819 8148	25
26	0.0695 6432	0.0731 9307	0.0769 0435	0.0806 9480	26
27	0.0682 9186	0.0719 5228	0.0756 9717	0.0795 2288	27
28	0.0671 2253	0.0708 1440	0.0745 9255	0.0784 5305	28
29	0.0660 4551	0.0697 6857	0.0735 7961	0.0774 7440	29
30	0.0650 5144	0.0688 0539	0.0726 4891	0.0765 7744	30
31	0.0641 3212	0.0679 1665	0.0717 9222	0.0757 5393	31
32	0.0632 8042	0.0670 9519	0.0710 0234	0.0749 9665	32
33	0.0624 9004	0.0663 3469	0.0702 7293	0.0742 9924	33
34	0.0617 5545	0.0656 2958	0.0695 9843	0.0736 5610	34
35	0.0610 7171	0.0649 7493	0.0689 7386	0.0730 6226	35
36	0.0604 3446	0.0643 6635	0.0683 9483	0.0725 1332	36
37	0.0598 3979	0.0637 9993	0.0678 5743	0.0720 0534	37
38	0.0592 8423	0.0632 7217	0.0673 5812	0.0715 3480	38
39	0.0587 6462	0.0627 7991	0.0668 9377	0.0710 9854	39
40	0.0582 7816	0.0623 2034	0.0664 6154	0.0706 9373	40
41	0.0578 2229	0.0618 9090	0.0660 5886	0.0703 1779	41
42	0.0573 9471	0.0614 8927	0.0656 8342	0.0699 6842	42
43	0.0569 9333	0.0611 1337	0.0653 3312	0.0696 4352	43
44	0.0566 1625	0.0607 6128	0.0650 0606	0.0693 4119	44
45	0.0562 6173	0.0604 3127	0.0647 0050	0.0690 5968	45
46	0.0559 2820	0.0601 2175	0.0644 1485	0.0687 9743	46
47	0.0556 1421	0.0598 3129	0.0641 4768	0.0685 5300	47
48	0.0553 1843	0.0595 5854	0.0638 9766	0.0683 2506	48
49	0.0550 3965	0.0593 0230	0.0636 6356	0.0681 1240	49
50	0.0547 7674	0.0590 6145	0.0634 4429	0.0679 1393	50

TABLE V.—Periodic Rent of Annuity Whose Present Value is 1

$$\frac{1}{a_{\overline{n}|i}} = \frac{i}{1-(1+i)^{-n}} \qquad \left[\frac{1}{s_{\overline{n}|i}} = \frac{1}{a_{\overline{n}|i}} - i\right]$$

n	5%	5½%	6%	6½%	n
51	0.0545 2867	0.0588 3495	0.0632 3880	0.0677 2861	51
52	0.0542 9450	0.0586 2186	0.0630 4617	0.0675 5553	52
53	0.0540 7334	0.0584 2130	0.0628 6551	0.0673 9382	53
54	0.0538 6438	0.0582 3245	0.0626 9602	0.0672 4267	54
55	0.0536 6686	0.0580 5458	0.0625 3696	0.0671 0137	55
56	0.0534 8010	0.0578 8698	0.0623 8765	0.0669 6923	56
57	0.0533 0343	0.0577 2900	0.0622 4744	0.0668 4563	57
58	0.0531 3626	0.0575 8006	0.0621 1574	0.0667 2999	58
59	0.0529 7802	0.0574 3959	0.0619 9200	0.0666 2177	59
60	0.0528 2818	0.0573 0707	0.0618 7572	0.0665 2047	60
61	0.0526 8627	0.0571 8202	0.0617 6642	0.0664 2564	61
62	0.0525 5183	0.0570 6400	0.0616 6366	0.0663 3684	62
63	0.0524 2442	0.0569 5258	0.0615 6704	0.0662 5367	63
64	0.0523 0365	0.0568 4737	0.0614 7615	0.0661 7577	64
65	0.0521 8915	0.0567 4800	0.0613 9066	0.0661 0280	65
66	0.0520 8057	0.0566 5413	0.0613 1022	0.0660 3442	66
67	0.0519 7757	0.0565 6544	0.0612 3454	0.0659 7034	67
68	0.0518 7986	0.0564 8163	0.0611 6330	0.0659 1029	68
69	0.0517 8715	0.0564 0242	0.0610 9625	0.0658 5400	69
70	0.0516 9915	0.0563 2754	0.0610 3313	0.0658 0124	70
71	0.0516 1563	0.0562 5675	0.0609 7370	0.0657 5177	71
72	0.0515 3633	0.0561 8982	0.0609 1774	0.0657 0539	72
73	0.0514 6103	0.0561 2652	0.0608 6505	0.0656 6190	73
74	0.0513 8953	0.0560 6665	0.0608 1542	0.0656 2112	74
75	0.0513 2161	0.0560 1002	0.0607 6867	0.0655 8287	75
76	0.0512 5709	0.0559 5645	0.0607 2463	0.0655 4699	76
77	0.0511 9580	0.0559 0577	0.0606 8315	0.0655 1335	77
78	0.0511 3756	0.0558 5781	0.0606 4407	0.0654 8178	78
79	0.0510 8222	0.0558 1243	0.0606 0724	0.0654 5217	79
80	0.0510 2962	0.0557 6948	0.0605 7254	0.0654 2440	80
81	0.0509 7963	0.0557 2884	0.0605 3984	0.0653 9834	81
82	0.0509 3211	0.0556 9036	0.0605 0903	0.0653 7388	82
83	0.0508 8694	0.0556 5395	0.0604 7998	0.0653 5094	83
84	0.0508 4399	0.0556 1947	0.0604 5261	0.0653 2941	84
85	0.0508 0316	0.0555 8683	0.0604 2681	0.0653 0921	85
86	0.0507 6433	0.0555 5593	0.0604 0249	0.0652 9026	86
87	0.0507 2740	0.0555 2667	0.0603 7956	0.0652 7247	87
88	0.0506 9228	0.0554 9896	0.0603 5795	0.0652 5577	88
89	0.0506 5888	0.0554 7273	0.0603 3757	0.0652 4010	89
90	0.0506 2711	0.0554 4788	0.0603 1836	0.0652 2540	90
91	0.0505 9689	0.0554 2435	0.0603 0025	0.0652 1160	91
92	0.0505 6815	0.0554 0207	0.0602 8318	0.0651 9864	92
93	0.0505 4080	0.0553 8096	0.0602 6708	0.0651 8649	93
94	0.0505 1478	0.0553 6097	0.0602 5190	0.0651 7507	94
95	0.0504 9003	0.0553 4204	0.0602 3758	0.0651 6436	95
96	0.0504 6648	0.0553 2410	0.0602 2408	0.0651 5431	96
97	0.0504 4407	0.0553 0711	0.0602 1135	0.0651 4487	97
98	0.0504 2274	0.0552 9101	0.0601 9935	0.0651 3601	98
99	0.0504 0245	0.0552 7577	0.0601 8803	0.0651 2769	99
100	0.0503 8314	0.0552 6132	0.0601 7736	0.0651 1988	100

TABLE V.—Periodic Rent of Annuity Whose Present Value is 1

$$\frac{1}{a_{\overline{n}|i}} = \frac{i}{1-(1+i)^{-n}} \qquad \left[\frac{1}{s_{\overline{n}|i}} = \frac{1}{a_{\overline{n}|i}} - i\right]$$

n	7%	7½%	8%	8½%	n
1	1.0700 0000	1.0750 0000	1.0800 0000	1.0850 0000	1
2	0.5530 9179	0.5569 2771	0.5607 6923	0.5646 1631	2
3	0.3810 5166	0.3845 3763	0.3880 3351	0.3915 3925	3
4	0.2952 2812	0.2985 6751	0.3019 2080	0.3052 8789	4
5	0.2438 9069	0.2471 6472	0.2504 5645	0.2537 6575	5
6	0.2097 9580	0.2130 4489	0.2163 1539	0.2196 0708	6
7	0.1855 5322	0.1888 0032	0.1920 7240	0.1953 6922	7
8	0.1674 6776	0.1707 2702	0.1740 1476	0.1773 3065	8
9	0.1534 8647	0.1567 6716	0.1600 7971	0.1634 2372	9
10	0.1423 7750	0.1456 8593	0.1490 2949	0.1524 0771	10
11	0.1333 5690	0.1366 9747	0.1400 7634	0.1434 9293	11
12	0.1259 0199	0.1292 7783	0.1326 9502	0.1361 5286	12
13	0.1196 5085	0.1230 6420	0.1265 2181	0.1300 2287	13
14	0.1143 4494	0.1177 9737	0.1212 9685	0.1248 4244	14
15	0.1097 9462	0.1132 8724	0.1168 2954	0.1204 2046	15
16	0.1058 5765	0.1093 9116	0.1129 7687	0.1166 1354	16
17	0.1024 2519	0.1060 0003	0.1096 2943	0.1133 1198	17
18	0.0994 1260	0.1030 2896	0.1067 0210	0.1104 3041	18
19	0.0967 5301	0.1004 1090	0.1041 2763	0.1079 0140	19
20	0.0943 9293	0.0980 9219	0.1018 5221	0.1056 7097	20
21	0.0922 8900	0.0960 2937	0.0998 3225	0.1036 9541	21
22	0.0904 0577	0.0941 8687	0.0980 3207	0.1019 3892	22
23	0.0887 1393	0.0925 3528	0.0964 2217	0.1003 7193	23
24	0.0871 8902	0.0910 5008	0.0949 7796	0.0989 6975	24
25	0.0858 1052	0.0897 1067	0.0936 7878	0.0977 1168	25
26	0.0845 6103	0.0884 9961	0.0925 0713	0.0965 8016	26
27	0.0834 2573	0.0874 0204	0.0914 4809	0.0955 6025	27
28	0.0823 9193	0.0864 0520	0.0904 8891	0.0946 3914	28
29	0.0814 4865	0.0854 9811	0.0896 1854	0.0938 0577	29
30	0.0805 8640	0.0846 7124	0.0888 2743	0.0930 5058	30
31	0.0797 9691	0.0839 1628	0.0881 0728	0.0923 6524	31
32	0.0790 7292	0.0832 2599	0.0874 5081	0.0917 4247	32
33	0.0784 0807	0.0825 9397	0.0868 5163	0.0911 7588	33
34	0.0777 9674	0.0820 1461	0.0863 0411	0.0906 5984	34
35	0.0772 3396	0.0814 8291	0.0858 0326	0.0901 8937	35
36	0.0767 1531	0.0809 9447	0.0853 4467	0.0897 6006	36
37	0.0762 3685	0.0805 4533	0.0849 2440	0.0893 6799	37
38	0.0757 9505	0.0801 3197	0.0845 3894	0.0890 0966	38
39	0.0753 8676	0.0797 5124	0.0841 8513	0.0886 8193	39
40	0.0750 0914	0.0794 0031	0.0838 6016	0.0883 8201	40
41	0.0746 5962	0.0790 7663	0.0835 6149	0.0881 0737	41
42	0.0743 3591	0.0787 7789	0.0832 8684	0.0878 5576	42
43	0.0740 3590	0.0785 0201	0.0830 3414	0.0876 2512	43
44	0.0737 5769	0.0782 4710	0.0828 0152	0 0874 1363	44
45	0.0734 9957	0.0780 1146	0.0825 8728	0.0872 1961	45
46	0.0732 5996	0.0777 9353	0.0823 8991	0.0870 4154	46
47	0.0730 3744	0.0775 9190	0.0822 0799	0.0868 7807	47
48	0.0728 3070	0.0774 0527	0.0820 4027	0.0867 2795	48
49	0.0726 3853	0.0772 3247	0.0818 8557	0.0865 9005	49
50	0.0724 5985	0.0770 7241	0.0817 4286	0.0864 6334	50

TABLE V.—Periodic Rent of Annuity Whose Present Value is 1

$$\frac{1}{a_{\overline{n}|i}} = \frac{i}{1-(1+i)^{-n}} \qquad \left[\frac{1}{s_{\overline{n}|i}} = \frac{1}{a_{\overline{n}|i}} - i\right]$$

n	7%	7½%	8%	8½%	n
51	0.0722 9365	0.0769 2411	0.0816 1116	0.0863 4688	51
52	0.0721 3901	0.0767 8668	0.0814 8959	0.0862 3983	52
53	0.0719 9509	0.0766 5927	0.0813 7735	0.0861 4139	53
54	0.0718 6110	0.0765 4112	0.0812 7370	0.0860 5087	54
55	0.0717 3633	0.0764 3155	0.0811 7796	0.0859 6761	55
56	0.0716 2011	0.0763 2991	0.0810 8952	0.0858 9101	56
57	0.0715 1183	0.0762 3559	0.0810 0780	0.0858 2053	57
58	0.0714 1093	0.0761 4807	0.0809 3227	0.0857 5568	58
59	0.0713 1689	0.0760 6683	0.0808 6247	0.0856 9599	59
60	0.0712 2923	0.0759 9142	0.0807 9795	0.0856 4106	60
61	0.0711 4749	0.0759 2140	0.0807 3830	0.0855 9049	61
62	0.0710 7127	0.0758 5638	0.0806 8314	0.0855 4393	62
63	0.0710 0019	0.0757 9600	0.0806 3214	0.0855 0107	63
64	0.0709 3388	0.0757 3992	0.0805 8497	0.0854 6160	64
65	0.0708 7203	0.0756 8782	0.0805 4135	0.0854 2526	65
66	0.0708 1431	0.0756 3942	0.0805 0100	0.0853 9179	66
67	0.0707 6046	0.0755 9446	0.0804 6367	0.0853 6097	67
68	0.0707 1021	0.0755 5268	0.0804 2914	0.0853 3258	68
69	0.0706 6331	0.0755 1386	0.0803 9719	0.0853 0643	69
70	0.0706 1953	0.0754 7778	0.0803 6764	0.0852 8234	70
71	0.0705 7866	0.0754 4425	0.0803 4029	0.0852 6016	71
72	0.0705 4051	0.0754 1308	0.0803 1498	0.0852 3972	72
73	0.0705 0490	0.0753 8412	0.0802 9157	0.0852 2089	73
74	0.0704 7164	0.0753 5719	0.0802 6989	0.0852 0354	74
75	0.0704 4060	0.0753 3216	0.0802 4984	0.0851 8756	75
76	0.0704 1160	0.0753 0889	0.0802 3128	0.0851 7284	76
77	0.0703 8453	0.0752 8726	0.0802 1410	0.0851 5927	77
78	0.0703 5924	0.0752 6714	0.0801 9820	0.0851 4677	78
79	0.0703 3563	0.0752 4844	0.0801 8349	0.0851 3526	79
80	0.0703 1357	0.0752 3106	0.0801 6987	0.0851 2465	80
81	0.0702 9297	0.0752 1489	0.0801 5726	0.0851 1487	81
82	0.0702 7373	0.0751 9986	0.0801 4559	0.0851 0586	82
83	0.0702 5576	0.0751 8588	0.0801 3479	0.0850 9756	83
84	0.0702 3897	0.0751 7288	0.0801 2479	0.0850 8990	84
85	0.0702 2329	0.0751 6079	0.0801 1553	0.0850 8285	85
86	0.0702 0863	0.0751 4955	0.0801 0696	0.0850 7636	86
87	0.0701 9495	0.0751 3910	0.0800 9903	0.0850 7037	87
88	0.0701 8216	0.0751 2938	0.0800 9168	0.0850 6485	88
89	0.0701 7021	0.0751 2034	0.0800 8489	0.0850 5977	89
90	0.0701 5905	0.0751 1103	0.0800 7859	0.0850 5508	90
91	0.0701 4863	0.0751 0411	0.0800 7277	0.0850 5077	91
92	0.0701 3888	0.0750 9684	0.0800 6737	0.0850 4679	92
93	0.0701 2978	0.0750 9007	0.0800 6238	0.0850 4312	93
94	0.0701 2128	0.0750 8378	0.0800 5775	0.0850 3974	94
95	0.0701 1333	0.0750 7793	0.0800 5347	0.0850 3663	95
96	0.0701 0590	0.0750 7249	0.0800 4951	0.0850 3375	96
97	0.0700 9897	0.0750 6743	0.0800 4584	0.0850 3111	97
98	0.0700 9248	0.0750 6272	0.0800 4244	0.0850 2867	98
99	0.0700 8643	0.0750 5834	0.0800 3930	0.0850 2642	99
100	0.0700 8076	0.0750 5427	0.0800 3638	0.0850 2435	100

TABLE VI. Six-place Common Logarithms of Numbers from 100 to 999

N.	0	1	2	3	4	5	6	7	8	9	D.
100	000000	000434	000868	001301	001734	002166	002598	003029	003461	003891	432
1	4321	4751	5181	5609	6038	6466	6894	7321	7748	8174	428
2	8600	9026	9451	9876	010300	010724	011147	011570	011993	012415	424
3	012837	013259	013680	014100	4521	4940	5360	5779	6197	6616	420
4	7033	7451	7868	8284	8700	9116	9532	9947	020361	020775	416
105	021189	021603	022016	022428	022841	023252	023664	024075	4486	4896	412
6	5306	5715	6125	6533	6942	7350	7757	8164	8571	8978	408
7	9384	9789	030195	030600	031004	031408	031812	032216	032619	033021	404
8	033424	033826	4227	4628	5029	5430	5830	6230	6629	7028	400
9	7426	7825	8223	8620	9017	9414	9811	040207	040602	040998	397
110	041393	041787	042182	042576	042969	043362	043755	044148	044540	044932	393
1	5323	5714	6105	6495	6885	7275	7664	8053	8442	8830	390
2	9218	9606	9993	050380	050766	051153	051538	051924	052309	052694	386
3	053078	053463	053846	4230	4613	4996	5378	5760	6142	6524	383
4	6905	7286	7666	8046	8426	8805	9185	9563	9942	060320	379
115	060698	061075	061452	061829	062206	062582	062958	063333	063709	4083	376
6	4458	4832	5206	5580	5953	6326	6699	7071	7443	7815	373
7	8186	8557	8928	9298	9668	070038	070407	070776	071145	071514	370
8	071882	072250	072617	072985	073352	3718	4085	4451	4816	5182	366
9	5547	5912	6276	6640	7004	7368	7731	8094	8457	8819	363
120	079181	079543	079904	080266	080626	080987	081347	081707	082067	082426	360
1	082785	083144	083503	3861	4219	4576	4934	5291	5647	6004	357
2	6360	6716	7071	7426	7781	8136	8490	8845	9198	9552	355
3	9905	090258	090611	090963	091315	091667	092018	092370	092721	093071	352
4	093422	3772	4122	4471	4820	5169	5518	5866	6215	6562	349
125	6910	7257	7604	7951	8298	8644	8990	9335	9681	100026	346
6	100371	100715	101059	101403	101747	102091	102434	102777	103119	3462	343
7	3804	4146	4487	4828	5169	5510	5851	6191	6531	6871	341
8	7210	7549	7888	8227	8565	8903	9241	9579	9916	110253	338
9	110590	110926	111263	111599	111934	112270	112605	112940	113275	3609	335
130	113943	114277	114611	114944	115278	115611	115943	116276	116608	116940	333
1	7271	7603	7934	8265	8595	8926	9256	9586	9915	120245	330
2	120574	120903	121231	121560	121888	122216	122544	122871	123198	3525	328
3	3852	4178	4504	4830	5156	5481	5806	6131	6456	6781	325
4	7105	7429	7753	8076	8399	8722	9045	9368	9690	130012	323
135	130334	130655	130977	131298	131619	131939	132260	132580	132900	3219	321
6	3539	3858	4177	4496	4814	5133	5451	5769	6086	6403	318
7	6721	7037	7354	7671	7987	8303	8618	8934	9249	9564	316
8	9879	140194	140508	140822	141136	141450	141763	142076	142389	142702	314
9	143015	3327	3639	3951	4263	4574	4885	5196	5507	5818	311
140	146128	146438	146748	147058	147367	147676	147985	148294	148603	148911	309
1	9219	9527	9835	150142	150449	150756	151063	151370	151676	151982	307
2	152288	152594	152900	3205	3510	3815	4120	4424	4728	5032	305
3	5336	5640	5943	6246	6549	6852	7154	7457	7759	8061	303
4	8362	8664	8965	9266	9567	9868	160168	160469	160769	161068	301
145	161368	161667	161967	162266	162564	162863	3161	3460	3758	4055	299
6	4353	4650	4947	5244	5541	5838	6134	6430	6726	7022	297
7	7317	7613	7908	8203	8497	8792	9086	9380	9674	9968	295
8	170262	170555	170848	171141	171434	171726	172019	172311	172603	172895	293
9	3186	3478	3769	4060	4351	4641	4932	5222	5512	5802	291
150	176091	176381	176670	176959	177248	177536	177825	178113	178401	178689	289
1	8977	9264	9552	9839	180126	180413	180699	180986	181272	181558	287
2	181844	182129	182415	182700	2985	3270	3555	3839	4123	4407	285
3	4691	4975	5259	5542	5825	6108	6391	6674	6956	7239	283
4	7521	7803	8084	8366	8647	8928	9209	9490	9771	190051	281
155	190332	190612	190892	191171	191451	191730	192010	192289	192567	2846	279
6	3125	3403	3681	3959	4237	4514	4792	5069	5346	5623	278
7	5900	6176	6453	6729	7005	7281	7556	7832	8107	8382	276
8	8657	8932	9206	9481	9755	200029	200303	200577	200850	201124	274
9	201397	201670	201943	202216	202488	2761	3033	3305	3577	3848	272
N.	0	1	2	3	4	5	6	7	8	9	D.

TABLE VI. Six-place Common Logarithms of Numbers from 100 to 999

N.	0	1	2	3	4	5	6	7	8	9	D.
160	204120	204391	204663	204934	205204	205475	205746	206016	206286	206556	271
1	6826	7096	7365	7634	7904	8173	8441	8710	8979	9247	269
2	9515	9783	210051	210319	210586	210853	211121	211388	211654	211921	267
3	212188	212454	2720	2986	3252	3518	3783	4049	4314	4579	266
4	4844	5109	5373	5638	5902	6166	6430	6694	6957	7221	264
165	7484	7747	8010	8273	8536	8798	9060	9323	9585	9846	262
6	220108	220370	220631	220892	221153	221414	221675	221936	222196	222456	261
7	2716	2976	3236	3496	3755	4015	4274	4533	4792	5051	259
8	5309	5568	5826	6084	6342	6600	6858	7115	7372	7630	258
9	7887	8144	8400	8657	8913	9170	9426	9682	9938	230193	256
170	230449	230704	230960	231215	231470	231724	231979	232234	232488	232742	255
1	2996	3250	3504	3757	4011	4264	4517	4770	5023	5276	253
2	5528	5781	6033	6285	6537	6789	7041	7292	7544	7795	252
3	8046	8297	8548	8799	9049	9299	9550	9800	240050	240300	250
4	240549	240799	241048	241297	241546	241795	242044	242293	2541	2790	249
175	3038	3286	3534	3782	4030	4277	4525	4772	5019	5266	248
6	5513	5759	6006	6252	6499	6745	6991	7237	7482	7728	246
7	7973	8219	8464	8709	8954	9198	9443	9687	9932	250176	245
8	250420	250664	250908	251151	251395	251638	251881	252125	252368	2610	243
9	2853	3096	3338	3580	3822	4064	4306	4548	4790	5031	242
180	255273	255514	255755	255996	256237	256477	256718	256958	257198	257439	241
1	7679	7918	8158	8398	8637	8877	9116	9355	9594	9833	239
2	260071	260310	260548	260787	261025	261263	261501	261739	261976	262214	238
3	2451	2688	2925	3162	3399	3636	3873	4109	4346	4582	237
4	4818	5054	5290	5525	5761	5996	6232	6467	6702	6937	235
185	7172	7406	7641	7875	8110	8344	8578	8812	9046	9279	234
6	9513	9746	9980	270213	270446	270679	270912	271144	271377	271609	233
7	271842	272074	272306	2538	2770	3001	3233	3464	3696	3927	232
8	4158	4389	4620	4850	5081	5311	5542	5772	6002	6232	230
9	6462	6692	6921	7151	7380	7609	7838	8067	8296	8525	229
190	278754	278982	279211	279439	279667	279895	280123	280351	280578	280806	228
1	281033	281261	281488	281715	281942	282169	2396	2622	2849	3075	227
2	3301	3527	3753	3979	4205	4431	4656	4882	5107	5332	226
3	5557	5782	6007	6232	6456	6681	6905	7130	7354	7578	225
4	7802	8026	8249	8473	8696	8920	9143	9366	9589	9812	223
195	290035	290257	290480	290702	290925	291147	291369	291591	291813	292034	222
6	2256	2478	2699	2920	3141	3363	3584	3804	4025	4246	221
7	4466	4687	4907	5127	5347	5567	5787	6007	6226	6446	220
8	6665	6884	7104	7323	7542	7761	7979	8198	8416	8635	219
9	8853	9071	9289	9507	9725	9943	300161	300378	300595	300813	218
200	301030	301247	301464	301681	301898	302114	302331	302547	302764	302980	217
1	3196	3412	3628	3844	4059	4275	4491	4706	4921	5136	216
2	5351	5566	5781	5996	6211	6425	6639	6854	7068	7282	215
3	7496	7710	7924	8137	8351	8564	8778	8991	9204	9417	213
4	9630	9843	310056	310268	310481	310693	310906	311118	311330	311542	212
205	311754	311966	2177	2389	2600	2812	3023	3234	3445	3656	211
6	3867	4078	4289	4499	4710	4920	5130	5340	5551	5760	210
7	5970	6180	6390	6599	6809	7018	7227	7436	7646	7854	209
8	8063	8272	8481	8689	8898	9106	9314	9522	9730	9938	208
9	320146	320354	320562	320769	320977	321184	321391	321598	321805	322012	207
210	322219	322426	322633	322839	323046	323252	323458	323665	323871	324077	206
1	4282	4488	4694	4899	5105	5310	5516	5721	5926	6131	205
2	6336	6541	6745	6950	7155	7359	7563	7767	7972	8176	204
3	8380	8583	8787	8991	9194	9398	9601	9805	330008	330211	203
4	330414	330617	330819	331022	331225	331427	331630	331832	2034	2236	202
215	2438	2640	2842	3044	3246	3447	3649	3850	4051	4253	202
6	4454	4655	4856	5057	5257	5458	5658	5859	6059	6260	201
7	6460	6660	6860	7060	7260	7459	7659	7858	8058	8257	200
8	8456	8656	8855	9054	9253	9451	9650	9849	340047	340246	199
9	340444	340642	340841	341039	341237	341435	341632	341830	2028	2225	198
N.	0	1	2	3	4	5	6	7	8	9	D.

TABLE VI. Six-place Common Logarithms of Numbers from 100 to 999

N.	0	1	2	3	4	5	6	7	8	9	D.
220	342423	342620	342817	343014	343212	343409	343606	343802	343999	344196	197
1	4392	4589	4785	4981	5178	5374	5570	5766	5962	6157	196
2	6353	6549	6744	6939	7135	7330	7525	7720	7915	8110	195
3	8305	8500	8694	8889	9083	9278	9472	9666	9860	350054	194
4	350248	350442	350636	350829	351023	351216	351410	351603	351796	1989	193
225	2183	2375	2568	2761	2954	3147	3339	3532	3724	3916	193
6	4108	4301	4493	4685	4876	5068	5260	5452	5643	5834	192
7	6026	6217	6408	6599	6790	6981	7172	7363	7554	7744	191
8	7935	8125	8316	8506	8696	8886	9076	9266	9456	9646	190
9	9835	360025	360215	360404	360593	360783	360972	361161	361350	361539	189
230	361728	361917	362105	362294	362482	362671	362859	363048	363236	363424	188
1	3612	3800	3988	4176	4363	4551	4739	4926	5113	5301	188
2	5488	5675	5862	6049	6236	6423	6610	6796	6983	7169	187
3	7356	7542	7729	7915	8101	8287	8473	8659	8845	9030	186
4	9216	9401	9587	9772	9958	370143	370328	370513	370698	370883	185
235	371068	371253	371437	371622	371806	1991	2175	2360	2544	2728	184
6	2912	3096	3280	3464	3647	3831	4015	4198	4382	4565	184
7	4748	4932	5115	5298	5481	5664	5846	6029	6212	6394	183
8	6577	6759	6942	7124	7306	7488	7670	7852	8034	8216	182
9	8398	8580	8761	8943	9124	9306	9487	9668	9849	380030	181
240	380211	380392	380573	380754	380934	381115	381296	381476	381656	381837	181
1	2017	2197	2377	2557	2737	2917	3097	3277	3456	3636	180
2	3815	3995	4174	4353	4533	4712	4891	5070	5249	5428	179
3	5606	5785	5964	6142	6321	6499	6677	6856	7034	7212	178
4	7390	7568	7746	7923	8101	8279	8456	8634	8811	8989	178
245	9166	9343	9520	9698	9875	390051	390228	390405	390582	390759	177
6	390935	391112	391288	391464	391641	1817	1993	2169	2345	2521	176
7	2697	2873	3048	3224	3400	3575	3751	3926	4101	4277	176
8	4452	4627	4802	4977	5152	5326	5501	5676	5850	6025	175
9	6199	6374	6548	6722	6896	7071	7245	7419	7592	7766	174
250	397940	398114	398287	398461	398634	398808	398981	399154	399328	399501	173
1	9674	9847	400020	400192	400365	400538	400711	400883	401056	401228	173
2	401401	401573	1745	1917	2089	2261	2433	2605	2777	2949	172
3	3121	3292	3464	3635	3807	3978	4149	4320	4492	4663	171
4	4834	5005	5176	5346	5517	5688	5858	6029	6199	6370	171
255	6540	6710	6881	7051	7221	7391	7561	7731	7901	8070	170
6	8240	8410	8579	8749	8918	9087	9257	9426	9595	9764	169
7	9933	410102	410271	410440	410609	410777	410964	411114	411283	411451	169
8	411620	1788	1956	2124	2293	2461	2629	2796	2964	3132	168
9	3300	3467	3635	3803	3970	4137	4305	4472	4639	4806	167
260	414973	415140	415307	415474	415641	415808	415974	416141	416308	416474	167
1	6641	6807	6973	7139	7306	7472	7638	7804	7970	8135	166
2	8301	8467	8633	8798	8964	9129	9295	9460	9625	9791	165
3	9956	420121	420286	420451	420616	420781	420945	421110	421275	421439	165
4	421604	1768	1933	2097	2261	2426	2590	2754	2918	3082	164
265	3246	3410	3574	3737	3901	4065	4228	4392	4555	4718	164
6	4882	5045	5208	5371	5534	5697	5860	6023	6186	6349	163
7	6511	6674	6836	6999	7161	7324	7486	7648	7811	7973	162
8	8135	8297	8459	8621	8783	8944	9106	9268	9429	9591	162
9	9752	9914	430075	430236	430398	430559	430720	430881	431042	431203	161
270	431364	431525	431685	431846	432007	432167	432328	432488	432649	432809	161
1	2969	3130	3290	3450	3610	3770	3930	4090	4249	4409	160
2	4569	4729	4888	5048	5207	5367	5526	5685	5844	6004	159
3	6163	6322	6481	6640	6799	6957	7116	7275	7433	7592	159
4	7751	7909	8067	8226	8384	8542	8701	8859	9017	9175	158
275	9333	9491	9648	9806	9964	440122	440279	440437	440594	440752	158
6	440909	441066	441224	441381	441538	1695	1852	2009	2166	2323	157
7	2480	2637	2793	2950	3106	3263	3419	3576	3732	3889	157
8	4045	4201	4357	4513	4669	4825	4981	5137	5293	5449	156
9	5604	5760	5915	6071	6226	6382	6537	6692	6848	7003	155
N.	0	1	2	3	4	5	6	7	8	9	D.

TABLE VI. Six-place Common Logarithms of Numbers from 100 to 999

N.	0	1	2	3	4	5	6	7	8	9	D.
280	447158	447313	447468	447623	447778	447933	448088	448242	448397	448552	155
1	8706	8861	9015	9170	9324	9478	9633	9787	9941	450095	154
2	450249	450403	450557	450711	450865	451018	451172	451326	451479	1633	154
3	1786	1940	2093	2247	2400	2553	2706	2859	3012	3165	153
4	3318	3471	3624	3777	3930	4082	4235	4387	4540	4692	153
285	4845	4997	5150	5302	5454	5606	5758	5910	6062	6214	152
6	6366	6518	6670	6821	6973	7125	7276	7428	7579	7731	152
7	7882	8033	8184	8336	8487	8638	8789	8940	9091	9242	151
8	9392	9543	9694	9845	9995	460146	460296	460447	460597	460748	151
9	460898	461048	461198	461348	461499	1649	1799	1948	2098	2248	150
290	462398	462548	462697	462847	462997	463146	463296	463445	463594	463744	150
1	3893	4042	4191	4340	4490	4639	4788	4936	5085	5234	149
2	5383	5532	5680	5829	5977	6126	6274	6423	6571	6719	149
3	6868	7016	7164	7312	7460	7608	7756	7904	8052	8200	148
4	8347	8495	8643	8790	8938	9085	9233	9380	9527	9675	148
295	9822	9969	470116	470263	470410	470557	470704	470851	470998	471145	147
6	471292	471438	1585	1732	1878	2025	2171	2318	2464	2610	146
7	2756	2903	3049	3195	3341	3487	3633	3779	3925	4071	146
8	4216	4362	4508	4653	4799	4944	5090	5235	5381	5526	146
9	5671	5816	5962	6107	6252	6397	6542	6687	6832	6976	145
300	477121	477266	477411	477555	477700	477844	477989	478133	478278	478422	145
1	8566	8711	8855	8999	9143	9287	9431	9575	9719	9863	144
2	480007	480151	480294	480438	480582	480725	480869	481012	481156	481299	144
3	1443	1586	1729	1872	2016	2159	2302	2445	2588	2731	143
4	2874	3016	3159	3302	3445	3587	3730	3872	4015	4157	143
305	4300	4442	4585	4727	4869	5011	5153	5295	5437	5579	142
6	5721	5863	6005	6147	6289	6430	6572	6714	6855	6997	142
7	7138	7280	7421	7563	7704	7845	7986	8127	8269	8410	141
8	8551	8692	8833	8974	9114	9255	9396	9537	9677	9818	141
9	9958	490099	490239	490380	490520	490661	490801	490941	491081	491222	140
310	491362	491502	491642	491782	491922	492062	492201	492341	492481	492621	140
1	2760	2900	3040	3179	3319	3458	3597	3737	3876	4015	139
2	4155	4294	4433	4572	4711	4850	4989	5128	5267	5406	139
3	5544	5683	5822	5960	6099	6238	6376	6515	6653	6791	139
4	6930	7068	7206	7344	7483	7621	7759	7897	8035	8173	138
315	8311	8448	8586	8724	8862	8999	9137	9275	9412	9550	138
6	9687	9824	9962	500099	500236	500374	500511	500648	500785	500922	137
7	501059	501196	501333	1470	1607	1744	1880	2017	2154	2291	137
8	2427	2564	2700	2837	2973	3109	3246	3382	3518	3655	136
9	3791	3927	4063	4199	4335	4471	4607	4743	4878	5014	136
320	505150	505286	505421	505557	505693	505828	505964	506099	506234	506370	136
1	6505	6640	6776	6911	7046	7181	7316	7451	7586	7721	135
2	7856	7991	8126	8260	8395	8530	8664	8799	8934	9068	135
3	9203	9337	9471	9606	9740	9874	510009	510143	510277	510411	134
4	510545	510679	510813	510947	511081	511215	1349	1482	1616	1750	134
325	1883	2017	2151	2284	2418	2551	2684	2818	2951	3084	133
6	3218	3351	3484	3617	3750	3883	4016	4149	4282	4415	133
7	4548	4681	4813	4946	5079	5211	5344	5476	5609	5741	133
8	5874	6006	6139	6271	6403	6535	6668	6800	6932	7064	132
9	7196	7328	7460	7592	7724	7855	7987	8119	8251	8382	132
330	518514	518646	518777	518909	519040	519171	519303	519434	519566	519697	131
1	9828	9959	520090	520221	520353	520484	520615	520745	520876	521007	131
2	521138	521269	1400	1530	1661	1792	1922	2053	2183	2314	131
3	2444	2575	2705	2835	2966	3096	3226	3356	3486	3616	130
4	3746	3876	4006	4136	4266	4396	4526	4656	4785	4915	130
335	5045	5174	5304	5434	5563	5693	5822	5951	6081	6210	129
6	6339	6469	6598	6727	6856	6985	7114	7243	7372	7501	129
7	7630	7759	7888	8016	8145	8274	8402	8531	8660	8788	129
8	8917	9045	9174	9302	9430	9559	9687	9815	9943	530072	128
9	530200	530328	530456	530584	530712	530840	530968	531096	531223	1351	128
N.	0	1	2	3	4	5	6	7	8	9	D.

TABLE VI. Six-place Common Logarithms of Numbers from 100 to 999

N.	0	1	2	3	4	5	6	7	8	9	D.
340	531479	531607	531734	531862	531990	532117	532245	532372	532500	532627	128
1	2754	2882	3009	3136	3264	3391	3518	3645	3772	3899	127
2	4026	4153	4280	4407	4534	4661	4787	4914	5041	5167	127
3	5294	5421	5547	5674	5800	5927	6053	6180	6306	6432	126
4	6558	6685	6811	6937	7063	7189	7315	7441	7567	7693	126
345	7819	7945	8071	8197	8322	8448	8574	8699	8825	8951	126
6	9076	9202	9327	9452	9578	9703	9829	9954	540079	540204	125
7	540329	540455	540580	540705	540830	540955	541080	541205	1330	1454	125
8	1579	1704	1829	1953	2078	2203	2327	2452	2576	2701	125
9	2825	2950	3074	3199	3323	3447	3571	3696	3820	3944	124
350	544068	544192	544316	544440	544564	544688	544812	544936	545060	545183	124
1	5307	5431	5555	5678	5802	5925	6049	6172	6296	6419	124
2	6543	6666	6789	6913	7036	7159	7282	7405	7529	7652	123
3	7775	7898	8021	8144	8267	8389	8512	8635	8758	8881	123
4	9003	9126	9249	9371	9494	9616	9739	9861	9984	550106	123
355	550228	550351	550473	550595	550717	550840	550962	551084	551206	1328	122
6	1450	1572	1694	1816	1938	2060	2181	2303	2425	2547	122
7	2668	2790	2911	3033	3155	3276	3398	3519	3640	3762	121
8	3883	4004	4126	4247	4368	4489	4610	4731	4852	4973	121
9	5094	5215	5336	5457	5578	5699	5820	5940	6061	6182	121
360	556303	556423	556544	556664	556785	556905	557026	557146	557267	557387	120
1	7507	7627	7748	7868	7988	8108	8228	8349	8469	8589	120
2	8709	8829	8948	9068	9188	9308	9428	9548	9667	9787	120
3	9907	560026	560146	560265	560385	560504	560624	560743	560863	560982	119
4	561101	1221	1340	1459	1578	1698	1817	1936	2055	2174	119
365	2293	2412	2531	2650	2769	2887	3006	3125	3244	3362	119
6	3481	3600	3718	3837	3955	4074	4192	4311	4429	4548	119
7	4666	4784	4903	5021	5139	5257	5376	5494	5612	5730	118
8	5848	5966	6084	6202	6320	6437	6555	6673	6791	6909	118
9	7026	7144	7262	7379	7497	7614	7732	7849	7967	8084	118
370	568202	568319	568436	568554	568671	568788	568905	569023	569140	569257	117
1	9374	9491	9608	9725	9842	9959	570076	570193	570309	570426	117
2	570543	570660	570776	570893	571010	571126	1243	1359	1476	1592	117
3	1709	1825	1942	2058	2174	2291	2407	2523	2639	2755	116
4	2872	2988	3104	3220	3336	3452	3568	3684	3800	3915	116
375	4031	4147	4263	4379	4494	4610	4726	4841	4957	5072	116
6	5188	5303	5419	5534	5650	5765	5880	5996	6111	6226	115
7	6341	6457	6572	6687	6802	6917	7032	7147	7262	7377	115
8	7492	7607	7722	7836	7951	8066	8181	8295	8410	8525	115
9	8639	8754	8868	8983	9097	9212	9326	9441	9555	9669	114
380	579784	579898	580012	580126	580241	580355	580469	580583	580697	580811	114
1	580925	581039	1153	1267	1381	1495	1608	1722	1836	1950	114
2	2063	2177	2291	2404	2518	2631	2745	2858	2972	3085	114
3	3199	3312	3426	3539	3652	3765	3879	3992	4105	4218	113
4	4331	4444	4557	4670	4783	4896	5009	5122	5235	5348	113
385	5461	5574	5686	5799	5912	6024	6137	6250	6362	6475	113
6	6587	6700	6812	6925	7037	7149	7262	7374	7486	7599	112
7	7711	7823	7935	8047	8160	8272	8384	8496	8608	8720	112
8	8832	8944	9056	9167	9279	9391	9503	9615	9726	9838	112
9	9950	590061	590173	590284	590396	590507	590619	590730	590842	590953	112
390	591065	591176	591287	591399	591510	591621	591732	591843	591955	592066	111
1	2177	2288	2399	2510	2621	2732	2843	2954	3064	3175	111
2	3286	3397	3508	3618	3729	3840	3950	4061	4171	4282	111
3	4393	4503	4614	4724	4834	4945	5055	5165	5276	5380	110
4	5496	5606	5717	5827	5937	6047	6157	6267	6377	6487	110
395	6597	6707	6817	6927	7037	7146	7256	7366	7476	7586	110
6	7695	7805	7914	8024	8134	8243	8353	8462	8572	8681	110
7	8791	8900	9009	9119	9228	9337	9446	9556	9665	9774	109
8	9883	9992	600101	600210	600319	600428	600537	600646	600755	600864	109
9	600973	601082	1191	1299	1408	1517	1625	1734	1843	1951	109
N.	0	1	2	3	4	5	6	7	8	9	D.

TABLE VI. Six-place Common Logarithms of Numbers from 100 to 999

N.	0	1	2	3	4	5	6	7	8	9	D.
400	602060	602169	602277	602386	602494	602603	602711	602819	602928	603036	108
1	3144	3253	3361	3469	3577	3686	3794	3902	4010	4118	108
2	4226	4334	4442	4550	4658	4766	4874	4982	5089	5197	108
3	5305	5413	5521	5628	5736	5844	5951	6059	6166	6274	108
4	6381	6489	6596	6704	6811	6919	7026	7133	7241	7348	107
405	7455	7562	7669	7777	7884	7991	8098	8205	8312	8419	107
6	8526	8633	8740	8847	8954	9061	9167	9274	9381	9488	107
7	9594	9701	9808	9914	610021	610128	610234	610341	610447	610554	107
8	610660	610767	610873	610979	1086	1192	1298	1405	1511	1617	106
9	1723	1829	1936	2042	2148	2254	2360	2466	2572	2678	106
410	612784	612890	612996	613102	613207	613313	613419	613525	613630	613736	106
1	3842	3947	4053	4159	4264	4370	4475	4581	4686	4792	106
2	4897	5003	5108	5213	5319	5424	5529	5634	5740	5845	105
3	5950	6055	6160	6265	6370	6476	6581	6686	6790	6895	105
4	7000	7105	7210	7315	7420	7525	7629	7734	7839	7943	105
415	8048	8153	8257	8362	8466	8571	8676	8780	8884	8989	105
6	9093	9198	9302	9406	9511	9615	9719	9824	9928	620032	104
7	620136	620240	620344	620448	620552	620656	620760	620864	620968	1072	104
8	1176	1280	1384	1488	1592	1695	1799	1903	2007	2110	104
9	2214	2318	2421	2525	2628	2732	2835	2939	3042	3146	104
420	623249	623353	623456	623559	623663	623766	623869	623973	624076	624179	103
1	4282	4385	4488	4591	4695	4798	4901	5004	5107	5210	103
2	5312	5415	5518	5621	5724	5827	5929	6032	6135	6238	103
3	6340	6443	6546	6648	6751	6853	6956	7058	7161	7263	103
4	7366	7468	7571	7673	7775	7878	7980	8082	8185	8287	102
425	8389	8491	8593	8695	8797	8900	9002	9104	9206	9308	102
6	9410	9512	9613	9715	9817	9919	630021	630123	630224	630326	102
7	630428	630530	630631	630733	630835	630936	1038	1139	1241	1342	102
8	1444	1545	1647	1748	1849	1951	2052	2153	2255	2356	101
9	2457	2559	2660	2761	2862	2963	3064	3165	3266	3367	101
430	633468	633569	633670	633771	633872	633973	634074	634175	634276	634376	101
1	4477	4578	4679	4779	4880	4981	5081	5182	5283	5383	101
2	5484	5584	5685	5785	5886	5986	6087	6187	6287	6388	100
3	6488	6588	6688	6789	6889	6989	7089	7189	7290	7390	100
4	7490	7590	7690	7790	7890	7990	8090	8190	8290	8389	100
435	8489	8589	8689	8789	8888	8988	9088	9188	9287	9387	100
6	9486	9586	9686	9785	9889	9984	640084	640183	640283	640382	99
7	640481	640581	640680	640779	640879	640978	1077	1177	1276	1375	99
8	1474	1573	1672	1771	1871	1970	2069	2168	2267	2366	99
9	2465	2563	2662	2761	2860	2959	3058	3156	3255	3354	99
440	643453	643551	643650	643749	643847	643946	644044	644143	644242	644340	98
1	4439	4537	4636	4734	4832	4931	5029	5127	5226	5324	98
2	5422	5521	5619	5717	5815	5913	6011	6110	6208	6306	98
3	6404	6502	6600	6698	6796	6894	6992	7089	7187	7285	98
4	7383	7481	7579	7676	7774	7872	7969	8067	8165	8262	98
445	8360	8458	8555	8653	8750	8848	8945	9043	9140	9237	97
6	9335	9432	9530	9627	9724	9821	9919	650016	650113	650210	97
7	650308	650405	650502	650599	650696	650793	650890	0987	1084	1181	97
8	1278	1375	1472	1569	1666	1762	1859	1956	2053	2150	97
9	2246	2343	2440	2536	2633	2730	2826	2923	3019	3116	97
450	653213	653309	653405	653502	653598	653695	653791	653888	653984	654080	96
1	4177	4273	4369	4465	4562	4658	4754	4850	4946	5042	96
2	5138	5235	5331	5427	5523	5619	5715	5810	5906	6002	96
3	6098	6194	6290	6386	6482	6577	6673	6769	6864	6960	96
4	7056	7152	7247	7343	7438	7534	7629	7725	7820	7916	96
455	8011	8107	8202	8298	8393	8488	8584	8679	8774	8870	95
6	8965	9060	9155	9250	9346	9441	9536	9631	9726	9821	95
7	9916	660011	660106	660201	660296	660391	660486	660581	660676	660771	95
8	660865	0960	1055	1150	1245	1339	1434	1529	1623	1718	95
9	1813	1907	2002	2096	2191	2286	2380	2475	2569	2663	95
N.	0	1	2	3	4	5	6	7	8	9	D.

TABLE VI. Six-place Common Logarithms of Numbers from 100 to 999

N.	0	1	2	3	4	5	6	7	8	9	D.
460	662758	662852	662947	663041	663135	663230	663324	663418	663512	663607	94
1	3701	3795	3889	3983	4078	4172	4266	4360	4454	4548	94
2	4642	4736	4830	4924	5018	5112	5206	5299	5393	5487	94
3	5581	5675	5769	5862	5956	6050	6143	6237	6331	6424	94
4	6518	6612	6705	6799	6892	6986	7079	7173	7266	7360	94
465	7453	7546	7640	7733	7826	7920	8013	8106	8199	8293	93
6	8386	8479	8572	8665	8759	8852	8945	9038	9131	9224	93
7	9317	9410	9503	9596	9689	9782	9875	9967	670060	670153	93
8	670246	670339	670431	670524	670617	670710	670802	670895	0988	1080	93
9	1173	1265	1358	1451	1543	1636	1728	1821	1913	2005	93
470	672098	672190	672283	672375	672467	672560	672652	672744	672836	672929	92
1	3021	3113	3205	3297	3390	3482	3574	3666	3758	3850	92
2	3942	4034	4126	4218	4310	4402	4494	4586	4677	4769	92
3	4861	4953	5045	5137	5228	5320	5412	5503	5595	5687	92
4	5778	5870	5962	6053	6145	6236	6328	6419	6511	6602	92
475	6694	6785	6876	6968	7059	7151	7242	7333	7424	7516	91
6	7607	7698	7789	7881	7972	8063	8154	8245	8336	8427	91
7	8518	8609	8700	8791	8882	8973	9064	9155	9246	9337	91
8	9428	9519	9610	9700	9791	9882	9973	680063	680154	680245	91
9	680336	680426	680517	680607	680698	680789	680879	0970	1060	1151	91
480	681241	681332	681422	681513	681603	681693	681784	681874	681964	682055	90
1	2145	2235	2326	2416	2506	2596	2686	2777	2867	2957	90
2	3047	3137	3227	3317	3407	3497	3587	3677	3767	3857	90
3	3947	4037	4127	4217	4307	4396	4486	4576	4666	4756	90
4	4845	4935	5025	5114	5204	5294	5383	5473	5563	5652	90
485	5742	5831	5921	6010	6100	6189	6279	6368	6458	6547	89
6	6636	6726	6815	6904	6994	7083	7172	7261	7351	7440	89
7	7529	7618	7707	7796	7886	7975	8064	8153	8242	8331	89
8	8420	8509	8598	8687	8776	8865	8953	9042	9131	9220	89
9	9309	9398	9486	9575	9664	9753	9841	9930	690019	690107	89
490	690196	690285	690373	690462	690550	690639	690728	690816	690905	690993	89
1	1081	1170	1258	1347	1435	1524	1612	1700	1789	1877	88
2	1965	2053	2142	2230	2318	2406	2494	2583	2671	2759	88
3	2847	2935	3023	3111	3199	3287	3375	3463	3551	3639	88
4	3727	3815	3903	3991	4078	4166	4254	4342	4430	4517	88
495	4605	4693	4781	4868	4956	5044	5131	5219	5307	5394	88
6	5482	5569	5657	5744	5832	5919	6007	6094	6182	6269	87
7	6356	6444	6531	6618	6706	6793	6880	6968	7055	7142	87
8	7229	7317	7404	7491	7578	7665	7752	7839	7926	8014	87
9	8101	8188	8275	8362	8449	8535	8622	8709	8796	8883	87
500	698970	699057	699144	699231	699317	699404	699491	699578	699664	699751	87
1	9838	9924	700011	700098	700184	700271	700358	700444	700531	700617	87
2	700704	700790	0877	0963	1050	1136	1222	1309	1395	1482	86
3	1568	1654	1741	1827	1913	1999	2086	2172	2258	2344	86
4	2431	2517	2603	2689	2775	2861	2947	3033	3119	3205	86
505	3291	3377	3463	3549	3635	3721	3807	3893	3979	4065	86
6	4151	4236	4322	4408	4494	4579	4665	4751	4837	4922	86
7	5008	5094	5179	5265	5350	5436	5522	5607	5693	5778	86
8	5864	5949	6035	6120	6206	6291	6376	6462	6547	6632	85
9	6718	6803	6888	6974	7059	7144	7229	7315	7400	7485	85
510	707570	707655	707740	707826	707911	707996	708081	708166	708251	708336	85
1	8421	8506	8591	8676	8761	8846	8931	9015	9100	9185	85
2	9270	9355	9440	9524	9609	9694	9779	9863	9948	710033	85
3	710117	710202	710287	710371	710456	710540	710625	710710	710794	0879	85
4	0963	1048	1132	1217	1301	1385	1470	1554	1639	1723	84
515	1807	1892	1976	2060	2144	2229	2313	2397	2481	2566	84
6	2650	2734	2818	2902	2986	3070	3154	3238	3323	3407	84
7	3491	3575	3659	3742	3826	3910	3994	4078	4162	4246	84
8	4330	4414	4497	4581	4665	4749	4833	4916	5000	5084	84
9	5167	5251	5335	5418	5502	5586	5669	5753	5836	5920	84
N.	0	1	2	3	4	5	6	7	8	9	D.

TABLE VI. Six-place Common Logarithms of Numbers from 100 to 999

N.	0	1	2	3	4	5	6	7	8	9	D.
520	716003	716087	716170	716254	716337	716421	716504	716588	716671	716754	83
1	6838	6921	7004	7088	7171	7254	7338	7421	7504	7587	83
2	7671	7754	7837	7920	8003	8086	8169	8253	8336	8419	83
3	8502	8585	8668	8751	8834	8917	9000	9083	9165	9248	83
4	9331	9414	9497	9580	9663	9745	9828	9911	9994	720077	83
525	720159	720242	720325	720407	720490	720573	720655	720738	720821	0903	83
6	0986	1068	1151	1233	1316	1398	1481	1563	1646	1728	82
7	1811	1893	1975	2058	2140	2222	2305	2387	2469	2552	82
8	2634	2716	2798	2881	2963	3045	3127	3209	3291	3374	82
9	3456	3538	3620	3702	3784	3866	3948	4030	4112	4194	82
530	724276	724358	724440	724522	724604	724685	724767	724849	724931	725013	82
1	5095	5176	5258	5340	5422	5503	5585	5667	5748	5830	82
2	5912	5993	6075	6156	6238	6320	6401	6483	6564	6646	82
3	6727	6809	6890	6972	7053	7134	7216	7297	7379	7460	81
4	7541	7623	7704	7785	7866	7948	8029	8110	8191	8273	81
535	8354	8435	8516	8597	8678	8759	8841	8922	9003	9084	81
6	9165	9246	9327	9408	9489	9570	9651	9732	9813	9893	81
7	9974	730055	730136	730217	730298	730378	730459	730540	730621	730702	81
8	730782	0863	0944	1024	1105	1186	1266	1347	1428	1508	81
9	1589	1669	1750	1830	1911	1991	2072	2152	2233	2313	81
540	732394	732474	732555	732635	732715	732796	732876	732956	733037	733117	80
1	3197	3278	3358	3438	3518	3598	3679	3759	3839	3919	80
2	3999	4079	4160	4240	4320	4400	4480	4560	4640	4720	80
3	4800	4880	4960	5040	5120	5200	5279	5359	5439	5519	80
4	5599	5679	5759	5838	5918	5998	6078	6157	6237	6317	80
545	6397	6476	6556	6635	6715	6795	6874	6954	7034	7113	80
6	7193	7272	7352	7431	7511	7590	7670	7749	7829	7908	79
7	7987	8067	8146	8225	8305	8384	8463	8543	8622	8701	79
8	8781	8860	8939	9018	9097	9177	9256	9335	9414	9493	79
9	9572	9651	9731	9810	9889	9968	740047	740126	740205	740284	79
550	740363	740442	740521	740600	740678	740757	740836	740915	740994	741073	79
1	1152	1230	1309	1388	1467	1546	1624	1703	1782	1860	79
2	1939	2018	2096	2175	2254	2332	2411	2489	2568	2647	79
3	2725	2804	2882	2961	3039	3118	3196	3275	3353	3431	78
4	3510	3588	3667	3745	3823	3902	3980	4058	4136	4215	78
555	4293	4371	4449	4528	4606	4684	4762	4840	4919	4997	78
6	5075	5153	5231	5309	5387	5465	5543	5621	5699	5777	78
7	5855	5933	6011	6089	6167	6245	6323	6401	6479	6556	78
8	6634	6712	6790	6868	6945	7023	7101	7179	7256	7334	78
9	7412	7489	7567	7645	7722	7800	7878	7955	8033	8110	78
560	748188	748266	748343	748421	748498	748576	748653	748731	748808	748885	77
1	8963	9040	9118	9195	9272	9350	9427	9504	9582	9659	77
2	9736	9814	9891	9968	750045	750123	750200	750277	750354	750431	77
3	750508	750586	750663	750740	0817	0894	0971	1048	1125	1202	77
4	1279	1356	1433	1510	1587	1664	1741	1818	1895	1972	77
565	2048	2125	2202	2279	2356	2433	2509	2586	2663	2740	77
6	2816	2893	2970	3047	3123	3200	3277	3353	3430	3506	77
7	3583	3660	3736	3813	3889	3966	4042	4119	4195	4272	77
8	4348	4425	4501	4578	4654	4730	4807	4883	4960	5036	76
9	5112	5189	5265	5341	5417	5494	5570	5646	5722	5799	76
570	755875	755951	756027	756103	756180	756256	756332	756408	756484	756560	76
1	6636	6712	6788	6864	6940	7016	7092	7168	7244	7320	76
2	7396	7472	7548	7624	7700	7775	7851	7927	8003	8079	76
3	8155	8230	8306	8382	8458	8533	8609	8685	8761	8836	76
4	8912	8988	9063	9139	9214	9290	9366	9441	9517	9592	76
575	9668	9743	9819	9894	9970	760045	760121	760196	760272	760347	75
6	760422	760498	760573	760649	760724	0799	0875	0950	1025	1101	75
7	1176	1251	1326	1402	1477	1552	1627	1702	1778	1853	75
8	1928	2003	2078	2153	2228	2303	2378	2453	2529	2604	75
9	2679	2754	2829	2904	2978	3053	3128	3203	3278	3353	75
N.	0	1	2	3	4	5	6	7	8	9	D.

TABLE VI. Six-place Common Logarithms of Numbers from 100 to 999

N.	0	1	2	3	4	5	6	7	8	9	D.
580	763428	763503	763578	763653	763727	763802	763877	763952	764027	764101	75
1	4176	4251	4326	4400	4475	4550	4624	4699	4774	4848	75
2	4923	4998	5072	5147	5221	5296	5370	5445	5520	5594	75
3	5669	5743	5818	5892	5966	6041	6115	6190	6264	6338	74
4	6413	6487	6562	6636	6710	6785	6859	6933	7007	7082	74
585	7156	7230	7304	7379	7453	7527	7601	7675	7749	7823	74
6	7898	7972	8046	8120	8194	8268	8342	8416	8490	8564	74
7	8638	8712	8786	8860	8934	9008	9082	9156	9230	9303	74
8	9377	9451	9525	9599	9673	9746	9820	9894	9968	770042	74
9	770115	770189	770263	770336	770410	770484	770557	770631	770705	0778	74
590	770852	770926	770999	771073	771146	771220	771293	771367	771440	771514	74
1	1587	1661	1734	1808	1881	1955	2028	2102	2175	2248	73
2	2322	2395	2468	2542	2615	2688	2762	2835	2908	2981	73
3	3055	3128	3201	3274	3348	3421	3494	3567	3640	3713	73
4	3786	3860	3933	4006	4079	4152	4225	4298	4371	4444	73
595	4517	4590	4663	4736	4809	4882	4955	5028	5100	5173	73
6	5246	5319	5392	5465	5538	5610	5683	5756	5829	5902	73
7	5974	6047	6120	6193	6265	6338	6411	6483	6556	6629	73
8	6701	6774	6846	6919	6992	7064	7137	7209	7282	7354	73
9	7427	7499	7572	7644	7717	7789	7862	7934	8006	8079	72
600	778151	778224	778296	778368	778441	778513	778585	778658	778730	778802	72
1	8874	8947	9019	9091	9163	9236	9308	9380	9452	9524	72
2	9596	9669	9741	9813	9885	9957	780029	780101	780173	780245	72
3	780317	780389	780461	780533	780605	780677	0749	0821	0893	0965	72
4	1037	1109	1181	1253	1324	1396	1468	1540	1612	1684	72
605	1755	1827	1899	1971	2042	2114	2186	2258	2329	2401	72
6	2473	2544	2616	2688	2759	2831	2902	2974	3046	3117	72
7	3189	3260	3332	3403	3475	3546	3618	3689	3761	3832	71
8	3904	3975	4046	4118	4189	4261	4332	4403	4475	4546	71
9	4617	4689	4760	4831	4902	4974	5045	5116	5187	5259	71
610	785330	785401	785472	785543	785615	785686	785757	785828	785899	785970	71
1	6041	6112	6183	6254	6325	6396	6467	6538	6609	6680	71
2	6751	6822	6893	6964	7035	7106	7177	7248	7319	7390	71
3	7460	7531	7602	7673	7744	7815	7885	7956	8027	8098	71
4	8168	8239	8310	8381	8451	8522	8593	8663	8734	8804	71
615	8875	8946	9016	9087	9157	9228	9299	9369	9440	9510	71
6	9581	9651	9722	9792	9863	9933	790004	790074	790144	790215	70
7	790285	790356	790426	790496	790567	790637	0707	0778	0848	0918	70
8	0988	1059	1129	1199	1269	1340	1410	1480	1550	1620	70
9	1691	1761	1831	1901	1971	2041	2111	2181	2252	2322	70
620	792392	792462	792532	792602	792672	792742	792812	792882	792952	793022	70
1	3092	3162	3231	3301	3371	3441	3511	3581	3651	3721	70
2	3790	3860	3930	4000	4070	4139	4209	4279	4349	4418	70
3	4488	4558	4627	4697	4767	4836	4906	4976	5045	5115	70
4	5185	5254	5324	5393	5463	5532	5602	5672	5741	5811	70
625	5880	5949	6019	6088	6158	6227	6297	6366	6436	6505	69
6	6574	6644	6713	6782	6852	6921	6990	7060	7129	7198	69
7	7268	7337	7406	7475	7545	7614	7683	7752	7821	7890	69
8	7960	8029	8098	8167	8236	8305	8374	8443	8513	8582	69
9	8651	8720	8789	8858	8927	8996	9065	9134	9203	9272	69
630	799341	799409	799478	799547	799616	799685	799754	799823	799892	799961	69
1	800029	800098	800167	800236	800305	800373	800442	800511	800580	800648	69
2	0717	0786	0854	0923	0992	1061	1129	1198	1266	1335	69
3	1404	1472	1541	1609	1678	1747	1815	1884	1952	2021	69
4	2089	2158	2226	2295	2363	2432	2500	2568	2637	2705	68
635	2774	2842	2910	2979	3047	3116	3184	3252	3321	3389	68
6	3457	3525	3594	3662	3730	3798	3867	3935	4003	4071	68
7	4139	4208	4276	4344	4412	4480	4548	4616	4685	4753	68
8	4821	4889	4957	5025	5093	5161	5229	5297	5365	5433	68
9	5501	5569	5637	5705	5773	5841	5908	5976	6044	6112	68
N.	0	1	2	3	4	5	6	7	8	9	D.

TABLE VI. Six-place Common Logarithms of Numbers from 100 to 999

N.	0	1	2	3	4	5	6	7	8	9	D.
640	806180	806248	806316	806384	806451	806519	806587	806655	806723	806790	68
1	6858	6926	6994	7061	7129	7197	7264	7332	7400	7467	68
2	7535	7603	7670	7738	7806	7873	7941	8008	8076	8143	68
3	8211	8279	8346	8414	8481	8549	8616	8684	8751	8818	67
4	8886	8953	9021	9088	9156	9223	9290	9358	9425	9492	67
645	9560	9627	9694	9762	9829	9896	9964	810031	810098	810165	67
6	810233	810300	810367	810434	810501	810569	810636	0703	0770	0837	67
7	0904	0971	1039	1106	1173	1240	1307	1374	1441	1508	67
8	1575	1642	1709	1776	1843	1910	1977	2044	2111	2178	67
9	2245	2312	2379	2445	2512	2579	2646	2713	2780	2847	67
650	812913	812980	813047	813114	813181	813247	813314	813381	813448	813514	67
1	3581	3648	3714	3781	3848	3914	3981	4048	4114	4181	67
2	4248	4314	4381	4447	4514	4581	4647	4714	4780	4847	67
3	4913	4980	5046	5113	5179	5246	5312	5378	5445	5511	66
4	5578	5644	5711	5777	5843	5910	5976	6042	6109	6175	66
655	6241	6308	6374	6440	6506	6573	6639	6705	6771	6838	66
6	6904	6970	7036	7102	7169	7235	7301	7367	7433	7499	66
7	7565	7631	7698	7764	7830	7896	7962	8028	8094	8160	66
8	8226	8292	8358	8424	8490	8556	8622	8688	8754	8820	66
9	8885	8951	9017	9083	9149	9215	9281	9346	9412	9478	66
660	819544	819610	819676	819741	819807	819873	819939	820004	820070	820136	66
1	820201	820267	820333	820399	820464	820530	820595	0661	0727	0792	66
2	0858	0924	0989	1055	1120	1186	1251	1317	1382	1448	66
3	1514	1579	1645	1710	1775	1841	1906	1972	2037	2103	65
4	2168	2233	2299	2364	2430	2495	2560	2626	2691	2756	65
665	2822	2887	2952	3018	3083	3148	3213	3279	3344	3409	65
6	3474	3539	3605	3670	3735	3800	3865	3930	3996	4061	65
7	4126	4191	4256	4321	4386	4451	4516	4581	4646	4711	65
8	4776	4841	4906	4971	5036	5101	5166	5231	5296	5361	65
9	5426	5491	5556	5621	5686	5751	5815	5880	5945	6010	65
670	826075	826140	826204	826269	826334	826399	826464	826528	826593	826658	65
1	6723	6787	6852	6917	6981	7046	7111	7175	7240	7305	65
2	7369	7434	7499	7563	7628	7692	7757	7821	7886	7951	65
3	8015	8080	8144	8209	8273	8338	8402	8467	8531	8595	64
4	8660	8724	8789	8853	8918	8982	9046	9111	9175	9239	64
675	9304	9368	9432	9497	9561	9625	9690	9754	9818	9882	64
6	9947	830011	830075	830139	830204	830268	830332	830396	830460	830525	64
7	830589	0653	0717	0781	0845	0909	0973	1037	1102	1166	64
8	1230	1294	1358	1422	1486	1550	1614	1678	1742	1806	64
9	1870	1934	1998	2062	2126	2189	2253	2317	2381	2445	64
680	832509	832573	832637	832700	832764	832828	832892	832956	833020	833083	64
1	3147	3211	3275	3338	3402	3466	3530	3593	3657	3721	64
2	3784	3848	3912	3975	4039	4103	4166	4230	4294	4357	64
3	4421	4484	4548	4611	4675	4739	4802	4866	4929	4993	64
4	5056	5120	5183	5247	5310	5373	5437	5500	5564	5627	63
685	5691	5754	5817	5881	5944	6007	6071	6134	6197	6261	63
6	6324	6387	6451	6514	6577	6641	6704	6767	6830	6894	63
7	6957	7020	7083	7146	7210	7273	7336	7399	7462	7525	63
8	7588	7652	7715	7778	7841	7904	7967	8030	8093	8156	63
9	8219	8282	8345	8408	8471	8534	8597	8660	8723	8786	63
690	838849	838912	838975	839038	839101	839164	839227	839289	839352	839415	63
1	9478	9541	9604	9667	9729	9792	9855	9918	9981	840043	63
2	840106	840169	840232	840294	840357	840420	840482	840545	840608	0671	63
3	0733	0796	0859	0921	0984	1046	1109	1172	1234	1297	63
4	1359	1422	1485	1547	1610	1672	1735	1797	1860	1922	63
695	1985	2047	2110	2172	2235	2297	2360	2422	2484	2547	62
6	2609	2672	2734	2796	2859	2921	2983	3046	3108	3170	62
7	3233	3295	3357	3420	3482	3544	3606	3669	3731	3793	62
8	3855	3918	3980	4042	4104	4166	4229	4291	4353	4415	62
9	4477	4539	4601	4664	4726	4788	4850	4912	4974	5036	62
N.	0	1	2	3	4	5	6	7	8	9	D.

TABLE VI. Six-place Common Logarithms of Numbers from 100 to 999

N.	0	1	2	3	4	5	6	7	8	9	D.
700	845098	845160	845222	845284	845346	845408	845470	845532	845594	845656	62
1	5718	5780	5842	5904	5966	6028	6090	6151	6213	6275	62
2	6337	6399	6461	6523	6585	6646	6708	6770	6832	6894	62
3	6955	7017	7079	7141	7202	7264	7326	7388	7449	7511	62
4	7573	7634	7696	7758	7819	7881	7943	8004	8066	8128	62
705	8189	8251	8312	8374	8435	8497	8559	8620	8682	8743	62
6	8805	8866	8928	8989	9051	9112	9174	9235	9297	9358	61
7	9419	9481	9542	9604	9665	9726	9788	9849	9911	9972	61
8	850033	850095	850156	850217	850279	850340	850401	850462	850524	850585	61
9	0646	0707	0769	0830	0891	0952	1014	1075	1136	1197	61
710	851258	851320	851381	851442	851503	851564	851625	851686	851747	851809	61
1	1870	1931	1992	2053	2114	2175	2236	2297	2358	2419	61
2	2480	2541	2602	2663	2724	2785	2846	2907	2968	3029	61
3	3090	3150	3211	3272	3333	3394	3455	3516	3577	3637	61
4	3698	3759	3820	3881	3941	4002	4063	4124	4185	4245	61
715	4306	4367	4428	4488	4549	4610	4670	4731	4792	4852	61
6	4913	4974	5034	5095	5156	5216	5277	5337	5398	5459	61
7	5519	5580	5640	5701	5761	5822	5882	5943	6003	6064	61
8	6124	6185	6245	6306	6366	6427	6487	6548	6608	6668	60
9	6729	6789	6850	6910	6970	7031	7091	7152	7212	7272	60
720	857332	857393	857453	857513	857574	857634	857694	857755	857815	857875	60
1	7935	7995	8056	8116	8176	8236	8297	8357	8417	8477	60
2	8537	8597	8657	8718	8778	8838	8898	8958	9018	9078	60
3	9138	9198	9258	9318	9379	9439	9499	9559	9619	9679	60
4	9739	9799	9859	9918	9978	860038	860098	860158	860218	860278	60
725	860338	860398	860458	860518	860578	0637	0697	0757	0817	0877	60
6	0937	0996	1056	1116	1176	1236	1295	1355	1415	1475	60
7	1534	1594	1654	1714	1773	1833	1893	1952	2012	2072	60
8	2131	2191	2251	2310	2370	2430	2489	2549	2608	2668	60
9	2728	2787	2847	2906	2966	3025	3085	3144	3204	3263	60
730	863323	863382	863442	863501	863561	863620	863680	863739	863799	863858	59
1	3917	3977	4036	4096	4155	4214	4274	4333	4392	4452	59
2	4511	4570	4630	4689	4748	4808	4867	4926	4985	5045	59
3	5104	5163	5222	5282	5341	5400	5459	5519	5578	5637	59
4	5696	5755	5814	5874	5933	5992	6051	6110	6169	6228	59
735	6287	6346	6405	6465	6524	6583	6642	6701	6760	6819	59
6	6878	6937	6996	7055	7114	7173	7232	7291	7350	7409	59
7	7467	7526	7585	7644	7703	7762	7821	7880	7939	7998	59
8	8056	8115	8174	8233	8292	8350	8409	8468	8527	8586	59
9	8644	8703	8762	8821	8879	8938	8997	9056	9114	9173	59
740	869232	869290	869349	869408	869466	869525	869584	869642	869701	869760	59
1	9818	9877	9935	9994	870053	870111	870170	870228	870287	870345	59
2	870404	870462	870521	870579	0638	0696	0755	0813	0872	0930	58
3	0989	1047	1106	1164	1223	1281	1339	1398	1456	1515	58
4	1573	1631	1690	1748	1806	1865	1923	1981	2040	2098	58
745	2156	2215	2273	2331	2389	2448	2506	2564	2622	2681	58
6	2739	2797	2855	2913	2972	3030	3088	3146	3204	3262	58
7	3321	3379	3437	3495	3553	3611	3669	3727	3785	3844	58
8	3902	3960	4018	4076	4134	4192	4250	4308	4366	4424	58
9	4482	4540	4598	4656	4714	4772	4830	4888	4945	5003	58
750	875061	875119	875177	875235	875293	875351	875409	875466	875524	875582	58
1	5640	5698	5756	5813	5871	5929	5987	6045	6102	6160	58
2	6218	6276	6333	6391	6449	6507	6564	6622	6680	6737	58
3	6795	6853	6910	6968	7026	7083	7141	7199	7256	7314	58
4	7371	7429	7487	7544	7602	7659	7717	7774	7832	7889	58
755	7947	8004	8062	8119	8177	8234	8292	8349	8407	8464	57
6	8522	8579	8637	8694	8752	8809	8866	8924	8981	9039	57
7	9096	9153	9211	9268	9325	9383	9440	9497	9555	9612	57
8	9669	9726	9784	9841	9898	9956	880013	880070	880127	880185	57
9	880242	880299	880356	880413	880471	880528	0585	0642	0699	0756	57
N.	0	1	2	3	4	5	6	7	8	9	D.

TABLE VI. Six-place Common Logarithms of Numbers from 100 to 999

N.	0	1	2	3	4	5	6	7	8	9	D.
760	880814	880871	880928	880985	881042	881099	881156	881213	881271	881328	57
1	1385	1442	1499	1556	1613	1670	1727	1784	1841	1898	57
2	1955	2012	2069	2126	2183	2240	2297	2354	2411	2468	57
3	2525	2581	2638	2695	2752	2809	2866	2923	2980	3037	57
4	3093	3150	3207	3264	3321	3377	3434	3491	3548	3605	57
765	3661	3718	3775	3832	3888	3945	4002	4059	4115	4172	57
6	4229	4285	4342	4399	4455	4512	4569	4625	4682	4739	57
7	4795	4852	4909	4965	5022	5078	5135	5192	5248	5305	57
8	5361	5418	5474	5531	5587	5644	5700	5757	5813	5870	57
9	5926	5983	6039	6096	6152	6209	6265	6321	6378	6434	56
770	886491	886547	886604	886660	886716	886773	886829	886885	886942	886998	56
1	7054	7111	7167	7223	7280	7336	7392	7449	7505	7561	56
2	7617	7674	7730	7786	7842	7898	7955	8011	8067	8123	56
3	8179	8236	8292	8348	8404	8460	8516	8573	8629	8685	56
4	8741	8797	8853	8909	8965	9021	9077	9134	9190	9246	56
775	9302	9358	9414	9470	9526	9582	9638	9694	9750	9806	56
6	9862	9918	9974	890030	890086	890141	890197	890253	890309	890365	56
7	890421	890477	890533	0589	0645	0700	0756	0812	0868	0924	56
8	0980	1035	1091	1147	1203	1259	1314	1370	1426	1482	56
9	1537	1593	1649	1705	1760	1816	1872	1928	1983	2039	56
780	892095	892150	892206	892262	892317	892373	892429	892484	892540	892595	56
1	2651	2707	2762	2818	2873	2929	2985	3040	3096	3151	56
2	3207	3262	3318	3373	3429	3484	3540	3595	3651	3706	56
3	3762	3817	3873	3928	3984	4039	4094	4150	4205	4261	55
4	4316	4371	4427	4482	4538	4593	4648	4704	4759	4814	55
785	4870	4925	4980	5036	5091	5146	5201	5257	5312	5367	55
6	5423	5478	5533	5588	5644	5699	5754	5809	5864	5920	55
7	5975	6030	6085	6140	6195	6251	6306	6361	6416	6471	55
8	6526	6581	6636	6692	6747	6802	6857	6912	6967	7022	55
9	7077	7132	7187	7242	7297	7352	7407	7462	7517	7572	55
790	897627	897682	897737	897792	897847	897902	897957	898012	898067	898122	55
1	8176	8231	8286	8341	8396	8451	8506	8561	8615	8670	55
2	8725	8780	8835	8890	8944	8999	9054	9109	9164	9218	55
3	9273	9328	9383	9437	9492	9547	9602	9656	9711	9766	55
4	9821	9875	9930	9985	900039	900094	900149	900203	900258	900312	55
795	900367	900422	900476	900531	0586	0640	0695	0749	0804	0859	55
6	0913	0968	1022	1077	1131	1186	1240	1295	1349	1404	55
7	1458	1513	1567	1622	1676	1731	1785	1840	1894	1948	54
8	2003	2057	2112	2166	2221	2275	2329	2384	2438	2492	54
9	2547	2601	2655	2710	2764	2818	2873	2927	2981	3036	54
800	903090	903144	903199	903253	903307	903361	903416	903470	903524	903578	54
1	3633	3687	3741	3795	3849	3904	3958	4012	4066	4120	54
2	4174	4229	4283	4337	4391	4445	4499	4553	4607	4661	54
3	4716	4770	4824	4878	4932	4986	5040	5094	5148	5202	54
4	5256	5310	5364	5418	5472	5526	5580	5634	5688	5742	54
805	5796	5850	5904	5958	6012	6066	6119	6173	6227	6281	54
6	6335	6389	6443	6497	6551	6604	6658	6712	6766	6820	54
7	6874	6927	6981	7035	7089	7143	7196	7250	7304	7358	54
8	7411	7465	7519	7573	7626	7680	7734	7787	7841	7895	54
9	7949	8002	8056	8110	8163	8217	8270	8324	8378	8431	54
810	908485	908539	908592	908646	908699	908753	908807	908860	908914	908967	54
1	9021	9074	9128	9181	9235	9289	9342	9396	9449	9503	54
2	9556	9610	9663	9716	9770	9823	9877	9930	9984	910037	53
3	910091	910144	910197	910251	910304	910358	910411	910464	910518	0571	53
4	0624	0678	0731	0784	0838	0891	0944	0998	1051	1104	53
815	1158	1211	1264	1317	1371	1424	1477	1530	1584	1637	53
6	1690	1743	1797	1850	1903	1956	2009	2063	2116	2169	53
7	2222	2275	2328	2381	2435	2488	2541	2594	2647	2700	53
8	2753	2806	2859	2913	2966	3019	3072	3125	3178	3231	53
9	3284	3337	3390	3443	3496	3549	3602	3655	3708	3761	53
N.	0	1	2	3	4	5	6	7	8	9	D.

TABLE VI. Six-place Common Logarithms of Numbers from 100 to 999

N.	0	1	2	3	4	5	6	7	8	9	D.
820	913814	913867	913920	913973	914026	914079	914132	914184	914237	914290	53
1	4343	4396	4449	4502	4555	4608	4660	4713	4766	4819	53
2	4872	4925	4977	5030	5083	5136	5189	5241	5294	5347	53
3	5400	5453	5505	5558	5611	5664	5716	5769	5822	5875	53
4	5927	5980	6033	6085	6138	6191	6243	6296	6349	6401	53
825	6454	6507	6559	6612	6664	6717	6770	6822	6875	6927	53
6	6980	7033	7085	7138	7190	7243	7295	7348	7400	7453	53
7	7506	7558	7611	7663	7716	7768	7820	7873	7925	7978	52
8	8030	8083	8135	8188	8240	8293	8345	8397	8450	8502	52
9	8555	8607	8659	8712	8764	8816	8869	8921	8973	9026	52
830	919078	919130	919183	919235	919287	919340	919392	919444	919496	919549	52
1	9601	9653	9706	9758	9810	9862	9914	9967	920019	920071	52
2	920123	920176	920228	920280	920332	920384	920436	920489	0541	0593	52
3	0645	0697	0749	0801	0853	0906	0958	1010	1062	1114	52
4	1166	1218	1270	1322	1374	1426	1478	1530	1582	1634	52
835	1686	1738	1790	1842	1894	1946	1998	2050	2102	2154	52
6	2206	2258	2310	2362	2414	2466	2518	2570	2622	2674	52
7	2725	2777	2829	2881	2933	2985	3037	3089	3140	3192	52
8	3244	3296	3348	3399	3451	3503	3555	3607	3658	3710	52
9	3762	3814	3865	3917	3969	4021	4072	4124	4176	4228	52
840	924279	924331	924383	924434	924486	924538	924589	924641	924693	924744	52
1	4796	4848	4899	4951	5003	5054	5106	5157	5209	5261	52
2	5312	5364	5415	5467	5518	5570	5621	5673	5725	5776	52
3	5828	5879	5931	5982	6034	6085	6137	6188	6240	6291	51
4	6342	6394	6445	6497	6548	6600	6651	6702	6754	6805	51
845	6857	6908	6959	7011	7062	7114	7165	7216	7268	7319	51
6	7370	7422	7473	7524	7576	7627	7678	7730	7781	7832	51
7	7883	7935	7986	8037	8088	8140	8191	8242	8293	8345	51
8	8396	8447	8498	8549	8601	8652	8703	8754	8805	8857	51
9	8908	8959	9010	9061	9112	9163	9215	9266	9317	9368	51
850	929419	929470	929521	929572	929623	929674	929725	929776	929827	929879	51
1	9930	9981	930032	930083	930134	930185	930236	930287	930338	930389	51
2	930440	930491	0542	0592	0643	0694	0745	0796	0847	0898	51
3	0949	1000	1051	1102	1153	1204	1254	1305	1356	1407	51
4	1458	1509	1560	1610	1661	1712	1763	1814	1865	1915	51
855	1966	2017	2068	2118	2169	2220	2271	2322	2372	2423	51
6	2474	2524	2575	2626	2677	2727	2778	2829	2879	2930	51
7	2981	3031	3082	3133	3183	3234	3285	3335	3386	3437	51
8	3487	3538	3589	3639	3690	3740	3791	3841	3892	3943	51
9	3993	4044	4094	4145	4195	4246	4296	4347	4397	4448	51
860	934498	934549	934599	934650	934700	934751	934801	934852	934902	934953	50
1	5003	5054	5104	5154	5205	5255	5306	5356	5406	5457	50
2	5507	5558	5608	5658	5709	5759	5809	5860	5910	5960	50
3	6011	6061	6111	6162	6212	6262	6313	6363	6413	6463	50
4	6514	6564	6614	6665	6715	6765	6815	6865	6916	6966	50
865	7016	7066	7117	7167	7217	7267	7317	7367	7418	7468	50
6	7518	7568	7618	7668	7718	7769	7819	7869	7919	7969	50
7	8019	8069	8119	8169	8219	8269	8320	8370	8420	8470	50
8	8520	8570	8620	8670	8720	8770	8820	8870	8920	8970	50
9	9020	9070	9120	9170	9220	9270	9320	9369	9419	9469	50
870	939519	939569	939619	939669	939719	939769	939819	939869	939918	939968	50
1	940018	940068	940118	940168	940218	940267	940317	940367	940417	940467	50
2	0516	0566	0616	0666	0716	0765	0815	0865	0915	0964	50
3	1014	1064	1114	1163	1213	1263	1313	1362	1412	1462	50
4	1511	1561	1611	1660	1710	1760	1809	1859	1909	1958	50
875	2008	2058	2107	2157	2207	2256	2306	2355	2405	2455	50
6	2504	2554	2603	2653	2702	2752	2801	2851	2901	2950	50
7	3000	3049	3099	3148	3198	3247	3297	3346	3396	3445	49
8	3495	3544	3593	3643	3692	3742	3791	3841	3890	3939	49
9	3989	4038	4088	4137	4186	4236	4285	4335	4384	4433	49
N.	0	1	2	3	4	5	6	7	8	9	D.

TABLE VI. Six-place Common Logarithms of Numbers from 100 to 999

N.	0	1	2	3	4	5	6	7	8	9	D.
880	944483	944532	944581	944631	944680	944729	944779	944828	944877	944927	49
1	4976	5025	5074	5124	5173	5222	5272	5321	5370	5419	49
2	5469	5518	5567	5616	5665	5715	5764	5813	5862	5912	49
3	5961	6010	6059	6108	6157	6207	6256	6305	6354	6403	49
4	6452	6501	6551	6600	6649	6698	6747	6796	6845	6894	49
885	6943	6992	7041	7090	7140	7189	7238	7287	7336	7385	49
6	7434	7483	7532	7581	7630	7679	7728	7777	7826	7875	49
7	7924	7973	8022	8070	8119	8168	8217	8266	8315	8364	49
8	8413	8462	8511	8560	8609	8657	8706	8755	8804	8853	49
9	8902	8951	8999	9048	9097	9146	9195	9244	9292	9341	49
890	949390	949439	949488	949536	949585	949634	949683	949731	949780	949829	49
1	9878	9926	9975	950024	950073	950121	950170	950219	950267	950316	49
2	950365	950414	950462	0511	0560	0608	0657	0706	0754	0803	49
3	0851	0900	0949	0997	1046	1095	1143	1192	1240	1289	49
4	1338	1386	1435	1483	1532	1580	1629	1677	1726	1775	49
895	1823	1872	1920	1969	2017	2066	2114	2163	2211	2260	48
6	2308	2356	2405	2453	2502	2550	2599	2647	2696	2744	48
7	2792	2841	2889	2938	2986	3034	3083	3131	3180	3228	48
8	3276	3325	3373	3421	3470	3518	3566	3615	3663	3711	48
9	3760	3808	3856	3905	3953	4001	4049	4098	4146	4194	48
900	954243	954291	954339	954387	954435	954484	954532	954580	954628	954677	48
1	4725	4773	4821	4869	4918	4966	5014	5062	5110	5158	48
2	5207	5255	5303	5351	5399	5447	5495	5543	5592	5640	48
3	5688	5736	5784	5832	5880	5928	5976	6024	6072	6120	48
4	6168	6216	6265	6313	6361	6409	6457	6505	6553	6601	48
905	6649	6697	6745	6793	6840	6888	6936	6984	7032	7080	48
6	7128	7176	7224	7272	7320	7368	7416	7464	7512	7559	48
7	7607	7655	7703	7751	7799	7847	7894	7942	7990	8038	48
8	8086	8134	8181	8229	8277	8325	8373	8421	8468	8516	48
9	8564	8612	8659	8707	8755	8803	8850	8898	8946	8994	48
910	959041	959089	959137	959185	959232	959280	959328	959375	959423	959471	48
1	9518	9566	9614	9661	9709	9757	9804	9852	9900	9947	48
2	9995	960042	960090	960138	960185	960233	960280	960328	960376	960423	48
3	960471	0518	0566	0613	0661	0709	0756	0804	0851	0899	48
4	0946	0994	1041	1089	1136	1184	1231	1279	1326	1374	48
915	1421	1469	1516	1563	1611	1658	1706	1753	1801	1848	47
6	1895	1943	1990	2038	2085	2132	2180	2227	2275	2322	47
7	2369	2417	2464	2511	2559	2606	2653	2701	2748	2795	47
8	2843	2890	2937	2985	3032	3079	3126	3174	3221	3268	47
9	3316	3363	3410	3457	3504	3552	3599	3646	3693	3741	47
920	963788	963835	963882	963929	963977	964024	964071	964118	964165	964212	47
1	4260	4307	4354	4401	4448	4495	4542	4590	4637	4684	47
2	4731	4778	4825	4872	4919	4966	5013	5061	5108	5155	47
3	5202	5249	5296	5343	5390	5437	5484	5531	5578	5625	47
4	5672	5719	5766	5813	5860	5907	5954	6001	6048	6095	47
925	6142	6189	6236	6283	6329	6376	6423	6470	6517	6564	47
6	6611	6658	6705	6752	6799	6845	6892	6939	6986	7033	47
7	7080	7127	7173	7220	7267	7314	7361	7408	7454	7501	47
8	7548	7595	7642	7688	7735	7782	7829	7875	7922	7969	47
9	8016	8062	8109	8156	8203	8249	8296	8343	8390	8436	47
930	968483	968530	968576	968623	968670	968716	968763	968810	968856	968903	47
1	8950	8996	9043	9090	9136	9183	9229	9276	9323	9369	47
2	9416	9463	9509	9556	9602	9649	9695	9742	9789	9835	47
3	9882	9928	9975	970021	970068	970114	970161	970207	970254	970300	47
4	970347	970393	970440	0486	0533	0579	0626	0672	0719	0765	46
935	0812	0858	0904	0951	0997	1044	1090	1137	1183	1229	46
6	1276	1322	1369	1415	1461	1508	1554	1601	1647	1693	46
7	1740	1786	1832	1879	1925	1971	2018	2064	2110	2157	46
8	2203	2249	2295	2342	2388	2434	2481	2527	2573	2619	46
9	2666	2712	2758	2804	2851	2897	2943	2989	3035	3082	46
N.	0	1	2	3	4	5	6	7	8	9	D.

TABLE VI. Six-place Common Logarithms of Numbers from 100 to 999

N.	0	1	2	3	4	5	6	7	8	9	D.
940	973128	973174	973220	973266	973313	973359	973405	973451	973497	973543	46
1	3590	3636	3682	3728	3774	3820	3866	3913	3959	4005	46
2	4051	4097	4143	4189	4235	4281	4327	4374	4420	4466	46
3	4512	4558	4604	4650	4696	4742	4788	4834	4880	4926	46
4	4972	5018	5064	5110	5156	5202	5248	5294	5340	5386	46
945	5432	5478	5524	5570	5616	5662	5707	5753	5799	5845	46
6	5891	5937	5983	6029	6075	6121	6167	6212	6258	6304	46
7	6350	6396	6442	6488	6533	6579	6625	6671	6717	6763	46
8	6808	6854	6900	6946	6992	7037	7083	7129	7175	7220	46
9	7266	7312	7358	7403	7449	7495	7541	7586	7632	7678	46
950	977724	977769	977815	977861	977906	977952	977998	978043	978089	978135	46
1	8181	8226	8272	8317	8363	8409	8454	8500	8546	8591	46
2	8637	8683	8728	8774	8819	8865	8911	8956	9002	9047	46
3	9093	9138	9184	9230	9275	9321	9366	9412	9457	9503	46
4	9548	9594	9639	9685	9730	9776	9821	9867	9912	9958	46
955	980003	980049	980094	980140	980185	980231	980276	980322	980367	980412	45
6	0458	0503	0549	0594	0640	0685	0730	0776	0821	0867	45
7	0912	0957	1003	1048	1093	1139	1184	1229	1275	1320	45
8	1366	1411	1456	1501	1547	1592	1637	1683	1728	1773	45
9	1819	1864	1909	1954	2000	2045	2090	2135	2181	2226	45
960	982271	982316	982362	982407	982452	982497	982543	982588	982633	982678	45
1	2723	2769	2814	2859	2904	2949	2994	3040	3085	3130	45
2	3175	3220	3265	3310	3356	3401	3446	3491	3536	3581	45
3	3626	3671	3716	3762	3807	3852	3897	3942	3987	4032	45
4	4077	4122	4167	4212	4257	4302	4347	4392	4437	4482	45
965	4527	4572	4617	4662	4707	4752	4797	4842	4887	4932	45
6	4977	5022	5067	5112	5157	5202	5247	5292	5337	5382	45
7	5426	5471	5516	5561	5606	5651	5696	5741	5786	5830	45
8	5875	5920	5965	6010	6055	6100	6144	6189	6234	6279	45
9	6324	6369	6413	6458	6503	6548	6593	6637	6682	6727	45
970	986772	986817	986861	986906	986951	986996	987040	987085	987130	987175	45
1	7219	7264	7309	7353	7398	7443	7488	7532	7577	7622	45
2	7666	7711	7756	7800	7845	7890	7934	7979	8024	8068	45
3	8113	8157	8202	8247	8291	8336	8381	8425	8470	8514	45
4	8559	8604	8648	8693	8737	8782	8826	8871	8916	8960	45
975	9005	9049	9094	9138	9183	9227	9272	9316	9361	9405	45
6	9450	9494	9539	9583	9628	9672	9717	9761	9806	9850	44
7	9895	9939	9983	990028	990072	990117	990161	990206	990250	990294	44
8	990339	990383	990428	0472	0516	0561	0605	0650	0694	0738	44
9	0783	0827	0871	0916	0960	1004	1049	1093	1137	1182	44
980	991226	991270	991315	991359	991403	991448	991492	991536	991580	991625	44
1	1669	1713	1758	1802	1846	1890	1935	1979	2023	2067	44
2	2111	2156	2200	2244	2288	2333	2377	2421	2465	2509	44
3	2554	2598	2642	2686	2730	2774	2819	2863	2907	2951	44
4	2995	3039	3083	3127	3172	3216	3260	3304	3348	3392	44
985	3436	3480	3524	3568	3613	3657	3701	3745	3789	3833	44
6	3877	3921	3965	4009	4053	4097	4141	4185	4229	4273	44
7	4317	4361	4405	4449	4493	4537	4581	4625	4669	4713	44
8	4757	4801	4845	4889	4933	4977	5021	5065	5108	5152	44
9	5196	5240	5284	5328	5372	5416	5460	5504	5547	5591	44
990	995635	995679	995723	995767	995811	995854	995898	995942	995986	996030	44
1	6074	6117	6161	6205	6249	6293	6337	6380	6424	6468	44
2	6512	6555	6599	6643	6687	6731	6774	6818	6862	6906	44
3	6949	6993	7037	7080	7124	7168	7212	7255	7299	7343	44
4	7386	7430	7474	7517	7561	7605	7648	7692	7736	7779	44
995	7823	7867	7910	7954	7998	8041	8085	8129	8172	8216	44
6	8259	8303	8347	8390	8434	8477	8521	8564	8608	8652	44
7	8695	8739	8782	8826	8869	8913	8956	9000	9043	9087	44
8	9131	9174	9218	9261	9305	9348	9392	9435	9479	9522	44
9	9565	9609	9652	9696	9739	9783	9826	9870	9913	9957	43
N.	0	1	2	3	4	5	6	7	8	9	D.

TABLE VII. Seven-place Common Logarithms of Numbers from 1000 to 1100

N.	0	1	2	3	4	5	6	7	8	9	D.
1000	000 0000	0434	0869	1303	1737	2171	2605	3039	3473	3907	434
1001	4341	4775	5208	5642	6076	6510	6943	7377	7810	8244	434
1002	8677	9111	9544	9977	*0411	*0844	*1277	*1710	*2143	*2576	433
1003	001 3009	3442	3875	4308	4741	5174	5607	6039	6472	6905	433
1004	7337	7770	8202	8635	9067	9499	9932	*0364	*0796	*1228	432
1005	002 1661	2093	2525	2957	3389	3821	4253	4685	5116	5548	432
1006	5980	6411	6843	7275	7706	8138	8569	9001	9432	9863	431
1007	003 0295	0726	1157	1588	2019	2451	2882	3313	3744	4174	431
1008	4605	5036	5467	5898	6328	6759	7190	7620	8051	8481	431
1009	8912	9342	9772	*0203	*0633	*1063	*1493	*1924	*2354	*2784	430
1010	004 3214	3644	4074	4504	4933	5363	5793	6223	6652	7082	430
1011	7512	7941	8371	8800	9229	9659	*0088	*0517	*0947	*1376	429
1012	005 1805	2234	2663	3092	3521	3950	4379	4808	5237	5666	429
1013	6094	6523	6952	7380	7809	8238	8666	9094	9523	9951	429
1014	006 0380	0808	1236	1664	2092	2521	2949	3377	3805	4233	428
1015	4660	5088	5516	5944	6372	6799	7227	7655	8082	8510	428
1016	8937	9365	9792	*0219	*0647	*1074	*1501	*1928	*2355	*2782	427
1017	007 3210	3637	4064	4490	4917	5344	5771	6198	6624	7051	427
1018	7478	7904	8331	8757	9184	9610	*0037	*0463	*0889	*1316	426
1019	008 1742	2168	2594	3020	3446	3872	4298	4724	5150	5576	426
1020	6002	6427	6853	7279	7704	8130	8556	8981	9407	9832	426
1021	009 0257	0683	1108	1533	1959	2384	2809	3234	3659	4084	425
1022	4509	4934	5359	5784	6208	6633	7058	7483	7907	8332	425
1023	8756	9181	9605	*0030	*0454	*0878	*1303	*1727	*2151	*2575	424
1024	010 3000	3424	3848	4272	4696	5120	5544	5967	6391	6815	424
1025	7239	7662	8086	8510	8933	9357	9780	*0204	*0627	*1050	424
1026	011 1474	1897	2320	2743	3166	3590	4013	4436	4859	5282	423
1027	5704	6127	6550	6973	7396	7818	8241	8664	9086	9509	423
1028	9931	*0354	*0776	*1198	*1621	*2043	*2465	*2887	*3310	*3732	422
1029	012 4154	4576	4998	5420	5842	6264	6685	7107	7529	7951	422
1030	8372	8794	9215	9637	*0059	*0480	*0901	*1323	*1744	*2165	422
1031	013 2587	3008	3429	3850	4271	4692	5113	5534	5955	6376	421
1032	6797	7218	7639	8059	8480	8901	9321	9742	*0162	*0583	421
1033	014 1003	1424	1844	2264	2685	3105	3525	3945	4365	4785	420
1034	5205	5625	6045	6465	6885	7305	7725	8144	8564	8984	420
1035	9403	9823	*0243	*0662	*1082	*1501	*1920	*2340	*2759	*3178	420
1036	015 3598	4017	4436	4855	5274	5693	6112	6531	6950	7369	419
1037	7788	8206	8625	9044	9462	9881	*0300	*0718	*1137	*1555	419
1038	016 1974	2392	2810	3229	3647	4065	4483	4901	5319	5737	418
1039	6155	6573	6991	7409	7827	8245	8663	9080	9498	9916	418
1040	017 0333	0751	1168	1586	2003	2421	2838	3256	3673	4090	417
1041	4507	4924	5342	5759	6176	6593	7010	7427	7844	8260	417
1042	8677	9094	9511	9927	*0344	*0761	*1177	*1594	*2010	*2427	417
1043	018 2843	3259	3676	4092	4508	4925	5341	5757	6173	6589	416
1044	7005	7421	7837	8253	8669	9084	9500	9916	*0332	*0747	416
1045	019 1163	1578	1994	2410	2825	3240	3656	4071	4486	4902	415
1046	5317	5732	6147	6562	6977	7392	7807	8222	8637	9052	415
1047	9467	9882	*0296	*0711	*1126	*1540	*1955	*2369	*2784	*3198	415
1048	020 3613	4027	4442	4856	5270	5684	6099	6513	6927	7341	414
1049	7755	8169	8583	8997	9411	9824	*0238	*0652	*1066	*1479	414
1050	021 1893	2307	2720	3134	3547	3961	4374	4787	5201	5614	413
N.	0	1	2	3	4	5	6	7	8	9	D.

TABLE VII. Seven-place Common Logarithms of Numbers from 1000 to 1100

N.	0	1	2	3	4	5	6	7	8	9	D.
1050	021 1893	2307	2720	3134	3547	3961	4374	4787	5201	5614	413
1051	6027	6440	6854	7267	7680	8093	8506	8919	9332	9745	413
1052	022 0157	0570	0983	1396	1808	2221	2634	3046	3459	3871	413
1053	4284	4696	5109	5521	5933	6345	6758	7170	7582	7994	412
1054	8406	8818	9230	9642	*0054	*0466	*0878	*1289	*1701	*2113	412
1055	023 2525	2936	3348	3759	4171	4582	4994	5405	5817	6228	411
1056	6639	7050	7462	7873	8284	8695	9106	9517	9928	*0339	411
1057	024 0750	1161	1572	1982	2393	2804	3214	3625	4036	4446	411
1058	4857	5267	5678	6088	6498	6909	7319	7729	8139	8549	410
1059	8960	9370	9780	*0190	*0600	*1010	*1419	*1829	*2239	*2649	410
1060	025 3059	3468	3878	4288	4697	5107	5516	5926	6335	6744	410
1061	7154	7563	7972	8382	8791	9200	9609	*0018	*0427	*0836	409
1062	026 1245	1654	2063	2472	2881	3289	3698	4107	4515	4924	409
1063	5333	5741	6150	6558	6967	7375	7783	8192	8600	9008	408
1064	9416	9824	*0233	*0641	*1049	*1457	*1865	*2273	*2680	*3088	408
1065	027 3496	3904	4312	4719	5127	5535	5942	6350	6757	7165	408
1066	7572	7979	8387	8794	9201	9609	*0016	*0423	*0830	*1237	407
1067	028 1644	2051	2458	2865	3272	3679	4086	4492	4899	5306	407
1068	5713	6119	6526	6932	7339	7745	8152	8558	8964	9371	406
1069	9777	*0183	*0590	*0996	*1402	*1808	*2214	*2620	*3026	*3432	406
1070	029 3838	4244	4649	5055	5461	5867	6272	6678	7084	7489	406
1071	7895	8300	8706	9111	9516	9922	*0327	*0732	*1138	*1543	405
1072	030 1948	2353	2758	3163	3568	3973	4378	4783	5188	5592	405
1073	5997	6402	6807	7211	7616	8020	8425	8830	9234	9638	405
1074	031 0043	0447	0851	1256	1660	2064	2468	2872	3277	3681	404
1075	4085	4489	4893	5296	5700	6104	6508	6912	7315	7719	404
1076	8123	8526	8930	9333	9737	*0140	*0544	*0947	*1350	*1754	403
1077	032 2157	2560	2963	3367	3770	4173	4576	4979	5382	5785	403
1078	6188	6590	6993	7396	7799	8201	8604	9007	9409	9812	403
1079	033 0214	0617	1019	1422	1824	2226	2629	3031	3433	3835	402
1080	4238	4640	5042	5444	5846	6248	6650	7052	7453	7855	402
1081	8257	8659	9060	9462	9864	*0265	*0667	*1068	*1470	*1871	402
1082	034 2273	2674	3075	3477	3878	4279	4680	5081	5482	5884	401
1083	6285	6686	7087	7487	7888	8289	8690	9091	9491	9892	401
1084	035 0293	0693	1094	1495	1895	2296	2696	3096	3497	3897	400
1085	4297	4698	5098	5498	5898	6298	6698	7098	7498	7898	400
1086	8298	8698	9098	9498	9898	*0297	*0697	*1097	*1496	*1896	400
1087	036 2295	2695	3094	3494	3893	4293	4692	5091	5491	5890	399
1088	6289	6688	7087	7486	7885	8284	8683	9082	9481	9880	399
1089	037 0279	0678	1076	1475	1874	2272	2671	3070	3468	3867	399
1090	4265	4663	5062	5460	5858	6257	6655	7053	7451	7849	398
1091	8248	8646	9044	9442	9839	*0237	*0635	*1033	*1431	*1829	398
1092	038 2226	2624	3022	3419	3817	4214	4612	5009	5407	5804	398
1093	6202	6599	6996	7393	7791	8188	8585	8982	9379	9776	397
1094	039 0173	0570	0967	1364	1761	2158	2554	2951	3348	3745	397
1095	4141	4538	4934	5331	5727	6124	6520	6917	7313	7709	397
1096	8106	8502	8898	9294	9690	*0086	*0482	*0878	*1274	*1670	396
1097	040 2066	2462	2858	3254	3650	4045	4441	4837	5232	5628	396
1098	6023	6419	6814	7210	7605	8001	8396	8791	9187	9582	395
1099	9977	*0372	*0767	*1162	*1557	*1952	*2347	*2742	*3137	*3532	395
1100	041 3927	4322	4716	5111	5506	5900	6295	6690	7084	7479	395
N.	0	1	2	3	4	5	6	7	8	9	D.

TABLE VIII.

Sums of the First Six Powers of the First 50 Natural Numbers

The following table, giving the sums of the first six powers of the first M natural numbers from $M = 1$ to $M = 50$ will be most frequently used in connection with the fitting of a trend line to time series. For that type of problem, M is the highest value of X used in the computation table. When

M	$\sum_{1}^{M} X$	$\sum_{1}^{M} X^2$	$\sum_{1}^{M} X^3$	$\sum_{1}^{M} X^4$	$\sum_{1}^{M} X^5$	$\sum_{1}^{M} X^6$
1	1	1	1	1	1	1
2	3	5	9	17	33	65
3	6	14	36	98	276	794
4	10	30	100	354	1 300	4 890
5	15	55	225	979	4 425	20 515
6	21	91	441	2 275	12 201	67 171
7	28	140	784	4 676	29 008	184 820
8	36	204	1 296	8 772	61 776	446 964
9	45	285	2 025	15 333	120 825	978 405
10	55	385	3 025	25 333	220 825	1 978 405
11	66	506	4 356	39 974	381 874	3 749 966
12	78	650	6 084	60 710	630 708	6 735 950
13	91	819	8 281	89 271	1 002 001	11 562 759
14	105	1 015	11 025	127 687	1 539 825	19 092 295
15	120	1 240	14 400	178 312	2 299 200	30 482 920
16	136	1 496	18 496	243 848	3 347 776	47 260 136
17	153	1 785	23 409	327 369	4 767 633	71 397 705
18	171	2 109	29 241	432 345	6 657 201	105 409 929
19	190	2 470	36 100	562 666	9 133 300	152 455 810
20	210	2 870	44 100	722 666	12 333 300	216 455 810
21	231	3 311	53 361	917 147	16 417 401	302 221 931
22	253	3 795	64 009	1 151 403	21 571 033	415 601 835
23	276	4 324	76 176	1 431 244	28 007 376	563 637 724
24	300	4 900	90 000	1 763 020	35 970 000	754 740 700
25	325	5 525	105 625	2 153 645	45 735 625	998 881 325
26	351	6 201	123 201	2 610 621	57 617 001	1 307 797 101
27	378	6 930	142 884	3 142 062	71 965 908	1 695 217 590
28	406	7 714	164 836	3 756 718	89 176 276	2 177 107 894
29	435	8 555	189 225	4 463 999	109 687 425	2 771 931 215
30	465	9 455	216 225	5 273 999	133 987 425	3 500 931 215
31	496	10 416	246 016	6 197 520	162 616 576	4 388 434 896
32	528	11 440	278 784	7 246 096	196 171 008	5 462 176 720
33	561	12 529	314 721	8 432 017	235 306 401	6 753 644 689
34	595	13 685	354 025	9 768 353	280 741 825	8 298 449 105
35	630	14 910	396 900	11 268 978	333 263 700	10 136 714 730
36	666	16 206	443 556	12 948 594	393 729 876	12 313 497 066
37	703	17 575	494 209	14 822 755	463 073 833	14 879 223 475
38	741	19 019	549 081	16 907 891	542 309 001	17 890 159 859
39	780	20 540	608 400	19 221 332	632 533 200	21 408 903 620
40	820	22 140	672 400	21 781 332	734 933 200	25 504 903 620
41	861	23 821	741 321	24 607 093	850 789 401	30 255 007 861
42	903	25 585	815 409	27 718 789	981 480 633	35 744 039 605
43	946	27 434	894 916	31 137 590	1 128 489 076	42 065 402 654
44	990	29 370	980 100	34 885 686	1 293 405 300	49 321 716 510
45	1 035	31 395	1 071 225	38 986 311	1 477 933 425	57 625 482 135
46	1 081	33 511	1 168 561	43 463 767	1 683 896 401	67 099 779 031
47	1 128	35 720	1 272 384	48 343 448	1 913 241 408	77 878 994 360
48	1 176	38 024	1 382 976	53 651 864	2 168 045 376	90 109 584 824
49	1 225	40 425	1 500 625	59 416 665	2 450 520 625	103 950 872 025
50	1 275	42 925	1 625 625	65 666 665	2 763 020 625	119 575 872 025

TABLE VIII.

the X origin has been taken at the center of the X values, it is necessary to multiply the summations shown in this table by two. When the origin has been taken at the first X value in a time series, N as used in the normal equations is $M + 1$; when the origin has been taken at the center of the X values in a time series, N is $2M + 1$.

The sums of the first six powers of the first M natural numbers may be obtained from the following expressions:

$$\sum_1^M X = \frac{M(M+1)}{2} \qquad \sum_1^M X^4 = \left(\frac{3M^2 + 3M - 1}{5}\right) \sum_1^M X^2$$

$$\sum_1^M X^2 = \left(\frac{2M+1}{3}\right) \sum_1^M X \qquad \sum_1^M X^5 = \left(\frac{2M^2 + 2M - 1}{3}\right) \sum_1^M X^3$$

$$\sum_1^M X^3 = \left(\sum_1^M X\right)^2 \qquad \sum_1^M X^6 = \left(\frac{3M^4 + 6M^3 - 3M + 1}{7}\right) \sum_1^M X^2$$

A table of the sums of the first 7 powers of the first 100 natural numbers may be found in E. S. Pearson and H. O. Hartley, *Biometrika Tables for Statisticians*, Volume I, Cambridge University Press, Cambridge, 1954, pp. 224–225, and in Karl Pearson, *Tables for Statisticians and Biometricians*, Part I, Cambridge University Press, Cambridge, 1948 (third edition), pp. 40–41. It appears also on the same pages in earlier editions.

TABLE IX.

Sums of the First Six Powers of the First 50 Odd Natural Numbers

This table shows the sums of the first six powers of the first M_o odd natural numbers from $M_o = 1$ to $M_o = 50$. Note that, when $M_o = 2$, we have the odd natural numbers 1 and 3; when $M_o = 3$, reference is to 1, 3, and 5; when $M_o = 4$, the numbers 1, 3, 5, and 7 are involved; and so

(Highest odd natural number)	M_o	$\sum_1^{M_o} X_o$	$\sum_1^{M_o} X_o^2$	$\sum_1^{M_o} X_o^3$	$\sum_1^{M_o} X_o^4$	$\sum_1^{M_o} X_o^5$	$\sum_1^{M_o} X_o^6$
1	1	1	1	1	1	1	1
3	2	4	10	28	82	244	730
5	3	9	35	153	707	3 369	16 355
7	4	16	84	496	3 108	20 176	134 004
9	5	25	165	1 225	9 669	79 225	665 445
11	6	36	286	2 556	24 310	240 276	2 437 006
13	7	49	455	4 753	52 871	611 569	7 263 815
15	8	64	680	8 128	103 496	1 370 944	18 654 440
17	9	81	969	13 041	187 017	2 790 801	42 792 009
19	10	100	1 330	19 900	317 338	5 266 900	89 837 890
21	11	121	1 771	29 161	511 819	9 351 001	175 604 011
23	12	144	2 300	41 328	791 660	15 787 344	323 639 900
25	13	169	2 925	56 953	1 182 285	25 552 969	567 780 525
27	14	196	3 654	76 636	1 713 726	39 901 876	955 201 014
29	15	225	4 495	101 025	2 421 007	60 413 025	1 550 024 335
31	16	256	5 456	130 816	3 344 528	89 042 176	2 437 528 016
33	17	289	6 545	166 753	4 530 449	128 177 569	3 728 995 985
35	18	324	7 770	209 628	6 031 074	180 699 444	5 567 261 610
37	19	361	9 139	260 281	7 905 235	250 043 401	8 132 988 019
39	20	400	10 660	319 600	10 218 676	340 267 600	11 651 731 780
41	21	441	12 341	388 521	13 044 437	456 123 801	16 401 836 021
43	22	484	14 190	468 028	16 463 238	603 132 244	22 723 199 070
45	23	529	16 215	559 153	20 563 863	787 660 369	31 026 964 695
47	24	576	18 424	662 976	25 443 544	1 017 005 376	41 806 180 024
49	25	625	20 825	780 625	31 208 345	1 299 480 625	55 647 467 225
51	26	676	23 426	913 276	37 973 546	1 644 505 876	73 243 755 026
53	27	729	26 235	1 062 153	45 864 027	2 062 701 369	95 408 116 155
55	28	784	29 260	1 228 528	55 014 652	2 565 985 744	123 088 756 780
57	29	841	32 509	1 413 721	65 570 653	3 167 677 801	157 385 204 029
59	30	900	35 990	1 619 100	77 688 014	3 882 602 100	199 565 737 670
61	31	961	39 711	1 846 081	91 533 855	4 727 198 401	251 086 112 031
63	32	1 024	43 680	2 096 128	107 286 816	5 719 634 944	313 609 614 240
65	33	1 089	47 905	2 370 753	125 137 441	6 879 925 569	389 028 504 865
67	34	1 156	52 394	2 671 516	145 288 562	8 230 050 676	479 486 887 034
69	35	1 225	57 155	3 000 025	167 955 683	9 794 082 025	587 405 050 115
71	36	1 296	62 196	3 357 936	193 367 364	11 598 311 376	715 505 334 036
73	37	1 369	67 525	3 746 953	221 765 605	13 671 382 969	866 839 560 325
75	38	1 444	73 150	4 168 828	253 406 230	16 044 429 844	1 044 818 075 950
77	39	1 521	79 079	4 625 361	288 559 271	18 751 214 001	1 253 240 456 039
79	40	1 600	85 320	5 118 400	327 509 352	21 828 270 400	1 496 327 911 560
81	41	1 681	91 881	5 649 841	370 556 073	25 315 054 801	1 778 757 448 041
83	42	1 764	98 770	6 221 628	418 014 394	29 254 095 444	2 105 697 821 410
85	43	1 849	105 995	6 835 753	470 215 019	33 691 148 569	2 482 847 337 035
87	44	1 936	113 564	7 494 256	527 504 780	38 675 357 776	2 916 473 538 044
89	45	2 025	121 485	8 199 225	590 247 021	44 259 417 225	3 413 454 829 005
91	46	2 116	129 766	8 952 796	658 821 982	50 499 738 676	3 981 324 081 046
93	47	2 209	138 415	9 757 153	733 627 183	57 456 622 369	4 628 314 264 495
95	48	2 304	147 440	10 614 528	815 077 808	65 194 431 744	5 363 406 155 120
97	49	2 401	156 849	11 527 201	903 607 089	73 781 772 001	6 196 378 160 049
99	50	2 500	166 650	12 497 500	999 666 690	83 291 672 500	7 137 858 309 450

on. For convenience, the table shows both the highest odd natural number and M_o. The sums shown here will be used almost exclusively in connection with the fitting of a trend line to a time series having an even number of years (or other periods) and where the origin is taken between the two center X values. Under these conditions: (1) the largest X value shown in the computation table is the highest odd natural number and M_o = (highest odd natural number + 1) ÷ 2; (2) the sums read from the table must be multiplied by 2; and (3) N as used in the normal equations is $2M_o$. X_o means "odd value of X."

The sums of the first six powers of the first M_o odd natural numbers may be obtained from the following:

$$\sum_{1}^{M_o} X_o = M_o^2 \qquad \sum_{1}^{M_o} X_o^4 = \left(\frac{12M_o^2 - 7}{5}\right)\sum_{1}^{M_o} X_o^2$$

$$\sum_{1}^{M_o} X_o^2 = \frac{4M_o^3 - M_o}{3} \qquad \sum_{1}^{M_o} X_o^5 = \left(\frac{16M_o^4 - 20M_o^2 + 7}{3}\right)\sum_{1}^{M_o} X_o$$

$$\sum_{1}^{M_o} X_o^3 = (2M_o^2 - 1)\sum_{1}^{M_o} X_o \qquad \sum_{1}^{M_o} X_o^6 = \left(\frac{48M_o^4 - 72M_o^2 + 31}{7}\right)\sum_{1}^{M_o} X_o^2$$

A table of the sums of the first six powers of the first 100 odd natural numbers is given in "Formulae for Facilitating Computations in Time Series Analysis," by Frank A. Ross, *Journal of The American Statistical Association*, March, 1925, pp.75–79.

TABLE X.

Squares, Square Roots, and Reciprocals, 1–1,000

No.	Square	Square Root	Reciprocal	No.	Square	Square Root	Reciprocal
1	1	1.0000000	1.000000000	51	26 01	7.1414284	.019607843
2	4	1.4142136	0.500000000	52	27 04	7.2111026	.019230769
3	9	1.7320508	.333333333	53	28 09	7.2801099	.018867925
4	16	2.0000000	.250000000	54	29 16	7.3484692	.018518519
5	25	2.2360680	.200000000	55	30 25	7.4161985	.018181818
6	36	2.4494897	.166666667	56	31 36	7.4833148	.017857143
7	49	2.6457513	.142857143	57	32 49	7.5498344	.017543860
8	64	2.8284271	.125000000	58	33 64	7.6157731	.017241379
9	81	3.0000000	.111111111	59	34 81	7.6811457	.016949153
10	1 00	3.1622777	.100000000	60	36 00	7.7459667	.016666667
11	1 21	3.3166248	.090909091	61	37 21	7.8102497	.016393443
12	1 44	3.4641016	.083333333	62	38 44	7.8740079	.016129032
13	1 69	3.6055513	.076923077	63	39 69	7.9372539	.015873016
14	1 96	3.7416574	.071428571	64	40 96	8.0000000	.015625000
15	2 25	3.8729833	.066666667	65	42 25	8.0622577	.015384615
16	2 56	4.0000000	.062500000	66	43 56	8.1240384	.015151515
17	2 89	4.1231056	.058823529	67	44 89	8.1853528	.014925373
18	3 24	4.2426407	.055555556	68	46 24	8.2462113	.014705882
19	3 61	4.3588989	.052631579	69	47 61	8.3066239	.014492754
20	4 00	4.4721360	.050000000	70	49 00	8.3666003	.014285714
21	4 41	4.5825757	.047619048	71	50 41	8.4261498	.014084507
22	4 84	4.6904158	.045454545	72	51 84	8.4852814	.013888889
23	5 29	4.7958315	.043478261	73	53 29	8.5440037	.013698630
24	5 76	4.8989795	.041666667	74	54 76	8.6023253	.013513514
25	6 25	5.0000000	.040000000	75	56 25	8.6602540	.013333333
26	6 76	5.0990195	.038461538	76	57 76	8.7177979	.013157895
27	7 29	5.1961524	.037037037	77	59 29	8.7749644	.012987013
28	7 84	5.2915026	.035714286	78	60 84	8.8317609	.012820513
29	8 41	5.3851648	.034482759	79	62 41	8.8881944	.012658228
30	9 00	5.4772256	.033333333	80	64 00	8.9442719	.012500000
31	9 61	5.5677644	.032258065	81	65 61	9.0000000	.012345679
32	10 24	5.6568542	.031250000	82	67 24	9.0553851	.012195122
33	10 89	5.7445626	.030303030	83	68 89	9.1104336	.012048193
34	11 56	5.8309519	.029411765	84	70 56	9.1651514	.011904762
35	12 25	5.9160798	.028571429	85	72 25	9.2195445	.011764706
36	12 96	6.0000000	.027777778	86	73 96	9.2736185	.011627907
37	13 69	6.0827625	.027027027	87	75 69	9.3273791	.011494253
38	14 44	6.1644140	.026315789	88	77 44	9.3808315	.011363636
39	15 21	6.2449980	.025641026	89	79 21	9.4339811	.011235955
40	16 00	6.3245553	.025000000	90	81 00	9.4868330	.011111111
41	16 81	6.4031242	.024390244	91	82 81	9.5393920	.010989011
42	17 64	6.4807407	.023809524	92	84 64	9.5916630	.010869565
43	18 49	6.5574385	.023255814	93	86 49	9.6436508	.010752688
44	19 36	6.6332496	.022727273	94	88 36	9.6953597	.010638298
45	20 25	6.7082039	.022222222	95	90 25	9.7467943	.010526316
46	21 16	6.7823300	.021739130	96	92 16	9.7979590	.010416667
47	22 09	6.8556546	.021276596	97	94 09	9.8488578	.010309278
48	23 04	6.9282032	.020833333	98	96 04	9.8994949	.010204082
49	24 01	7.0000000	.020408163	99	98 01	9.9498744	.010101010
50	25 00	7.0710678	.020000000	100	1 00 00	10.0000000	.010000000

TABLE X.

No.	Square	Square Root	Reciprocal .00
101	1 02 01	10.0498756	9900990
102	1 04 04	10.0995049	9803922
103	1 06 09	10.1488916	9708738
104	1 08 16	10.1980390	9615385
105	1 10 25	10.2469508	9523810
106	1 12 36	10.2956301	9433962
107	1 14 49	10.3440804	9345794
108	1 16 64	10.3923048	9259259
109	1 18 81	10.4403065	9174312
110	1 21 00	10.4880885	9090909
111	1 23 21	10.5356538	9009009
112	1 25 44	10.5830052	8928571
113	1 27 69	10.6301458	8849558
114	1 29 96	10.6770783	8771930
115	1 32 25	10.7238053	8695652
116	1 34 56	10.7703296	8620690
117	1 36 89	10.8166538	8547009
118	1 39 24	10.8627805	8474576
119	1 41 61	10.9087121	8403361
120	1 44 00	10.9544512	8333333
121	1 46 41	11.0000000	8264463
122	1 48 84	11.0453610	8196721
123	1 51 29	11.0905365	8130081
124	1 53 76	11.1355287	8064516
125	1 56 25	11.1803399	8000000
126	1 58 76	11.2249722	7936508
127	1 61 29	11.2694277	7874016
128	1 63 84	11.3137085	7812500
129	1 66 41	11.3578167	7751938
130	1 69 00	11.4017543	7692308
131	1 71 61	11.4455231	7633588
132	1 74 24	11.4891253	7575758
133	1 76 89	11.5325626	7518797
134	1 79 56	11.5758369	7462687
135	1 82 25	11.6189500	7407407
136	1 84 96	11.6619038	7352941
137	1 87 69	11.7046999	7299270
138	1 90 44	11.7473401	7246377
139	1 93 21	11.7898261	7194245
140	1 96 00	11.8321596	7142857
141	1 98 81	11.8743422	7092199
142	2 01 64	11.9163753	7042254
143	2 04 49	11.9582607	6993007
144	2 07 36	12.0000000	6944444
145	2 10 25	12.0415946	6896552
146	2 13 16	12.0830460	6849315
147	2 16 09	12.1243557	6802721
148	2 19 04	12.1655251	6756757
149	2 22 01	12.2065556	6711409
150	2 25 00	12.2474487	6666667

No.	Square	Square Root	Reciprocal .00
151	2 28 01	12.2882057	6622517
152	2 31 04	12.3288280	6578947
153	2 34 09	12.3693169	6535948
154	2 37 16	12.4096736	6493506
155	2 40 25	12.4498996	6451613
156	2 43 36	12.4899960	6410256
157	2 46 49	12.5299641	6369427
158	2 49 64	12.5698051	6329114
159	2 52 81	12.6095202	6289308
160	2 56 00	12.6491106	6250000
161	2 59 21	12.6885775	6211180
162	2 62 44	12.7279221	6172840
163	2 65 69	12.7671453	6134969
164	2 68 96	12.8062485	6097561
165	2 72 25	12.8452326	6060606
166	2 75 56	12.8840987	6024096
167	2 78 89	12.9228480	5988024
168	2 82 24	12.9614814	5952381
169	2 85 61	13.0000000	5917160
170	2 89 00	13.0384048	5882353
171	2 92 41	13.0766968	5847953
172	2 95 84	13.1148770	5813953
173	2 99 29	13.1529464	5780347
174	3 02 76	13.1909060	5747126
175	3 06 25	13.2287566	5714286
176	3 09 76	13.2664992	5681818
177	3 13 29	13.3041347	5649718
178	3 16 84	13.3416641	5617978
179	3 20 41	13.3790882	5586592
180	3 24 00	13.4164079	5555556
181	3 27 61	13.4536240	5524862
182	3 31 24	13.4907376	5494505
183	3 34 89	13.5277493	5464481
184	3 38 56	13.5646600	5434783
185	3 42 25	13.6014705	5405405
186	3 45 96	13.6381817	5376344
187	3 49 69	13.6747943	5347594
188	3 53 44	13.7113092	5319149
189	3 57 21	13.7477271	5291005
190	3 61 00	13.7840488	5263158
191	3 64 81	13.8202750	5235602
192	3 68 64	13.8564065	5208333
193	3 72 49	13.8924440	5181347
194	3 76 36	13.9283883	5154639
195	3 80 25	13.9642400	5128205
196	3 84 16	14.0000000	5102041
197	3 88 09	14.0356688	5076142
198	3 92 04	14.0712473	5050505
199	3 96 01	14.1067360	5025126
200	4 00 00	14.1421356	5000000

TABLE X.

No.	Square	Square Root	Reciprocal .00
201	4 04 01	14.1774469	4975124
202	4 08 04	14.2126704	4950495
203	4 12 09	14.2478068	4926108
204	4 16 16	14.2828569	4901961
205	4 20 25	14.3178211	4878049
206	4 24 36	14.3527001	4854369
207	4 28 49	14.3874946	4830918
208	4 32 64	14.4222051	4807692
209	4 36 81	14.4568323	4784689
210	4 41 00	14.4913767	4761905
211	4 45 21	14.5258390	4739336
212	4 49 44	14.5602198	4716981
213	4 53 69	14.5945195	4694836
214	4 57 96	14.6287388	4672897
215	4 62 25	14.6628783	4651163
216	4 66 56	14.6969385	4629630
217	4 70 89	14.7309199	4608295
218	4 75 24	14.7648231	4587156
219	4 79 61	14.7986486	4566210
220	4 84 00	14.8323970	4545455
221	4 88 41	14.8660687	4524887
222	4 92 84	14.8996644	4504505
223	4 97 29	14.9331845	4484305
224	5 01 76	14.9666295	4464286
225	5 06 25	15.0000000	4444444
226	5 10 76	15.0332964	4424779
227	5 15 29	15.0665192	4405286
228	5 19 84	15.0996689	4385965
229	5 24 41	15.1327460	4366812
230	5 29 00	15.1657509	4347826
231	5 33 61	15.1986842	4329004
232	5 38 24	15.2315462	4310345
233	5 42 89	15.2643375	4291845
234	5 47 56	15.2970585	4273504
235	5 52 25	15.3297097	4255319
236	5 56 96	15.3622915	4237288
237	5 61 69	15.3948043	4219409
238	5 66 44	15.4272486	4201681
239	5 71 21	15.4596248	4184100
240	5 76 00	15.4919334	4166667
241	5 80 81	15.5241747	4149378
242	5 85 64	15.5563492	4132231
243	5 90 49	15.5884573	4115226
244	5 95 36	15.6204994	4098361
245	6 00 25	15.6524758	4081633
246	6 05 16	15.6843871	4065041
247	6 10 09	15.7162336	4048583
248	6 15 04	15.7480157	4032258
249	6 20 01	15.7797338	4016064
250	6 25 00	15.8113883	4000000
251	6 30 01	15.8429795	3984064
252	6 35 04	15.8745079	3968254
253	6 40 09	15.9059737	3952569
254	6 45 16	15.9373775	3937008
255	6 50 25	15.9687194	3921569
256	6 55 36	16.0000000	3906250
257	6 60 49	16.0312195	3891051
258	6 65 64	16.0623784	3875969
259	6 70 81	16.0934769	3861004
260	6 76 00	16.1245155	3846154
261	6 81 21	16.1554944	3831418
262	6 86 44	16.1864141	3816794
263	6 91 69	16.2172747	3802281
264	6 96 96	16.2480768	3787879
265	7 02 25	16.2788206	3773585
266	7 07 56	16.3095064	3759398
267	7 12 89	16.3401346	3745318
268	7 18 24	16.3707055	3731343
269	7 23 61	16.4012195	3717472
270	7 29 00	16.4316767	3703704
271	7 34 41	16.4620776	3690037
272	7 39 84	16.4924225	3676471
273	7 45 29	16.5227116	3663004
274	7 50 76	16.5529454	3649635
275	7 56 25	16.5831240	3636364
276	7 61 76	16.6132477	3623188
277	7 67 29	16.6433170	3610108
278	7 72 84	16.6733320	3597122
279	7 78 41	16.7032931	3584229
280	7 84 00	16.7332005	3571429
281	7 89 61	16.7630546	3558719
282	7 95 24	16.7928556	3546099
283	8 00 89	16.8226038	3533569
284	8 06 56	16.8522995	3521127
285	8 12 25	16.8819430	3508772
286	8 17 96	16.9115345	3496503
287	8 23 69	16.9410743	3484321
288	8 29 44	16.9705627	3472222
289	8 35 21	17.0000000	3460208
290	8 41 00	17.0293864	3448276
291	8 46 81	17.0587221	3436426
292	8 52 64	17.0880075	3424658
293	8 58 49	17.1172428	3412969
294	8 64 36	17.1464282	3401361
295	8 70 25	17.1755640	3389831
296	8 76 16	17.2046505	3378378
297	8 82 09	17.2336879	3367003
298	8 88 04	17.2626765	3355705
299	8 94 01	17.2916165	3344482
300	9 00 00	17.3205081	3333333

TABLE X.

No.	Square	Square Root	Reciprocal .00
301	9 06 01	17.3493516	3322259
302	9 12 04	17.3781472	3311258
303	9 18 09	17.4068952	3300330
304	9 24 16	17.4355958	3289474
305	9 30 25	17.4642492	3278689
306	9 36 36	17.4928557	3267974
307	9 42 49	17.5214155	3257329
308	9 48 64	17.5499288	3246753
309	9 54 81	17.5783958	3236246
310	9 61 00	17.6068169	3225806
311	9 67 21	17.6351921	3215434
312	9 73 44	17.6635217	3205128
313	9 79 69	17.6918060	3194888
314	9 85 96	17.7200451	3184713
315	9 92 25	17.7482393	3174603
316	9 98 56	17.7763888	3164557
317	10 04 89	17.8044938	3154574
318	10 11 24	17.8325545	3144654
319	10 17 61	17.8605711	3134796
320	10 24 00	17.8885438	3125000
321	10 30 41	17.9164729	3115265
322	10 36 84	17.9443584	3105590
323	10 43 29	17.9722008	3095975
324	10 49 76	18.0000000	3086420
325	10 56 25	18.0277564	3076923
326	10 62 76	18.0554701	3067485
327	10 69 29	18.0831413	3058104
328	10 75 84	18.1107703	3048780
329	10 82 41	18.1383571	3039514
330	10 89 00	18.1659021	3030303
331	10 95 61	18.1934054	3021148
332	11 02 24	18.2208672	3012048
333	11 08 89	18.2482876	3003003
334	11 15 56	18.2756669	2994012
335	11 22 25	18.3030052	2985075
336	11 28 96	18.3303028	2976190
337	11 35 69	18.3575598	2967359
338	11 42 44	18.3847763	2958580
339	11 49 21	18.4119526	2949853
340	11 56 00	18.4390889	2941176
341	11 62 81	18.4661853	2932551
342	11 69 64	18.4932420	2923977
343	11 76 49	18.5202592	2915452
344	11 83 36	18.5472370	2906977
345	11 90 25	18.5741756	2898551
346	11 97 16	18.6010752	2890173
347	12 04 09	18.6279360	2881844
348	12 11 04	18.6547581	2873563
349	12 18 01	18.6815417	2865330
350	12 25 00	18.7082869	2857143

No.	Square	Square Root	Reciprocal .00
351	12 32 01	18.7349940	2849003
352	12 39 04	18.7616630	2840909
353	12 46 09	18.7882942	2832861
354	12 53 16	18.8148877	2824859
355	12 60 25	18.8414437	2816901
356	12 67 36	18.8679623	2808989
357	12 74 49	18.8944436	2801120
358	12 81 64	18.9208879	2793296
359	12 88 81	18.9472953	2785515
360	12 96 00	18.9736660	2777778
361	13 03 21	19.0000000	2770083
362	13 10 44	19.0262976	2762431
363	13 17 69	19.0525589	2754821
364	13 24 96	19.0787840	2747253
365	13 32 25	19.1049732	2739726
366	13 39 56	19.1311265	2732240
367	13 46 89	19.1572441	2724796
368	13 54 24	19.1833261	2717391
369	13 61 61	19.2093727	2710027
370	13 69 00	19.2353841	2702703
371	13 76 41	19.2613603	2695418
372	13 83 84	19.2873015	2688172
373	13 91 29	19.3132079	2680965
374	13 98 76	19.3390796	2673797
375	14 06 25	19.3649167	2666667
376	14 13 76	19.3907194	2659574
377	14 21 29	19.4164878	2652520
378	14 28 84	19.4422221	2645503
379	14 36 41	19.4679223	2638522
380	14 44 00	19.4935887	2631579
381	14 51 61	19.5192213	2624672
382	14 59 24	19.5448203	2617801
383	14 66 89	19.5703858	2610966
384	14 74 56	19.5959179	2604167
385	14 82 25	19.6214169	2597403
386	14 89 96	19.6468827	2590674
387	14 97 69	19.6723156	2583979
388	15 05 44	19.6977156	2577320
389	15 13 21	19.7230829	2570694
390	15 21 00	19.7484177	2564103
391	15 28 81	19.7737199	2557545
392	15 36 64	19.7989899	2551020
393	15 44 49	19.8242276	2544529
394	15 52 36	19.8494332	2538071
395	15 60 25	19.8746069	2531646
396	15 68 16	19.8997487	2525253
397	15 76 09	19.9248588	2518892
398	15 84 04	19.9499373	2512563
399	15 92 01	19.9749844	2506266
400	16 00 00	20.0000000	2500000

TABLE X.

No.	Square	Square Root	Reciprocal .00
401	16 08 01	20.0249844	2493766
402	16 16 04	20.0499377	2487562
403	16 24 09	20.0748599	2481390
404	16 32 16	20.0997512	2475248
405	16 40 25	20.1246118	2469136
406	16 48 36	20.1494417	2463054
407	16 56 49	20.1742410	2457002
408	16 64 64	20.1990099	2450980
409	16 72 81	20.2237484	2444988
410	16 81 00	20.2484567	2439024
411	16 89 21	20.2731349	2433090
412	16 97 44	20.2977831	2427184
413	17 05 69	20.3224014	2421308
414	17 13 96	20.3469899	2415459
415	17 22 25	20.3715488	2409639
416	17 30 56	20.3960781	2403846
417	17 38 89	20.4205779	2398082
418	17 47 24	20.4450483	2392344
419	17 55 61	20.4694895	2386635
420	17 64 00	20.4939015	2380952
421	17 72 41	20.5182845	2375297
422	17 80 84	20.5426386	2369668
423	17 89 29	20.5669638	2364066
424	17 97 76	20.5912603	2358491
425	18 06 25	20.6155281	2352941
426	18 14 76	20.6397674	2347418
427	18 23 29	20.6639783	2341920
428	18 31 84	20.6881609	2336449
429	18 40 41	20.7123152	2331002
430	18 49 00	20.7364414	2325581
431	18 57 61	20.7605395	2320186
432	18 66 24	20.7846097	2314815
433	18 74 89	20.8086520	2309469
434	18 83 56	20.8326667	2304147
435	18 92 25	20.8566536	2298851
436	19 00 96	20.8806130	2293578
437	19 09 69	20.9045450	2288330
438	19 18 44	20.9284495	2283105
439	19 27 21	20.9523268	2277904
440	19 36 00	20.9761770	2272727
441	19 44 81	21.0000000	2267574
442	19 53 64	21.0237960	2262443
443	19 62 49	21.0475652	2257336
444	19 71 36	21.0713075	2252252
445	19 80 25	21.0950231	2247191
446	19 89 16	21.1187121	2242152
447	19 98 09	21.1423745	2237136
448	20 07 04	21.1660105	2232143
449	20 16 01	21.1896201	2227171
450	20 25 00	21.2132034	2222222
451	20 34 01	21.2367606	2217295
452	20 43 04	21.2602916	2212389
453	20 52 09	21.2837967	2207506
454	20 61 16	21.3072758	2202643
455	20 70 25	21.3307290	2197802
456	20 79 36	21.3541565	2192982
457	20 88 49	21.3775583	2188184
458	20 97 64	21.4009346	2183406
459	21 06 81	21.4242853	2178649
460	21 16 00	21.4476106	2173913
461	21 25 21	21.4709106	2169197
462	21 34 44	21.4941853	2164502
463	21 43 69	21.5174348	2159827
464	21 52 96	21.5406592	2155172
465	21 62 25	21.5638587	2150538
466	21 71 56	21.5870331	2145923
467	21 80 89	21.6101828	2141328
468	21 90 24	21.6333077	2136752
469	21 99 61	21.6564078	2132196
470	22 09 00	21.6794834	2127660
471	22 18 41	21.7025344	2123142
472	22 27 84	21.7255610	2118644
473	22 37 29	21.7485632	2114165
474	22 46 76	21.7715411	2109705
475	22 56 25	21.7944947	2105263
476	22 65 76	21.8174242	2100840
477	22 75 29	21.8403297	2096436
478	22 84 84	21.8632111	2092050
479	22 94 41	21.8860686	2087683
480	23 04 00	21.9089023	2083333
481	23 13 61	21.9317122	2079002
482	23 23 24	21.9544984	2074689
483	23 32 89	21.9772610	2070393
484	23 42 56	22.0000000	2066116
485	23 52 25	22.0227155	2061856
486	23 61 96	22.0454077	2057613
487	23 71 69	22.0680765	2053388
488	23 81 44	22.0907220	2049180
489	23 91 21	22.1133444	2044990
490	24 01 00	22.1359436	2040816
491	24 10 81	22.1585198	2036660
492	24 20 64	22.1810730	2032520
493	24 30 49	22.2036033	2028398
494	24 40 36	22.2261108	2024291
495	24 50 25	22.2485955	2020202
496	24 60 16	22.2710575	2016129
497	24 70 09	22.2934968	2012072
498	24 80 04	22.3159136	2008032
499	24 90 01	22.3383079	2004008
500	25 00 00	22.3606798	2000000

TABLE X.

No.	Square	Square Root	Reciprocal .00
501	25 10 01	22.3830293	1996008
502	25 20 04	22.4053565	1992032
503	25 30 09	22.4276615	1988072
504	25 40 16	22.4499443	1984127
505	25 50 25	22.4722051	1980198
506	25 60 36	22.4944438	1976285
507	25 70 49	22.5166605	1972387
508	25 80 64	22.5388553	1968504
509	25 90 81	22.5610283	1964637
510	26 01 00	22.5831796	1960784
511	26 11 21	22.6053091	1956947
512	26 21 44	22.6274170	1953125
513	26 31 69	22.6495033	1949318
514	26 41 96	22.6715681	1945525
515	26 52 25	22.6936114	1941748
516	26 62 56	22.7156334	1937984
517	26 72 89	22.7376340	1934236
518	26 83 24	22.7596134	1930502
519	26 93 61	22.7815715	1926782
520	27 04 00	22.8035085	1923077
521	27 14 41	22.8254244	1919386
522	27 24 84	22.8473193	1915709
523	27 35 29	22.8691933	1912046
524	27 45 76	22.8910463	1908397
525	27 56 25	22.9128785	1904762
526	27 66 76	22.9346899	1901141
527	27 77 29	22.9564806	1897533
528	27 87 84	22.9782506	1893939
529	27 98 41	23.0000000	1890359
530	28 09 00	23.0217289	1886792
531	28 19 61	23.0434372	1883239
532	28 30 24	23.0651252	1879699
533	28 40 89	23.0867928	1876173
534	28 51 56	23.1084400	1872659
535	28 62 25	23.1300670	1869159
536	28 72 96	23.1516738	1865672
537	28 83 69	23.1732605	1862197
538	28 94 44	23.1948270	1858736
539	29 05 21	23.2163735	1855288
540	29 16 00	23.2379001	1851852
541	29 26 81	23.2594067	1848429
542	29 37 64	23.2808935	1845018
543	29 48 49	23.3023604	1841621
544	29 59 36	23.3238076	1838235
545	29 70 25	23.3452351	1834862
546	29 81 16	23.3666429	1831502
547	29 92 09	23.3880311	1828154
548	30 03 04	23.4093998	1824818
549	30 14 01	23.4307490	1821494
550	30 25 00	23.4520788	1818182
551	30 36 01	23.4733892	1814882
552	30 47 04	23 4946802	1811594
553	30 58 09	23 5159520	1808318
554	30 69 16	23.5372046	1805054
555	30 80 25	23.5584380	1801802
556	30 91 36	23.5796522	1798561
557	31 02 49	23.6008474	1795332
558	31 13 64	23.6220236	1792115
559	31 24 81	23 6431808	1788909
560	31 36 00	23.6643191	1785714
561	31 47 21	23.6854386	1782531
562	31 58 44	23.7065392	1779359
563	31 69 69	23.7276210	1776199
564	31 80 96	23.7486842	1773050
565	31 92 25	23.7697286	1769912
566	32 03 56	23.7907545	1766784
567	32 14 89	23.8117618	1763668
568	32 26 24	23.8327506	1760563
569	32 37 61	23.8537209	1757469
570	32 49 00	23.8746728	1754386
571	32 60 41	23.8956063	1751313
572	32 71 84	23.9165215	1748252
573	32 83 29	23.9374184	1745201
574	32 94 76	23.9582971	1742160
575	33 06 25	23.9791576	1739130
576	33 17 76	24.0000000	1736111
577	33 29 29	24.0208243	1733102
578	33 40 84	24.0416306	1730104
579	33 52 41	24.0624188	1727116
580	33 64 00	24.0831891	1724138
581	33 75 61	24.1039416	1721170
582	33 87 24	24.1246762	1718213
583	33 98 89	24.1453929	1715266
584	34 10 56	24.1660919	1712329
585	34 22 25	24.1867732	1709402
586	34 33 96	24.2074369	1706485
587	34 45 69	24.2280829	1703578
588	34 57 44	24.2487113	1700680
589	34 69 21	24.2693222	1697793
590	34 81 00	24.2899156	1694915
591	34 92 81	24.3104916	1692047
592	35 04 64	24.3310501	1689189
593	35 16 49	24.3515913	1686341
594	35 28 36	24.3721152	1683502
595	35 40 25	24.3926218	1680672
596	35 52 16	24.4131112	1677852
597	35 64 09	24.4335834	1675042
598	35 76 04	24.4540385	1672241
599	35 88 01	24.4744765	1669449
600	36 00 00	24.4948974	1666667

TABLE X.

No.	Square	Square Root	Reciprocal .00
601	36 12 01	24.5153013	1663894
602	36 24 04	24.5356883	1661130
603	36 36 09	24.5560583	1658375
604	36 48 16	24.5764115	1655629
605	36 60 25	24.5967478	1652803
606	36 72 36	24.6170673	1650165
607	36 84 49	24.6373700	1647446
608	36 96 64	24.6576560	1644737
609	37 08 81	24.6779254	1642036
610	37 21 00	24.6981781	1639344
611	37 33 21	24.7184142	1636661
612	37 45 44	24.7386338	1633987
613	37 57 69	24.7588368	1631321
614	37 69 96	24.7790234	1628664
615	37 82 25	24.7991935	1626016
616	37 94 56	24.8193473	1623377
617	38 06 89	24.8394847	1620746
618	38 19 24	24.8596058	1618123
619	38 31 61	24.8797106	1615509
620	38 44 00	24.8997992	1612903
621	38 56 41	24.9198716	1610306
622	38 68 84	24.9399278	1607717
623	38 81 29	24.9599679	1605136
624	38 93 76	24.9799920	1602564
625	39 06 25	25.0000000	1600000
626	39 18 76	25.0199920	1597444
627	39 31 29	25.0399681	1594896
628	39 43 84	25.0599282	1592357
629	39 56 41	25.0798724	1589825
630	39 69 00	25.0998008	1587302
631	39 81 61	25.1197134	1584786
632	39 94 24	25.1396102	1582278
633	40 06 89	25.1594913	1579779
634	40 19 56	25.1793566	1577287
635	40 32 25	25.1992063	1574803
636	40 44 96	25.2190404	1572327
637	40 57 69	25.2388589	1569859
638	40 70 44	25.2586619	1567398
639	40 83 21	25.2784493	1564945
640	40 96 00	25.2982213	1562500
641	41 08 81	25.3179778	1560062
642	41 21 64	25 3377189	1557632
643	41 34 49	25.3574447	1555210
644	41 47 36	25.3771551	1552795
645	41 60 25	25.3968502	1550388
646	41 73 16	25.4165301	1547988
647	41 86 09	25.4361947	1545595
648	41 99 04	25.4558441	1543210
649	42 12 01	25.4754784	1540832
650	42 25 00	25.4950976	1538462

No.	Square	Square Root	Reciprocal .00
651	42 38 01	25.5147016	1536098
652	42 51 04	25.5342907	1533742
653	42 64 09	25.5538647	1531394
654	42 77 16	25.5734237	1529052
655	42 90 25	25.5929678	1526718
656	43 03 36	25.6124969	1524390
657	43 16 49	25.6320112	1522070
658	43 29 64	25.6515107	1519757
659	43 42 81	25.6709953	1517451
660	43 56 00	25.6904652	1515152
661	43 69 21	25.7099203	1512859
662	43 82 44	25.7293607	1510574
663	43 95 69	25.7487864	1508296
664	44 08 96	25.7681975	1506024
665	44 22 25	25.7875939	1503759
666	44 35 56	25.8069758	1501502
667	44 48 89	25.8263431	1499250
668	44 62 24	25.8456960	1497006
669	44 75 61	25.8650343	1494768
670	44 89 00	25.8843582	1492537
671	45 02 41	25.9036677	1490313
672	45 15 84	25.9229628	1488095
673	45 29 29	25.9422435	1485884
674	45 42 76	25.9615100	1483680
675	45 56 25	25.9807621	1481481
676	45 69 76	26.0000000	1479290
677	45 83 29	26.0192237	1477105
678	45 96 84	26.0384331	1474926
679	46 10 41	26.0576284	1472754
680	46 24 00	26.0768096	1470588
681	46 37 61	26.0959767	1468429
682	46 51 24	26.1151297	1466276
683	46 64 89	26.1342687	1464129
684	46 78 56	26.1533937	1461988
685	46 92 25	26.1725047	1459854
686	47 05 96	26.1916017	1457726
687	47 19 69	26.2106848	1455604
688	47 33 44	26.2297541	1453488
689	47 47 21	26.2488095	1451379
690	47 61 00	26.2678511	1449275
691	47 74 81	26.2868789	1447178
692	47 88 64	26.3058929	1445087
693	48 02 49	26.3248932	1443001
694	48 16 36	26 3438797	1440922
695	48 30 25	26.3628527	1438849
696	48 44 16	26.3818119	1436782
697	48 58 09	26.4007576	1434720
698	48 72 04	26.4196896	1432665
699	48 86 01	26.4386081	1430615
700	49 00 00	26.4575131	1428571

TABLE X.

No.	Square	Square Root	Reciprocal .00
701	49 14 01	26.4764046	1426534
702	49 28 04	26.4952826	1424501
703	49 42 09	26.5141472	1422475
704	49 56 16	26.5329983	1420455
705	49 70 25	26.5518361	1418440
706	49 84 36	26.5706605	1416431
707	49 98 49	26.5894716	1414427
708	50 12 64	26.6082694	1412429
709	50 26 81	26.6270539	1410437
710	50 41 00	26.6458252	1408451
711	50 55 21	26.6645833	1406470
712	50 69 44	26.6833281	1404494
713	50 83 69	26.7020598	1402525
714	50 97 96	26.7207784	1400560
715	51 12 25	26.7394839	1398601
716	51 26 56	26.7581763	1396648
717	51 40 89	26.7768557	1394700
718	51 55 24	26.7955220	1392758
719	51 69 61	26.8141754	1390821
720	51 84 00	26.8328157	1388889
721	51 98 41	26.8514432	1386963
722	52 12 84	26.8700577	1385042
723	52 27 29	26.8886593	1383126
724	52 41 76	26.9072481	1381215
725	52 56 25	26.9258240	1379310
726	52 70 76	26.9443872	1377410
727	52 85 29	26.9629375	1375516
728	52 99 84	26.9814751	1373626
729	53 14 41	27.0000000	1371742
730	53 29 00	27.0185122	1369863
731	53 43 61	27.0370117	1367989
732	53 58 24	27.0554985	1366120
733	53 72 89	27.0739727	1364256
734	53 87 56	27.0924344	1362398
735	54 02 25	27.1108834	1360544
736	54 16 96	27.1293199	1358696
737	54 31 69	27.1477439	1356852
738	54 46 44	27.1661554	1355014
739	54 61 21	27.1845544	1353180
740	54 76 00	27.2029410	1351351
741	54 90 81	27.2213152	1349528
742	55 05 64	27.2396769	1347709
743	55 20 49	27.2580263	1345895
744	55 35 36	27.2763634	1344086
745	55 50 25	27.2946881	1342282
746	55 65 16	27.3130006	1340483
747	55 80 09	27.3313007	1338688
748	55 95 04	27.3495887	1336898
749	56 10 01	27.3678644	1335113
750	56 25 00	27.3861279	1333333

No.	Square	Square Root	Reciprocal .00
751	56 40 01	27.4043792	1331558
752	56 55 04	27.4226184	1329787
753	56 70 09	27.4408455	1328021
754	56 85 16	27.4590604	1326260
755	57 00 25	27.4772633	1324503
756	57 15 36	27.4954542	1322751
757	57 30 49	27.5136330	1321004
758	57 45 64	27.5317998	1319261
759	57 60 81	27.5499546	1317523
760	57 76 00	27.5680975	1315789
761	57 91 21	27.5862284	1314060
762	58 06 44	27.6043475	1312336
763	58 21 69	27.6224546	1310616
764	58 36 96	27.6405499	1308901
765	58 52 25	27.6586334	1307190
766	58 67 56	27.6767050	1305483
767	58 82 89	27.6947648	1303781
768	58 98 24	27.7128129	1302083
769	59 13 61	27.7308492	1300390
770	59 29 00	27.7488739	1298701
771	59 44 41	27.7668868	1297017
772	59 59 84	27.7848880	1295337
773	59 75 29	27.8028775	1293661
774	59 90 76	27.8208555	1291990
775	60 06 25	27.8388218	1290323
776	60 21 76	27.8567766	1288660
777	60 37 29	27.8747197	1287001
778	60 52 84	27.8926514	1285347
779	60 68 41	27.9105715	1283697
780	60 84 00	27.9284801	1282051
781	60 99 61	27.9463772	1280410
782	61 15 24	27.9642629	1278772
783	61 30 89	27.9821372	1277139
784	61 46 56	28.0000000	1275510
785	61 62 25	28.0178515	1273885
786	61 77 96	28.0356915	1272265
787	61 93 69	28.0535203	1270648
788	62 09 44	28.0713377	1269036
789	62 25 21	28.0891438	1267427
790	62 41 00	28.1069386	1265823
791	62 56 81	28.1247222	1264223
792	62 72 64	28.1424946	1262626
793	62 88 49	28.1602557	1261034
794	63 04 36	28.1780056	1259446
795	63 20 25	28.1957444	1257862
796	63 36 16	28.2134720	1256281
797	63 52 09	28.2311884	1254705
798	63 68 04	28.2488938	1253133
799	63 84 01	28.2665881	1251564
800	64 00 00	28.2842712	1250000

TABLE X.

No.	Square	Square Root	Reciprocal .00
801	64 16 01	28:3019434	1248439
802	64 32 04	28.3196045	1246883
803	64 48 09	28.3372546	1245330
804	64 64 16	28.3548938	1243781
805	64 80 25	28.3725219	1242236
806	64 96 36	28.3901391	1240695
807	65 12 49	28.4077454	1239157
808	65 28 64	28.4253408	1237624
809	65 44 81	28.4429253	1236094
810	65 61 00	28.4604989	1234568
811	65 77 21	28.4780617	1233046
812	65 93 44	28.4956137	1231527
813	66 09 69	28.5131549	1230012
814	66 25 96	28.5306852	1228501
815	66 42 25	28.5482048	1226994
816	66 58 56	28.5657137	1225490
817	66 74 89	28.5832119	1223990
818	66 91 24	28.6006993	1222494
819	67 07 61	28.6181760	1221001
820	67 24 00	28.6356421	1219512
821	67 40 41	28.6530976	1218027
822	67 56 84	28.6705424	1216545
823	67 73 29	28.6879766	1215067
824	67 89 76	28.7054002	1213592
825	68 06 25	28.7228132	1212121
826	68 22 76	28.7402157	1210654
827	68 39 29	28.7576077	1209190
828	68 55 84	28.7749891	1207729
829	68 72 41	28.7923601	1206273
830	68 89 00	28.8097206	1204819
831	69 05 61	28.8270706	1203369
832	69 22 24	28.8444102	1201923
833	69 38 89	28.8617394	1200480
834	69 55 56	28.8790582	1199041
835	69 72 25	28.8963666	1197605
836	69 88 96	28.9136646	1196172
837	70 05 69	28.9309523	1194743
838	70 22 44	28.9482297	1193317
839	70 39 21	28.9654967	1191895
840	70 56 00	28.9827535	1190476
841	70 72 81	29.0000000	1189061
842	70 89 64	29.0172363	1187648
843	71 06 49	29.0344623	1186240
844	71 23 36	29.0516781	1184834
845	71 40 25	29.0688837	1183432
846	71 57 16	29.0860791	1182033
847	71 74 09	29.1032644	1180638
848	71 91 04	29.1204396	1179245
849	72 08 01	29.1376046	1177856
850	72 25 00	29.1547595	1176471
851	72 42 01	29.1719043	1175088
852	72 59 04	29.1890390	1173709
853	72 76 09	29.2061637	1172333
854	72 93 16	29.2232784	1170960
855	73 10 25	29 2403830	1169591
856	73 27 36	29.2574777	1168224
857	73 44 49	29.2745623	1166861
858	73 61 64	29.2916370	1165501
859	73 78 81	29.3087018	1164144
860	73 96 00	29.3257566	1162791
861	74 13 21	29.3428015	1161440
862	74 30 44	29.3598365	1160093
863	74 47 69	29.3768616	1158749
864	74 64 96	29.3938769	1157407
865	74 82 25	29.4108823	1156069
866	74 99 56	29.4278779	1154734
867	75 16 89	29.4448637	1153403
868	75 34 24	29.4618397	1152074
869	75 51 61	29.4788059	1150748
870	75 69 00	29.4957624	1149425
871	75 86 41	29.5127091	1148106
872	76 03 84	29.5296461	1146789
873	76 21 29	29.5465734	1145475
874	76 38 76	29.5634910	1144165
875	76 56 25	29.5803989	1142857
876	76 73 76	29.5972972	1141553
877	76 91 29	29.6141858	1140251
878	77 08 84	29.6310648	1138952
879	77 26 41	29.6479342	1137656
880	77 44 00	29.6647939	1136364
881	77 61 61	29.6816442	1135074
882	77 79 24	29.6984848	1133787
883	77 96 89	29.7153159	1132503
884	78 14 56	29.7321375	1131222
885	78 32 25	29.7489496	1129944
886	78 49 96	29.7657521	1128668
887	78 67 69	29.7825452	1127396
888	78 85 44	29.7993289	1126126
889	79 03 21	29.8161030	1124859
890	79 21 00	29.8328678	1123596
891	79 38 81	29.8496231	1122334
892	79 56 64	29.8663690	1121076
893	79 74 49	29.8831056	1119821
894	79 92 36	29.8998328	1118568
895	80 10 25	29.9165506	1117318
896	80 28 16	29.9332591	1116071
897	80 46 09	29.9499583	1114827
898	80 64 04	29.9666481	1113586
899	80 82 01	29.9833287	1112347
900	81 00 00	30.0000000	1111111

TABLE X.

No.	Square	Square Root	Reciprocal .00
901	81 18 01	30.0166620	1109878
902	81 36 04	30.0333148	1108647
903	81 54 09	30.0499584	1107420
904	81 72 16	30.0665928	1106195
905	81 90 25	30.0832170	1104972
906	82 08 36	30.0998339	1103753
907	82 26 49	30.1164407	1102536
908	82 44 64	30.1330383	1101322
909	82 62 81	30.1496269	1100110
910	82 81 00	30.1662063	1098901
911	82 99 21	30.1827765	1097695
912	83 17 44	30.1993377	1096491
913	83 35 69	30.2158899	1095290
914	83 53 96	30.2324329	1094092
915	83 72 25	30.2489669	1092896
916	83 90 56	30.2654919	1091703
917	84 08 89	30.2820079	1090513
918	84 27 24	30.2985148	1089325
919	84 45 61	30.3150128	1088139
920	84 64 00	30.3315018	1086957
921	84 82 41	30.3479818	1085776
922	85 00 84	30.3644529	1084599
923	85 19 29	30.3809151	1083424
924	85 37 76	30.3973683	1082251
925	85 56 25	30.4138127	1081081
926	85 74 76	30.4302481	1079914
927	85 93 29	30.4466747	1078749
928	86 11 84	30.4630924	1077586
929	86 30 41	30.4795013	1076426
930	86 49 00	30.4959014	1075269
931	86 67 61	30.5122926	1074114
932	86 86 24	30.5286750	1072961
933	87 04 89	30.5450487	1071811
934	87 23 56	30.5614136	1070664
935	87 42 25	30.5777697	1069519
936	87 60 96	30.5941171	1068376
937	87 79 69	30.6104557	1067236
938	87 98 44	30.6267857	1066098
939	88 17 21	30.6431069	1064963
940	88 36 00	30.6594194	1063830
941	88 54 81	30.6757233	1062699
942	88 73 64	30.6920185	1061571
943	88 92 49	30.7083051	1060445
944	89 11 36	30.7245830	1059322
945	89 30 25	30.7408523	1058201
946	89 49 16	30.7571130	1057082
947	89 68 09	30.7733651	1055966
948	89 87 04	30.7896086	1054852
949	90 06 01	30.8058436	1053741
950	90 25 00	30.8220700	1052632
951	90 44 01	30.8382879	1051525
952	90 63 04	30.8544972	1050420
953	90 82 09	30.8706981	1049318
954	91 01 16	30.8868904	1048218
955	91 20 25	30.9030743	1047120
956	91 39 36	30.9192497	1046025
957	91 58 49	30.9354166	1044932
958	91 77 64	30.9515751	1043841
959	91 96 81	30.9677251	1042753
960	92 16 00	30.9838668	1041667
961	92 35 21	31.0000000	1040583
962	92 54 44	31.0161248	1039501
963	92 73 69	31.0322413	1038422
964	92 92 96	31.0483494	1037344
965	93 12 25	31.0644491	1036269
966	93 31 56	31.0805405	1035197
967	93 50 89	31.0966236	1034126
968	93 70 24	31.1126984	1033058
969	93 89 61	31.1287648	1031992
970	94 09 00	31.1448230	1030928
971	94 28 41	31.1608729	1029866
972	94 47 84	31.1769145	1028807
973	94 67 29	31.1929479	1027749
974	94 86 76	31.2089731	1026694
975	95 06 25	31.2249900	1025641
976	95 25 76	31.2409987	1024590
977	95 45 29	31.2569992	1023541
978	95 64 84	31.2729915	1022495
979	95 84 41	31.2889757	1021450
980	96 04 00	31.3049517	1020408
981	96 23 61	31.3209195	1019368
982	96 43 24	31.3368792	1018330
983	96 62 89	31.3528308	1017294
984	96 82 56	31.3687743	1016260
985	97 02 25	31.3847097	1015228
986	97 21 96	31.4006369	1014199
987	97 41 69	31.4165561	1013171
988	97 61 44	31.4324673	1012146
989	97 81 21	31.4483704	1011122
990	98 01 00	31.4642654	1010101
991	98 20 81	31.4801525	1009082
992	98 40 64	31.4960315	1008065
993	98 60 49	31.5119025	1007049
994	98 80 36	31.5277655	1006036
995	99 00 25	31.5436206	1005025
996	99 20 16	31.5594677	1004016
997	99 40 09	31.5753068	1003009
998	99 60 04	31.5911380	1002004
999	99 80 01	31.6069613	1001001
1000	1 00 00 00	31.6227766	1000000

TABLE XI.

Areas Under the Normal Curve

From the Arithmetic Mean to Distances* $\frac{x}{s}$ or $\frac{x}{\sigma}$ from the Arithmetic Mean, Expressed as Decimal Fractions of the Total Area 1.0000

This table shows the black area:

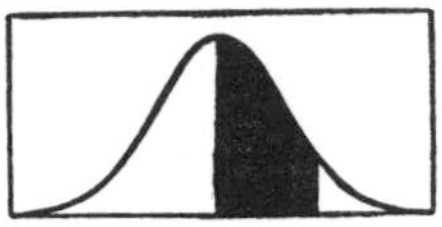

$\frac{x}{s}$ or $\frac{x}{\sigma}$	.00	.01	.02	.03	.04	.05	.06	.07	.08	.09
0.0	.0000	.0040	.0080	.0120	.0160	.0199	.0239	.0279	.0319	.0359
0.1	.0398	.0438	.0478	.0517	.0557	.0596	.0636	.0675	.0714	.0753
0.2	.0793	.0832	.0871	.0910	.0948	.0987	.1026	.1064	.1103	.1141
0.3	.1179	.1217	.1255	.1293	.1331	.1368	.1406	.1443	.1480	.1517
0.4	.1554	.1591	.1628	.1664	.1700	.1736	.1772	.1808	.1844	.1879
0.5	.1915	.1950	.1985	.2019	.2054	.2088	.2123	.2157	.2190	.2224
0.6	.2257	.2291	.2324	.2357	.2389	.2422	.2454	.2486	.2518	.2549
0.7	.2580	.2612	.2642	.2673	.2704	.2734	.2764	.2794	.2823	.2852
0.8	.2881	.2910	.2939	.2967	.2995	.3023	.3051	.3078	.3106	.3133
0.9	.3159	.3186	.3212	.3238	.3264	.3289	.3315	.3340	.3365	.3389
1.0	.3413	.3438	.3461	.3485	.3508	.3531	.3554	.3577	.3599	.3621
1.1	.3643	.3665	.3686	.3708	.3729	.3749	.3770	.3790	.3810	.3830
1.2	.3849	.3869	.3888	.3907	.3925	.3944	.3063	.3980	.3997	.4015
1.3	.4032	.4049	.4066	.4082	.4099	.4115	.4131	.4147	.4162	.4177
1.4	.4192	.4207	.4222	.4236	.4251	.4265	.4279	.4292	.4306	.4319
1.5	.4332	.4345	.4357	.4370	.4382	.4394	.4406	.4418	.4429	.4441
1.6	.4452	.4463	.4474	.4484	.4495	.4505	.4515	.4525	.4535	.4545
1.7	.4554	.4564	.4573	.4582	.4591	.4599	.4608	.4616	.4625	.4633
1.8	.4641	.4649	.4656	.4664	.4671	.4678	.4686	.4693	.4699	.4706
1.9	.4713	.4719	.4726	.4732	.4738	.4744	.4750	.4756	.4761	.4767
2.0	.4772	.4778	.4783	.4788	.4793	.4798	.4803	.4808	.4812	.4817
2.1	.4821	.4826	.4830	.4834	.4838	.4842	.4846	.4850	.4854	.4857
2.2	.4861	.4864	.4868	.4871	.4875	.4878	.4881	.4884	.4887	.4890
2.3	.4893	.4896	.4898	.4901	.4904	.4906	.4909	.4911	.4913	.4916
2.4	.4918	.4920	.4922	.4925	.4927	.4929	.4931	.4932	.4934	.4936
2.5	.4938	.4940	.4941	.4943	.4945	.4946	.4948	.4949	.4951	.4952
2.6	.4953	.4955	.4956	.4957	.4959	.4960	.4961	.4962	.4963	.4964
2.7	.4965	.4966	.4967	.4968	.4969	.4970	.4971	.4972	.4973	.4974
2.8	.4974	.4975	.4976	.4977	.4977	.4978	.4979	.4979	.4980	.4981
2.9	.4981	.4982	.4982	.4983	.4984	.4984	.4985	.4985	.4986	.4986
3.0	.49865	.4987	.4987	.4988	.4988	.4989	.4989	.4989	.4990	.4990
3.1	.49903	.4991	.4991	.4991	.4992	.4992	.4992	.4992	.4993	.4993
3.2	.4993129									
3.3	.4995166									
3.4	.4996631									
3.5	.4997674									
3.6	.4998409									
3.7	.4998922									
3.8	.4999277									
3.9	.4999519									
4.0	.4999683									
4.5	.4999966									
5.0	.4999997133									

* The expression $\frac{x}{s}$ is used when fitting a normal curve (pp. 590–607); $\frac{x}{\sigma}$ is employed when making a test of significance involving the standard deviation of the population and the normal curve (pp. 635–642, 663–666, 670–671, 673–675, 679–680, and 723–725).

Largely from Rugg's *Statistical Methods Applied to Education* (with corrections), by arrangement with the publishers, Houghton Mifflin Company. A more detailed table of normal-curve areas, but in two directions from the arithmetic mean, is given in Federal Works Agency, Work Projects Administration for the City of New York, *Tables of Probability Functions*, National Bureau of Standards, New York, 1942, Vol. II, pp. 2–338.

TABLE XII.

Ordinates of the Normal Curve

Erected at Distances $\frac{x}{s}$ from $\bar{X}$, Expressed as Decimal Fractions of the Maximum Ordinate Y_0

The maximum ordinate is computed from the expression $Y_0 = \frac{Ni}{s\sqrt{2\pi}} = \frac{Ni}{2.5066s}$.

The values tabled below result from solving the expression $e^{\frac{-x^2}{2s^2}}$.

The proportional height of an ordinate to be erected at any given value on the X axis can be read from the table by determining x (the deviation of the given value from the mean) and computing $\frac{x}{s}$. Thus, if $\bar{X}$ = \$25.00, s = \$4.00, Y_0 = 1950, and it is desired to ascertain the height of an ordinate to be erected at \$23.00; x = \$2.00 and $\frac{x}{s} = \frac{\$2.00}{\$4.00} = 0.50$. From the table the ordinate is found to be 0.88250 of the maximum ordinate Y_0, or $0.88250 \times 1950 = 1721$.

TABLE XII. —*Continued*

Ordinates of the Normal Curve

$\frac{x}{s}$	0	.01	.02	.03	.04	.05	.06	.07	.08	.09
0.0	1.00000	.99995	.99980	.99955	.99920	.99875	.99820	.99755	.99685	.99596
0.1	.99501	.99396	.99283	.99158	.99025	.98881	.98728	.98565	.98393	.98211
0.2	.98020	.97819	.97609	.97390	.97161	.96923	.96676	.96420	.96156	.95882
0.3	.95600	.95309	.95010	.94702	.94387	.94055	.93723	.93382	.93024	.92677
0.4	.92312	.91939	.91558	.91169	.90774	.90371	.89961	.89543	.89119	.88688
0.5	.88250	.87805	.87353	.86896	.86432	.85962	.85488	.85006	.84519	.84060
0.6	.83527	.83023	.82514	.82010	.81481	.80957	.80429	.79896	.79359	.78817
0.7	.78270	.77721	.77167	.76610	.76048	.75484	.74916	.74342	.73769	.73193
0.8	.72615	.72033	.71448	.70861	.70272	.69681	.69087	.68493	.67896	.67298
0.9	.66689	.66097	.65494	.64891	.64287	.63683	.63077	.62472	.61865	.61259
1.0	.60653	.60047	.59440	.58834	.58228	.57623	.57017	.56414	.55810	.55209
1.1	.54607	.54007	.53409	.52812	.52214	.51620	.51027	.50437	.49848	.49260
1.2	.48675	.48092	.47511	.46933	.46357	.45783	.45212	.44644	.44078	.43516
1.3	.42956	.42399	.41845	.41294	.40747	.40202	.39661	.39123	.38569	.38058
1.4	.37531	.37007	.36487	.35971	.35459	.34950	.34445	.33944	.33447	.32954
1.5	.32465	.31980	.31500	.31023	.30550	.30082	.29618	.29158	.28702	.28251
1.6	.27804	.27361	.26923	.26489	.26059	.25634	.25213	.24797	.24385	.23978
1.7	.23575	.23176	.22782	.22392	.22008	.21027	.21251	.20879	.20511	.20148
1.8	.19790	.19436	.19086	.18741	.18400	.18064	.17732	.17404	.17081	.16762
1.9	.16448	.16137	.15831	.15530	.15232	.14939	.14650	.14364	.14083	.13806
2.0	.13534	.13265	.13000	.12740	.12483	.12230	.11981	.11737	.11496	.11259
2.1	.11025	.10795	.10570	.10347	.10129	.09914	.09702	.09495	.09290	.09090
2.2	.08892	.08698	.08507	.08320	.08136	.07956	.07778	.07604	.07433	.07265
2.3	.07100	.06939	.06780	.06624	.06471	.06321	.06174	.06029	.05888	.05750
2.4	.05614	.05481	.05350	.05222	.05096	.04973	.04852	.04734	.04618	.04505
2.5	.04394	.04285	.04179	.04074	.03972	.03873	.03775	.03680	.03586	.03494
2.6	.03405	.03317	.03232	.03148	.03066	.02986	.02908	.02831	.02757	.02684
2.7	.02612	.02542	.02474	.02408	.02343	.02280	.02218	.02157	.02098	.02040
2.8	.01984	.01929	.01876	.01823	.01772	.01723	.01674	.01627	.01581	.01536
2.9	.01492	.01449	.01408	.01367	.01328	.01288	.01252	.01215	.01179	.01145

$\frac{x}{s}$	0	.1	.2	.3	.4	.5	.6	.7	.8	.9
3.	.01111	.00819	.00598	.00432	.00309	.00219	.00153	.00106	.00073	.00050
4.	.00034	.00022	.00015	.00010	.00006	.00004	.00003	.00002	.00001	.00001
5.	.00000									

Largely from Rugg's *Statistical Methods Applied to Education*, by arrangement with the publishers, Houghton Mifflin Company. More detailed tables of normal-curve ordinates may be found in E. S. Pearson and H. O. Hartley, *Biometrika Tables for Statisticians*, Volume I, Cambridge University Press, Cambridge, 1954, pp. 104–110; in Karl Pearson, *Tables for Statisticians and Biometricians, Part I*, The University Press, Cambridge, England, 1948 (third edition), pp. 2–8; and in Federal Works Agency, Work Projects Administration for the City of New York, *Tables of Probability Functions*, National Bureau of Standards, New York, 1942, Vol. II, pp. 2–238. The values shown in these tables should be multiplied by $\sqrt{2\pi} = 2.5066$ to agree with those shown above.

TABLE OF 73,500 RANDOM DECIMAL DIGITS*

Introduction

The use of tables of random numbers in sampling and in other statistical problems has been frequently discussed,[1] and tables of random numbers such as those compiled by Tippett, and by Kendall and Smith have been in use for some time.[2] The table of 73,500 numbers which follows may be used in the manner described in these various statistical discussions, the digits included having been developed by a process which closely approximates an underlying rectangular distribution. It is also possible by the use of suitable transformations to obtain from the 73,500 numbers in this set, other sets of random numbers, which will follow any given distribution function.[a]

The Randomizing Process

The mathematical principle involved in producing the accompanying set of random numbers has been explained elsewhere.[3] Briefly, this process consists of adding groups of digits module their base (n) to obtain random digits for the final table.[b] By this method, the probability of each digit converges to $1/n$ under very general conditions. Thus, it is unnecessary to attempt to design a machine or a process which will have equal probabilities for each digit in single trials. Rather it is sufficient that the trials be independent and that the device (or process) be irregular in the sense that the probability of obtaining each digit in each trial should be different from zero, or more precisely,

$$\text{Prs} \geqq \varepsilon \text{ for all } r \text{ and all } s,$$

where Prs represents the probability of obtaining the rth digit in the sth trial, and ε is a fixed positive number, arbitrarily small.[c] If this condition is satisfied, the probabilities of individual digits in the final set can be made as nearly equal as desired. This can be accomplished by increasing the number of digits (original set) added modulo n to obtain each digit of the final set.

---

*Published by permission of Bureau of Transport Economics and Statistics, Interstate Commerce Commission, Washington 25, D. C.

[a]Let $y = \int_{-\infty}^{x} \phi(z)\,dz.$

If y is distributed between 0 and 1 with uniform probability, x will be distributed according to $\phi(x)$, where ϕ is any probability density function.

[b]This operation amounts to reading only the units position of a sum. For example, $(3 + 7 + 9 + 4) \bmod 10 = 3$, this being the remainder after division of the sum by 10.

[c]Actually, convergence to equal probabilities occurs under more general conditions. For details see first reference in 3.

Production of a Random Set

In producing this particular set of random decimal digits it was calculated that addition modulo 10 of 10 decimal digits from the original set would yield a set with probabilities in the range $1/10 \pm 10^{-7}$. This derived set was produced by tabulating 75,000 machine cards which had been punched from waybills received during three months in the regular course of the Commission's work. Fourteen columns, which apparently were independent, were selected from these cards. These included positions from such fields as the shipment weight, revenue, serial number of the car, etc. Each of these columns was then tabulated by wiring into counters with no carryover and so controlled that the total in the units position of the counter would be cut in a summary card at the end of each 10 cards. The totals (mod 10) of the 14 columns for each block of ten cards were cut in the first 14 columns of the summary cards until 1,500 summary cards had been completed from the first 15,000 cards of the original set. The 1,500 summary cards were then replaced in the summary punch which was wired to punch in the next 14 columns, using totals from the second 15,000 cards of the original set. This operation was repeated until 70 columns of the summary cards had been punched. The tabulation following this discussion is a listing of the completed summary cards.

Tests for Randomness

Any number of tests for local randomness may be devised. This particular set was subjected to three of the four tests used by Kendall and Smith.[1] These tests, with the results of tests of significance are presented below. Table 1 shows the results of the frequency test in which the digits are merely counted and the totals compared with the theoretical expectation of 10,500 of each.

TABLE 1

Digit	0	1	2	3	4	5
Actual frequency	10,420	10,496	10,540	10,507	10,445	10,569
Expected frequency	10,500	10,500	10,500	10,500	10,500	10,500

	6	7	8	9	Total
Actual frequency	10,544	10,476	10,533	10,470	105,000
Expected frequency	10,500	10,500	10,500	10,500	105,000

Test Results: $\chi^2 = 1.938 \quad P = .99$

In the serial test adjacent pairs of digits are tabulated. According to the hypothesis of randomness, the frequencies of digits following any specified digit should be equal, within tolerable statistical limits. The results of this test are presented in Table 2.

TABLE 2

i^{th} digit	$(i+1)^{th}$ digit 0	1	2	3	4	5	6	7	8	9	Total
0	1,041	1,073	1,005	1,095	1,016	1,021	1,017	1,063	1,042	1,047	10,420
1	1,030	1,024	1,043	1,024	1,057	1,081	1,117	1,043	1,037	1,040	10,496
2	1,063	995	1,045	1,144	1,066	1,071	1,005	1,063	1,056	1,032	10,540
3	1,035	1,082	1,056	1,026	1,069	1,026	1,072	1,035	1,039	1,067	10,507
4	1,035	1,061	1,106	1,028	1,011	1,082	1,028	983	1,053	1,058	10,445
5	1,049	1,065	1,086	1,046	1,057	1,068	1,056	1,038	1,060	1,044	10,569
6	1,046	1,060	1,070	1,102	1,038	1,029	1,063	1,080	1,008	1,048	10,544
7	1,000	1,049	1,036	1,023	1,062	1,066	1,080	1,053	1,079	1,028	10,476
8	1,091	1,078	1,004	1,027	1,019	1,032	1,065	1,071	1,088	1,058	10,533
9	1,030	1,009	1,089	992	1,050	1,093	1,041	1,047	1,071	1,048	10,470
Total	10,420	10,496	10,540	10,507	10,445	10,569	10,544	10,476	10,533	10,470	105,000

Test Results: $\chi^2 = 75.461$; $P = .96$

In the gap test the number of non-zero digits appearing between successive zeros is tabulated.[d] The theoretical probability of occurrence of a gap of length k is given by $p(k) = (9/10)^k (1/10)$. Also, the probability of occurrence of a gap of length greater than or equal to k is given by: $P(k) = (9/10)^k$. It should be noted that two adjacent zeros are tabulated as a gap of length zero. The total number of gaps between zeros is one less than the number of zeros. The product of this total and the theoretical probabilities yields the expected frequencies for various gap lengths. The actual frequencies were compared with the theoretical frequencies, the results appearing in Table 3. The gap test could, of course, be applied to any digit, but due to the time required to make the test only gaps between zeros were tabulated.

TABLE 3

Length of Gap	0-1	2-3	4-6	7-10	11-16	17 & over	Total
Actual Frequency	1,962	1,620	1,857	1,683	1,505	1,792	10,419
Expected Frequency	1,980	1,603	1,852	1,714	1,532	1,738	10,419

Test Results: $\chi^2 = 3.072$; $P = .69$

The machine methods used in running tests of local randomness did not lend themselves easily to tests of subsets of the 73,500 digits. Tabulations for the serial and gap tests were run by columns, although the reading was horizontal. The tests of significance applied to individual tabulations of the serial tests (by single columns) and the gap tests (by groups of ten columns) gave a set of 77 probabilities which should be evenly distributed from 0 to 1. A χ^2 test of the distribution of these probabilities is presented in Table 4.

[d]The gap test is one of a large group of tests which may be based on runs.

TABLE 4

	(tenths)										
Probability Interval	0–1	1–2	2–3	3–4	4–5	5–6	6–7	7–8	8–9	9–10	Total
Actual Frequency	8	9	5	9	8	10	7	11	4	6	77
Expected Frequency	7.7	7.7	7.7	7.7	7.7	7.7	7.7	7.7	7.7	7.7	77

Test Results: $\chi^2 = 5.727$; $P = .77$

On the basis of the results of these tests it appears that the set of 73,500 digits presented herein is locally random.

Use of Machine Methods of Selection

In many sampling problems it is desirable to have sets of random numbers in a form suitable for machine use. In most such cases machines and sources of numerical data are available from which sets of any size can be constructed. Random selection of machine cards may also be accomplished without the use of recorded random numbers. Data recorded on the cards themselves can be used to generate random digits by addition modulo 10, and these digits may be used to make the selection as the cards pass through the machine. For example, a listing of a 10 percent random sample from a deck of cards could be obtained without disturbing the order of the cards. Several columns in the cards would be selected for independence and irregularity and the digits in these columns added into separate counters. The counters would not be cleared, so that at any time the digit in the units position of each counter would be the result of addition modulo 10 of the digits in the column wired to it. The units digits read successively from the counters would form a random sequence which could be used to control the listing. Extensions of this principle to other problems and for other types of equipment will suggest themselves.

REFERENCES

[1]Kendall, M. G., and Smith, B. Babington, Randomness and random sampling numbers, *Jour. Roy., Stat. Soc.*, Vol. 101 (1938), pp. 147–166; Kendall, M. G., and Smith, B. Babington, Second paper on random sampling numbers, *Jour. Roy., Stat. Soc. Supp.*, Vol. 6 (1939), pp. 51–61.

[2]Tippett, L. H. C., Random sampling numbers, *Tracts for Computers*, No. 15 (1927), Cambridge; Kendall, M. G., and Smith, B. Babington, Tables of random sampling numbers, *Tracts for Computers*, No. 24 (1939), Cambridge.

[3]H. Burke Horton and R. Tynes Smith III, A direct method for producing random digits in any number system, *Annals of Math. Stat.*, Vol. 20 (1949), pp. 82–90; H. Burke Horton, A method for obtaining random numbers, *Annals of Math. Stat.*, Vol. 19 (1948), pp. 81–85.

Line \ Col.	(1)	(2)	(3)	(4)	(5)	(6)
1	10480	15011	01536	02011	81647	91646
2	22368	46573	25595	85393	30995	89198
3	24130	48360	22527	97265	76393	64809
4	42167	93093	06243	61680	07856	16376
5	37570	39975	81837	16656	06121	91782
6	77921	06907	11008	42751	27756	53498
7	99562	72905	56420	69994	98872	31016
8	96301	91977	05463	07972	18876	20922
9	89579	14342	63661	10281	17453	18103
10	85475	36857	53342	53988	53060	59533
11	28918	69578	88231	33276	70997	79936
12	63553	40961	48235	03427	49626	69445
13	09429	93969	52636	92737	88974	33488
14	10365	61129	87529	85689	48237	52267
15	07119	97336	71048	08178	77233	13916
16	51085	12765	51821	51259	77452	16308
17	02368	21382	52404	60268	89368	19885
18	01011	54092	33362	94904	31273	04146
19	52162	53916	46369	58586	23216	14513
20	07056	97628	33787	09998	42698	06691
21	48663	91245	85828	14346	09172	30168
22	54164	58492	22421	74103	47070	25306
23	32639	32363	05597	24200	13363	38005
24	29334	27001	87637	87308	58731	00256
25	02488	33062	28834	07351	19731	92420
26	81525	72295	04839	96423	24878	82651
27	29676	20591	68086	26432	46901	20849
28	00742	57392	39064	66432	84673	40027
29	05366	04213	25669	26422	44407	44048
30	91921	26418	64117	94305	26766	25940
31	00582	04711	87917	77341	42206	35126
32	00725	69884	62797	56170	86324	88072
33	69011	65795	95876	55293	18988	27354
34	25976	57948	29888	88604	67917	48708
35	09763	83473	73577	12908	30883	18317
36	91567	42595	27958	30134	04024	86385
37	17955	56349	90999	49127	20044	59931
38	46503	18584	18845	49618	02304	51038
39	92157	89634	94824	78171	84610	82834
40	14577	62765	35605	48263	39667	47358
41	98427	07523	33362	64270	01638	92477
42	34914	63976	88720	82765	34476	17032
43	70060	28277	39475	46473	23219	53416
44	53976	54914	06990	67245	68350	82948
45	76072	29515	40980	07391	58745	25774
46	90725	52210	83974	29992	65831	38857
47	64364	67412	33339	31926	14883	24413
48	08962	00358	31662	25388	61642	34072
49	95012	68379	93526	70765	10592	04542
50	15664	10493	20492	38391	91132	21999

(7)	(8)	(9)	(10)	(11)	(12)	(13)	(14)
69179	14194	62590	36207	20969	99570	91291	90700
27982	53402	93965	34095	52666	19174	39615	99505
15179	24830	49340	32081	30680	19655	63348	58629
39440	53537	71341	57004	00849	74917	97758	16379
60468	81305	49684	60672	14110	06927	01263	54613
18602	70659	90655	15053	21916	81825	44394	42880
71194	18738	44013	48840	63213	21069	10634	12952
94595	56869	69014	60045	18425	84903	42508	32307
57740	84378	25331	12566	58678	44947	05585	56941
38867	62300	08158	17983	16439	11458	18593	64952
56865	05859	90106	31595	01547	85590	91610	78188
18663	72695	52180	20847	12234	90511	33703	90322
36320	17617	30015	08272	84115	27156	30613	74952
67689	93394	01511	26358	85104	20285	29975	89868
47564	81056	97735	85977	29372	74461	28551	90707
60756	92144	49442	53900	70960	63990	75601	40719
55322	44819	01188	65255	64835	44919	05944	55157
18594	29852	71585	85030	51132	01915	92747	64951
83149	98736	23495	64350	94738	17752	35156	35749
76988	13602	51851	46104	88916	19509	25625	58104
90229	04734	59193	22178	30421	61666	99904	32812
76468	26384	58151	06646	21524	15227	96909	44592
94342	28728	35806	06912	17012	64161	18296	22851
45834	15398	46557	41135	10367	07684	36188	18510
60952	61280	50001	67658	32586	86679	50720	94953
66566	14778	76797	14780	13300	87074	79666	95725
89768	81536	86645	12659	92259	57102	80428	25280
32832	61362	98947	96067	64760	64584	96096	98253
37937	63904	45766	66134	75470	66520	34693	90449
39972	22209	71500	64568	91402	42416	07844	69618
74087	99547	81817	42607	43808	76655	62028	76630
76222	36086	84637	93161	76038	65855	77919	88006
26575	08625	40801	59920	29841	80150	12777	48501
18912	82271	65424	69774	33611	54262	85963	03547
28290	35797	05998	41688	34952	37888	38917	88050
29880	99730	55536	84855	29080	09250	79656	73211
06115	20542	18059	02008	73708	83517	36103	42791
20655	58727	28168	15475	56942	53389	20562	87338
09922	25417	44137	48413	25555	21246	35509	20468
56873	56307	61607	49518	89636	20103	77490	18062
66969	98420	04880	45585	46565	04102	46880	45709
87589	40836	32427	70002	70663	88863	77775	69348
94970	25832	69975	94884	19661	72828	00102	66794
11398	42878	80287	88267	47363	46634	06541	97809
22987	80059	39911	96189	41151	14222	60697	59583
50490	83765	55657	14361	31720	57375	56228	41546
59744	92351	97473	89286	35931	04110	23726	51900
81249	35648	56891	69352	48373	45578	78547	81788
76463	54328	02349	17247	28865	14777	62730	92277
59516	81652	27195	48223	46751	22923	32261	85653

Line \ Col.	(1)	(2)	(3)	(4)	(5)	(6)
51	16408	81899	04153	53381	79401	21438
52	18629	81953	05520	91962	04739	13092
53	73115	35101	47498	87637	99016	71060
54	57491	16703	23167	49323	45021	33132
55	30405	83946	23792	14422	15059	45799
56	16631	35006	85900	98275	32388	52390
57	96773	20206	42559	78985	05300	22164
58	38935	64202	14349	82674	66523	44133
59	31624	76384	17403	53363	44167	64486
60	78919	19474	23632	27889	47914	02584
61	03931	33309	57047	74211	63445	17361
62	74426	33278	43972	10119	89917	15665
63	09066	00903	20795	95452	92648	45454
64	42238	12426	87025	14267	20979	04508
65	16153	08002	26504	41744	81959	65642
66	21457	40742	29820	96783	29400	21840
67	21581	57802	02050	89728	17937	37621
68	55612	78095	83197	33732	05810	24813
69	44657	66999	99324	51281	84463	60563
70	91340	84979	46949	81973	37949	61023
71	91227	21199	31935	27022	84067	05462
72	50001	38140	66321	19924	72163	09538
73	65390	05224	72958	28609	81406	39147
74	27504	96131	83944	41575	10573	08619
75	37169	94851	39117	89632	00959	16487
76	11508	70225	51111	38351	19444	66499
77	37449	30362	06694	54690	04052	53115
78	46515	70331	85922	38329	57015	15765
79	30986	81223	42416	58353	21532	30502
80	63798	64995	46583	09785	44160	78128
81	82486	84846	99254	67632	43218	50076
82	21885	32906	92431	09060	64297	51674
83	60336	98782	07408	53458	13564	59089
84	43937	46891	24010	25560	86355	33941
85	97656	63175	89303	16275	07100	92063
86	03299	01221	05418	38982	55758	92237
87	79626	06486	03574	17668	07785	76020
88	85636	68335	47539	03129	65651	11977
89	18039	14367	61337	06177	12143	46609
90	08362	15656	60627	36478	65648	16764
91	79556	29068	04142	16268	15387	12856
92	92608	82674	27072	32534	17075	27698
93	23982	25835	40055	67006	12293	02753
94	09915	96306	05908	97901	28395	14186
95	59037	33300	26695	62247	69927	76123
96	42488	78077	69882	61657	34136	79180
97	46764	86273	63003	93017	31204	36692
98	03237	45430	55417	63282	90816	17349
99	86591	81482	52667	61582	14972	90053
100	38534	01715	94964	87288	65680	43772

(7)	(8)	(9)	(10)	(11)	(12)	(13)	(14)
83035	92350	36693	31238	59649	91754	72772	02338
97662	24822	94730	06496	35090	04822	86774	98289
88824	71013	18735	20286	23153	72924	35165	43040
12544	41035	80780	45393	44812	12515	98931	91202
22716	19792	09983	74353	68668	30429	70735	25499
16815	69298	82732	38480	73817	32523	41961	44437
24369	54224	35083	19687	11052	91491	60383	19746
00697	35552	35970	19124	63318	29686	03387	59846
64758	75366	76554	31601	12614	33072	60332	92325
37680	20801	72152	39339	34806	08930	85001	87820
62825	39908	05607	91284	68833	25570	38818	46920
52872	73823	73144	88662	88970	74492	51805	99378
09552	88815	16553	51125	79375	97596	16296	66092
64535	31355	86064	29472	47689	05974	52468	16834
74240	56302	00033	67107	77510	70625	28725	34191
15035	34537	33310	06116	95240	15957	16572	06004
47075	42080	97403	48626	68995	43805	33386	21597
86902	60397	16489	03264	88525	42786	05269	92532
79312	93454	68876	25471	93911	25650	12682	73572
43997	15263	80644	43942	89203	71795	99533	50501
35216	14486	29891	68607	41867	14951	91696	85065
12151	06878	91903	18749	34405	56087	82790	70925
25549	48542	42627	45233	57202	94617	23772	07896
64482	73923	36152	05184	94142	25299	84387	34925
65536	49071	39782	17095	02330	74301	00275	48280
71945	05422	13442	78675	84081	66938	93654	59894
62757	95348	78662	11163	18651	50245	34971	52924
97161	17869	45349	61796	66345	81073	49106	79860
32305	86482	05174	07901	54339	58861	74818	46942
83991	42865	92520	83531	80377	35909	81250	54238
21361	64816	51202	88124	41870	52689	51275	83556
64126	62570	26123	05155	59194	52799	28225	85762
26445	29789	85205	41001	12535	12133	14645	23541
25786	54990	71899	15475	95434	98227	21824	19585
21942	18611	47348	20203	18534	03862	78095	50136
26759	86367	21216	98442	08303	56613	91511	75928
79924	25651	83325	88428	85076	72811	22717	50585
02510	26113	99447	68645	34327	15152	55230	93448
32989	74014	64708	00533	35398	58408	13261	47908
53412	09013	07832	41574	17639	82163	60859	75567
66227	38358	22478	73373	88732	09443	82558	05250
98204	63863	11951	34648	88022	56148	34925	57031
14827	23235	35071	99704	37543	11601	35503	85171
00821	80703	70426	75647	76310	88717	37890	40129
50842	43834	86654	70959	79725	93872	28117	19233
97526	43092	04098	73571	80799	76536	71255	64239
40202	35275	87306	55543	53203	18098	47625	88684
88298	90183	36600	78406	06216	95787	42579	90730
89534	76036	49199	43716	97548	04379	46370	28672
39560	12918	86537	62738	19636	51132	25739	56947

Line \ Col.	(1)	(2)	(3)	(4)	(5)	(6)
101	13284	16834	74151	92027	24670	36665
102	21224	00370	30420	03883	94648	89428
103	99052	47887	81085	64933	66279	80432
104	00199	50993	98603	38452	87890	94624
105	60578	06483	28733	37867	07936	98710
106	91240	18312	17441	01929	18163	69201
107	97458	14229	12063	59611	32249	90466
108	35249	38646	34475	72417	60514	69257
109	38980	46600	11759	11900	46743	27860
110	10750	52745	38749	87365	58959	53731
111	36247	27850	73958	20673	37800	63835
112	70994	66986	99744	72438	01174	42159
113	99638	94702	11463	18148	81386	80431
114	72055	15774	43857	99805	10419	76939
115	24038	65541	85788	55835	38835	59399
116	74976	14631	35908	28221	39470	91548
117	35553	71628	70189	26436	63407	91178
118	35676	12797	51434	82976	42010	26344
119	74815	67523	72985	23183	02446	63594
120	45246	88048	65173	50989	91060	89894
121	76509	47069	86378	41797	11910	49672
122	19689	90332	04315	21358	97248	11188
123	42751	35318	97513	61537	54955	08159
124	11946	22681	45045	13964	57517	59419
125	96518	48688	20996	11090	48396	57177
126	35726	58643	76869	84622	39098	36083
127	39737	42750	48968	70536	84864	64952
128	97025	66492	56177	04049	80312	48028
129	62814	08075	09788	56350	76787	51591
130	25578	22950	15227	83291	41737	79599
131	68763	69576	88991	49662	46704	63362
132	17900	00813	64361	60725	88974	61005
133	71944	60227	63551	71109	05624	43836
134	54684	93691	85132	64399	29182	44324
135	25946	27623	11258	65204	52832	50880
136	01353	39318	44961	44972	91766	90262
137	99083	88191	27662	99113	57174	35571
138	52021	45406	37945	75234	24327	86978
139	78755	47744	43776	83098	03225	14281
140	25282	69106	59180	16257	22810	43609
141	11959	94202	02743	86847	79725	51811
142	11644	13792	98190	01424	30078	28197
143	06307	97912	68110	59812	95448	43244
144	76285	75714	89585	99296	52640	46518
145	55322	07598	39600	60866	63007	20007
146	78017	90928	90220	92503	83375	26986
147	44768	43342	20696	26331	43140	69744
148	25100	19336	14605	86603	51680	97678
149	83612	46623	62876	85197	07824	91392
150	41347	81666	82961	60413	71020	83658

(7)	(8)	(9)	(10)	(11)	(12)	(13)	(14)
00770	22878	02179	51602	07270	76517	97275	45960
41583	17564	27395	63904	41548	49197	82277	24120
65793	83287	34142	13241	30590	97760	35848	91983
69721	57484	67501	77638	44331	11257	71131	11059
98539	27186	31237	80612	44488	97819	70401	95419
31211	54288	39296	37318	65724	90401	79017	62077
33216	19358	02591	54263	88449	01912	07436	50813
12489	51924	86871	92446	36607	11458	30440	52639
77940	39298	97838	95145	32378	68038	89351	37005
89295	59062	39404	13198	59960	70408	29812	83126
71051	84724	52492	22342	78071	17456	96104	18327
11392	20724	54322	36923	70009	23233	65438	59685
90628	52506	02016	85151	88598	47821	00265	82525
25993	03544	21560	83471	43989	90770	22965	44247
13790	35112	01324	39520	76210	22467	83275	32286
12854	30166	09073	75887	36782	00268	97121	57676
90348	55359	80392	41012	36270	77786	89578	21059
92920	92155	58807	54644	58581	95331	78629	73344
98924	20633	58842	85961	07648	70164	34994	67662
36036	32819	68559	99221	49475	50558	34698	71800
88575	97966	32466	10083	54728	81972	58975	30761
39062	63312	52496	07349	79178	33692	57352	72862
00337	80778	27507	95478	21252	12746	37554	97775
58045	44067	58716	58840	45557	96345	33271	53464
83867	86464	14342	21545	46717	72364	86954	55580
72505	92265	23107	60278	05822	46760	44294	07672
38404	94317	65402	13589	01055	79044	19308	83623
26408	43591	75528	65341	49044	95495	81256	53214
54509	49295	85830	59860	30883	89660	96142	18354
96191	71845	86899	70694	24290	01551	80092	82118
56625	00481	73323	91427	15264	06969	57048	54149
99709	30666	26451	11528	44323	34778	60342	60388
58254	26160	32116	63403	35404	57146	10909	07346
14491	55226	78793	34107	30374	48429	51376	09559
22273	05554	99521	73791	85744	29276	70326	60251
56073	06606	51826	18893	83448	31915	97764	75091
99884	13951	71057	53961	61448	74909	07322	80960
22644	87779	23753	99926	63898	54886	18051	96314
83637	55984	13300	52212	58781	14905	46502	04472
12224	25643	89884	31149	85423	32581	34374	70873
12998	76844	05320	54236	53891	70226	38632	84776
55583	05197	47714	68440	22016	79204	06862	94451
31262	88880	13040	16458	43813	89416	42482	33939
55486	90754	88932	19937	57119	23251	55619	23679
66819	84164	61131	81429	60676	42807	78286	29015
74399	30885	88567	29169	72816	53357	15428	86932
82928	24988	94237	46138	77426	39039	55596	12655
24261	02464	86563	74812	60069	71674	15478	47642
58317	37726	84628	42221	10268	20692	15699	29167
0241-	33322	66036	98712	46795	16308	28413	05417

Line \ Col.	(1)	(2)	(3)	(4)	(5)	(6)
151	38128	51178	75096	13609	16110	73533
152	60950	00455	73254	96067	50717	13878
153	90524	17320	29832	96118	75792	25326
154	49897	18278	67160	39408	97056	43517
155	18494	99209	81060	19488	65596	59787
156	65373	72984	30171	37741	70203	94094
157	40653	12843	04213	70925	95360	55774
158	51638	22238	56344	44587	83231	50317
159	69742	99303	62578	83575	30337	07488
160	58012	74072	67488	74580	47992	69482
161	18348	19855	42887	08279	43206	47077
162	59614	09193	58064	29086	44385	45740
163	75688	28630	39210	52897	62748	72658
164	13941	77802	69101	70061	35460	34576
165	96656	86420	96475	86458	54463	96419
166	03363	82042	15942	14549	38324	87094
167	70366	08390	69155	25496	13240	57407
168	47870	36605	12927	16043	53257	93796
169	79504	77606	22761	30518	28373	73898
170	46967	74841	50923	15339	37755	98995
171	14558	50769	35444	59030	87516	48193
172	12440	25057	01132	38611	28135	68089
173	32293	29938	68653	10497	98919	46587
174	10640	21875	72462	77981	56550	55999
175	47615	23169	39571	56972	20628	21788
176	16948	11128	71624	72754	49084	96303
177	21258	61092	66634	70335	92448	17354
178	15072	48853	15178	30730	47481	48490
179	99154	57412	09858	65671	70655	71479
180	08759	61089	23706	32994	35426	36666
181	67323	57839	61114	62192	47547	58023
182	09255	13986	84834	20764	72206	89393
183	36304	74712	00374	10107	85061	69228
184	15884	67429	86612	47367	10242	44880
185	18745	32031	35303	08134	33925	03004
186	72934	40086	88292	65728	38300	42323
187	17626	02944	20910	57662	80181	38579
188	27117	61399	50967	41399	81636	16663
189	93995	18678	90012	63645	85701	85269
190	67392	89421	09623	80725	62620	84162
191	04910	12261	37566	80016	21245	69377
192	81453	20283	79929	59839	23875	13245
193	19480	75790	48539	23703	15537	48885
194	21456	13162	74608	81011	55512	07481
195	89406	20912	46189	76376	25538	87212
196	09866	07414	55977	16419	01101	69343
197	86541	24681	23421	13521	28000	94917
198	10414	96941	06205	72222	57167	83902
199	49942	06683	41479	58982	56288	42853
200	23995	68882	42291	23374	24299	27024

(7)	(8)	(9)	(10)	(11)	(12)	(13)	(14)
42564	59870	29399	67834	91055	89917	51096	89011
03216	78274	65863	37011	91283	33914	91303	49326
22940	24904	80523	38928	91374	55597	97567	38914
84426	59650	20247	19293	02019	14790	02852	05819
47939	91225	98768	43688	00438	05548	09443	82897
87261	30056	58124	70133	18936	02138	59372	09075
76439	61768	52817	81151	52188	31940	54273	49032
74541	07719	25472	41602	77318	15145	57515	07633
51941	84316	42067	49692	28616	29101	03013	73449
58624	17106	47538	13452	22620	24260	40155	74716
42637	45606	00011	20662	14642	49984	94509	56380
70752	05663	49081	26960	57454	99264	24142	74648
98059	67202	72789	01869	13496	14663	87645	89713
15412	81304	58757	35498	94830	75521	00603	97701
55417	41375	76886	19008	66877	35934	59801	00497
19069	67590	11087	68570	22591	65232	85915	91499
91407	49160	07379	34444	94567	66035	38918	65708
52721	73120	48025	76074	95605	67422	41646	14557
30550	76684	77366	32276	04690	61667	64798	66276
40162	89561	69199	42257	11647	47603	48779	97907
02945	00922	48189	04724	21263	20892	92955	90251
10954	10097	54243	06460	50856	65435	79377	53890
77701	99119	93165	67788	17638	23097	21468	36992
87310	69643	45124	00349	25748	00844	96831	30651
51736	33133	72696	32605	41569	76148	91544	21121
27830	45817	67867	18062	87453	17226	72904	71474
83432	49608	66520	06442	59664	20420	39201	69549
41436	25015	49932	20474	53821	51015	79841	32405
63520	31357	56968	06729	34465	70685	04184	25250
63988	98844	37533	08269	27021	45886	22835	78451
64630	34886	98777	75442	95592	06141	45096	73117
34548	93438	88730	61805	78955	18952	46436	58740
81969	92216	03568	39630	81869	52824	50937	27954
12060	44309	46629	55105	66793	93173	00480	13311
59929	95418	04917	57596	24878	61733	92834	64454
64068	98373	48971	09049	59943	36538	05976	82118
24580	90529	52303	50436	29401	57824	86039	81062
15634	79717	94696	59240	25543	97989	63306	90946
62263	68331	00389	72571	15210	20769	44686	96176
87368	29560	00519	84545	08004	24526	41252	14521
50420	85658	55263	68667	78770	04533	14513	18099
46808	74124	74703	35769	95588	21014	37078	39170
02861	86587	74539	65227	90799	58789	96257	02708
93551	72189	76261	91206	89941	15132	37738	59284
20748	12831	57166	35026	16817	79121	18929	40628
13305	94302	80703	57910	36933	57771	42546	03003
07423	57523	97234	63951	42876	46829	09781	58160
07460	69507	10600	08858	07685	44472	64220	27040
92196	20632	62045	78812	35895	51851	83534	10689
67460	94783	40937	16961	26053	78749	46704	21983

Line \ Col.	(1)	(2)	(3)	(4)	(5)	(6)
201	78994	36244	02673	25475	84953	61793
202	04909	58485	70686	93930	34880	73059
203	46582	73570	33004	51795	86477	46736
204	29242	89792	88634	60285	07190	07795
205	68104	81339	97090	20601	78940	20228
206	17156	02182	82504	19880	93747	80910
207	50711	94789	07171	02103	99057	98775
208	39449	52409	75095	77720	39729	03205
209	75629	82729	76916	72657	58992	32756
210	01020	55151	36132	51971	32155	60735
211	08337	89989	24260	08618	66798	25889
212	76829	47229	19706	30094	69430	92399
213	39708	30641	21267	56501	95182	72442
214	89836	55817	56747	75195	06818	83043
215	25903	61370	66081	54076	67442	52964
216	71345	03422	01015	68025	19703	77313
217	61454	92263	14647	08473	34124	10740
218	80376	08909	30470	40200	46558	61742
219	45144	54373	05505	90074	24783	86299
220	12191	88527	58852	51175	11534	87218
221	62936	59120	73957	35969	21598	47287
222	31588	96798	43668	12611	01714	77266
223	20787	96048	84726	17512	39450	43618
224	45603	00745	84635	43079	52724	14262
225	31606	64782	34027	56734	09365	20008
226	10452	33074	76718	99556	16026	00013
227	37016	64633	67301	50949	91298	74968
228	66725	97865	25409	37498	00816	99262
229	07380	74438	82120	17890	40963	55757
230	71621	57688	58256	47702	74724	89419
231	03466	13263	23917	20417	11315	52805
232	12692	32931	97387	34822	53775	91674
233	52192	30941	44998	17833	94563	23062
234	56691	72529	66063	73570	86860	68125
235	74952	43041	58869	15677	78598	43520
236	18752	43693	32867	53017	22661	39610
237	61691	04944	43111	28325	82319	65589
238	49197	63948	38947	60207	70667	39843
239	19436	87291	71684	74859	76501	93456
240	39143	64893	14606	13543	09621	68301
241	82244	67549	76491	09761	74494	91307
242	55847	56155	42878	23708	97999	40131
243	94095	95970	07826	25991	37584	56966
244	11751	69469	25521	44097	07511	88976
245	69902	08995	27821	11758	64989	61902
246	21850	25352	25556	92161	23592	43294
247	75850	46992	25165	55906	62339	88958
248	29648	22086	42581	85677	20251	39641
249	82740	28443	42734	25518	82827	35825
250	36842	42092	52075	83926	42875	71500

(7)	(8)	(9)	(10)	(11)	(12)	(13)	(14)
50243	63423	69309	80308	49977	18075	43227	08266
06823	80257	44193	08337	47655	75932	29209	41954
60460	70345	37322	19987	67143	41129	89514	46892
27011	85941	01852	43096	31173	43730	48505	17958
22803	96070	10251	62711	66200	74330	13820	18966
78260	25136	62018	62919	73801	57195	83457	70597
37997	18325	88281	61091	97889	79977	04544	72963
09313	43545	43786	70443	41350	73369	42405	80516
01154	84890	04107	17469	59346	68651	97433	89491
64867	35424	25257	93844	39928	52519	34368	02114
52860	57375	52815	43539	18072	44270	27309	56535
98749	22081	52564	90431	35208	40323	87505	10227
21445	17276	90344	33199	02522	97883	09515	65930
47403	58266	52630	75573	91088	41118	27195	40650
23823	02718	28786	06121	29680	55295	67086	57574
04555	83425	46763	95315	23150	15116	18017	42730
40839	05620	62418	73374	92577	06755	21856	56272
11643	92121	22294	26648	69676	46198	00331	85186
20900	15144	26506	53770	76431	23861	71208	80694
04876	85584	78465	82182	03412	13217	14313	70593
39394	08778	38036	30140	89117	32054	44603	61849
55079	24690	84716	77732	35363	85525	17015	56344
30629	24356	05294	34236	65299	36922	46995	65765
05750	89373	79088	38088	65082	92504	80545	03090
93559	78384	99219	61747	96111	86965	33233	29812
78411	95107	10786	44886	44612	06830	27848	87597
73631	57397	08632	04762	69328	34926	07403	60916
14471	10232	19035	21695	07540	96447	20743	92472
13492	68294	87170	49468	40164	13374	23021	17006
08025	68519	95188	54788	32999	34374	05780	17506
33072	07723	87876	75258	22709	99869	11609	46666
76549	37635	91118	31062	89441	31839	88614	78168
95725	38463	03665	49189	46359	37401	73407	61817
40436	31303	79330	59083	34862	00540	21734	75535
97521	83248	52173	17636	77106	01044	22990	74874
03796	02622	78267	24503	73518	76545	99088	08369
66048	98498	46941	81427	44447	70357	18864	15525
60607	15328	09528	17277	84278	04463	12188	35359
95714	92518	10683	75617	78841	25315	74041	71554
69817	52140	03976	48795	60266	99592	68334	18790
64222	66592	67270	38593	18094	95095	08649	25047
52360	90390	73108	40475	80487	07787	35238	50990
68623	83454	49461	97707	12479	25041	40565	18313
30122	67542	54825	03274	02765	67162	40312	76127
32121	28165	21326	97375	44801	66977	08232	06807
10479	37879	21825	11453	29584	70067	09471	16319
91717	15756	78817	35541	01177	06869	10543	57652
65786	80689	49066	14456	91681	69371	18292	39377
90288	32911	79666	52959	01475	83321	24991	80102
69216	01350	92846	84792	87455	06842	22422	77379

Line \ Col.	(1)	(2)	(3)	(4)	(5)	(6)
251	89429	26726	15563	94972	78739	04419
252	43427	25412	25587	21276	44426	17369
253	58575	81958	51846	02676	67781	95137
254	61888	71246	24246	23487	78639	92006
255	73891	47025	40937	71907	26827	98865
256	40938	73894	40854	15997	55293	95033
257	98053	43567	17292	86908	71364	06089
258	59774	29138	46993	39836	99596	59050
259	09765	07548	63043	59782	81449	13652
260	38991	64502	24770	29209	82909	66610
261	25622	27100	56128	62145	82388	45197
262	31864	74120	66231	82306	91784	33177
263	81171	75639	60863	49562	28846	81581
264	69874	52803	28544	51569	56090	44558
265	27848	51107	05761	02159	53911	01952
266	69407	69736	75375	31488	67528	84234
267	29418	03091	06364	13151	40663	43633
268	38222	31231	79415	44558	62490	26936
269	94720	83796	93251	03568	62484	29140
270	45275	16852	02284	41361	73733	61486
271	97260	09352	82626	42915	45847	87401
272	01990	65259	60684	78175	43825	45211
273	24633	42314	81192	50253	67516	59076
274	98071	52677	74920	74461	52266	26967
275	34101	79442	28403	48541	13010	16596
276	77186	93967	25918	66403	73837	73445
277	23114	05481	42335	51396	60823	22680
278	59988	49944	41038	99977	16348	41119
279	11852	42254	82304	05588	75165	20179
280	59992	87922	56299	01700	07003	97507
281	42116	86593	22828	41422	18176	03250
282	39663	61401	21471	42702	70588	53144
283	53542	72009	96296	68908	58657	87117
284	25996	76108	98476	36397	89457	19577
285	91106	26450	14451	50328	29084	32332
286	37133	88924	27845	13024	90687	23726
287	13982	25736	10087	16762	02564	27250
288	26663	36187	81688	25005	46677	75851
289	62572	08275	16313	24936	81680	53829
290	65925	95455	08383	24643	72962	08172
291	97978	74676	08942	48919	51592	71196
292	01914	42524	67820	47985	91773	10383
293	68565	44811	39238	70394	78555	33539
294	54370	31672	03893	32423	54092	69375
295	79954	89601	23881	46951	69084	33477
296	55479	01069	44229	56975	06785	80930
297	38114	70330	42157	86699	46212	74692
298	29766	83452	66202	02488	72704	97821
299	31771	70640	34779	41831	33456	53194
300	77522	87188	83577	99067	83235	48662

(7)	(8)	(9)	(10)	(11)	(12)	(13)	(14)
60523	31022	23728	37647	16476	11170	68376	56874
29010	45337	90245	92053	41447	14897	18753	68291
88430	78260	66962	31812	12759	06427	40337	50115
63846	92263	33212	26516	93662	72399	88244	33922
38882	25757	26662	91441	89357	87803	61521	80600
31736	75068	91314	75293	04895	39355	54837	57203
92394	73691	57883	09983	35643	79309	53449	95334
25419	04130	54632	17223	94604	22973	97731	99476
94420	74460	46707	94303	85523	95244	70995	10742
84418	66214	26001	78685	69117	72446	79783	22305
97609	83942	01120	71717	32858	58679	97165	02810
17681	18963	07216	49288	43185	62797	00735	27085
10249	23190	53440	32357	16472	99013	24328	93670
42095	92311	57915	13368	13719	15833	38744	56065
59273	32250	39647	29908	49075	23061	07795	95047
76462	13628	21286	13736	67478	45218	27867	93049
87954	69800	24773	62596	52476	60631	50503	94116
49682	16307	98535	44822	99574	58487	85020	68881
14152	37044	90398	92042	35099	31640	99753	44409
33189	08907	41159	08147	15472	33250	17361	79961
13339	53850	34931	00602	75307	99708	77863	04924
86287	78190	02431	66251	74970	50246	23975	80697
92006	65676	87343	89231	15760	73706	69426	01979
68284	31612	40335	28865	98949	64492	96905	29184
72001	38546	76305	22119	82668	84017	44111	40302
86663	15929	08237	05647	15785	70444	58670	95967
50459	05429	35227	92559	24136	13126	22099	52388
51548	19511	90142	65604	16147	63445	60525	10480
94198	25700	33473	59554	30974	69973	57629	38550
69260	53349	86947	27517	80159	01899	46890	53850
06079	85467	32052	56922	96804	51060	33157	83948
27087	05591	57759	51394	98873	45625	61069	78783
21483	28879	20480	57309	95552	09826	79928	17141
65877	04802	61938	25032	09190	74932	36925	82686
08635	25192	31337	20249	95073	93800	70022	99968
11212	30414	42185	49224	46560	80447	24334	74866
79316	83848	38684	20552	44402	85153	94526	41256
73938	73044	05132	61204	90354	90296	03182	36672
40412	01479	24241	58488	65341	93414	07135	43446
37824	87587	40698	34964	50166	74756	77033	41501
48534	16955	25759	95645	03148	10646	15660	86520
89514	07557	02084	16736	39198	69697	62485	61938
56310	40809	63204	14479	19635	97299	66947	58010
63308	08016	28407	98287	22874	57545	72695	01604
87968	15639	82409	34125	36864	52112	27102	87334
26443	44892	77561	51123	34495	31376	06238	15973
92603	91306	58558	57280	50639	80563	71370	81487
70614	53616	39050	30355	15340	97298	41795	35185
19602	74194	61154	51774	76822	73794	54182	45264
31503	54829	54723	13177	15307	26073	68915	88415

Line \ Col.	(1)	(2)	(3)	(4)	(5)	(6)
301	64670	10396	82981	58320	71478	08143
302	25771	02205	73984	28436	88192	11470
303	27551	13537	54984	89406	88326	33993
304	91224	22417	44820	26189	57541	87558
305	75179	64320	71523	67868	38883	09674
306	64654	91085	65818	03313	39273	46384
307	98059	81123	67832	04102	66188	78200
308	38765	63585	18810	95805	11414	58096
309	01921	03564	71754	10213	80383	13473
310	16211	93671	27704	66778	96307	06732
311	70232	86076	61527	56123	48514	53935
312	22332	94265	67627	85815	00394	75271
313	81333	45965	64171	84367	15052	37965
314	39333	47453	66174	04546	10594	64271
315	29195	20825	50878	80273	26285	90070
316	74420	64037	06960	25109	08821	60143
317	22763	16508	24866	13177	07464	51730
318	72919	54618	40616	33287	51274	78491
319	92385	42402	15922	90033	21555	31647
320	85431	19857	97246	46118	71222	82744
321	40778	12451	14921	51464	45331	75822
322	88903	46592	60637	65231	08778	86813
323	29830	34899	85457	19548	83355	52479
324	22832	47422	08073	10107	46772	92299
325	75159	14809	11930	83531	51239	86298
326	99390	08217	56276	09263	82685	30451
327	68622	80897	08902	10867	91379	30068
328	92393	95901	41179	72129	72502	91097
329	53122	66033	38229	51879	29925	45574
330	43251	11941	86631	93264	53433	70281
331	16613	24901	34866	75002	55163	68308
332	12010	60852	92603	70393	17989	95755
333	85528	97879	27814	08219	02908	71582
334	32590	55079	33556	83169	92087	77939
335	92934	30650	16449	15805	61551	38689
336	80614	10150	09389	61892	79477	14522
337	62398	12034	90764	52872	22285	50592
338	02222	46811	05145	67916	15184	02636
339	08690	31785	61664	61322	24149	21471
340	61187	73897	66168	12885	73191	89432
341	12324	61149	85643	64999	63738	46671
342	47635	42279	98620	70677	52386	50904
343	70965	00390	08878	15373	70276	71889
344	58764	15262	96814	54548	00042	19721
345	07429	05609	31207	50254	68389	07714
346	15665	28659	54952	53217	76898	88931
347	64208	53232	99459	43605	04553	48451
348	17952	73276	52567	48489	64264	24220
349	60531	43217	39999	38615	97195	76928
350	76692	39999	43254	68110	88053	88727

(7)	(8)	(9)	(10)	(11)	(12)	(13)	(14)
48294	42631	45464	58092	14187	12271	98179	87812
11775	67385	66360	59884	93873	29948	66302	82227
92324	13249	35271	60400	70762	08343	76456	90068
45835	28461	54835	92411	44369	47512	49508	02841
27645	76240	47587	01677	38342	85598	12482	30749
66677	14148	87552	38383	67435	21072	63866	74644
67466	46043	65406	22834	08620	17509	51424	25187
00295	82626	42683	44518	12209	83245	53771	95469
94128	62199	59411	46782	62871	51149	87146	40129
63750	04191	40003	51653	54228	14916	05361	08884
86784	42351	67586	07432	61499	01773	97463	58815
98385	53697	56378	50592	77441	88505	89791	16331
03122	81914	69381	70034	92563	61804	58326	97895
61026	39471	55981	18628	67943	35599	37209	34061
79586	12449	77293	36577	59192	03658	90056	83145
34485	19257	29417	72713	72326	41572	41553	46946
65802	95718	28560	11332	74272	59189	53167	13133
53604	66742	97777	64468	98224	45485	17257	31561
22288	75692	20592	84620	58679	24587	83517	55327
67892	77155	10785	00344	19641	98279	18716	13895
46859	66829	35803	27645	76095	41535	25508	53066
47819	19218	46837	89671	77661	08518	85216	62664
77801	01596	48890	56104	68733	40830	58611	59181
42975	86376	27869	52954	07900	75918	51398	87598
72661	63015	98804	98491	99565	42801	71816	84000
25742	41105	74711	42007	02082	93025	86641	28952
84289	45020	92459	03831	08531	63496	98230	42884
09488	84896	37720	68104	73817	67626	16221	63527
53938	72801	64067	76328	28941	43645	37181	95329
55000	24550	74751	32855	25399	95743	85393	20261
20070	36953	39378	71191	84510	47599	93608	24379
14672	58786	41996	02893	94163	36156	54203	94138
31439	00360	72264	87245	65903	42298	28061	81889
53792	78795	58159	86394	41749	91623	26973	81474
59179	85485	18537	70496	98694	19796	76804	03673
40270	45744	29582	29717	39590	10223	43049	78775
42505	80560	38213	18917	10015	03887	62589	15851
59078	57773	21259	86090	56705	65556	04487	95954
23328	03093	31266	14840	30703	01640	07874	16630
65414	41886	75911	35708	43208	59193	04727	31037
25408	69313	54455	04917	35047	09951	72776	84697
97403	03931	42090	28179	98028	47728	45696	74176
86953	37931	23286	20508	40100	22486	37323	35429
78869	85937	36639	29135	12633	67225	69588	74178
92268	64698	32823	60122	46213	05646	54742	98304
25786	55912	85269	29212	84976	08888	94332	58528
68154	49436	49891	65524	65133	55163	76765	26006
55498	97548	98437	26033	39026	17377	43519	27425
87688	99010	90189	12522	00675	01995	82781	95130
14187	98623	84225	78440	67082	37425	40559	16838

Line \ Col.	(1)	(2)	(3)	(4)	(5)	(6)
351	06433	80674	24520	18222	10610	05794
352	39298	47829	72648	37414	75755	04717
353	89884	59651	67533	68123	17730	95862
354	61512	32155	51906	61662	64130	16688
355	99653	47635	12506	88535	36553	23757
356	95913	11085	13772	76638	48423	25018
357	55864	44004	13122	44115	01601	50541
358	35334	82410	91601	40617	72876	33967
359	57729	88646	76487	11622	96297	24160
360	86648	89317	63677	70119	94739	25875
361	30574	06039	07967	32422	76791	39725
362	81307	13114	83580	79974	45929	85113
363	02410	96385	79007	54939	21410	86980
364	18969	87444	52233	62319	08598	09066
365	87863	80514	66860	62297	80198	19347
366	68397	10538	15438	62311	72844	60203
367	28529	45247	58729	10854	99058	18260
368	44285	09452	15867	70418	57012	72122
369	86299	22510	33571	23309	57040	29285
370	84842	05748	90894	61658	15001	94055
371	56970	10799	52098	04184	54967	72938
372	83125	85077	60490	44369	66130	72936
373	55503	21383	02464	26141	68779	66388
374	47019	06683	33203	29608	54553	25971
375	84828	61152	79526	29554	84580	37859
376	68921	31331	79227	05748	51276	57143
377	36458	28285	30424	98420	72925	40729
378	95752	96065	36847	87729	81679	59126
379	26768	02513	58454	56958	20575	76746
380	42613	72456	43636	58085	06766	60227
381	95457	12176	65482	25596	02678	54592
382	95276	67524	63564	95958	39750	64379
383	66954	53574	64776	92345	95110	59448
384	17457	44151	14113	62462	02798	54977
385	03704	23322	83214	59337	01695	60666
386	21538	16997	33210	60337	27976	70661
387	57178	16739	98310	70348	11317	71623
388	31048	40058	94953	55866	96283	46620
389	69799	83300	16498	80733	96422	58078
390	90595	65017	59231	17772	67831	33317
391	33570	34761	98939	78784	09977	29398
392	15340	82760	57477	13898	48431	72936
393	64079	07733	36512	56186	99098	48850
394	63491	84886	67118	62063	74958	20946
395	92003	76568	41034	28260	79708	00770
396	52360	46658	66511	04172	73085	11795
397	74622	12142	68355	65635	21828	39539
398	04157	50079	61343	64315	70836	82857
399	86003	60070	66241	32836	27573	11479
400	41268	80187	20351	09636	84668	42486

(7)	(8)	(9)	(10)	(11)	(12)	(13)	(14)
37515	48619	62866	33963	14045	79451	04934	45576
29899	78817	03509	78673	73181	29973	18664	04555
08034	19473	63971	37271	31445	49019	49405	46925
37275	51262	11569	08697	91120	64156	40365	74297
34209	55803	96275	26130	47949	14877	69594	83041
99041	77529	81360	18180	97421	55541	90275	18213
00147	77685	58788	33016	61173	93049	04694	43534
73830	15405	96554	88265	34537	38526	67924	40474
09903	14047	22917	60718	66487	46346	30949	03173
38829	68377	43918	77653	04127	69930	43283	35766
53711	93385	13421	67957	20384	58731	53396	59723
72268	09858	52104	32014	53115	03727	98624	84616
91772	93307	34116	49516	42148	57740	31198	70336
95288	04794	01534	92058	03157	91758	80611	45357
73234	86265	49096	97021	92582	61422	75890	86442
46412	65943	79232	45702	67055	39024	57383	44424
38765	90038	94209	04055	27393	61517	23002	96560
36634	97283	95943	78363	36498	40662	94188	18202
67870	21913	72958	75637	99936	58715	07943	23748
36308	41161	37341	81838	19389	80336	46346	91895
56834	23777	98392	31417	98547	92058	02277	50315
69848	59973	08144	61070	73094	27059	69181	55623
75242	82690	74099	77885	23813	10054	11900	44653
69573	83854	24715	48866	65745	31131	47636	45137
28504	61980	34997	41825	11623	07320	15003	56774
31926	99915	45821	97702	87125	44488	77613	56823
22337	48293	86847	43186	42951	37804	85129	28993
59437	33225	31280	41232	34750	91097	60752	69783
49878	06846	32828	24425	30249	78801	26977	92074
96414	32671	45587	79620	84831	38156	74211	82752
63607	82096	21913	75544	55228	89796	05694	91552
46059	51666	10433	10945	55306	78562	89630	41230
77249	54044	67942	24145	42294	27427	84875	37022
48349	66738	60184	75679	38120	17640	36242	99357
97410	55064	17427	89180	74018	44865	53197	74810
08250	69599	60264	84549	78007	88450	06488	72274
55510	64756	87759	92354	78694	63638	80939	98644
52087	80817	74533	68407	55862	32476	19326	95558
99643	39847	96884	84657	33697	39578	90197	80532
00520	90401	41700	95510	61166	33757	23279	85523
93896	78227	90110	81378	96659	37008	04050	04228
78160	87240	52716	87697	79433	16336	52862	69149
72527	08486	10951	26832	39763	02485	71688	90936
28147	39338	32169	03713	93510	61244	73774	01245
88643	21188	01850	69629	49426	49128	14660	14143
52594	13287	22531	04388	64693	11934	35051	68576
18988	53609	04001	19648	14053	49623	10840	31915
35335	87900	36194	31567	53506	34304	39910	79630
94114	81641	00496	36058	75899	46620	70024	88753
71303	19512	50277	71508	20116	79520	06269	74173

Line \ Col.	(1)	(2)	(3)	(4)	(5)	(6)
401	05073	90103	85167	53900	19720	41488
402	93320	80269	56684	39192	53220	74539
403	18806	70257	96424	13606	14356	76599
404	22253	45923	29815	18578	23316	30896
405	93640	45982	40011	74142	29106	45729
406	47630	45980	76619	57138	57492	00030
407	01781	55061	07455	47083	71870	90597
408	69694	45054	33587	03664	95007	31567
409	51236	05052	26503	94651	29874	73492
410	89445	51039	73837	26720	38650	47322
411	40867	96834	02162	41517	88937	26099
412	92946	56944	93407	05010	54896	33173
413	75898	02275	90768	31902	52114	36634
414	22729	21695	90824	80500	09332	54667
415	28733	62663	23644	16416	47135	39137
416	51323	37770	42114	79742	59905	38480
417	69325	65551	49927	68073	56979	49454
418	11333	60801	36992	76128	27959	41306
419	86347	03703	36778	72501	95229	65735
420	73452	36179	82893	92262	43850	31888
421	75483	74009	73699	05870	36804	89338
422	73302	84917	75128	34085	86208	98399
423	42785	24350	05933	65282	12832	75382
424	40429	33209	58622	09308	38098	55947
425	92876	58271	99325	12301	72957	22690
426	32951	39844	99126	94838	48715	36586
427	09772	28139	48130	73301	35915	90923
428	78459	91322	50072	77941	65046	78363
429	14419	96517	99075	43664	81119	63487
430	97769	50967	24427	21011	92226	44380
431	09175	37545	39088	06879	21277	05153
432	52062	95519	54087	14072	50953	63477
433	70558	85169	01086	97202	10390	01819
434	22553	61317	08968	67521	16627	48855
435	95216	75263	60351	02643	00063	20824
436	49087	61399	47781	32173	96672	04528
437	24808	79068	70787	43106	97133	37236
438	89879	79942	43781	05069	80143	59176
439	61178	79295	58926	21977	28435	32631
440	37444	56047	23208	34710	12147	28558
441	99633	00363	16853	20789	87674	03938
442	87363	59239	42023	78056	51254	95644
443	23923	87269	85277	34727	78036	74471
444	45610	26370	13094	34500	36750	54517
445	44166	80095	08286	38126	48834	73423
446	81875	27486	53925	22330	37168	97954
447	79400	83852	52174	42577	18553	14023
448	42799	46647	36718	49704	17150	07935
449	09302	36408	64569	93033	95645	56791
450	88078	81456	17242	84590	93660	34619

(7)	(8)	(9)	(10)	(11)	(12)	(13)	(14)
57476	39458	16621	69774	47953	35039	39283	21573
26393	00787	94490	23386	38454	33466	32159	77439
25390	63236	04513	16358	30504	10551	32498	18685
64771	11220	86218	75956	22399	36234	61644	80682
43406	21457	04301	39651	76025	73819	11462	97385
77897	76236	64990	35985	57748	11606	72081	18359
10151	59606	96919	31174	99872	15843	99173	79512
25334	26433	75002	67607	33135	07076	82984	82675
88941	08488	09418	08173	63380	82067	58143	64983
68474	95047	20404	41577	46865	39849	78735	99192
56047	49164	35127	64916	75451	79160	14014	00445
30548	23667	43171	47849	40449	91072	91092	17613
46803	97970	92216	55398	75320	70475	82931	20172
46696	38166	02005	24615	85613	25948	75389	25765
62190	31032	58702	03805	67252	23712	92697	19071
25293	32993	36946	62701	51198	72941	52215	85257
79451	60753	70872	07422	06399	75240	80847	78231
93543	15926	99159	27102	98684	80175	98732	45405
14269	50220	77270	68604	05677	23347	43686	31584
71151	40682	49775	63628	45415	96270	31735	01509
73891	40740	98753	74566	74733	34777	05786	38294
79433	61960	01720	87458	24023	89971	09532	68155
29826	33197	81781	53542	63985	57022	22712	61343
12001	73526	23170	13721	37856	86502	74299	01346
62705	73892	01974	77759	92733	11331	08323	86196
42076	15283	19280	29166	24522	73131	83401	38920
19255	75242	84655	30163	75510	83315	98529	93805
21951	42319	46472	67617	34134	05905	61251	51040
95589	51785	07398	23245	10086	49097	46173	00507
23422	10654	43617	80504	90663	60751	79728	41132
81855	84043	35307	59465	75395	74758	09427	84460
64635	34552	75243	70222	75023	81454	70606	31861
88167	21851	87837	85287	69883	08289	74968	46947
97263	94242	93354	72446	28840	88195	82751	94352
67468	89441	84055	47035	29741	47972	61914	66864
15881	46764	20115	03226	79308	31970	49804	85150
77888	48451	20788	44648	70350	54965	57715	94826
47392	70372	26899	16228	71205	14564	97087	95690
23062	31822	70462	05965	22312	33013	74612	23733
58817	98807	56775	08129	08794	23646	92846	61706
36077	41012	08813	51168	78822	37353	61281	31172
90527	41398	74996	94977	22149	96616	54435	52469
12157	11655	25194	47557	26181	67825	80224	41490
85011	26567	01021	32485	58903	43529	24191	91832
13617	08853	16286	16023	77901	39118	14288	39385
11967	03309	97096	64221	11318	98720	01100	13651
69629	61913	41050	69689	57284	38160	57756	16762
62372	39933	20838	27652	54801	41067	08240	35163
14830	81699	45057	85796	63756	93944	60649	84847
51965	85618	36558	54410	68456	98504	83011	19393

Line \ Col.	(1)	(2)	(3)	(4)	(5)	(6)
451	85018	23508	91507	76455	54941	72711
452	11904	73678	08272	62941	02349	71389
453	75344	98489	86268	73652	98210	44546
454	65566	65614	01443	07607	11826	91326
455	51872	72294	95432	53555	96810	17100
456	03805	37913	98633	81009	81060	33449
457	21055	78685	71250	10329	56135	80647
458	48977	36794	56054	59243	57361	65304
459	93077	72941	92779	23581	24548	56415
460	84533	26564	91583	83411	66504	02036
461	11338	12903	14514	27585	45068	05520
462	23853	68500	92274	87026	99717	01542
463	94096	74920	25822	98026	05394	61840
464	83160	82362	09350	98536	38155	42661
465	97425	47335	69709	01386	74319	04318
466	83951	11954	24317	20345	18134	90062
467	93085	35203	05740	03206	92012	42710
468	33762	83193	58045	89880	78101	44392
469	49665	85397	85137	30496	23469	42846
470	37541	82627	80051	72521	35342	56119
471	22145	85304	35348	82854	55846	18076
472	27153	08662	61078	52433	22184	33998
473	00301	49425	66682	25442	83668	66236
474	43815	43272	73778	63469	50083	70696
475	14689	86482	74157	46012	97765	27552
476	16680	55936	82453	19532	49988	13176
477	86938	60429	01137	86168	78257	86249
478	33944	29219	73161	46061	30946	22210
479	16045	67736	18608	18198	19468	76358
480	37044	52523	25627	63107	30806	80857
481	61471	45322	35340	35132	42163	69332
482	47422	21296	16785	66393	39249	51463
483	24133	39719	14484	58613	88717	29289
484	67253	67064	10748	16006	16767	57345
485	62382	76941	01635	35829	77516	98468
486	98011	16503	09201	03523	87192	66483
487	37366	24386	20654	85117	74078	64120
488	73587	83993	54176	05221	94119	20108
489	33583	68291	50547	96085	62180	27453
490	02878	33223	39199	49536	56199	05993
491	91498	41673	17195	33175	04994	09879
492	91127	19815	30219	55591	21725	43827
493	12997	55013	18662	81724	24305	37661
494	96098	13651	15393	69995	14762	69734
495	97627	17837	10472	18983	28387	99781
496	40064	47981	31484	76603	54088	91095
497	16239	68743	71374	55863	22672	91609
498	58354	24913	20435	30965	17453	65623
499	52567	65085	60220	84641	18273	49604
500	06236	29052	91392	07551	83532	68130

(7)	(8)	(9)	(10)	(11)	(12)	(13)	(14)
39406	94620	27963	96478	21559	19246	88097	44926
45605	60947	60775	73181	43264	56895	04232	59604
27174	27499	53523	63110	57106	20865	91683	80688
29664	01603	23156	89223	43429	95353	44662	59433
35066	00815	01552	06392	31437	70385	45863	75971
68055	83844	90942	74857	52419	68723	47830	63010
51404	06626	10042	93629	37609	57215	08409	81906
93258	56760	63348	24949	11859	29793	37457	59377
61927	64416	29934	00755	09418	14230	62887	92683
02922	63569	17906	38076	32135	19096	96970	75917
56321	22693	35089	07694	04252	23791	60249	83010
72990	43413	59744	44595	71326	91382	45114	20245
83089	09224	78530	33996	49965	04851	18280	14039
02363	67625	34683	95372	74733	63558	09665	22610
99387	86874	12549	38369	54952	91579	26023	81076
10761	54548	49505	52685	63903	13193	33905	66936
34650	73236	66167	21788	03581	40699	10396	81827
53767	15220	66319	72953	14071	59148	95154	72852
94810	16151	08020	50551	03091	38313	34016	18671
97190	43635	84249	61254	80993	55431	90793	62603
12415	30193	42776	85611	57635	51362	79907	77364
87436	37430	45246	11400	20986	43996	73122	88474
79655	88312	93047	12088	86937	70794	01041	74867
13558	98995	58159	04700	90443	13168	31553	67891
49617	51734	20849	70198	67906	00880	82899	66065
94219	88698	41755	56216	66852	17748	04963	54859
46134	51865	09836	73966	65711	41699	11732	17173
79302	40300	08852	27528	84648	79589	95295	72895
69203	02760	28625	70476	76410	32988	10194	94917
84383	78450	26245	91763	73117	33047	03577	62599
98851	50252	56911	62693	73817	98693	18728	94741
95963	07929	66728	47761	81472	44806	15592	71357
77360	09030	39605	87507	85446	51257	89555	75520
42285	56670	88445	85799	76200	21795	38894	58070
51686	48140	13583	94911	13318	64741	64336	95103
55649	36764	86132	12463	28385	94242	32063	45233
04643	14351	71381	28133	68269	65145	28152	39087
78101	81276	00835	63835	87174	42446	08882	27067
18567	55524	86088	00069	59254	24654	77371	26409
71201	78852	65889	32719	13758	23937	90740	16866
70337	11861	69032	51915	23510	32050	52052	24004
78862	67699	01009	07050	73324	06732	27510	33761
18956	50064	39500	17450	18030	63124	48061	59412
89150	93126	17700	94400	76075	08317	27324	72723
52977	01657	92602	41043	05686	15650	29970	95877
00010	13800	76690	75133	60456	28491	03845	11507
51514	98135	42870	48578	29036	69876	86563	61729
93058	08313	99293	00990	13595	77457	79969	11339
47418	90974	83965	62732	85161	54330	22406	86253
56970	33273	61993	88407	69399	17301	70975	99129

Line \ Col.	(1)	(2)	(3)	(4)	(5)	(6)
501	88188	99345	94118	40373	50387	24802
502	05200	50533	59428	02797	16833	10038
503	82828	41316	92617	31346	89263	06589
504	71006	99318	19269	35233	79183	78538
505	05937	00875	32264	82808	00229	03868
506	06021	04370	93070	90737	05354	68427
507	54789	10960	44023	57857	56556	83993
508	90400	05707	29128	14859	84117	72206
509	51424	01651	99970	73521	82356	03297
510	79743	88757	43370	86536	07166	06401
511	77418	00322	98854	51507	00565	33066
512	17580	49302	16408	05678	75532	46218
513	15489	45559	28548	64330	42126	43145
514	56342	66773	18536	32600	73958	75993
515	20202	19216	23762	47856	04623	70728
516	84877	51708	69357	67914	55372	97225
517	01647	00311	44989	21900	96079	15793
518	45652	89311	45302	14539	32045	86727
519	79975	06153	08932	59185	71386	19070
520	49744	54713	37053	77467	15348	03383
521	40922	94903	29638	46870	14108	84391
522	53319	48020	77444	51447	07916	99506
523	76682	10559	85446	56236	85919	76388
524	48869	97229	69581	84581	71728	45150
525	95961	19279	38078	17473	43945	21562
526	16521	25945	94076	91281	92272	41233
527	78282	26332	44072	55104	16895	98311
528	43473	39179	53174	43498	72674	13087
529	06513	31352	09177	21367	64725	23784
530	48734	39737	03448	99009	98136	34562
531	54832	70111	48339	75270	11652	41697
532	55844	69515	22658	75438	83086	41325
533	42829	54398	93338	90705	00626	97752
534	81128	63461	10925	44382	73365	98875
535	62885	26354	10368	78026	00186	46783
536	19525	10375	27010	42791	49471	90607
537	26570	99202	73924	59888	01827	93314
538	04772	17749	01537	96036	02102	02622
539	49129	12491	62552	64323	44856	29045
540	19937	75104	57780	95871	94547	53541
541	52571	67962	72775	28480	87411	12075
542	54943	80723	81195	84069	28144	48106
543	16375	88048	29625	08111	92924	53335
544	38745	91458	30363	95005	55854	38628
545	09937	17776	86425	88916	80594	28347
546	30097	47192	27960	15937	42080	61048
547	02410	60124	62825	42947	74590	89730
548	44804	80165	19442	72194	76910	40274
549	37352	79142	51032	58844	03167	57351
550	60640	14199	48263	71533	94235	42431

(7)	(8)	(9)	(10)	(11)	(12)	(13)	(14)
81352	61640	56614	71506	75541	37818	88047	94144
18901	40743	99449	49825	44637	72724	42649	67052
07121	07151	23905	98435	50453	12983	04738	76421
06326	62715	28701	52809	56581	05925	85210	17745
71072	11519	44876	34508	07859	62424	54319	32842
25554	11165	00123	80338	03876	85648	24978	01687
70787	28193	65872	33723	00125	99818	85571	69509
53740	00464	51853	78852	83593	82926	48985	64355
36288	93531	69269	84798	78962	06336	95618	89718
14413	23643	21527	91902	91384	31444	54783	38760
65791	47857	32483	38493	52606	91078	13631	67863
74359	77556	82242	00134	70154	09027	79459	18730
81287	73884	69312	03395	06879	49662	40000	61598
84250	19254	06677	54192	53422	58200	74464	73949
86657	70801	53719	25214	65635	07565	49977	45525
52837	46723	00256	96221	26641	00309	36009	48392
13148	01433	78721	02647	25454	53913	97554	41578
40595	55953	93448	07805	53622	27330	18749	57867
87098	19392	13899	56096	83645	45871	35950	52272
96086	93295	12413	55774	97318	66402	11209	52495
87313	65969	43349	85142	25650	01896	48680	51236
83504	22290	63835	45589	04884	92760	70462	00538
59850	03262	60347	31077	07165	26588	31296	56112
16901	88717	62688	24828	89469	35483	76532	30256
90937	52140	73771	56084	08775	94820	78139	25987
58614	18912	58454	34011	85969	83621	92099	19131
56005	23331	21939	03463	53828	78930	30987	40988
54261	01844	45738	93150	13240	16694	59155	67589
18125	74873	83971	92678	96950	69821	41119	43312
30339	93143	07350	94289	76144	47238	08110	00037
43277	58089	70520	96997	71007	87803	52458	06637
04694	40359	28351	53492	73134	02370	72313	53039
93482	27726	51835	23966	50279	26329	25754	43530
77605	27351	49177	36914	50258	62361	38229	89608
02059	98892	98061	15330	31705	71923	29266	72716
98103	31752	04842	13693	84292	48485	76178	41716
63949	35394	12989	05867	11568	45056	16609	20470
06007	52239	61201	57415	35609	38761	19589	24238
76871	80449	81351	73642	48643	23848	48390	56829
77723	54114	90290	62627	65151	15687	81062	06729
45177	08796	99297	48807	88310	75454	45456	85394
04169	16575	62665	97861	71650	56981	61794	94285
09525	88290	17679	08945	25816	11848	95106	22031
13599	73065	40870	82576	37089	86738	16284	44725
08092	64255	55604	78635	13197	72213	95102	36723
14358	44508	72683	51088	55368	85587	27046	11198
16073	28184	30078	92578	83789	08044	76238	47599
93861	06568	92482	70037	66779	63312	00619	94053
51850	92810	35331	78995	44221	41532	51606	26430
44114	90993	41149	06159	39242	11163	14764	19246

Line \ Col.	(1)	(2)	(3)	(4)	(5)	(6)
551	31630	67734	78201	94545	80152	62327
552	25101	98983	36993	40028	58036	14075
553	86207	09805	46240	70644	76012	37000
554	31611	47643	28795	48115	17223	63161
555	10649	89132	59781	12373	35999	30832
556	68210	16228	34801	40972	22887	89759
557	32367	69587	66162	44358	69844	73042
558	14684	42446	01751	37459	31945	03627
559	64260	04661	39957	01200	84800	27930
560	66035	77943	70861	32037	96699	56314
561	20966	71492	32323	11867	47523	24094
562	20498	68176	02027	22358	15907	13247
563	56320	79875	60634	17556	52153	63549
564	50559	90270	33571	88091	34749	56784
565	49366	90095	73459	12225	28483	35358
566	29022	19268	03003	96622	30239	20482
567	77212	76531	68842	37777	20085	38703
568	41121	90499	83459	71424	27596	74645
569	06613	95412	94751	60763	56611	73508
570	66430	95324	60108	42377	56350	67861
571	39380	09648	47285	62864	03421	34292
572	27595	63289	75149	03348	91237	28372
573	43525	45549	58819	48478	14007	11384
574	60024	79858	72015	01236	27444	47010
575	35914	73076	05158	40190	41294	72776
576	58253	32995	54370	34437	98365	17630
577	85887	54618	23532	73821	80904	05950
578	88988	60426	34636	40601	57718	93925
579	65381	17333	32358	49608	36893	43453
580	20214	88406	06098	07770	51679	64857
581	04970	56425	74303	94793	55055	44762
582	87556	31521	19669	16311	01767	67301
583	34615	85796	30299	56090	41453	82886
584	95769	07371	49569	42262	74097	44317
585	57338	58325	53918	08075	69395	08189
586	08882	30762	14602	54767	67683	57818
587	62644	32814	31337	06011	80623	36021
588	55358	48010	24440	51092	89263	82352
589	02254	43319	79888	86311	57615	69666
590	61023	48494	57279	47133	89534	37085
591	41900	90881	96080	35258	70734	59465
592	94500	19764	94752	73077	74726	86176
593	66375	34653	37125	84780	92759	09781
594	27141	20959	02318	57546	45467	06653
595	25670	88933	19316	57014	52797	83779
596	06590	67256	21117	69351	98168	81043
597	36429	99750	38004	64992	25021	45680
598	52011	93461	06334	23801	34422	13728
599	09443	77694	26882	15663	45983	29425
600	25862	81855	15254	28462	95680	42433

(7)	(8)	(9)	(10)	(11)	(12)	(13)	(14)
83165	31035	82295	11824	06765	29501	62849	50419
05980	57094	45527	18766	77741	12985	14112	65058
98321	97197	30645	56169	09363	44394	29087	96569
29677	69820	77159	20762	94296	94528	82984	71418
02508	93055	57173	79848	25439	18861	26742	54970
09095	00587	03998	13659	64179	98567	69313	84637
88091	07288	74971	47066	36927	53520	58309	58605
47690	97813	45272	42789	99315	26662	15833	37246
98937	76108	11043	29101	01767	78894	92922	66537
75755	68667	04730	15256	13957	52743	42306	87515
23334	78839	81588	67374	43855	24512	81956	75721
44784	82957	53009	73379	44093	58405	38515	85531
03661	78290	96447	04192	30157	63198	75932	02367
98486	06018	27447	00884	29564	51522	35571	69208
99941	63054	54358	80748	54049	85937	64718	21466
50028	16632	57708	78559	70241	47977	78645	48550
31753	18608	52524	08585	91711	63572	57007	11379
68790	66478	78885	53799	02026	24596	88692	55936
88479	86151	78563	31633	92321	23004	77153	86639
47478	11961	78516	95316	64393	52020	44994	88205
36084	39604	89838	03635	30064	72710	26327	65521
65330	00966	73904	17477	34953	08975	83142	48425
19576	68138	30774	51898	24711	72537	18360	95682
80938	15828	86484	92753	04322	27171	41828	79025
38528	22272	34709	34561	65554	53461	61776	03585
42196	49736	39619	16731	71792	38047	85559	56700
63441	86109	79900	14063	03152	39235	74289	42342
67763	67671	21739	87534	83385	91492	45796	04621
38580	27639	52832	01522	11108	59992	23168	04414
36998	95796	46745	36780	56791	34690	61634	85411
22800	02663	91182	13102	07408	50545	21312	11365
63016	01227	29273	79256	50368	88653	23329	86500
33077	99791	86553	64640	61529	88660	66941	15936
40304	05346	90342	73324	81555	82769	23559	55238
66668	11663	84852	93146	27182	34936	97267	63996
98756	49119	91258	71916	65948	24841	38607	39412
81846	71868	98242	72307	25917	56240	73499	45106
95072	68828	28001	48991	19201	90963	34192	63336
60651	49084	39681	66415	10201	53931	44245	42850
28495	39162	89121	52021	23143	14829	55792	84641
49227	01431	90694	96186	57811	54512	30108	01261
31623	14569	89225	09606	73432	95276	21237	36807
06912	96802	92502	97497	67702	49763	25950	49924
99212	60612	26046	53553	59757	70491	69632	46009
56495	33104	26858	07662	41253	97688	76883	29444
26682	00063	96223	30436	21987	15450	56574	45011
46501	92943	99165	20707	43410	53746	54716	17090
35016	80605	86628	21689	34082	26035	11928	41817
12085	96233	29036	91135	28258	27709	90674	09705
70311	09702	71615	72688	85922	58369	89734	08750

Line \ Col.	(1)	(2)	(3)	(4)	(5)	(6)
601	60359	07603	81594	66235	48154	61257
602	34992	97880	79115	47587	76167	47086
603	04887	64208	71842	97885	32616	23280
604	09332	86232	88199	66094	72594	30100
605	42326	62962	06485	04978	96639	96214
606	49187	42836	17042	35179	31880	48444
607	09228	57404	42180	07949	98750	31506
608	69720	73477	91252	48009	81393	76401
609	82222	13787	98611	95257	34753	36674
610	30703	00513	54586	05623	43999	55387
611	86369	62151	70713	41166	79321	52215
612	83331	99035	68506	96734	91074	24356
613	43053	60600	98921	43720	77342	26186
614	57104	49148	18487	01775	71782	04679
615	33177	11409	13925	18130	54242	13460
616	05424	76714	05732	29415	01183	45054
617	92950	58665	41191	69259	50244	55322
618	54925	20502	71767	82737	64847	04496
619	41980	43710	55304	57526	29616	92314
620	83825	70977	67987	61545	92066	71215
621	84047	83627	37763	07081	33048	57895
622	12776	69127	67921	57611	85876	30744
623	81419	55440	69506	09115	45032	48343
624	59844	03603	96297	58028	93069	35674
625	18350	74940	07044	11210	53622	00779
626	79960	18784	13376	03415	84450	78874
627	45420	24157	16374	22384	56892	84941
628	13945	09559	68152	56960	39453	51654
629	91206	33871	60730	96821	95808	29763
630	24847	08724	81499	72905	95102	63004
631	94303	08209	27804	49372	66392	50578
632	22732	95331	60954	93333	71142	38827
633	82809	24004	65983	01091	70431	91145
634	62700	79965	09610	97213	48579	43574
635	89870	73755	48525	32765	50818	71468
636	81493	24124	67928	12735	41249	24180
637	43630	32189	08532	43055	08080	84208
638	60234	18992	13283	96334	39746	07272
639	00107	21861	60367	48999	71634	34053
640	09657	36088	05976	88267	62683	57675
641	93948	38350	63464	08008	96607	73505
642	42746	29761	72298	48186	88584	90141
643	12939	04181	27698	48297	20574	30169
644	71032	55283	94804	00202	12254	22920
645	09188	78876	95736	70659	32725	23024
646	79236	54729	47052	49717	22312	06735
647	41337	52635	48056	43317	11599	26382
648	73732	99966	30485	45994	30195	40239
649	92113	55625	03726	76886	64237	33300
650	63797	22667	74860	99731	06975	63055

(7)	(8)	(9)	(10)	(11)	(12)	(13)	(14)
27978	64695	63165	44593	08210	16863	09655	00855
57064	16730	74172	60317	83215	38133	06303	05466
11783	19852	64266	24446	14189	77419	30991	92130
23673	68705	66989	42666	81857	34651	36167	24221
91478	12408	21457	19862	99102	91426	10181	51762
89877	50915	37426	21556	25999	84256	82314	18813
78442	45809	12725	49774	11276	46371	81681	00623
48168	25967	33372	84414	21506	46131	46046	12354
44326	66070	61131	70620	42865	89251	54844	04013
67189	95058	91174	13121	27557	16512	77963	40635
94358	28962	35868	22796	87221	40014	68875	71420
03035	66926	32197	54944	76781	86722	11769	27368
64554	46226	64244	10703	49564	69737	32948	43060
64369	06208	71669	63046	10470	54194	96709	86502
39174	63528	22670	31810	04313	50669	20653	31779
13493	44006	61641	80304	96504	52181	05359	72203
75137	90193	31989	17381	43795	26981	15326	02303
35921	42670	08584	54090	52907	75331	09155	54187
85883	21584	55045	81997	62277	58884	01590	13532
93967	63071	69928	98917	05699	35957	04679	58769
42182	73279	08032	19165	01701	35656	03328	81785
40886	68396	79787	76434	71221	86769	15104	19062
78352	39075	31689	76469	64918	15149	88457	97144
38479	54639	54455	10300	73946	94827	53164	07458
36027	51496	01694	57895	84570	18271	54461	42210
22050	19730	92598	54291	60658	73188	03446	49864
97157	99656	33978	81436	10955	98991	10456	35727
10617	55628	47933	85161	52998	75414	59552	03546
39678	73104	43398	38181	44314	58343	28884	94613
22223	19808	90777	54986	97234	18458	22889	83960
02966	90907	33164	83044	97985	78526	00983	29271
48222	21779	35598	95957	58844	82319	19780	08330
88207	52216	94846	75303	85105	89486	08182	56504
37652	12447	80233	42473	94585	84840	99926	74778
37876	28334	07762	16180	45346	78324	20422	85784
54740	44290	58903	38681	04066	69393	84595	42173
06295	07813	24068	67549	43051	78581	02095	03471
25295	07871	34201	49620	52178	07290	89767	63890
28265	02064	06290	10620	17941	81086	51759	57028
85265	10856	06525	37911	52332	55752	25054	30436
75513	91238	11042	40972	62837	30260	84002	99947
72879	54531	99127	60063	22374	76895	63812	94877
45545	04462	91067	43847	62739	31141	30385	30098
73225	51484	73943	08431	45681	32663	67097	15644
04656	48102	15904	19019	09882	87431	16879	61253
58347	04402	03838	97049	35378	38579	24489	86899
41305	04589	92877	52732	53130	45275	30183	15962
52751	64124	67778	60982	12167	63134	10730	11350
48004	37440	76329	80441	74766	70630	97855	88039
72287	81976	43983	97018	25559	96618	93350	67143

Line \ Col.	(1)	(2)	(3)	(4)	(5)	(6)
651	98707	41348	74106	43550	16638	72858
652	65496	87176	71726	09722	85667	37498
653	17617	18337	83583	73510	52998	02570
654	85006	32658	83348	38599	77549	70275
655	77279	66357	38044	75041	06698	16798
656	84133	32224	55350	73251	64120	86718
657	86535	01806	18470	94806	18228	71262
658	58459	99005	64939	57060	34609	06739
659	38783	61870	02744	23773	74163	30029
660	49454	76832	17745	75922	40087	51566
661	71219	82115	51031	28586	91328	59635
662	57770	63699	49430	82846	13285	69178
663	94539	92056	65825	27167	69783	48976
664	94992	45377	75471	45547	34348	61707
665	60717	63093	60684	08910	30296	12345
666	28040	08603	43675	64665	40567	76211
667	69841	63836	53186	49970	05485	65171
668	80931	69365	75077	19929	67852	63937
669	94000	24074	95072	32602	89373	78009
670	70609	17467	26861	51035	44534	49774
671	24016	76531	77282	21820	61170	37198
672	36008	76472	60324	45386	67266	98846
673	65769	02131	95850	61875	52572	82826
674	71033	43026	99601	18102	33654	29885
675	25152	11755	33527	05149	71696	63492
676	81251	78313	53908	66912	84868	51859
677	37401	18809	83908	01638	72548	80521
678	01383	28893	13771	99613	39531	20895
679	03921	79304	91058	03175	33155	58344
680	19882	28056	10093	45334	89019	23914
681	55339	29655	37282	26504	70059	91780
682	01725	18314	40197	00964	44112	60484
683	45073	49109	77778	46092	30928	16111
684	60861	39467	17392	05446	26083	65352
685	88775	27006	69664	22246	77064	40312
686	20497	65297	17965	97094	26451	47473
687	76692	21880	39663	77289	36681	47935
688	00528	63679	57762	88094	26402	25925
689	57718	09889	94003	43899	32989	87707
690	85652	55278	23342	30372	47987	19936
691	16543	93477	41421	34710	59498	55069
692	50315	17150	14006	10453	96007	41512
693	73876	27245	79551	56241	53843	66714
694	26749	07215	99485	51013	50210	69934
695	89438	39457	58255	75693	72570	17885
696	24388	81801	22581	26331	47945	11717
697	19688	39199	20531	96205	50355	14725
698	07943	07018	03516	05747	94259	73583
699	90391	97135	97952	83722	35578	82905
700	61564	65108	76451	71430	08671	84975

(7)	(8)	(9)	(10)	(11)	(12)	(13)	(14)
32375	50634	80903	43867	54215	65017	70776	09596
03926	72585	15193	45615	67073	65110	42404	28419
37334	82042	07261	97361	93327	81104	17979	15192
85147	08030	20980	86223	58024	56948	10793	81858
83023	84686	53539	86491	70402	31779	09591	22398
61061	66146	36275	48583	74783	85824	87328	39207
39195	99049	75632	67645	26117	89606	83976	53307
40489	08146	74014	24803	50699	05588	73658	24352
64988	67851	68279	53341	88122	03631	97916	27003
38620	92988	84531	99883	40785	53456	03864	20593
15746	09832	53937	07006	00272	00914	31619	73222
66391	44979	69923	02920	98234	68478	52861	04824
07466	76421	71439	98358	21989	77098	86413	62724
77657	29541	67815	56777	91185	00390	17361	18119
22178	71824	11973	61293	25937	61542	76603	48032
18715	62133	75336	98118	88984	44341	11202	34471
40135	67168	42593	37922	55146	40354	32803	63430
67390	94560	76131	58351	72302	68973	72689	28187
38009	60982	27122	29283	08881	91436	80644	09688
88833	15577	80076	68625	42230	94087	97450	13569
16941	14009	97386	61256	11687	70360	18405	85586
17763	98235	53433	01295	74947	71106	33976	55405
09571	61125	81326	72388	40377	93419	38458	13301
48692	09691	95837	77697	69896	47214	85897	59723
32871	48386	37657	82062	02643	34598	36128	42411
15959	31119	92964	94054	57594	61310	42452	76262
02945	29410	37736	96301	32848	16332	63069	35975
92322	01032	66104	86756	84812	10692	73677	58045
13242	02686	57998	84750	88695	99642	86560	79808
12549	69492	09859	46366	22224	63308	95897	20408
59955	01729	92886	28616	52061	47284	02989	20385
07486	10883	23106	18254	23711	26458	09878	12981
15372	76016	15402	98293	24495	79618	69649	19768
24501	20502	13346	11151	37472	05548	35893	47964
14388	70861	47198	24261	69913	07368	78156	07858
07292	03191	47612	36599	67827	74007	48783	12329
76260	96157	44019	73403	83985	84210	58091	88097
10598	09606	41596	90916	25311	91501	63286	87423
46639	53512	25509	92751	60744	24239	13608	90176
89623	38221	45073	67291	57082	13194	39749	75753
70504	08544	80118	77512	88070	03943	84969	02116
36027	60557	57141	50554	80556	47441	56506	62857
24050	26354	14915	62391	75724	57468	34621	22325
73613	95543	94599	13955	29586	62507	90618	52247
07259	10273	25229	52788	55762	14772	50200	55909
42187	06031	02488	09199	74752	65757	27989	81532
38656	79167	44771	43966	73425	79632	77181	84817
43619	99509	02102	08279	57372	53487	10885	95017
41761	66670	43482	34931	94438	93341	60927	31368
36182	70787	79442	29461	01209	20022	93055	28312

Line \ Col.	(1)	(2)	(3)	(4)	(5)	(6)
701	79681	63467	02907	86515	71330	04490
702	30305	20743	10302	71391	18138	23412
703	32763	33847	58250	64362	87550	94978
704	59166	21978	40556	13084	31782	00518
705	55843	94845	30006	51045	17428	50657
706	33537	82468	52422	32155	54419	61661
707	13533	29605	31430	07663	95274	11484
708	24626	54219	12284	06890	05239	42846
709	48002	32024	17230	37523	47488	31080
710	03742	00004	98249	12256	94253	95378
711	17749	89193	37944	53702	49918	65397
712	34837	36219	22048	97047	68804	09633
713	99451	37922	90191	39229	07564	41077
714	74045	00036	53137	15250	19646	20451
715	98998	98774	98159	00032	97323	81490
716	61513	02266	36871	85993	23028	67082
717	67056	19960	53863	63917	68283	31123
718	83036	04625	93284	14368	10979	95800
719	71901	25497	76987	74388	41605	39295
720	46484	77860	02062	92917	70275	40593
721	18312	05137	64361	86541	17794	32313
722	63093	94089	17729	19607	19340	19022
723	38109	69439	62094	49578	37728	17809
724	41421	22003	36770	32741	10325	30892
725	92320	12828	57972	83551	63054	95028
726	42226	72413	67949	96906	17848	21446
727	01094	08525	21349	41981	55232	76652
728	75760	51119	37218	16828	89127	42801
729	62568	56665	42394	67135	03069	93275
730	77151	67677	85258	46925	92504	87860
731	71920	39074	15464	36753	86550	24330
732	99411	04216	66076	90718	67214	03688
733	05654	88507	03119	93043	06951	35126
734	65937	81013	09884	97787	85851	00011
735	87649	70531	88258	21822	97418	67341
736	57827	19642	95661	23788	19164	78112
737	78911	81376	22392	42570	33512	17996
738	91302	54963	94112	60597	31843	40120
739	82950	87509	65702	14385	86299	23769
740	21888	66504	85577	67163	46317	92073
741	73799	60026	87226	26744	12037	98558
742	48237	10339	99550	86134	30229	39131
743	24293	69496	20243	17738	55798	96178
744	18748	01580	73315	84924	81621	67021
745	94470	36824	89203	23689	37016	18462
746	87639	11791	63380	25952	20838	13638
747	65676	78482	33343	65797	56005	15782
748	94357	62236	54083	37960	43467	79372
749	06595	83512	74524	10051	97759	64738
750	34033	69035	18588	88893	83679	27789

(7)	(8)	(9)	(10)	(11)	(12)	(13)	(14)
47372	68791	27576	02044	03784	94581	60105	75131
11858	47818	22324	52031	10600	49892	34101	71430
22888	78355	34651	41604	51892	89533	81610	72641
18621	60508	93095	74017	17416	76900	25261	63227
68237	02969	30500	43569	28051	22505	07159	78162
64835	06496	16377	92607	86248	89492	49306	95414
42579	15718	54485	08857	93691	02973	26687	90437
24773	15025	15161	51340	54739	99433	54328	47800
29352	61444	04011	56275	19259	72475	53451	43397
88918	98167	46646	19727	24181	83358	28999	11769
72597	63520	77429	68355	21003	00657	02157	68031
28689	80484	59331	77577	30376	10021	78267	78049
91554	46657	74652	84677	49671	94805	82406	99797
46677	53620	74712	17246	96626	28587	33618	46845
21552	35001	10913	48910	91005	62408	83253	19770
93486	45110	86288	34493	66710	04268	04955	49074
17443	32019	19695	85622	46808	03535	91566	36785
72182	77004	07320	79516	00915	53209	00884	65464
75622	41203	87987	09672	81312	08728	49867	95245
93265	92722	39193	47099	39046	85989	24607	72287
52847	08862	36752	32624	11035	92500	35016	18519
50080	21998	49864	07107	64287	41647	75264	09230
11563	10073	17299	69238	88068	04754	51698	11641
14112	34880	92387	45169	96668	89183	10099	44382
50857	40315	04962	36431	54964	33961	89397	70359
35722	10376	84226	16403	14642	23253	07162	57664
00857	77173	63362	64936	96601	95816	14729	35398
01084	78402	28359	41533	83339	69672	64909	55192
11662	23607	00878	53800	14840	28975	51693	97620
85299	45952	76388	72989	12170	03449	28315	95994
17873	20798	15221	80763	69974	95552	66857	85097
71088	92479	27623	97466	27560	63689	35799	28078
26154	26820	68861	37807	17485	58902	92005	57597
66801	02686	73801	19522	67200	80477	73121	88815
54342	80836	46142	04718	08348	75316	53030	90533
07304	32337	12845	12588	70054	12267	96360	43459
29406	47329	66928	89312	16994	87633	71914	52038
00386	35486	27379	02873	69868	03803	29671	74165
87183	66267	13819	58266	16843	06546	00521	50286
68325	46664	03841	58572	46048	04635	78350	53233
66640	32882	11415	64686	78236	05844	76840	80802
76976	56296	89453	79556	48059	70552	45852	06593
86022	42073	16407	53031	48671	82154	04054	90741
99065	43590	82522	71919	25097	49536	03140	63610
59404	27230	78689	88837	41119	95462	94394	13374
32782	23841	16936	91384	20472	81876	85484	35003
27311	64066	28230	36207	06446	09976	09463	56698
26370	08273	18180	84100	30757	33315	28583	53434
10370	07874	28301	08201	07624	63508	82486	82993
22340	12208	00381	06023	77844	28666	24220	19220

Line \ Col.	(1)	(2)	(3)	(4)	(5)	(6)
751	03548	52011	53722	62927	01693	90948
752	05066	74263	11659	84658	52063	42299
753	19814	89956	36256	19896	56654	69424
754	44928	11206	21377	35086	62233	93761
755	52158	08923	94812	04443	32028	96465
756	53211	58616	05135	52204	51079	11341
757	27334	43976	14685	38119	29486	57290
758	66166	06709	69495	42150	38018	43875
759	01837	16750	96491	33095	30383	48804
760	38295	51093	63495	13203	93562	94132
761	72510	80830	39948	94133	00780	14167
762	16354	00336	06494	30078	46134	62486
763	45168	70700	04592	35281	47737	28881
764	68137	13619	84666	78104	83546	72551
765	31848	95753	76858	89517	91138	62356
766	17216	37292	05495	50885	98994	32966
767	73211	42922	57386	95490	56100	08977
768	29217	56753	90171	87554	57421	35839
769	66780	34571	71684	28798	47123	25232
770	55780	48081	93674	70837	92534	65892
771	05788	64237	58140	63279	60170	17229
772	21911	51065	51525	65122	52608	52836
773	32645	38561	25181	18042	31903	46525
774	72304	15382	01151	63162	23656	69649
775	27637	04122	86132	22538	98976	90718
776	66305	85906	87925	50081	37585	63674
777	53470	40332	81044	00558	50403	48029
778	01355	77096	64828	02445	94511	09503
779	66954	04728	86153	10933	86557	10877
780	53734	15628	08080	24011	04187	65722
781	23114	08743	07186	23825	04298	72839
782	16803	91335	64192	13631	20332	74852
783	57233	99034	38028	32038	81270	77809
784	83203	59665	72314	67942	01320	24467
785	79299	97340	04568	65386	04876	31514
786	99442	63865	14360	83898	98873	17471
787	77773	19621	81557	84629	18808	89056
788	18581	12572	15185	57989	87644	88902
789	80978	13327	19682	53353	96223	04775
790	96884	95522	04791	93463	20316	84054
791	61113	82511	44196	73740	16111	73200
792	01272	75657	28365	17431	93603	32457
793	82357	77572	75628	93073	38281	72103
794	20434	70899	44243	19741	59954	73617
795	38580	10399	44894	25476	04984	64543
796	20211	12980	45261	82527	87534	39405
797	98954	03124	09433	19894	01380	18962
798	99749	02140	46641	56354	78746	89410
799	47167	24716	84417	40097	46608	11667
800	65812	77947	27864	98144	01818	28214

(7)	(8)	(9)	(10)	(11)	(12)	(13)	(14)
75340	16660	00939	77148	52778	20615	97851	58353
94340	20391	00080	43359	44231	06891	86588	88565
84446	95294	00919	60267	34349	64353	92469	01606
56000	42066	35898	48944	32352	33177	16239	76624
94430	42834	22836	88818	44467	18329	30144	31536
20366	86248	35160	31485	92436	69726	12722	52722
34141	18058	91299	58001	17944	00296	13949	94904
44534	48712	98089	76889	55720	09038	95667	57007
21228	10863	08350	25610	80866	00115	27666	94607
54810	11410	73776	55752	36138	52297	31528	77790
83322	32747	97291	66126	64996	21354	64615	64234
70923	17400	28797	83599	78655	67488	09715	69232
57221	79935	99756	61564	36936	55668	87148	95939
40848	52138	36343	93975	09556	58888	08125	80961
66405	98171	66239	49761	88800	29069	30175	31267
83496	54614	75214	34959	15500	32107	81638	46696
78499	53540	41745	09805	67110	53329	92776	32312
60961	87828	24777	19688	42464	35569	84904	13130
67995	39562	35855	61645	64448	65170	46792	77081
32422	02887	03170	05372	48068	65758	62376	94055
69038	02500	21071	26294	95005	47815	87991	93358
86157	19943	63173	34921	11943	36931	74722	06193
96290	24323	68269	45841	73918	13720	52336	48416
54580	33479	62899	33716	53668	86735	36746	21939
81840	33461	28526	96231	28082	89710	16038	26648
65144	75814	87596	04642	07590	82276	59336	84262
07719	83340	20258	49737	45499	72241	90103	96141
12283	15264	32845	55594	03668	05664	67999	06001
97049	40124	87071	03864	29526	42888	09057	82966
82863	59616	60664	76761	84417	72560	77869	42603
43963	52136	60923	88568	55458	87335	81939	67361
67813	68131	56695	93253	71650	81735	13302	30319
99813	67091	56997	62005	95516	34011	52035	79500
27813	74783	56696	84101	93852	12016	20869	57009
78813	77887	66697	51048	28395	62626	42911	99130
01813	81541	66913	52874	10563	59450	16885	16009
48194	65899	26244	74431	24232	33299	58332	18314
49946	76235	92633	10232	84241	66467	86018	92272
05590	55237	21695	31870	48893	94058	88943	77040
68980	56907	77188	54803	67622	57968	78532	66688
65980	66320	77327	14715	24759	08145	28077	32303
57980	66157	27797	55887	57788	29337	73409	35682
39980	71150	87282	01585	25850	46138	21777	97555
11661	81574	05903	25909	38638	32196	41345	22152
14141	97911	89418	97980	49571	60483	94714	51753
03701	94321	23777	61546	21541	69603	61768	40328
40701	05185	23280	04945	49801	98051	77848	62320
35701	00250	23508	51246	09460	02313	71279	74223
40701	06155	23784	68961	34289	04531	12752	08516
83701	10257	33945	08795	30976	14017	59161	31388

Line \ Col.	(1)	(2)	(3)	(4)	(5)	(6)
801	33993	51249	78123	16507	57399	77922
802	39041	05779	74278	75301	01779	60768
803	56011	26839	38501	03321	43259	73148
804	07397	95853	45764	43803	76659	57736
805	74998	53337	13860	89430	95825	65893
806	59572	95893	69765	43597	90570	60909
807	74645	13920	28640	00127	04261	17650
808	42765	23855	38451	11462	32671	52126
809	66561	56130	30356	54034	53996	98874
810	50670	13172	31460	20224	34193	59458
811	53971	08701	38356	36149	10891	05178
812	47177	03085	37432	94053	87057	61859
813	41494	89270	48063	12253	00383	96010
814	07409	32874	03514	84943	74421	86708
815	03097	12212	43093	46224	14431	15065
816	34722	88896	59205	18004	96431	41366
817	48117	83879	52509	29339	87735	97499
818	14628	89161	66972	19180	40852	91738
819	61512	79376	88184	29415	50716	93393
820	99954	55656	01946	57035	64418	29700
821	61455	28229	82511	11622	60786	18442
822	10398	50239	70191	37585	98373	04651
823	59075	81492	40669	16391	12148	38538
824	91497	76797	82557	55301	61570	69577
825	74619	62316	80041	53053	81252	32739
826	12536	80792	44581	12616	49740	86946
827	10246	49556	07610	59950	34387	70013
828	92506	24397	19145	24185	24479	70118
829	65745	27223	22831	39446	65808	95534
830	01707	04494	48168	58480	74983	63091
831	66959	80109	88908	38759	80716	36340
832	79278	02746	50718	90196	28394	82035
833	11343	22312	41379	22297	71703	78729
834	40415	10553	65932	34938	43977	39262
835	72774	25480	30264	08291	93796	22281
836	75886	86543	47020	14493	38363	64238
837	64628	20234	07967	46676	42907	60909
838	45905	77701	98976	70056	80502	68650
839	77691	00408	64191	11006	39212	26862
840	39172	12824	43379	57590	45307	72206
841	67120	01558	99762	79752	17139	52265
842	88264	85390	92841	63811	64423	50910
843	78097	59495	45090	74592	47474	56157
844	41888	69798	82296	09312	04150	07616
845	46618	07254	28714	18244	53214	39560
846	29213	42101	25089	11881	77558	72738
847	38601	25735	04726	36544	67842	93937
848	92207	10011	64210	77096	00011	79218
849	30610	13236	33241	68731	30955	40587
850	74544	72806	62226	65685	37996	00377

(7)	(8)	(9)	(10)	(11)	(12)	(13)	(14)
38198	63494	00278	30782	33119	64943	17239	69020
22023	07510	67883	55288	67391	54188	31913	29733
43615	49093	91641	77179	50837	48734	85187	41210
44801	45623	23714	69657	87971	24757	94493	78723
96572	73975	19577	87947	23962	78235	64839	73456
06478	77692	30911	08272	81887	57749	02952	51524
34050	78788	57948	36189	88382	72324	59253	30258
23800	02691	57034	34532	19711	71567	90495	55980
78001	29707	91938	72016	16429	69726	41990	33673
24410	01366	68825	22798	52873	18370	15577	63271
55653	31553	20037	39346	28591	13505	04446	92130
97943	81113	62161	11369	54419	58886	89956	12857
41457	54657	46881	75255	29242	07537	53186	95083
34267	66071	62262	99391	61245	95839	75203	93984
18267	60039	62089	38572	70988	17279	05469	28591
50982	92400	59369	43605	26404	04176	05106	08366
42848	81449	80024	81312	59469	91169	70851	90165
23920	75518	32041	13411	61334	52386	33582	72143
96220	82277	64510	43374	09107	28813	41848	08813
99242	42586	11583	82768	44966	39192	82144	05810
36508	98936	19050	57242	33045	54278	21720	87812
67804	84062	27380	75486	63171	24529	60070	66939
73873	68596	25538	83646	61066	45210	24182	18687
23301	31921	09862	73089	69329	41916	41165	34503
65201	92165	93792	30912	59105	76944	70998	00317
41819	85104	25705	92481	95287	61769	29390	05764
64460	96719	43056	24268	23303	19863	43644	76986
42708	54311	95989	08402	77608	98356	47034	01635
03348	11435	24166	62726	99878	59302	81164	08010
81027	72579	67249	48089	34219	71727	86665	94975
30082	43295	37551	18531	43903	94975	31049	19033
03255	39574	41483	12450	32494	65192	54772	97431
65082	57759	79579	41516	46248	37348	34631	88164
95828	98617	27401	50226	17322	44024	23133	57899
51434	66771	20118	00502	07738	31841	90200	46348
16322	45503	90723	35607	43715	85751	15888	80645
73293	38588	31035	12226	37746	45008	43271	32015
24469	15574	40018	90057	96540	47174	03943	37553
99863	58155	66052	96864	61790	11064	49308	94510
53283	75882	93451	44830	06300	45456	49567	51673
97997	66806	55559	62043	51324	32423	88325	99634
38189	88183	56625	22910	52250	70491	71111	37202
88287	47032	66341	38328	70538	91105	12056	36125
34572	83202	58691	27354	37015	11278	49697	65667
68753	16825	48639	38228	95166	53649	05071	26894
57234	28458	74313	29665	97366	94714	48704	07033
68745	62979	97750	28293	75851	08362	71546	17993
52123	29841	76145	82364	55774	15462	44555	26844
45206	11949	28295	12666	98479	82498	49195	46254
59917	91100	07993	15046	51303	19515	25055	56386

Line \ Col.	(1)	(2)	(3)	(4)	(5)	(6)
851	76385	05431	82252	79850	31192	86315
852	08059	15958	10514	86124	29817	19044
853	30636	03463	50326	69684	38422	59826
854	23794	51463	67574	48953	73512	46239
855	01117	60216	29314	65537	84029	00741
856	29527	19577	01414	35290	70174	37019
857	64236	24229	17970	92022	64164	17873
858	92331	30325	61918	71623	38040	51375
859	93454	37190	23790	40058	03758	01774
860	17101	42181	45798	68745	24190	16539
861	30742	93358	95730	52535	34404	76057
862	02472	01280	67106	47893	93551	76697
863	80718	72187	67178	77179	06212	37409
864	85406	73687	02116	57637	94701	46754
865	00563	67156	88141	13491	92592	35746
866	89190	58965	55213	24337	58807	36123
867	01438	81590	83758	45361	76209	65081
868	79127	53282	50510	80129	23960	78423
869	33952	92823	32840	94420	51193	69652
870	57146	14126	71734	56942	83371	31526
871	33158	61761	73207	01764	81696	55137
872	63615	69083	00118	47991	99521	88655
873	89010	46915	70186	55657	76955	25430
874	32547	43398	30909	62599	53105	27460
875	61992	28258	27359	61002	16882	44018
876	78326	74541	22198	48380	45919	76160
877	35493	53008	78622	38329	27611	12327
878	19130	59917	28850	76593	02389	80759
879	00317	05769	03497	42174	32653	23663
880	84122	36454	70776	17000	83017	07027
881	76320	32120	91585	39640	23470	86000
882	09234	36233	94404	42812	39210	25967
883	16206	70598	95378	70573	42636	53862
884	04071	51662	67884	73911	08708	66287
885	97545	87732	23795	38027	90239	80044
886	53253	56120	42720	25660	36921	30891
887	66817	18439	53188	35155	24309	88284
888	28077	26409	11443	22200	23129	32407
889	18889	00291	13701	12401	26466	67700
890	10598	64974	66296	33329	30560	73380
891	18656	81152	45498	14400	92435	67664
892	79044	10440	25777	05486	65659	22183
893	74042	20365	42672	34850	60670	56980
894	87249	06640	09090	03242	68467	85678
895	82839	52537	00518	60559	43669	44297
896	07749	62249	01611	43795	17129	44447
897	37171	34598	87234	28324	85927	23465
898	55432	45030	85336	49128	40487	63959
899	43658	35437	83506	11209	24770	87123
900	59536	79475	04874	50831	16996	04750

(7)	(8)	(9)	(10)	(11)	(12)	(13)	(14)
75612	59985	76421	39300	64976	27951	17855	02220
03555	80725	67857	31395	68780	16560	79952	41739
47858	90601	50834	88109	43882	15687	06212	19886
10953	04622	60650	35048	34705	90502	31011	81004
40851	96344	13861	43421	57107	60813	06877	52161
80223	62206	22928	63414	03940	02188	20345	13183
41189	28240	60697	26495	87634	75899	09741	84939
91127	93903	83715	93244	04366	57679	70829	90088
90696	81674	53791	15559	42798	46892	57960	06575
32330	21732	65547	94356	38651	35102	16327	17886
21325	87526	93020	94861	83865	61393	89645	00773
56598	67982	77376	33312	58893	69370	59118	95277
48788	68930	21672	88783	59304	82369	19410	93050
54019	96344	93343	47764	57490	21321	29075	40086
72117	37593	72780	78271	75915	85972	58615	71755
09235	95541	96979	03336	34380	66288	98659	46572
34785	68423	04408	73827	78494	02765	46174	83192
31988	78571	79458	95043	23997	97528	21631	63898
04332	81675	64644	68673	33718	02256	34414	87710
13444	11912	03152	66411	42853	08437	35667	26251
41834	81860	81310	14711	36599	78042	62086	41752
94451	67445	99377	75528	40794	30140	82298	85868
91951	56473	34225	68103	25353	89595	04715	20102
56734	41954	47696	82113	38508	88941	49983	36899
85376	66756	14395	66865	67036	78374	43612	44134
10974	03127	58980	18350	22089	54977	94019	84739
52541	00861	62380	65890	79729	99710	64836	43706
18481	02724	57578	35705	89265	25033	13767	95888
29569	36342	85908	29572	60063	41170	59957	14755
98058	41274	22476	27436	30798	62287	21235	00249
68204	23980	17625	53197	35128	76385	02848	61680
12232	38195	16649	96739	64610	96067	89561	15772
81334	65439	28858	97619	59608	61460	00581	43226
89261	73451	81146	77733	70162	42449	44755	56401
64677	47912	82144	85918	93508	05816	57549	74831
42042	80370	97880	62507	01218	19202	22323	81363
74644	25454	19606	61460	52684	36568	68108	45653
52401	78416	63693	35633	77724	86835	89829	81383
55805	63818	16067	95185	97241	66126	16774	39342
94905	04959	80213	14228	97242	94826	64276	37466
86229	74358	76537	87066	42293	91743	49462	42808
82080	04351	19530	49941	29181	34667	28910	70927
88333	75288	64996	26913	62379	55068	91239	85752
23411	53443	19526	03205	29261	36061	34325	03761
75071	17146	35492	60718	38106	06409	75657	66013
95197	25088	22150	54427	11578	77560	26460	55002
80833	62872	40826	10066	64858	33605	24848	30881
25879	60415	26744	38584	51543	17333	47300	13834
21494	85056	56630	75919	26005	90077	50380	09261
02246	08846	82410	50997	45824	55547	08168	16679

Line \ Col.	(1)	(2)	(3)	(4)	(5)	(6)
901	77583	63193	14378	66314	92154	31173
902	41435	82033	40363	74800	79198	03991
903	17163	74517	11281	83105	16146	27577
904	47909	53647	99896	13016	53708	18549
905	88024	64045	70954	56434	73860	50310
906	51540	26148	65528	66246	74154	47254
907	29122	04072	85663	33914	63587	20151
908	34873	53537	85834	11394	44898	92403
909	26132	07856	14223	02824	66094	88093
910	26892	74387	97124	32851	83465	51300
911	73485	32215	29894	87362	47818	52494
912	45678	13831	93961	93558	34050	42936
913	71687	79185	46096	22818	19051	39123
914	11833	28572	61695	36928	50851	98599
915	90529	59895	55565	57955	75623	55721
916	31697	92763	05134	45963	15725	39771
917	47212	92010	40601	23364	72705	15989
918	56686	61285	36139	18867	12877	89109
919	50669	06740	74638	62054	53083	22790
920	16821	64195	64269	62235	41829	93374
921	30608	94750	38092	42230	85443	34743
922	83211	45796	33370	31291	76074	40065
923	51774	53905	66945	65882	70352	38447
924	89095	90943	76279	78323	37210	77141
925	54047	41638	45626	98549	20648	89365
926	81549	98773	68979	28308	53686	57192
927	72335	08233	56777	99798	57340	54203
928	02540	14032	90858	26020	28174	91563
929	09226	10658	79614	84200	53035	16839
930	18050	79976	70461	19890	08214	77015
931	44378	42627	16636	69923	89122	92792
932	92101	13475	15373	53642	77422	26662
933	27926	69613	88880	95537	08518	66627
934	06900	75222	25385	63569	03483	90973
935	08717	31244	56529	97336	17309	32629
936	79966	02658	18012	59422	86272	69447
937	85668	03060	61274	14020	16594	72642
938	29530	85435	54205	01781	88806	28369
939	69284	91923	11744	13051	69350	55403
940	41503	48684	36452	06825	80218	76395
941	47063	45686	78929	82808	67899	16936
942	90503	44995	53753	88362	99077	14510
943	08367	68828	82856	56380	26969	16987
944	05207	94071	56234	12584	21319	90050
945	15445	53683	92875	02502	48973	00564
946	99603	19507	68314	12524	57700	39240
947	82736	02198	84682	18512	42010	69026
948	04925	66489	08883	69176	95712	25057
949	48692	63679	55426	75873	21338	78242
950	23766	44510	30176	02784	65111	89090

(7)	(8)	(9)	(10)	(11)	(12)	(13)	(14)
75223	92947	81041	91385	89091	83989	34982	66565
01635	43666	02630	46039	53273	86262	91450	79883
33565	39621	27321	06387	51838	37591	54290	54527
75241	22312	53261	80185	69888	12646	64464	98505
29601	52204	93295	05735	15486	39857	83584	59587
65546	75309	90415	17346	20559	29568	30124	11974
36720	25827	13447	17082	74817	92523	81519	65724
01979	22785	94354	33271	44579	40756	70108	30514
35794	69015	67498	97087	25936	52239	07472	74585
58546	12579	43451	48661	79351	58231	11824	77723
27684	83573	91237	03585	13266	63905	94600	43823
00860	66594	36783	56939	47057	55257	16555	65642
08793	18798	79528	05621	12131	88365	51154	46175
76466	73848	76675	68072	50077	27709	60895	55306
43773	98277	38842	05069	31590	31482	38040	71541
54430	76890	52975	52037	06071	14710	84160	05126
02965	78394	53956	48542	35568	09897	20287	54478
48963	58636	18825	47664	74509	53250	61778	43202
82404	85132	17634	35664	26876	54191	61412	08062
74377	17728	84164	32762	18275	91425	96275	97711
00348	36016	74853	00499	03387	07739	96416	28578
50006	74244	44355	96978	79518	51941	26627	39503
50881	25003	88424	98825	47209	16332	48104	50130
50200	95786	00463	82949	55660	93650	41134	43309
10934	10799	37862	71684	98288	94592	70961	51028
65423	47225	27490	78045	57512	11431	50502	11301
12334	16800	91872	82213	79086	33896	31707	48739
65006	14401	58189	32658	13812	72382	19169	24151
83058	55540	32716	03834	05299	58331	90479	34808
86657	29965	21658	72049	74959	95217	71503	74950
95380	20397	06649	02752	46279	99681	05154	56400
58069	86649	38783	30050	20087	26681	05859	41218
61173	27188	55705	29607	24361	83286	00052	41181
86572	53485	23353	18345	24553	43494	84651	48483
34184	47240	07490	86150	78423	82309	01762	33463
45731	19344	49685	95236	60922	09665	50176	98674
59596	70634	58195	78404	80798	60696	00686	75274
69095	26496	77711	62699	92045	74777	97537	69768
75969	64260	42303	54467	61374	22426	70625	96732
85109	67756	71072	04047	38520	31872	00118	84181
94990	90513	44712	51443	78685	61446	11529	64531
95018	53155	71938	99420	15408	44461	27981	90368
20563	11277	42307	32736	99532	65361	64300	76678
20768	27895	83856	69778	39159	68796	17739	30795
70805	92775	34093	00317	34349	79168	87667	98240
96194	11150	67555	95582	47540	91542	35023	35235
15920	14305	46477	35022	30006	35516	48513	09493
80789	87303	24848	46375	92999	26747	77435	49786
14907	30788	79299	34428	88050	39956	35155	55514
99467	74257	98806	10498	63125	99067	24489	32313

Line \ Col.	(1)	(2)	(3)	(4)	(5)	(6)
951	17222	24847	14225	43238	39943	20269
952	51117	86027	85128	33442	59152	67511
953	98122	85707	47835	60583	81100	24151
954	07079	03751	09486	74453	95050	28861
955	91827	97079	74080	85168	67841	92785
956	63924	46330	97808	84837	61032	98609
957	27527	61690	11334	66616	74361	26430
958	62640	79415	84174	76251	22673	44026
959	24485	14761	49553	21948	82300	95215
960	31163	12555	57763	73074	54090	95819
961	75829	90951	85627	98027	69242	44145
962	50265	07807	43138	62890	82977	38769
963	71200	80801	81289	44767	02901	61530
964	88107	27970	99234	22295	36871	14761
965	61197	02791	14924	93662	36173	00145
966	83405	26615	87854	03164	98061	64144
967	02276	39832	64484	17204	96556	46324
968	13020	23251	09546	06687	39893	85402
969	50766	20504	47573	87991	62684	10921
970	74813	19126	38598	77307	59250	62431
971	34150	68179	87177	64247	40979	62952
972	95035	52598	27655	90383	76468	08022
973	76846	66076	01650	77548	03009	48350
974	24146	49880	75124	54340	74297	31307
975	27427	83596	07262	58388	43212	81674
976	62277	00386	94965	57568	04965	52742
977	26218	09494	96963	28005	15942	13443
978	95828	98777	58855	21092	97414	28481
979	06052	32502	47874	51676	13316	43804
980	79103	19996	36294	42929	95081	45359
981	69040	75170	31286	93852	19394	43743
982	02688	26065	29875	54689	12247	67229
983	59669	62317	56242	90656	43992	64306
984	03409	78084	23818	21489	87944	11732
985	05188	62591	48883	62080	49460	32772
986	91857	24665	14441	83430	90899	23068
987	78853	88643	78621	02377	02253	06181
988	57803	03002	43966	52273	88993	47814
989	20414	62347	23572	02107	86764	95612
990	76748	64133	70898	44429	28121	56265
991	98506	47155	93726	32281	64505	56978
992	54242	81976	67665	70890	07185	20131
993	81990	00775	05836	34512	64536	69060
994	44250	04275	16365	24813	43750	62646
995	27942	19415	30541	10707	42525	84144
996	64300	38752	56657	85280	28224	84314
997	14653	08589	09404	81557	16276	63464
998	95087	67947	29851	06124	04054	73563
999	08774	32723	44960	29042	94665	36955
1000	37039	97547	64673	31546	99314	66854

(7)	(8)	(9)	(10)	(11)	(12)	(13)	(14)
52593	99929	69993	66806	16035	74175	04974	75631
36916	93946	25402	53934	83623	18774	21413	37540
58693	46274	83783	68899	42100	14798	30325	01988
19001	56932	51925	60421	43291	13854	87524	26618
85584	97685	18369	02716	04330	45215	67343	98098
67177	96231	44689	05224	72408	37347	30369	45386
06353	29841	87500	03627	42526	26924	64139	45052
59218	78743	90058	54715	88307	88689	51172	47812
58519	81521	21773	21559	07775	96603	12156	58338
02558	92149	15685	15315	84154	89401	53301	70641
74974	58554	71020	36095	41778	51657	99796	93408
11754	81428	56568	40473	43510	66127	10806	57208
67617	50078	88909	40539	31521	68964	47991	59963
74494	02770	94610	89209	52688	92319	56341	04119
81019	63834	09891	16660	20541	48016	48620	66704
81948	49844	07816	04927	68917	11008	96965	74719
12068	68780	30396	01443	36666	76408	18082	19438
96369	71504	04242	80485	66151	39141	52873	13346
29624	44384	82938	30828	72266	20455	32794	18715
25603	49204	72792	87154	34140	45891	44767	55879
88828	81184	83310	49826	78268	84810	34755	76708
90814	78356	95077	65538	77477	12978	72000	34428
61844	17850	10898	75323	23270	74928	29066	50899
87627	14922	55793	78307	61406	73263	29927	21784
09745	74206	19310	11767	88334	52762	50280	77990
85423	87258	25805	97116	03662	40715	26670	51038
96330	50222	50856	27308	78353	83501	28171	69667
39244	80530	45700	78547	36536	86420	71140	25607
85364	25972	77144	32777	81828	16275	99252	28637
82772	10679	34236	27171	90309	42230	97146	91977
79837	38978	99397	91989	25596	24940	91964	97249
69268	72790	59095	68115	52432	03486	47945	00001
01038	22952	49953	72014	05599	06801	92765	39212
69494	98213	41356	65383	25792	96224	57038	19936
09094	13547	94514	38094	93755	39313	56688	30338
39436	65648	90795	04028	44670	88737	54796	80249
15150	41361	65890	86631	08289	15996	31647	89466
41363	97015	32977	09224	77829	77519	42395	21926
22638	02471	49752	86400	21017	92299	36523	28074
53054	85704	25631	56706	54899	25569	71394	48333
48469	71323	70581	72004	67535	79545	88388	46777
73487	53010	31677	34437	88622	03580	41811	40951
23223	57511	61764	85828	21119	66098	83996	70640
97455	01174	23358	71401	28580	92308	62973	72123
17237	38447	76318	03660	59959	76447	37567	66990
58118	97734	35701	06593	03690	50302	97271	97034
79223	12993	51056	57233	75099	31082	01867	25094
67625	44199	40748	52598	76137	26030	34138	76445
46376	14300	13280	88986	81039	34211	38168	67630
97855	99965	26373	61701	24760	52014	96547	65403

Line \ Col.	(1)	(2)	(3)	(4)	(5)	(6)
1001	25145	84834	23009	51584	66754	77785
1002	98433	54725	18864	65866	76918	78825
1003	97965	68548	81545	82933	93545	85959
1004	78049	67830	14624	17563	25697	07734
1005	50203	25658	91478	08509	23308	48130
1006	40059	67825	18934	64998	49807	71126
1007	84350	67241	54031	34535	04093	35062
1008	30954	51637	91500	48722	60988	60029
1009	86723	36464	98305	08009	00866	29255
1010	50188	22554	86160	92250	14021	63859
1011	50014	00463	13906	35936	71761	95755
1012	66023	21428	14742	94674	23308	58533
1013	04458	61862	63119	09541	01715	87901
1014	57510	36314	30458	09712	37714	95482
1015	43373	58939	95848	28288	60341	52174
1016	40704	48823	65963	39359	12717	56201
1017	07318	44623	00843	33299	59872	86774
1018	94550	23299	45557	07923	75126	00808
1019	34348	81191	21027	77087	10909	03676
1020	92277	57115	50789	68111	75305	58289
1021	61500	12763	64433	02268	57905	72347
1022	78938	71312	99705	71546	42274	23915
1023	64287	93218	35793	43671	64055	88729
1024	35314	29631	06937	54546	04470	75463
1025	96864	11554	70445	24841	04779	76774
1026	96093	58302	52236	64756	50273	61566
1027	16623	17849	96701	94971	94758	08845
1028	50848	93982	66451	32143	05441	10399
1029	48006	58200	98367	66577	68583	21108
1030	56640	27890	28825	96509	21363	53657
1031	01554	40592	26557	79189	81099	03951
1032	63799	48415	28087	17196	42784	58377
1033	77654	05943	43283	63181	72300	50360
1034	51058	95654	72648	60349	59563	59021
1035	14982	68789	41999	84797	17743	18775
1036	22305	50900	77277	32383	41723	35868
1037	51375	62050	18718	88109	36767	27440
1038	14590	70151	63862	02246	33710	46456
1039	60312	56009	52588	65722	46072	26273
1040	48513	62172	46711	56744	52250	95301
1041	19052	03511	71346	50933	10108	19747
1042	11246	92882	40354	14700	66716	93470
1043	34268	97508	69711	07165	69844	07591
1044	22931	31857	95595	48438	78029	07045
1045	11476	16553	10297	23643	06192	72478
1046	57005	88551	02117	87827	00151	39027
1047	76056	48776	41451	27779	86241	63562
1048	11961	67214	64606	51982	87588	67464
1049	28009	20616	02614	15759	65618	92266
1050	09194	83950	36645	00734	74652	87328

(7)	(8)	(9)	(10)	(11)	(12)	(13)	(14)
52357	25532	46346	39806	70361	41836	33098	03790
58210	76835	72248	43023	85884	08785	41152	11830
63282	61454	27337	10560	76390	36976	62785	77529
48243	94318	85992	15716	48891	74601	90030	82376
65047	77873	02912	52675	62971	40993	79767	19178
77818	56893	06714	25147	69782	56399	55494	29547
58168	14205	87257	59443	29927	30667	99040	61060
60873	37423	62206	78386	10008	03027	69882	99663
18514	49158	93679	84854	27953	73627	45315	94563
16237	72296	86715	17588	24327	69905	43592	52283
87002	71667	21899	50605	44017	48019	01348	33230
26507	11208	85354	34288	33031	06081	45402	54274
91260	03079	17350	91991	46955	16951	42276	18627
30507	68475	49167	54279	89734	24807	23802	60439
11879	18115	91925	93506	10331	52809	06032	98707
22811	24863	62130	86396	12606	40352	44181	56860
06926	12672	23096	62738	48877	98889	77375	72317
01312	46689	56900	74653	65614	94333	44775	42054
97723	34469	08852	51465	38544	25247	00105	14825
39751	45760	76922	62810	47392	47765	69009	41520
49498	21871	80128	71588	34936	93724	47479	30366
38906	18779	96970	81430	77457	90793	53509	79535
11168	60260	97668	29687	78958	71480	75638	32812
77112	77126	46942	35873	21104	70323	07091	25408
96129	73594	67259	08958	45986	91442	28529	91358
61962	93280	54750	91572	22825	35238	34955	77692
32280	59823	97638	63913	81772	20605	13104	86762
17775	74169	04324	00195	97321	71104	70286	44675
41361	20732	39538	95746	91363	37416	08833	72639
60119	75385	83475	94949	94360	64076	24305	66042
60438	94263	21708	82714	33487	15713	24149	90641
02026	79893	28219	95848	29099	68424	97854	87967
38411	08823	83158	85734	18917	92697	20102	13956
18616	93244	67666	36344	60506	10937	69837	92511
61437	55258	36401	21686	20416	77429	99664	16803
61829	75281	73850	09094	10748	87175	35537	42489
73438	87774	65688	13701	38111	44531	10728	25248
50225	35742	46423	27373	95388	90238	81178	95956
32049	89647	81900	49167	81910	98790	66208	92721
20401	96558	22600	59000	44669	97303	25080	61986
84712	35431	27652	36130	67396	98295	58395	54493
48587	12514	20234	20769	86575	53071	84995	46531
64588	58016	26532	17957	59119	70048	14130	72848
04453	46783	97341	34526	02731	34808	65028	61054
75968	23807	70533	73805	64118	60682	17286	45369
66060	38915	55240	10473	52382	74523	13452	18918
98013	21109	57835	56161	76084	85338	65491	85719
54389	52910	37447	71173	85880	06581	73833	62987
13545	39578	36021	09262	71240	16627	28570	44003
53507	71924	47057	83163	16248	76396	17886	46311

INDEX